AP ENVIRONMENTAL SCIENCE

AP ENVIRONMENTAL SCIENCE

Meet the writing team

Tracey Greenwood
I have been writing resources for students since 1993. I have a Ph.D in biology, specialising in lake ecology and I have taught both graduate and undergraduate biology.

Kent Pryor
I have a BSc from Massey University majoring in zoology and ecology and taught secondary school biology and chemistry for 9 years before joining BIOZONE as an author in 2009.

Lissa Bainbridge-Smith
I worked in industry in a research and development capacity for 8 years before joining BIOZONE in 2006. I have a M.Sc from Waikato University.

Richard Allan
I have had 11 years experience teaching senior secondary school biology. I have a Masters degree in biology and founded BIOZONE in the 1980s after developing resources for my own students.

Cover photograph

3D rendering of Earth focused on Mexico and the United States with detailed exaggerated relief. Images of the Earth at night emphasize how much of the planet is occupied by humans and their urban centers.

PHOTO: ©Anton Balazh 2019/www.stock.adobe.com

ISBN 978-1-98-856632-0

First Edition

Fifth Printing

Published by **BIOZONE International Ltd**

Printed by Replika Press Pvt. Ltd. using paper produced from renewable and waste materials.

Thanks to:

The staff at BIOZONE, including Clare Mansfield for design and graphics support, Paolo Curray and James Leggett for IT support, Felix Hicks for illustration and production support, Allan Young for office handling, Anu Chauhan for office logistics, and the BIOZONE sales team.

Purchases of this book may be made direct from the publisher:

BIOZONE Corporation
USA and Canada
FREE phone: 1-855-246-4555
FREE fax: 1-855-935-3555
Email: sales@thebiozone.com
Web: www.thebiozone.com

Contents

CODES: **Activity** is marked: ☐ to be done ☑ when completed ● Includes practical investigation

Contents

CODES: **Activity** is marked: ❑ to be done ☑ when completed ● Includes practical investigation

Contents

Using This Book

This book is structured on the AP Environmental Science Course and Exam Description (CED). It comprises 9 units, with an additional concluding chapter covering background and support for science practices (Chapter 10). The activities cover the course content, each one corresponding to a specific topic. These are outlined in the Unit Introduction (below).

UNIT INTRODUCTIONS

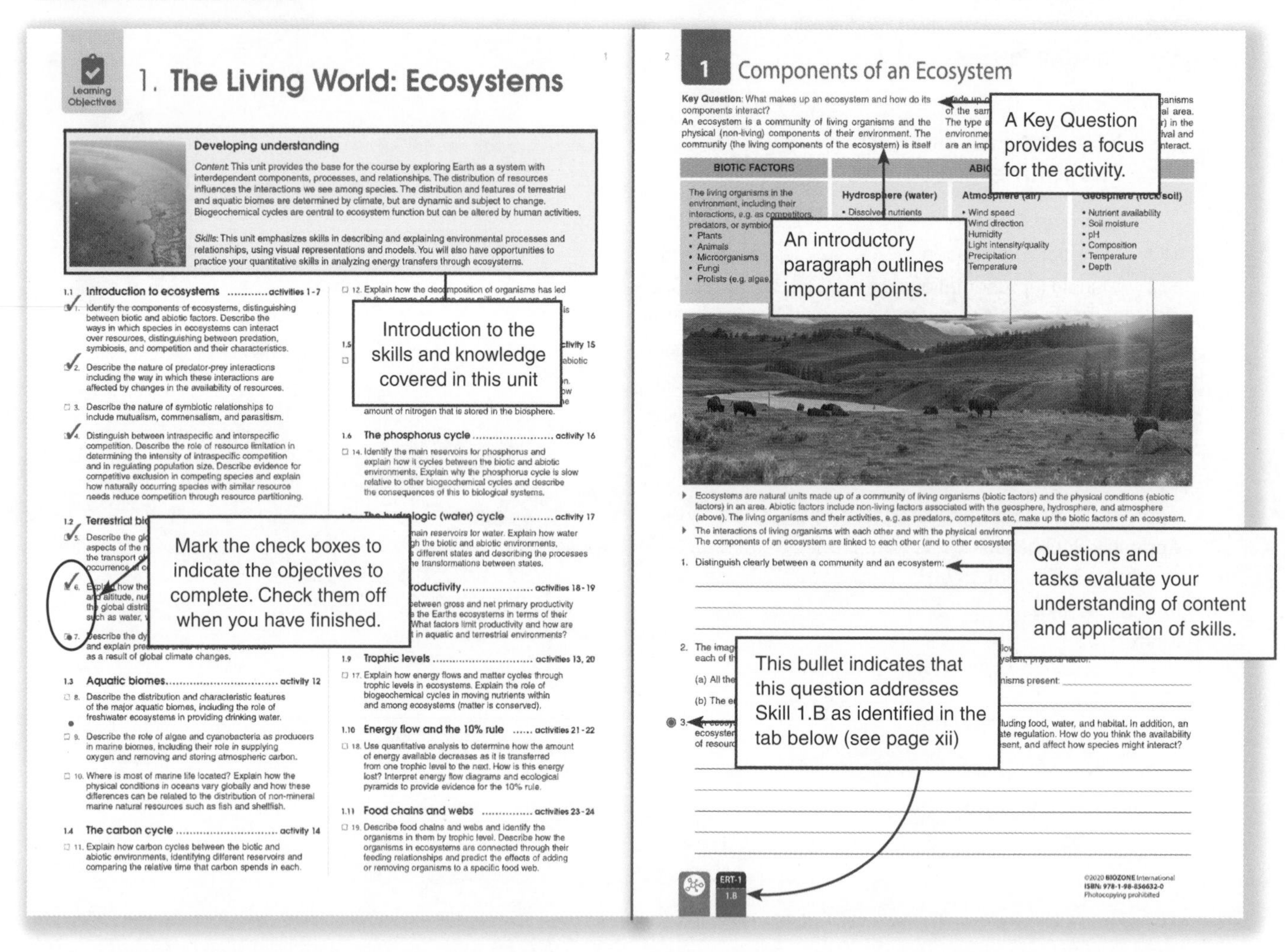

The unit introductions begin with a synopsis of the skills and understanding you will develop in the unit. This is followed by a list of **learning objectives** aligned to the activities in the book. Tick off the objectives as you complete each activity and can answer the questions asked.

Activities make up most of the book. They present data and information as graphs, tables, diagrams, text, and labeled images. Questions and tasks allow you to test your understanding of content and competency in science practices. Skills addressed throughout the activity are identified with a colored bullet in the margin (see page xii).

PRACTICAL INVESTIGATIONS

This book includes a number of simple practical investigations. In addition, some of the Personal Progress Checks (see opposite) require you to design investigations to ask and answer questions about some aspect of an environmental concept or process.

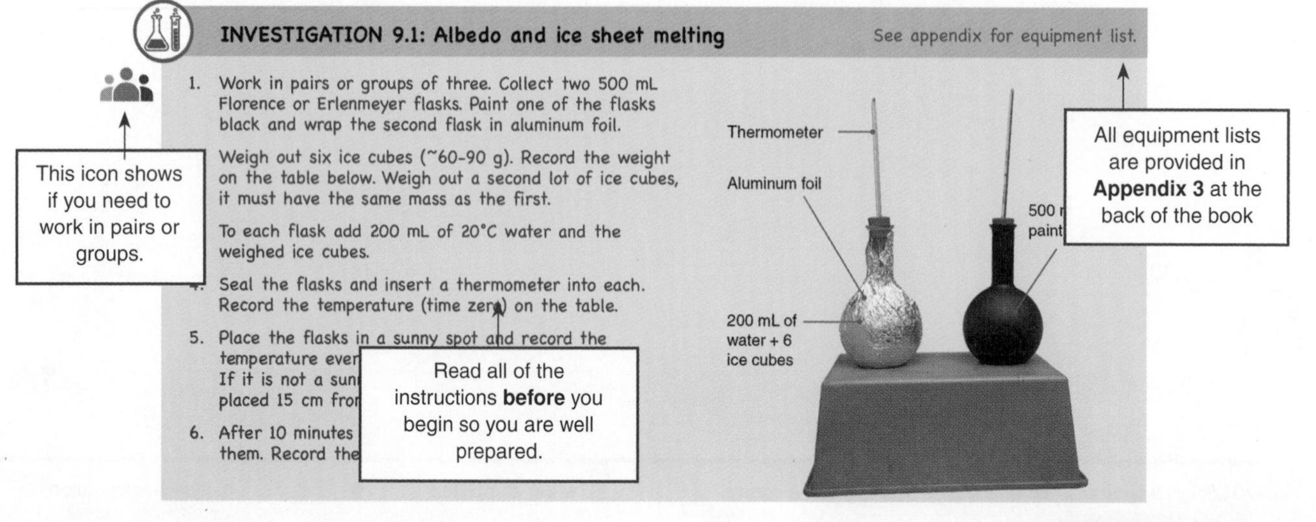

FINDING YOUR WAY AROUND THIS BOOK

The activities in this book are furnished with a simple, easy-to-use tab system to help you identify the **big ideas** and the **science practices** and their associated **skills**. It will also help you to identify where the activity (or part of it) is supported with resources on **BIOZONE's Resource Hub**. Some of the tabs are at the bottom of the first page, while others are margin icons.

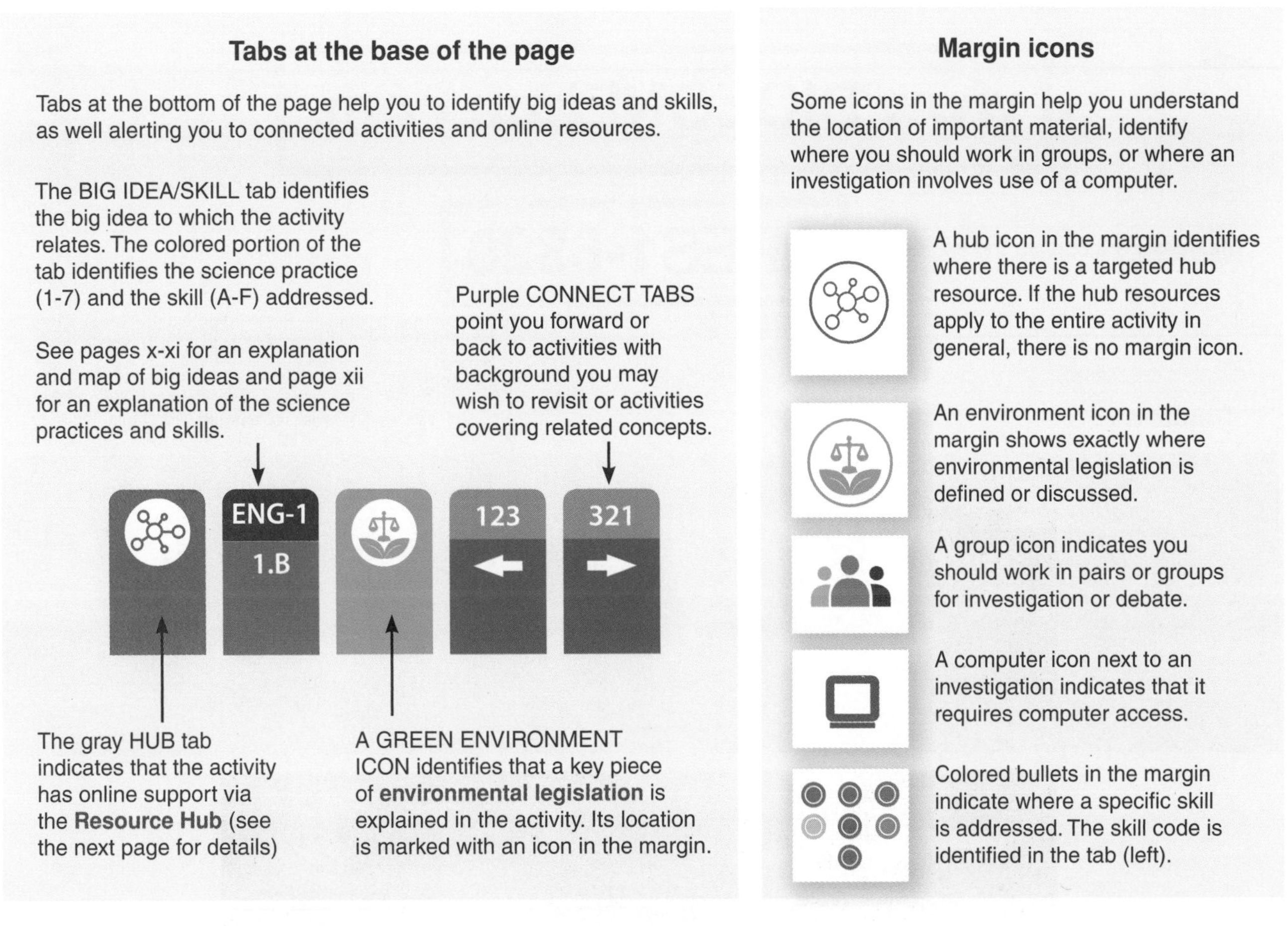

Tabs at the base of the page

Tabs at the bottom of the page help you to identify big ideas and skills, as well alerting you to connected activities and online resources.

The BIG IDEA/SKILL tab identifies the big idea to which the activity relates. The colored portion of the tab identifies the science practice (1-7) and the skill (A-F) addressed.

See pages x-xi for an explanation and map of big ideas and page xii for an explanation of the science practices and skills.

Purple CONNECT TABS point you forward or back to activities with background you may wish to revisit or activities covering related concepts.

The gray HUB tab indicates that the activity has online support via the **Resource Hub** (see the next page for details)

A GREEN ENVIRONMENT ICON identifies that a key piece of **environmental legislation** is explained in the activity. Its location is marked with an icon in the margin.

Margin icons

Some icons in the margin help you understand the location of important material, identify where you should work in groups, or where an investigation involves use of a computer.

A hub icon in the margin identifies where there is a targeted hub resource. If the hub resources apply to the entire activity in general, there is no margin icon.

An environment icon in the margin shows exactly where environmental legislation is defined or discussed.

A group icon indicates you should work in pairs or groups for investigation or debate.

A computer icon next to an investigation indicates that it requires computer access.

Colored bullets in the margin indicate where a specific skill is addressed. The skill code is identified in the tab (left).

PERSONAL PROGRESS CHECKS

Each unit in this book finishes with a three-page Personal Progress Check (PPC), which will help you in your preparation for the AP Environmental Science exam. The first two pages are ~20-30 multiple choice questions. The final page is a free response question. Some involve analyzing a problem. Others involve experimental design. See pages x-xi for the details of the PPCs for each unit.

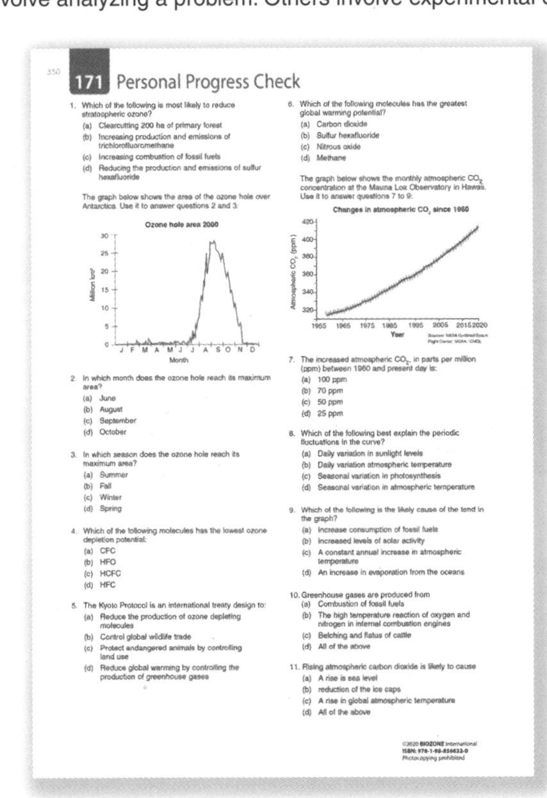

350

171 Personal Progress Check

1. Which of the following is most likely to reduce stratospheric ozone?
(a) Clearcutting 200 ha of primary forest
(b) Increasing production and emissions of trichlorofluoromethane
(c) Increasing combustion of fossil fuels
(d) Reducing the production and emissions of sulfur hexafluoride

The graph below shows the area of the ozone hole over Antarctica. Use it to answer questions 2 and 3:

Ozone hole area 2000

2. In which month does the ozone hole reach its maximum area?
(a) June
(b) August
(c) September
(d) October

3. In which season does the ozone hole reach its maximum area?
(a) Summer
(b) Fall
(c) Winter
(d) Spring

4. Which of the following molecules has the lowest ozone depletion potential:
(a) CFC
(b) HFO
(c) HCFC
(d) HFC

5. The Kyoto Protocol is an international treaty design to:
(a) Reduce the production of ozone depleting molecules
(b) Control global wildlife trade
(c) Protect endangered animals by controlling land use
(d) Reduce global warming by controlling the production of greenhouse gases

6. Which of the following molecules has the greatest global warming potential?
(a) Carbon dioxide
(b) Sulfur hexafluoride
(c) Nitrous oxide
(d) Methane

The graph below shows the monthly atmospheric CO_2 concentration at the Mauna Loa Observatory in Hawaii. Use it to answer questions 7 to 9:

Changes in atmospheric CO_2 since 1960

7. The increased atmospheric CO_2, in parts per million (ppm) between 1960 and present day is:
(a) 100 ppm
(b) 70 ppm
(c) 50 ppm
(d) 25 ppm

8. Which of the following best explain the periodic fluctuations in the curve?
(a) Daily variation in sunlight levels
(b) Daily variation atmospheric temperature
(c) Seasonal variation in photosynthesis
(d) Seasonal variation in atmospheric temperature

9. Which of the following is the likely cause of the trend in the graph?
(a) Increase consumption of fossil fuels
(b) Increased levels of solar activity
(c) A constant annual increase in atmospheric temperature
(d) An increase in evaporation from the oceans

10. Greenhouse gases are produced from
(a) Combustion of fossil fuels
(b) The high temperature reaction of oxygen and nitrogen in internal combustion engines
(c) Belching and flatus of cattle
(d) All of the above

11. Rising atmospheric carbon dioxide is likely to cause
(a) A rise in sea level
(b) reduction of the ice caps
(c) A rise in global atmospheric temperature
(d) All of the above

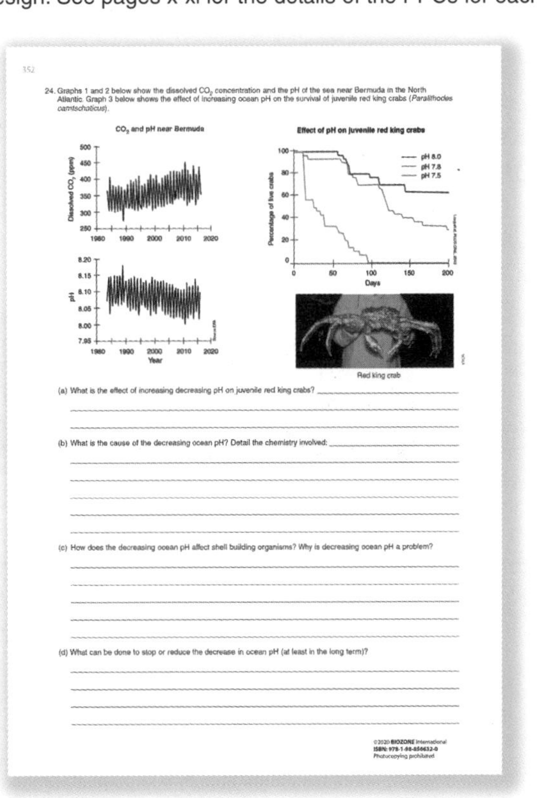

352

24. Graphs 1 and 2 below show the dissolved CO_2 concentration and the pH of the sea near Bermuda in the North Atlantic. Graph 3 below shows the effect of increasing ocean pH on the survival of juvenile red king crabs (*Paralithodes camtschaticus*).

CO_2 and pH near Bermuda

Effect of pH on juvenile red king crabs

Red king crab

(a) What is the effect of increasing decreasing pH on juvenile red king crabs?

(b) What is the cause of the decreasing ocean pH? Detail the chemistry involved:

(c) How does the decreasing ocean pH affect shell building organisms? Why is decreasing ocean pH a problem?

(d) What can be done to stop or reduce the decrease in ocean pH (at least in the long term)?

Using BIOZONE's Resource Hub

- **BIOZONE's Resource Hub** provides links to online content supporting the activities in the book. From this page, you can also check for any errata or clarifications to the book since printing.
- Many of these external websites are narrowly focused animations and video clips directly relevant to that part of the activity identified by the hub icon. There is also material for research tasks, data exploration, and some fact sheets, as well as 3D models and spreadsheet models. The hub provides great support to help your understanding.

Then enter the code in the text field **APES1-6320**

Search for an activity here.

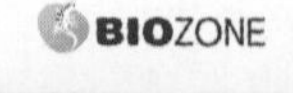

Search activity number, title, keyword...

AP Environmental Science

BIOZONE's Resource Hub provides links to online content that supports the activities in the book. From this page, you can also check for any errata or clarifications to the book or model answers since printing.

The external websites are, for the most part, narrowly focused animations and video clips directly relevant to some aspect of the activity on which they are cited. They provide great support to help your understanding.

The unit title (following the APES Course and Exam Description)

Unit 1 - The Living World: Ecosystems

1 Components of an Ecosystem
2 Resources and the Interactions between species
3 Predator-P
4 The Nature
5 Intraspecifi
6 Intraspecifi
7 Resource Partitioning
8 Climate Drivers and the World's Biomes
9 The World's Terrestrial Biomes
12 Aquatic Biomes
13 Nutrient Cycles
14 The Carbon Cycle

Click on an activity title to go directly to the resources available for that activity.

View resources →

Unit 2 - The Living World: Biodiversity

26 What is Biodiversity?
27 Stability of Ecosystems
28 Effect of Habitat Loss on Ecosystems
29 Measuring Biodiversity
30 Ecosystem Services
31 Island Biogeography
32 Ecological Tolerance
33 Natural Ecosystem Changes
34 Responding to Environmental Change
35 Adaptation and Environmental Change
36 Primary Succession
37 Secondary Succession

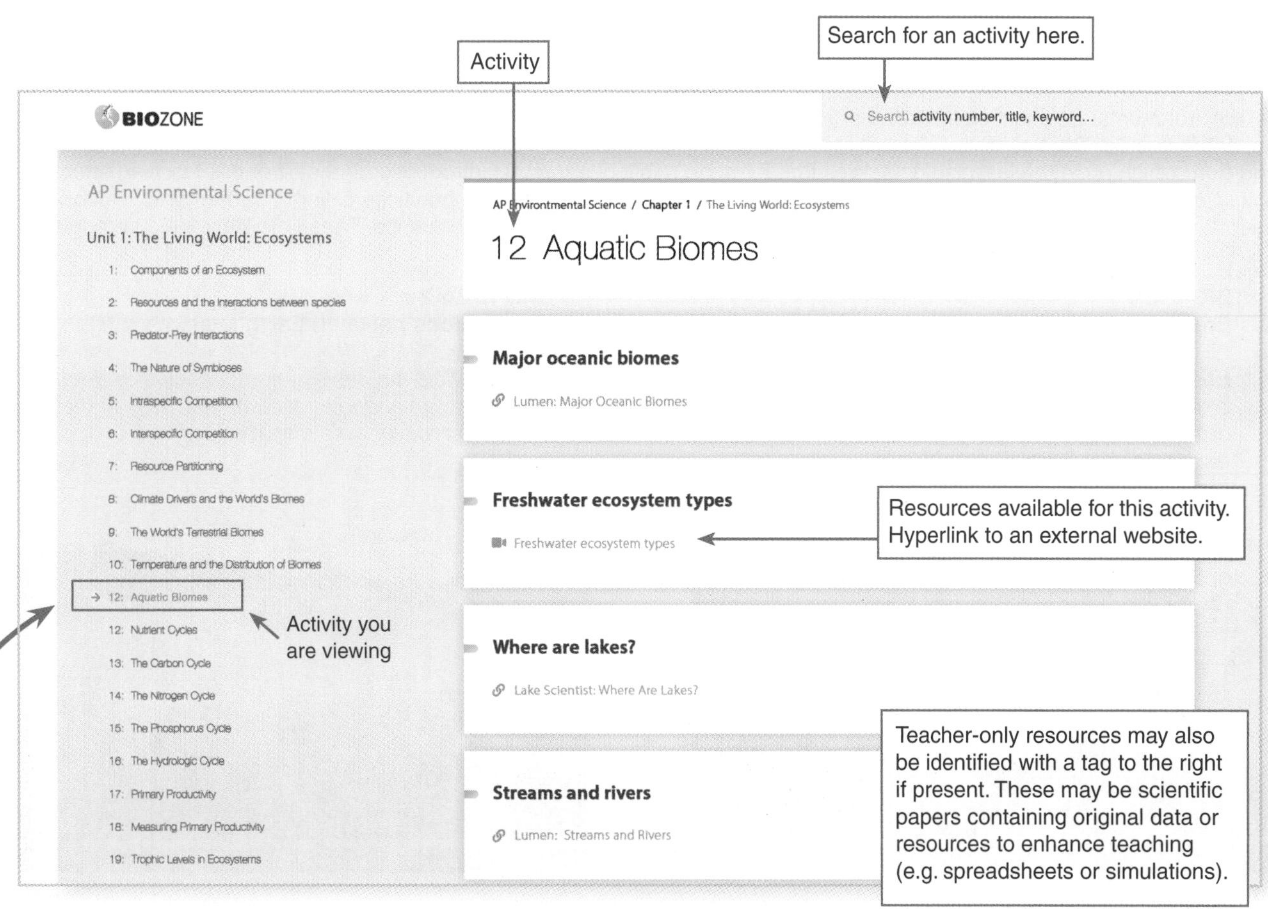

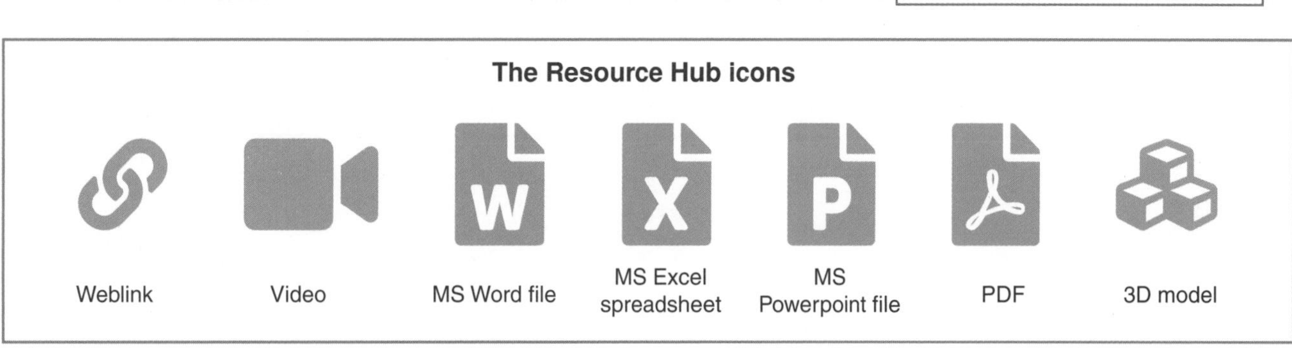

Explore videos

Explore spreadsheet modeling

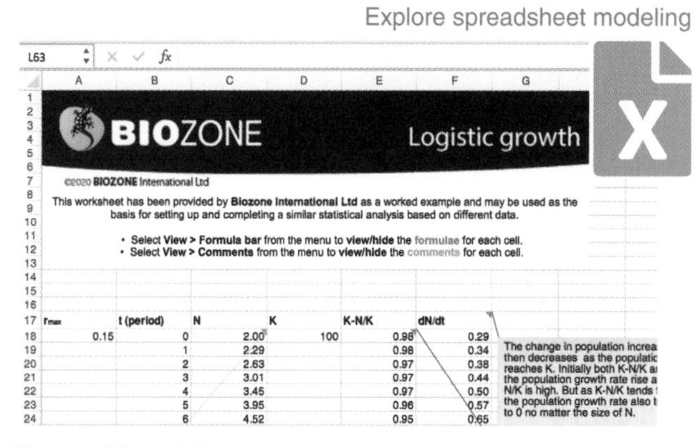

Explore web based resources

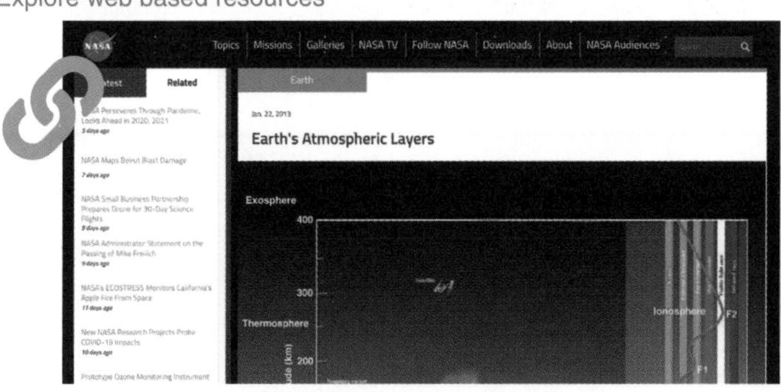

Explore 3D models

Big Ideas and Enduring Understandings

AP Environmental Science is structured around four BIG IDEAS (below). These big ideas form threads that run throughout the entire course. The big ideas relate to several ENDURING UNDERSTANDINGS, which form the key concepts for learning and from which arise the learning objectives that form the basis of each unit introduction. As part of this learning structure, key science practices are integrated into the activities of this book. The science practices cover important skills students need to describe and analyze scientific ideas and data related to environmental science. These are described on page xii.

BIG IDEA 1
Energy transfer (ENG):

Energy conversions underlie all ecological processes. Energy cannot be created or destroyed, only transferred and transformed. At each transfer energy is lost from the system to the environment.

BIG IDEA 2
Interactions between Earth systems (ERT):

The Earth is a complex interconnected system. Systems can change over time and vary in their ability to recover from disturbances.

Big Ideas	Unit 1 The Living World: Ecosystems	Unit 2 The Living World: Biodiversity	Unit 3 Populations	Unit 4 Earth Systems and Resources
Energy transfer ENG	**ENG1** Energy can be converted from one form to another.			**ENG-2** Most of the Earth's atmospheric processes are driven by input of energy from the Sun.
Interactions between Earth systems ERT	**ERT-1** Ecosystems are the result of biotic and abiotic interactions.	**ERT-2** Ecosystems have structure and diversity that change over time.	**ERT-3** Populations change over time in the reaction to a variety of factors.	**ERT-4** Earth's systems interact, resulting in a state of balance over time.
Interactions between different species and their environment EIN			**EIN-1** Human populations change in reaction to a variety of factors, including social and cultural factors.	
Sustainability STB				
PERSONAL PROGRESS CHECKS	24 multiple choice **Free response question** Analyze an environmental problem and propose a solution.	21 multiple choice **Free response question** Design an investigation.	24 multiple choice **Free response question** Analyze an environmental problem and propose a solution doing calculations.	15 multiple choice **Free response question** Design an investigation.

BIG IDEA 3
Interactions between different species and their environment (EIN):

Humans have altered the environment for millennia. The rate and scale of these changes are increasing as technology advances and the human population increases.

BIG IDEA 4
Sustainability (STB):

Human survival depends on developing sustainable solutions for managing resources that take into account social, cultural, and economic factors.

Unit 5 Land and Water Use	**Unit 6** Energy Resources and Consumption	**Unit 7** Atmospheric Pollution	**Unit 8** Aquatic and Terrestrial Pollution	**Unit 9** Global Change
	ENG-3 Humans use energy from a variety of sources, resulting in positive and negative consequences.			
EIN-2 When humans use natural resources, they alter natural systems.			**EIN-3** Pollutants can have both direct and indirect impacts on the health of organisms, including humans.	**EIN-4** The health of a species is closely tied to its ecosystem, and minor environmental changes can have a large impact.
STB-1 Humans can mitigate their impact on land and water resources through sustainable use.		**STB-2** Human activities have physical, chemical, and biological consequences for the atmosphere.	**STB-3** Human activities, including the use of resources, have physical, chemical, and biological consequences for ecosystems.	**STB-4** Local and regional human activities can have impacts at the global level.
22 multiple choice **Free response question** Analyze an environmental problem and propose a solution.	28 multiple choice **Free response question** Analyze an environmental problem and propose a solution doing calculations.	28 multiple choice **Free response question** Design an investigation.	26 multiple choice **Free response question** Analyze an environmental problem and propose a solution doing calculations.	23 multiple choice **Free response question** Analyze an environmental problem and propose a solution.

Science Practices and Skills

Science practices are things that scientists do in their everyday work, such as analyzing text and data, conducting experiments, and designing and evaluating solutions to problems. Competency in the skills associated with important practices in science are an integral part of the APES course. The skills associated with each science practice (1-7) are identified in every activity and described below. As described on page vii, a margin bullet identifies exactly where on the page the skill is addressed. You will gain confidence and competence in these skills as you complete the activities. To help you, **refer at any time to the final chapter of this book**, which has an activity dedicated to each science practice.

Practice

1 Concept explanation
Explain environmental concepts, processes, and models given in written format.

SKILL

1.A	1.B	1.C
Describe environmental concepts and processes.	Explain environmental concepts and processes.	Explain environmental concepts, processes, or models in applied contexts.

2 Visual representation
Analyze visual representations of environmental concepts and processes.

SKILL

2.A	2.B	2.C
Describe characteristics of an environmental concept, process, or model represented visually.	Explain relationships between different characteristics of environmental concepts, processes, or models represented visually, in theoretical and applied contexts.	Explain how environmental concepts and processes represented visually relate to broader environmental issues.

3 Text analysis
Analyze sources of information about environmental issues.

SKILL

3.A	3.B	3.C	3.D	3.E
Identify the author's claim.	Describe the author's perspective and assumptions.	Describe the author's reasoning (use of evidence to support a claim).	Evaluate the credibility of a source (not assessed), including bias and scientific accuracy.	Evaluate the validity of conclusions of a source or research study (not assessed).

4 Scientific explanation
Analyze research studies that test environmental principles.

SKILL

4.A	4.B	4.C	4.D	4.E
Identify a testable hypothesis or scientific question for an investigation.	Identify a research method, design, and/or measure used.	Describe an aspect of a research method, design, and/or measure used.	Make observations or collect data from laboratory setups (not assessed).	Explain modifications to an experimental procedure that will alter results.

5 Data analysis
Analyze and interpret quantitative data represented in tables, charts, and graphs.

SKILL

5.A	5.B	5.C	5.D	5.E
Describe patterns or trends in data.	Describe relationships among variables in data represented.	Explain patterns and trends in data to draw conclusions.	Interpret experimental data and results in relation to a given hypothesis.	Explain what the data implies or illustrates about environmental issues.

6 Mathematical routines
Apply quantitative methods to address environmental concepts.

SKILL

6.A	6.B	6.C
Determine an approach or method aligned with the problem to be solved.	Apply appropriate mathematical relationships to solve a problem, with work shown (e.g. dimensional analysis).	Calculate an accurate numeric answer with appropriate units.

7 Environmental solutions
Propose and justify solutions to environmental problems.

SKILL

7.A	7.B	7.C	7.D	7.E	7.F
Describe environmental problems.	Describe potential responses or approaches to environmental problems.	Describe disadvantages, advantages, or unintended consequences for potential solutions.	Use data and evidence to support a potential solution.	Make a claim that proposes a solution to an environmental problem in an applied context.	Justify a proposed solution, by explaining potential advantages.

1. The Living World: Ecosystems

Developing understanding

Content: This unit provides the base for the course by exploring Earth as a system with interdependent components, processes, and relationships. The distribution of resources influences the interactions we see among species. The distribution and features of terrestrial and aquatic biomes are determined by climate, but are dynamic and subject to change. Biogeochemical cycles are central to ecosystem function but can be altered by human activities.

Skills: This unit emphasizes skills in describing and explaining environmental processes and relationships, using visual representations and models. You will also have opportunities to practice your quantitative skills in analyzing energy transfers through ecosystems.

1.1 Introduction to ecosystems ....activities 1 - 7

☐ 1. Identify the components of ecosystems, distinguishing between biotic and abiotic factors. Describe the ways in which species in ecosystems can interact over resources, distinguishing between predation, symbiosis, and competition and their characteristics.

☐ 2. Describe the nature of predator-prey interactions including the way in which these interactions are affected by changes in the availability of resources.

☐ 3. Describe the nature of symbiotic relationships to include mutualism, commensalism, and parasitism.

☐ 4. Distinguish between intraspecific and interspecific competition. Describe the role of resource limitation in determining the intensity of intraspecific competition and in regulating population size. Describe evidence for competitive exclusion in competing species and explain how naturally occurring species with similar resource needs reduce competition through resource partitioning.

1.2 Terrestrial biomes .... activities 8 - 11

☐ 5. Describe the global distribution and main environmental aspects of the major terrestrial biomes. Explain how the transport of heat around the globe accounts for the occurrence of certain biomes in particular regions.

☐ 6. Explain how the combination of climate, geography, latitude and altitude, nutrient availability, and soil type influence the global distribution of non-mineral terrestrial resources such as water, wood, coal, peat, soil, and gravel.

☐ 7. Describe the dynamic nature of biome distribution and explain predicted shifts in biome distribution as a result of global climate changes.

1.3 Aquatic biomes................................ activity 12

☐ 8. Describe the distribution and characteristic features of the major aquatic biomes, including the role of freshwater ecosystems in providing drinking water.

☐ 9. Describe the role of algae and cyanobacteria as producers in marine biomes, including their role in supplying oxygen and removing and storing atmospheric carbon.

☐ 10. Where is most of marine life located? Explain how the physical conditions in oceans vary globally and how these differences can be related to the distribution of non-mineral marine natural resources such as fish and shellfish.

1.4 The carbon cycle .... activity 14

☐ 11. Explain how carbon cycles between the biotic and abiotic environments, identifying different reservoirs and comparing the relative time that carbon spends in each.

☐ 12. Explain how the decomposition of organisms has led to the storage of carbon over millions of years and describe the processes by which this stored carbon is being rapidly moved into the atmospheric reservoir.

1.5 The nitrogen cycle .... activity 15

☐ 13. Explain how nitrogen cycles between the biotic and abiotic environments, with emphasis on the role of bacteria in nitrogen transformations, including nitrogen fixation. Identify the main reservoir of nitrogen and explain how humans intervene in the nitrogen cycle by altering the amount of nitrogen that is stored in the biosphere.

1.6 The phosphorus cycle .... activity 16

☐ 14. Identify the main reservoirs for phosphorus and explain how it cycles between the biotic and abiotic environments. Explain why the phosphorus cycle is slow relative to other biogeochemical cycles and describe the consequences of this to biological systems.

1.7 The hydrologic (water) cycle .... activity 17

☐ 15. Identify the main reservoirs for water. Explain how water cycles through the biotic and abiotic environments, identifying its different states and describing the processes involved in the transformations between states.

1.8 Primary productivity..................... activities 18 - 19

☐ 16. Distinguish between gross and net primary productivity and compare the Earths ecosystems in terms of their productivity. What factors limit productivity and how are they different in aquatic and terrestrial environments?

1.9 Trophic levels .... activities 13, 20

☐ 17. Explain how energy flows and matter cycles through trophic levels in ecosystems. Explain the role of biogeochemical cycles in moving nutrients within and among ecosystems (matter is conserved).

1.10 Energy flow and the 10% rule ...... activities 21 - 22

☐ 18. Use quantitative analysis to determine how the amount of energy available decreases as it is transferred from one trophic level to the next. How is this energy lost? Interpret energy flow diagrams and ecological pyramids to provide evidence for the 10% rule.

1.11 Food chains and webs .... activities 23 - 24

☐ 19. Describe food chains and webs and identify the organisms in them by trophic level. Describe how the organisms in ecosystems are connected through their feeding relationships and predict the effects of adding or removing organisms to a specific food web.

1 Components of an Ecosystem

Key Question: What makes up an ecosystem and how do its components interact?

An ecosystem is a community of living organisms and the physical (non-living) components of their environment. The community (the living components of the ecosystem) is itself made up of a number of populations, these being organisms of the same species living in the same geographical area. The type and availability of resources (such as water) in the environment determine species distribution and survival and are an important influence on how different species interact.

BIOTIC FACTORS	ABIOTIC FACTORS		
	Hydrosphere (water)	**Atmosphere (air)**	**Geosphere (rock/soil)**
The living organisms in the environment, including their interactions, e.g. as competitors, predators, or symbionts. • Plants • Animals • Microorganisms • Fungi • Protists (e.g. algae, protozoans)	• Dissolved nutrients • pH • Salinity • Dissolved oxygen • Precipitation • Temperature	• Wind speed • Wind direction • Humidity • Light intensity/quality • Precipitation • Temperature	• Nutrient availability • Soil moisture • pH • Composition • Temperature • Depth

- Ecosystems are natural units made up of a community of living organisms (biotic factors) and the physical conditions (abiotic factors) in an area. Abiotic factors include non-living factors associated with the geosphere, hydrosphere, and atmosphere (above). The living organisms and their activities, e.g. as predators, competitors etc, make up the biotic factors of an ecosystem.
- The interactions of living organisms with each other and with the physical environment help determine an ecosystem's features. The components of an ecosystem are linked to each other (and to other ecosystems) through nutrient cycles and energy flows.

1. Distinguish clearly between a community and an ecosystem: A community is only biotic while ecosystem has biotic & abiotic

2. The image above depicts buffalo in Yellowstone National Park. From the following list, assign the appropriate term to each of the features described below. **Terms**: population, community, ecosystem, physical factor.

   (a) All the buffalo present: population

   (b) The entire National Park: ecosystem

   (c) All the organisms present: community

   (d) The river: physical factor

3. An ecosystem provides resources to its community of living organisms, including food, water, and habitat. In addition, an ecosystem provides essential services such as nutrient recycling and climate regulation. How do you think the availability of resources might influence the distribution and abundance of species present, and affect how species might interact?

   Availability of resources could increase or decrease distribution while making species more or less aggressive

ERT-1
1.B

ISBN: 978-1-98-856632-0

2 Resources and the Interactions Between Species

Key Question: How do species interact within ecosystems and how are their interactions influenced by resources?

Organisms do not live in isolation. The interactions within and between species are an important component of the biotic factors that structure every ecosystem. Many of these relationships involve exploitation: a predator eats its prey and herbivores eat plants. Other relationships involve two or more species being entirely or partly reliant on their very close ecological relationship. Such a relationship is called a symbiosis. Symbioses can be beneficial for both parties (a mutualism) or exploitative (as in parasitism). Resource availability often influences the extent to which species interact. While this is most obvious for species competing for limited resources, it is important in other interactions also.

Type of interaction between species

Mutualism	Commensalism	Parasitism	Predation	Competition
A symbiosis in which both species benefit. If both species depend on the symbiosis for survival, the mutualism is obligate. Mutualism can involve more than two species. **Examples**: Flowering plants and their insect pollinators. The flowers are pollinated and the insect gains food. Ruminants and their rumen protozoa and bacteria. The microbes digest the cellulose in plant material and produce short-chain fatty acids, which the ruminant uses as an energy source.	A symbiosis in which one species benefits and the other is unaffected. It is likely that most commensal relationships involve some small benefit to the apparently neutral party. **Example**: The squat anemone shrimp (or sexy shrimp), lives among the tentacles of sea anemones, where it gains protection and scavenges scraps of food from the anemone. The anemone appears to be neither harmed, nor gain any benefit.	A symbiotic relationship in which the parasite lives in or on the host, taking all its nutrition from it. The host is harmed but not usually killed, at least not directly. Parasites may have multiple hosts and their transmission is often linked to food webs. **Example**: Parasitic tongue-replacing isopods cut the blood supply to the tongue of the host fish, causing it to fall off. The parasite attaches to what is left of the tongue, feeding on blood or mucus.	A predator kills the prey and eats it. Predators may take a range of species as prey or they may prey exclusively on one other species. Predation is a consumer-resource interaction and a type of exploitation. **Examples**: Praying mantis consuming insect prey. Canada lynx eating snowshoe hare. The ochre sea star feeding on its primary prey, mussels. They also eat chitons, barnacles, and limpets.	Individuals of the same or different species compete for the same limited resources. Both parties are detrimentally affected. **Examples**: Neighboring plants of the same and different species compete for light and soil nutrients. Vultures compete for the remains of a carcass. Insectivorous birds compete for suitable food in a forest. Tree-nesting birds with similar requirements compete for nest sites.
		Luc Viatour www.Lucnix.be	Marco vinci cc 3.0	
A ⇄ B Benefits Benefits				

1. In the spaces above, draw a simple model to show whether each species/individual in the interaction described is harmed or benefits. The first one has been completed for you.

2. Ticks are obligate blood feeders (meaning they must obtain blood to pass from one life stage to the next). Ticks attach to the outside of hosts where they suck blood and fluids and cause irritation.

   (a) Identify this type of interaction: Paratism

   (b) How would the tick population be affected if the host became rare? Their food would be scarce

3. Competition is common both within and between species. Predict which would be the most intense and explain why:

   Between species would be more intense because most animals dont attack same species

ISBN: 978-1-98-856632-0

3 Predator-Prey Interactions

Key Question: How does resource availability influence the interactions between populations of predators and their prey?

A predator eating its prey is one of the most obvious ecological interactions we see between species. Predators are well adapted to locate and subdue their prey, and prey species are equally well adapted to avoid being eaten and to maintain their populations despite predation. Vertebrate predators generally do not control their prey populations, which tend to fluctuate seasonally depending on available food supply. However, predator populations are heavily influenced by the availability of prey, especially when there is little opportunity for switching to alternative prey species.

Strategies of predators: capture

The strategies of predators to capture prey are diverse. Strategies for prey capture will depend on the habitat (forested, open), the adaptations of the predator and its prey species (teeth, claws, venom, speed), and whether the predator is social or solitary. Ambush predators conceal themselves and capture prey by surprise. Pursuit predators use speed to chase down prey, while persistence predators rely on endurance to follow prey until it tires. Others, such as spiders, use lures or traps to ensnare prey.

Canids are persistence predators, using endurance to follow prey until it tires.

Pursuit predators such as cheetah and dragonflies use speed to outrun prey.

Ambush predators (snakes, lizards, spiders) are concealed until they attack.

Strategies of predators: how to select prey?

The resources in ecosystems are not usually uniform because environments are patchy. This applies to prey seeking the resources they need to survive and to predators seeking prey. Predators show behaviors that will increase their chances of finding prey and optimize their energy gains from foraging. There are many ecological studies, particularly of bird predators, that indicate predators will forage in a way that maximizes energy gain for energy spent.

Aggregation: Predators will often aggregate for short periods of time in areas of high prey density, maximizing exploitation of rich food patches. This behavior is seen in marine birds that feed at sea as well as wading birds exploiting patchy estuarine environments.

Prey size selection: Given a range of prey sizes, predators will often select a prey size that is optimum for maximum energy gain per handling time. Small prey do not provide enough energy, whereas larger prey are too difficult to handle. Energy gain is often balanced against handling time (or risk).

Right: Pied wagtails take medium sized prey (dung flies and beetles) in amounts out of proportion to their availability in the environment. This correlates with the maximum energy gain for the time they spend handling their prey.

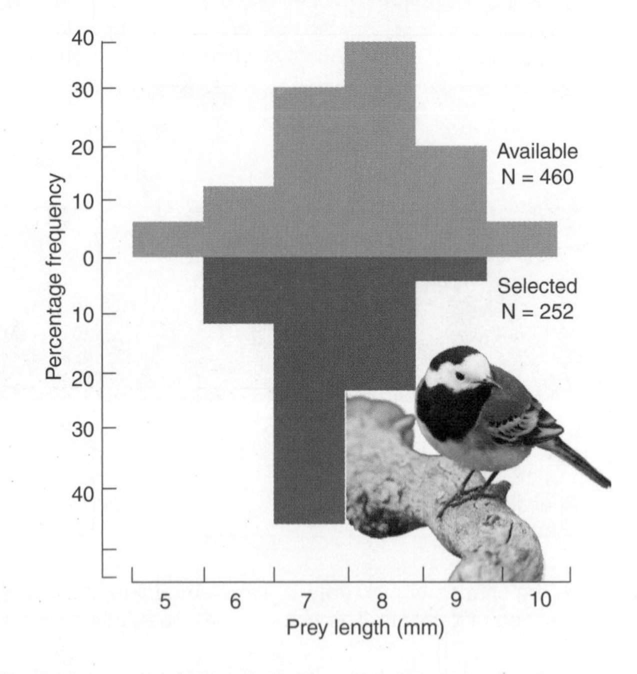

1. Describe the effect of resource distribution on the occurrence of prey and their predators:

Greater resource distribution creates more prey

2. What evidence is there that predators hunt in a way that maximizes the gain in energy for the time spent hunting?

In the passage above

ERT-1
1.A

ISBN: 978-1-98-856632-0

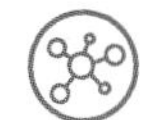

How do predators respond to increases in prey?

Time lagged numerical responses: In many herbivore-carnivore systems, prey populations fluctuate seasonally with changes in vegetation growth. Predators may respond to increases in prey by increasing their rate of reproduction. This type of numerical response shows a time lag, associated with the time it takes for the predator population to respond by producing more young. The most famous of these time-lagged predator-prey cycles is that recorded for the Canada lynx and its prey, the snowshoe hare (below).

Figure right: Population cycles in Canada lynx and snowshoe hare
Image (below left): Canada lynx, a specialist predator of snowshoe hares, taking almost no other prey.
Image (below right): Snowshoe hare, the primary prey of the lynx.

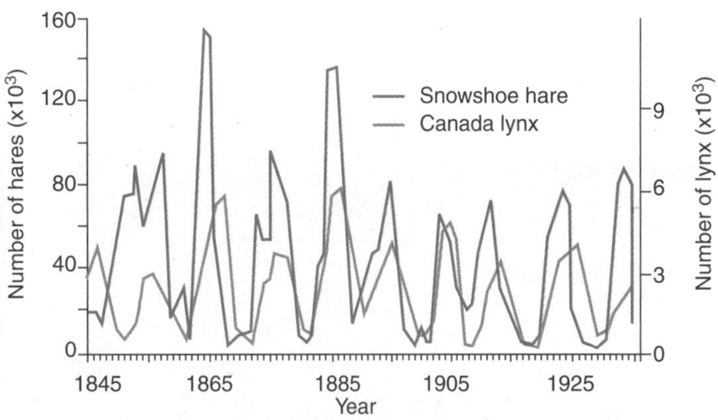

No-lag numerical responses: Predators can show an immediate numerical response to increases in prey availability. In one study, numbers of kestrels fluctuated with the density of voles, their prey (below). The birds could track the vole populations without a time lag because of their high mobility. An increase in vole numbers was accompanied by a rapid immigration of birds into the area.

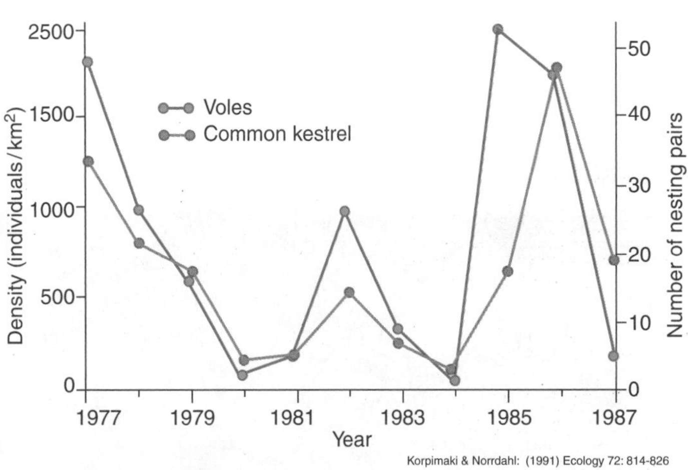

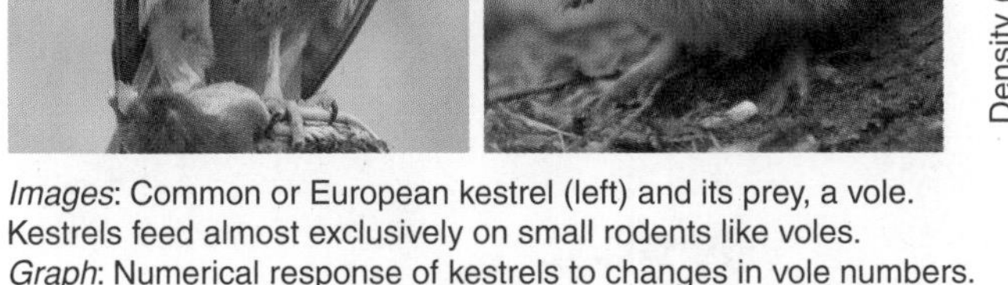

Images: Common or European kestrel (left) and its prey, a vole. Kestrels feed almost exclusively on small rodents like voles.
Graph: Numerical response of kestrels to changes in vole numbers. Study area was 47 km^2 of farmland in western Finland.

3. (a) Describe how seasonal fluctuations in resources relate to cycles of abundance of Canada lynx and snowshoe hare:

   (b) Explain why the fluctuations in lynx numbers lag slightly behind those of the hare:

   (c) Why do you think the cycle of lynx abundance is so closely linked to the hare abundance?

4. Describe three ways in which predator behavior responds to differences in resource (prey) abundance in ecosystems. Use examples to illustrate your answer:

ISBN: 978-1-98-856632-0

4 The Nature of Symbioses

Key Question: How does resource availability influence the type of symbiotic relationship we see between species?

As we saw earlier, a symbiosis is a close ecological relationship (literally meaning "living together"). Symbioses include mutualistic and commensal relationships, as well as parasitism. As we saw, the partners in a mutualistic relationship benefit from the association. This contrasts with parasitism, where the symbiosis involves exploitation of one species by another. As in all species interactions, there is a strong resource component to all symbiotic relationships.

Types of mutualistic relationships

Resource-resource relationships: One resource is traded for another (usually food or a nutrient)

Staghorn coral

Reef building corals rely on a mutualism with algae in their tissues. The algae supply the coral with energy (glucose and glycerol) and, in return, obtain a habitat and the compounds they need for photosynthesis and growth (CO_2 and nitrogen). This symbiosis is crucial to recycling nutrients within the reef.

Worker termite

Althepal cc 2.5

Termites eat wood and rely on a community of microbes in their gut to break down the cellulose in wood and produce the fatty acids they use for energy. The obligate relationship provides food for both microbes and termites. Termites are responsible for recycling most of the dead wood in tropical ecosystems.

Service-resource relationships: A service is performed in exchange for a resource, e.g. food for protection

Ant guards its aphids

viamoi cc 2.0

Some species of ants "farm" aphids by protecting the aphids from their ladybug predators. In return the ants harvest and consume the honeydew excreted by the aphids. Aphids will also increase their honeydew production when attended by the ants.

Honeybee pollinating a purple crocus

Many flowering plant species have a mutualistic relationship with their bee pollinators. The bee obtains food (nectar) and the plant receives a service (pollination). The mutualism is facultative; neither species depends exclusively on the other for survival.

1. Using examples, describe how symbiotic relationships increase resource availability for the species involved:

2. In ecosystems, resources such as food are usually limited. Suggest how resource limitation might help to strengthen and shape mutualistic relationships to the point that both species depend on the relationship for survival:

ISBN: 978-1-98-856632-0

How do parasitic relationships persist when parasites harm their hosts?

Parasites exploit their hosts for the resources they provide. They do not kill their host directly as a predator does, but hosts may succumb to parasites through ill health, poor reproduction, or secondary disease. Although parasitism can regulate host populations (through increased death rates and lower birth rates) it is not in the parasite's interests to eliminate its host. This accounts for how most host-parasite relationships evolve into a mutual tolerance with low grade widespread infection.

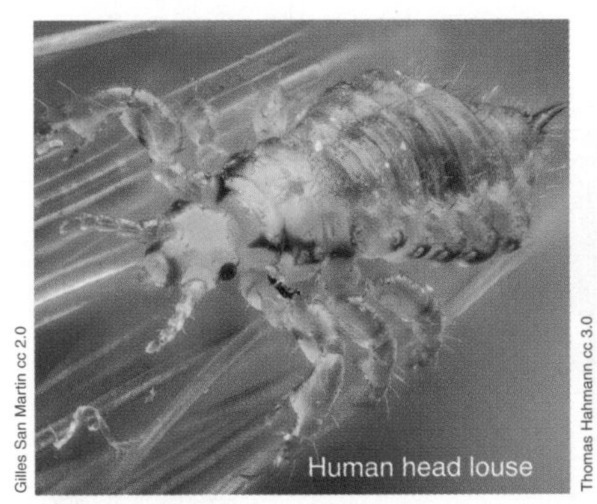

Gilles San Martin cc 2.0

Human head louse

The human head louse is an ectoparasite (it attaches to the outside of the host's body). Its relationship with humans is obligate, meaning it cannot complete its life cycle without its host. It spends its entire life on the human scalp, sucking blood. Humans are the only host species.

Thomas Hahmann cc 3.0

Snail with parasitized eyestalk

The green-banded broodsac is a parasitic flatworm with two hosts. It enters its intermediate host, a snail, when the snail feeds on bird droppings. The reproductive stage invades the snail's eyestalk, mimicking a grub, and is eaten by a bird (the definitive host) to complete the cycle.

Charles J Sharp cc 4.0

Oxpeckers- not so helpful

The relationship between oxpeckers and large grazers was once thought to be mutualistic. However, research indicates that the relationship is parasitic in nature. Oxpeckers will remove parasites such as ticks, but they also create or reopen wounds and drink the animal's blood, and there is no evidence that they reduce its parasite load.

Parasite transmission and the impact of host patchiness

Tick infestation of a deer

Mite infestation of harvestman

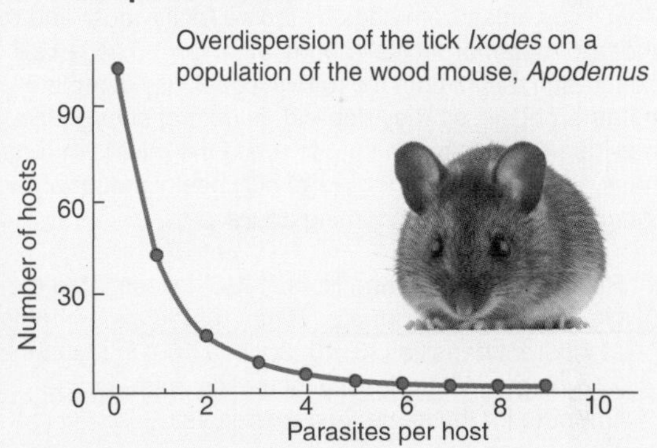

Transmission of parasites that multiply outside the host (e.g. ticks) is affected by patchy distribution of hosts (the resource). This leads to a phenomenon called overdispersion in which a small proportion of the host population carries most of the parasite load (above).

3. The mutualism between corals and the algae in their tissues is obligate (neither can survive without the other). Increasing ocean temperatures can cause the corals to expel their algae. This causes them to bleach (lose their color). The coral will eventually die unless recolonized. Describe some likely effects of coral bleaching on the reef ecosystem:

____

____

____

____

4. (a) Describe the effect of patchy resource (host) distribution on parasite populations: _______________

____

____

(b) Explain how this might allow parasite and host populations to persist, despite the parasite's exploitation of the host:

____

____

ISBN: 978-1-98-856632-0

5 Intraspecific Competition

Key Question: How does competition for resources among individuals of the same species affect the growth and distribution of individuals in the population?

Intraspecific competition describes competition among individuals of the same species. These individuals share the same resource requirements so competition for resources (food, habitat, mates) is more intense than competition between different species. Resource limitation affects individual and population growth and often determines the distribution of individuals within the environment.

Scramble competition
Direct competition between individuals for a finite resource is called scramble competition. These birch sawfly larvae feed along the birch leaf edges. Larvae compete for the same food and those hatching too late in the season are unlikely to survive.

Mike Baird

Contest competition
In contest competition, there is a winner and a loser and resources are obtained completely or not at all. For example, male elephant seals fight for territory and mates. Unsuccessful males may not mate at all.

Competition in social species
In many social species, dominance hierarchies ensure that dominant individuals have priority access to resources. Lower ranked individuals must contest what remains. If food is scarce, only dominant individuals may receive enough to survive.

Resource competition limits population growth

Most frogs hatch from eggs as larvae (pollywogs) and then undergo metamorphosis into the adult form. The larvae must reach a minimum mass to successfully complete metamorphosis, so they depend on getting enough food. Individuals that take too long to reach the minimum required mass decrease their chances of successful metamorphosis and often die before becoming adults.

- Researchers Dash and Hota (1980) investigated the growth rate of frog larvae (*Rana*) reared experimentally at different densities (5, 40, 80, and 160) in the same 2 L volume. When density increases, more larvae compete for the same food resources.
- The results are plotted right. The increase in mean body mass over time indicates growth rate. The flattening of the curve indicates size at metamorphosis.

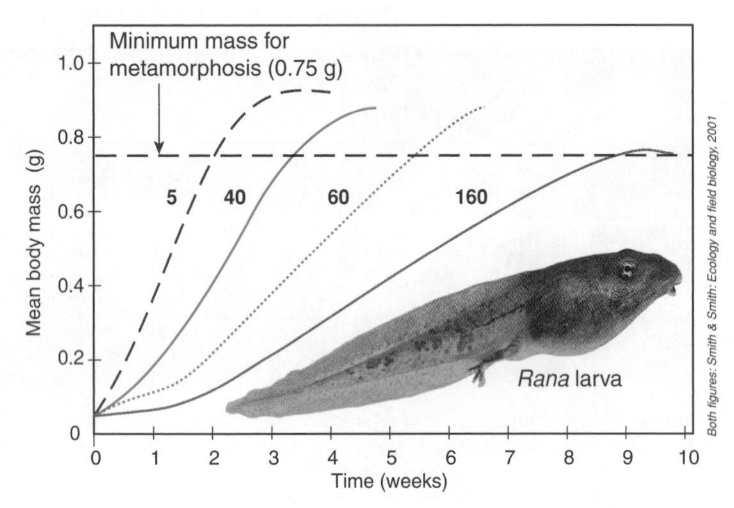

Both figures: Smith & Smith: Ecology and field biology, 2001

1. Describe the difference between scramble competition and contest competition: ______

2. Answer the following questions based on evidence from the *Rana* growth rate data:

(a) What is the effect of increasing density on individual growth rate of *Rana* larvae? ______

(b) Explain the likely effect of strong resource competition on population size of *Rana*: ______

ISBN: 978-1-98-856632-0

Territories and limitations of population size

- Territoriality in birds and other animals is usually a result of intraspecific competition. A territory is a defended area containing the resources required by an individual or breeding pair to survive and reproduce. Territories space organisms out in the habitat according to the availability of resources. Those without territories usually do not breed.
- In the South American rufous-collared sparrow, males and females occupy small territories (below). These birds make up 50% of the population. The remaining 50% of the population, called floaters, occupy home ranges (which are undefended areas) within the territory boundaries. They are tolerated by the territory owners, but these floaters do not breed.
- By using tagging studies and removal of birds, researchers found that when a territory owner (male or female) dies or disappears, it is replaced by a floater of the appropriate sex. This is shown for the females in the left diagram as a darker region.
- Territoriality can limit population size in some circumstances. If there is no lower limit to territory size and all individuals or pairs gain a territory then the population becomes spaced out but not limited. However, if territories have a lower size limit, then only a limited number of individuals or pairs can claim a territory. Those that fail to do so must leave and this limits population numbers.

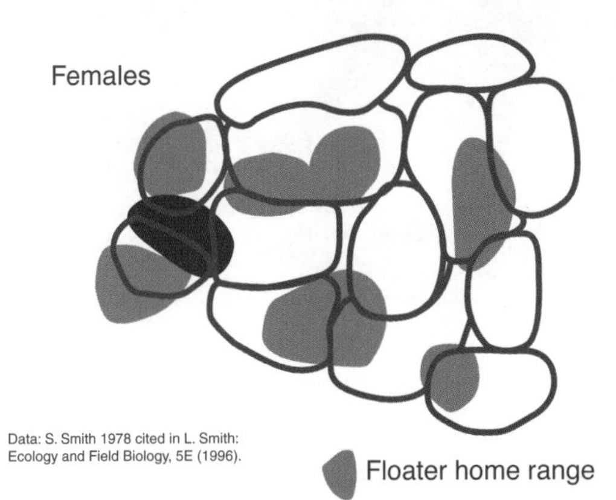

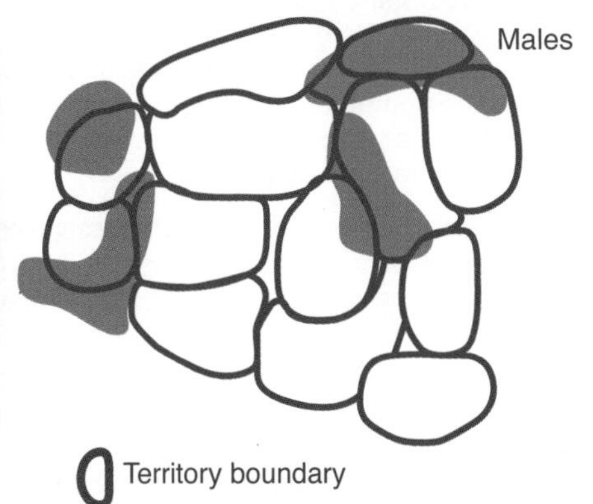

3. Intraspecific competition is considered to be a density-dependent process. What do you think this means?

____

____

4. Territoriality is a way to ensure that at least some individuals have the resources to survive and reproduce. The territories are established and maintained by direct conflict and by calls and displays.

   (a) Describe the benefits of possessing a territory: ____

   ____

   ____

   (b) What costs are likely to be associated with having a territory? ____

   ____

   ____

   (c) What evidence is there from the rufous-collared sparrow study to show that territoriality can limit population size?

   ____

   ____

   ____

   ____

   ____

5. In many animals, crowding and increased competition for resources after the breeding season leads to dispersal. In vertebrates, particularly rodents (right), young are driven away. In some insects, such as aphids, dispersing individuals become winged. Describe the advantages of dispersal in terms of resource competition:

____

____

____

ISBN: 978-1-98-856632-0

6 Interspecific Competition

Key Question: What do different species compete for and why can one species sometimes exclude another?

Competition between different species (or interspecific competition) is usually less intense than competition within a species because different species usually do not depend on exactly the same resources. Laboratory studies of interspecific competition in enclosures with limited resources provide evidence that competition can drive one species to extinction. However, in natural populations, competing species usually exist in a more or less stable equilibrium.

Interspecific competition is an important biotic factor in natural communities

Competition between different species takes one of two forms. As with all competition, there is a negative effect on all species involved, because fewer resources are available to each.

Exploitative competition occurs when two or more species use the same resource. This often results in neither species having enough of the resource to meet their needs.

Interference competition involves a direct interaction between competitors. In animals, this is usually aggressive behavior. In plants, the interaction is passive.

- Interspecific competition is usually less intense than competition between members of the same species because competing species have different requirements for at least some resources (e.g. different habitat or food preferences).
- Interspecific competition can be an important influence on the species present in an ecosystem or their distribution. However, in naturally occurring populations, it is generally less effective at limiting population size than intraspecific competition, especially in animals. This is because different species usually exploit a different spectrum of resources to avoid direct competition most of the time.
- Interspecific competition in natural plant communities is very dependent on nutrient availability and will be greater when soil nutrients are low. Fast growing plants with large, dense root systems can absorb large amounts of nitrogen, depleting soil nitrogen so that other plants cannot grow close to them. Similarly, fast growing plants may quickly grow tall enough to intercept the available light and prevent the germination of plants nearby. Pest plants often have this strategy and become very difficult to control (see the example of purple loosestrife, opposite).
- Sometimes, humans may introduce a species with the same resource requirements as a native species. The resulting competition can lead to the decline of the native species. For example, the American gray squirrel was introduced to England in the 1800s where it has displaced the smaller native red squirrel from much of its former range.

In some communities, many different species may be competing for the same resource. This is called interference competition because individuals directly interfere with the access of others to a resource. In the example above, a spotted hyena and black backed jackal compete for the hyena's kill.

In plant communities, the level of competition depends on how close individuals are to each other. Each individual affects the environment of its neighbor by using resources (e.g. mineral nutrients) and modifying the environment, e.g. by shading.

1. (a) Describe an example of interspecific competition, identifying the resource(s) the species are contesting: ___________

   (b) Why is interspecific competition generally less effective at limiting population size than intraspecific competition?

2. Describe the role of competition in the displacement of a native species: ___________

ISBN: 978-1-98-856632-0

One competing species can exclude another in a manipulated environment

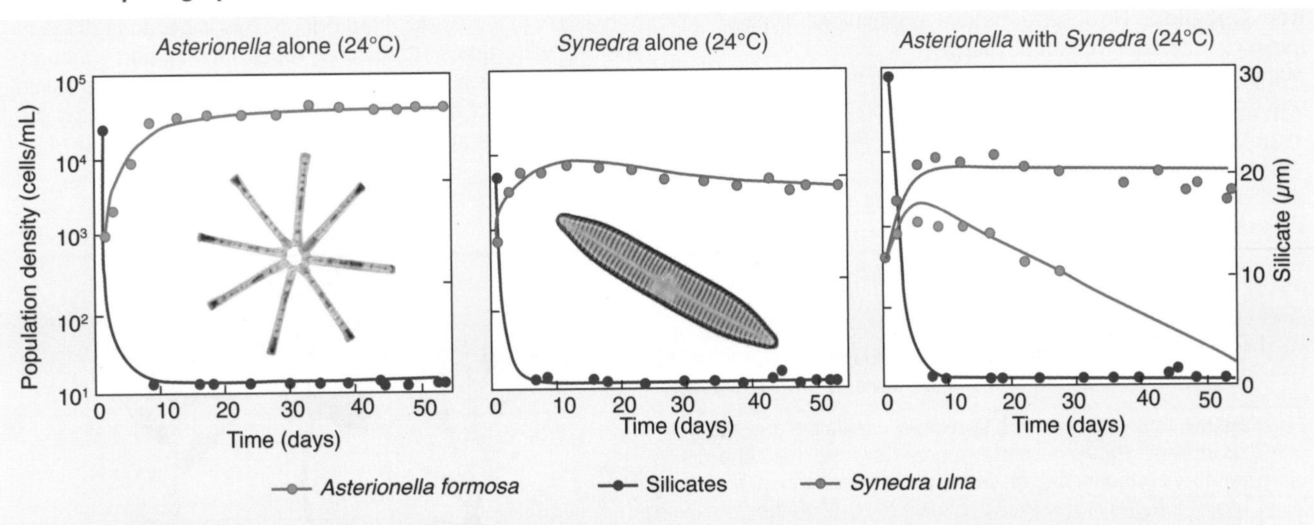

- Experimental studies in which two competing species are grown in controlled and manipulated conditions typically result in one species out-competing the other. These findings support the **competitive exclusion principle**, which states that two species with the same resource requirements cannot coexist.
- In one laboratory study, two diatom species were grown both alone and together in a nutrient medium that supplied continual silica. Diatoms are algae that require silica to form their cell walls. Grown alone, each species reduced the silica to a low level but the populations were stable. However, *Synedra* depleted the silica to a lower level than did *Asterionella*. When grown together, *Synedra* depleted the silica to a level that caused the *Asterionella* population to die out (above right).

Data and plots (redrawn) from Tilman, Mattson, and Langer (1981) Limnology and Oceanography 26.

Introduced species can exclude native species

Naturally occurring populations normally reach a competitive balance and it is rare for one to exclude the other. However species that are naturally or deliberately introduced to a new region may out-compete resident natives through more efficient resource exploitation or by being more aggressive competitors in direct interactions. Not all introduced species out-compete native residents, but many do.

- A well known example in the US is **purple loosestrife** (*Lythrum salicaria*). This species is native to Europe, Asia, and parts of Africa and Australia. It was introduced to North America as a contaminant in ship ballast and as an herbal remedy for dysentery, and it quickly became established. Its range now extends throughout Canada and to all US states except Hawaii and Florida.
- Purple loosestrife crowds out native wetland plant species and disrupts water flow in rivers and canals. It produces vast numbers of seeds and can produce vegetatively from root fragments also. The image right shows it dominating the Cooper Marsh conservation area in Ontario.

Saffron Blaze cc 3.0

3. (a) Using the example of the diatoms above, describe the experimental evidence for the role of resource competition in the exclusion of one species by another:

(b) Suggest why these manipulated environments are unlikely to represent the usual situation in a natural ecosystem:

ISBN: 978-1-98-856632-0

7 Resource Partitioning

Key Question: How have natural populations evolved to minimize interspecific competition?

Many species in natural ecosystems utilize many of the same resources, and so are in competition at least some of the time. Yet we see that most appear able to obtain the resources necessary to survive and reproduce. This is because different species with similar ecological requirements and resource needs can reduce competition by exploiting resources within different parts of the same environment or by exploiting the same resources at different times of the day or year.

Many field studies have indicated that different species partition the available resources to avoid direct competition.

Right: In three species of annual plants growing on unplowed prairie soil, water resources are partitioned by root depth. The shallow fibrous roots of the bristly foxtail contrast with the deep tap root of the smartweed. Foxtail is drought tolerant, whereas smartweed's deep tap root ensures water is always available.

Below: In a study of three species of coexisting grassland sparrows in Pennsylvania, researchers found that although territory boundaries of all three species overlapped, they made use of the gradient in the vegetation to partition the grassland habitat and avoid competition. All species eat insects and seeds. Henslow's and grasshopper sparrows have a similar beak size but the savannah sparrow has a smaller beak and exploits slightly different food sizes than the grasshopper sparrow with which it has a 35% habitat overlap.

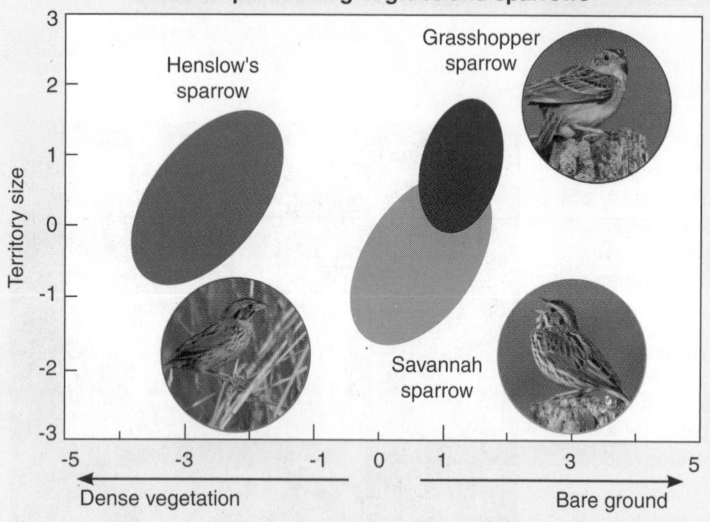

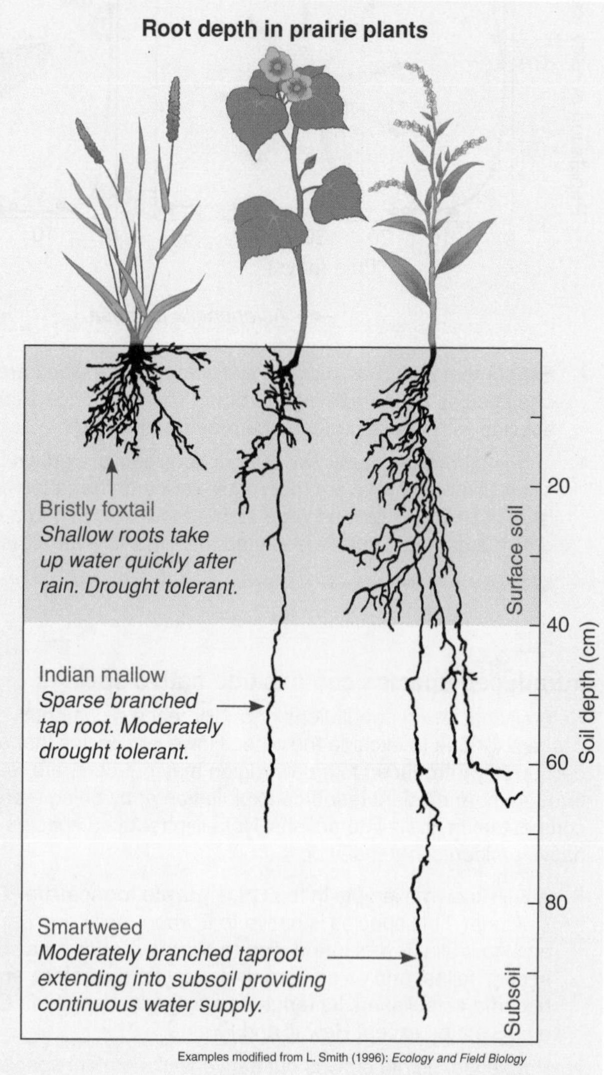

Examples modified from L. Smith (1996): *Ecology and Field Biology*

1. Study the diagram of resource partitioning in grassland sparrows. Describe two ways in which the species minimize the competition between them in their grassland ecosystem:

2. Describe the different strategies of prairie annual plants to obtaining water when growing in the same soil environment:

ISBN: 978-1-98-856632-0

8 Climate Drivers and the World's Biomes

Key Question: How does circulation of air and water masses distribute heat and influence climate zones?

Biomes are distinct biological communities that occur as a result of a shared physical climate. These biomes exist in part because of the climate zones created by the Earth's air and ocean circulation, its rotation, and its topography. The Earth is circled in the Northern and Southern hemispheres by three air cells. The cells form areas of rising or descending air, affecting the amount of rainfall. Surface features, such as oceans and mountain ranges, affect the final positions and size of these biomes but four general climate-defined regions in each hemisphere can be identified (lower blue panel).

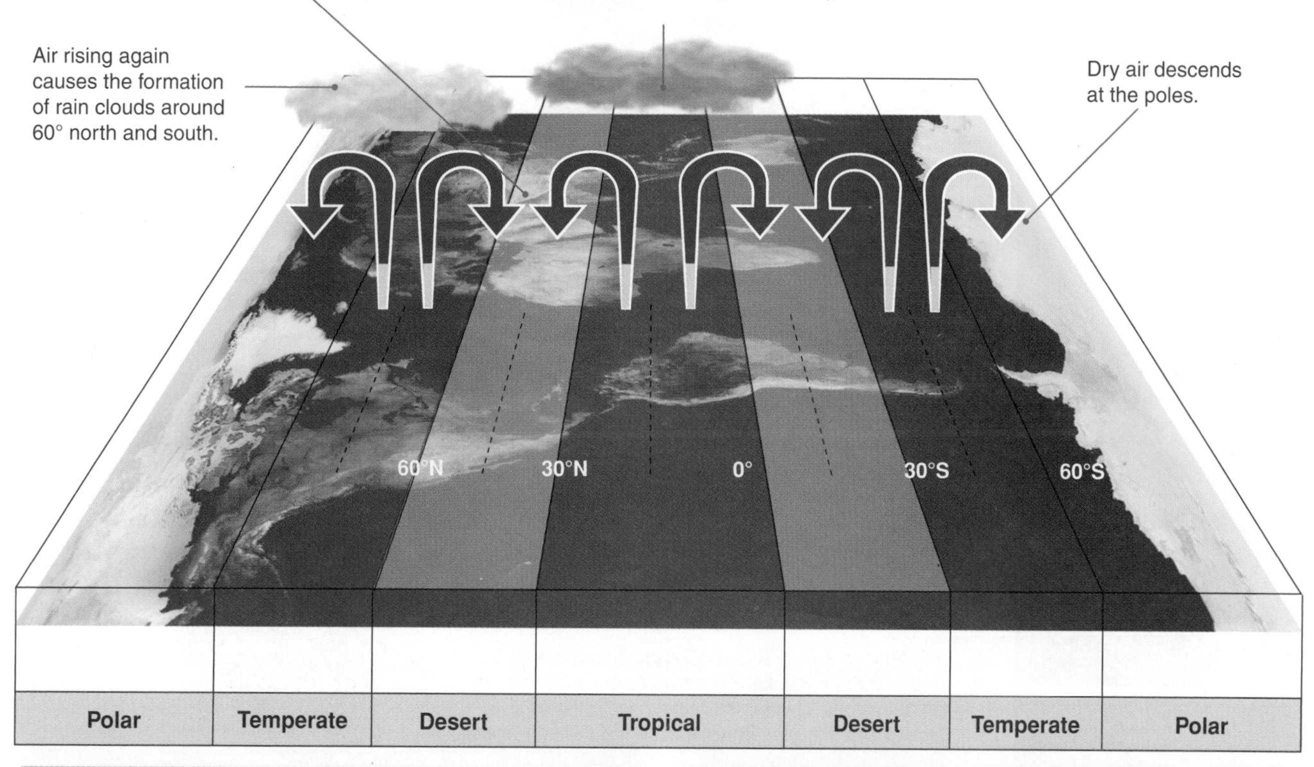

Polar	Temperate	Desert	Tropical	Desert	Temperate	Polar

Global atmospheric circulation leads to areas of high rainfall, like the tropical rainforests, and areas of dry air, like deserts. The movement of air as it rises, cools, and descends creates the east-to-west prevailing winds that flow in equatorial regions and the prevailing westerlies the mid-latitudes.

Atmospheric circulation redistributes most of the heat from the tropics towards the poles (~78% in the Northern Hemisphere and 92% in the Southern Hemisphere). Ocean circulation transports the rest of the heat. These include warmer surface, wind-driven currents and deeper saltier, density currents.

1. Explain why the tropics tend to be both hot and wet: ____________________

2. Explain why the distribution of biomes in the Northern Hemisphere is similar, but not identical to, the distribution of biomes in the Southern Hemisphere:

____

ISBN: 978-1-98-856632-0

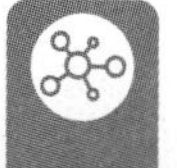

9 The World's Terrestrial Biomes

Key Question: What factors determine the distribution of the world's distinct biological communities?

Global patterns of vegetation distribution are closely related to climate. Although they are complex, major vegetation **biomes** can be recognized. These are large areas where a distinctive vegetation type has formed in response to a particular physical environment. Biomes have characteristic features, but the boundaries between them are not distinct. The same biome may occur in widely separated regions of the world wherever the climatic and soil conditions are similar.

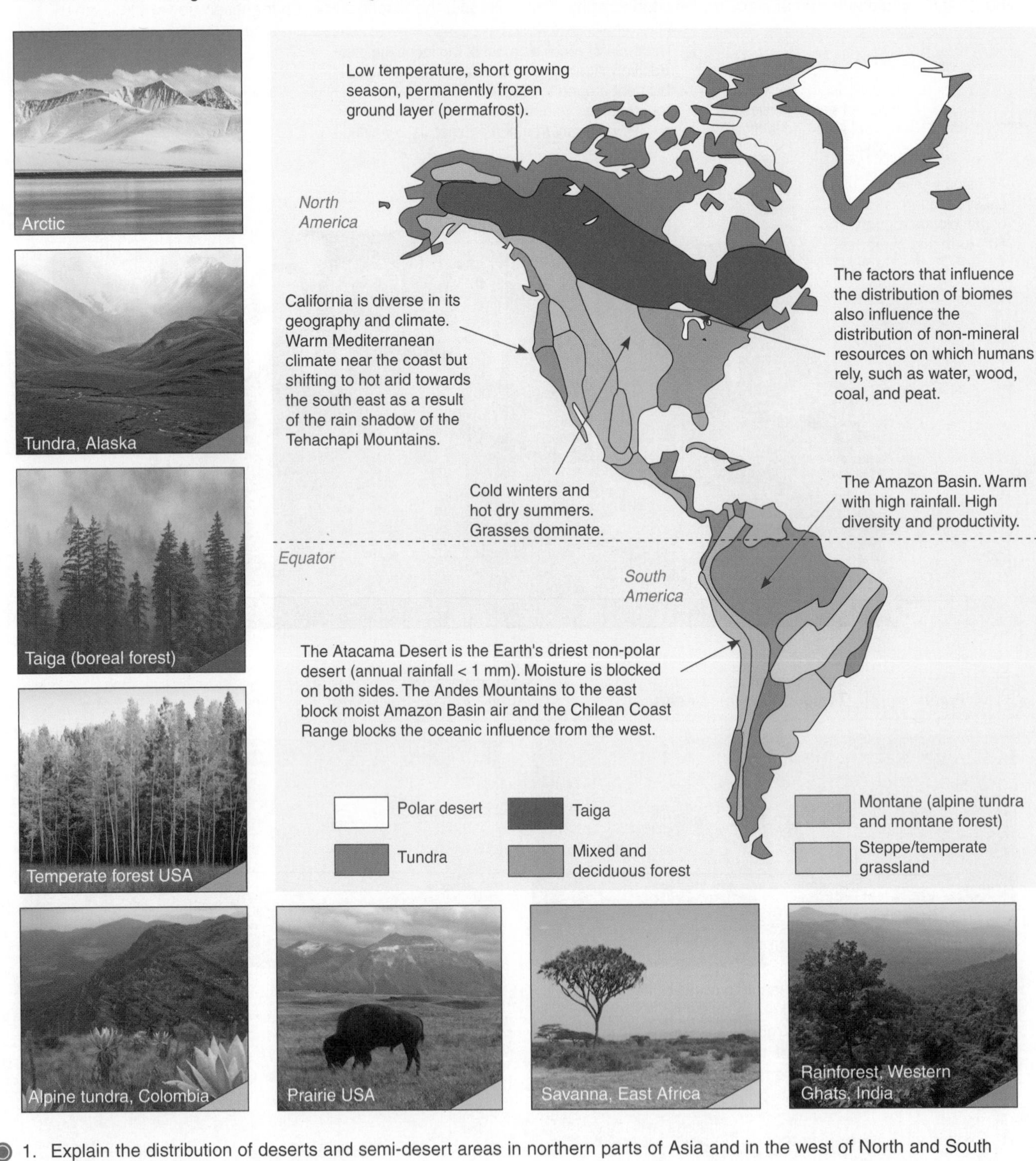

1. Explain the distribution of deserts and semi-desert areas in northern parts of Asia and in the west of North and South America (away from equatorial regions):

____

____

____

____

____

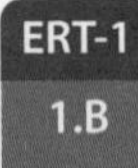

ISBN: 978-1-98-856632-0

Vegetation patterns are determined largely by climate, which in turn is heavily influenced by topography and proximity to the ocean. Where there are large mountain ranges, wind is deflected upwards causing rain on the windward side and a drier 'rain shadow' on the leeward side. Rain shadowing governs the occurrence of many deserts globally, and some of the world's driest regions, including the Atacama Desert in Chile and Death Valley in California, are in rain shadows. Wherever they occur, montane regions are associated with their own altitude adapted vegetation. Biome classification may vary considerably and is not necessarily static as environments shift under patterns of changing climate and human influence. However, most classifications recognize desert, tundra, grassland and forest types and distinguish them on the basis of latitude.

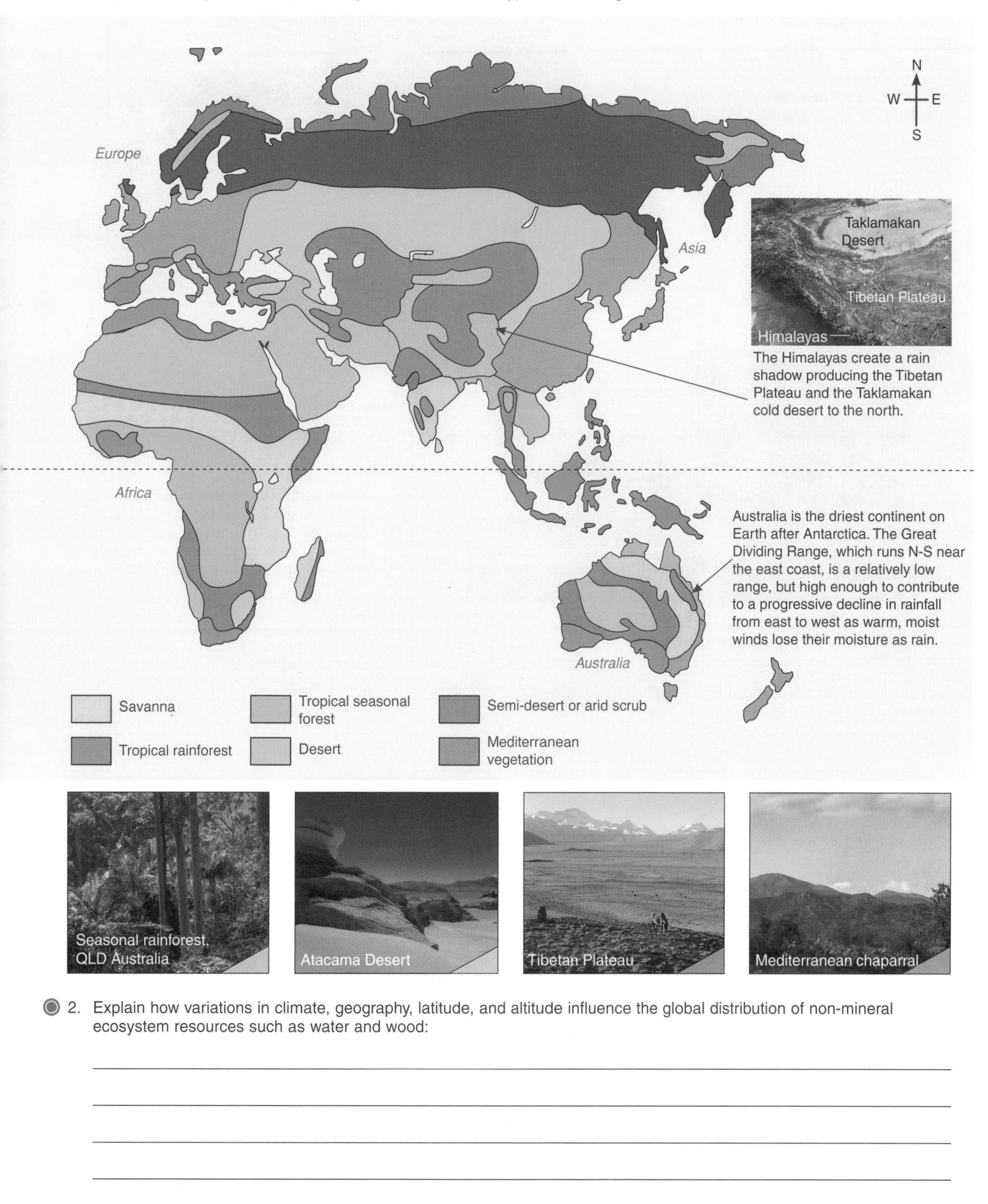

2. Explain how variations in climate, geography, latitude, and altitude influence the global distribution of non-mineral ecosystem resources such as water and wood:

ISBN: 978-1-98-856632-0

10 Temperature and the Distribution of Biomes

Key Question: What is the role of temperature and rainfall in determining the geographical location of terrestrial biomes? Temperature and precipitation are excellent predictors of biome distribution. Temperature decreases from the equator to the poles. Temperature and precipitation act together as limiting factors to determine the type of desert, grassland, or forest biome in a region. Latitude directly affects solar input and temperature.

Within a single latitudinal region, the level of precipitation (rainfall) governs the type of plant community found. Note that the effect of altitude is similar to that of latitude (ice will occur at high altitudes even at low-latitudes).

Cold

Hot

Wet

Dry

Latitudinal region	0–250	250–1000	1000–4000	4000+
Polar / Arctic	Snow & ice			
Arctic	Tundra			
Subarctic	Boreal forest (taiga)	Boreal forest (taiga)		
Temperate	Chaparral	Chaparral	Temperate forests	
Temperate	Desert	Grassland	Temperate forests	
Equatorial / Tropical	Desert	Semi-desert	Savanna	Tropical forest

Latitudinal region: Equatorial → Polar

Annual precipitation (mm): 0, 250, 1000, 4000

Desert → Tropical

As the Earth curves towards the poles, solar energy is spread out over an ever increasing area. This energy must also travel through a greater amount of the atmosphere, expending more energy than at low latitudes.

1. Explain how temperature and rainfall affect the distribution of biomes:

2. Explain why biomes are not evenly distributed about the globe:

3. Explain how the landscape can modify climate:

4. Explain why higher latitudes receive less solar energy than lower latitudes:

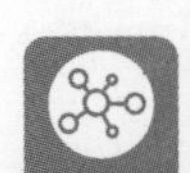

ERT-1

1.B

ISBN: 978-1-98-856632-0

11 Changing Biomes

Key Question: How and why has the distribution of biomes changed over time and how might it change in the future? The worldwide distribution of biomes is not fixed. Biome distribution has continually changed as global climates have shifted between warmer and cooler periods (below). The increase in average global temperature currently being experienced on Earth is already seeing current biomes shift as alpine areas shrink and sea levels rise.

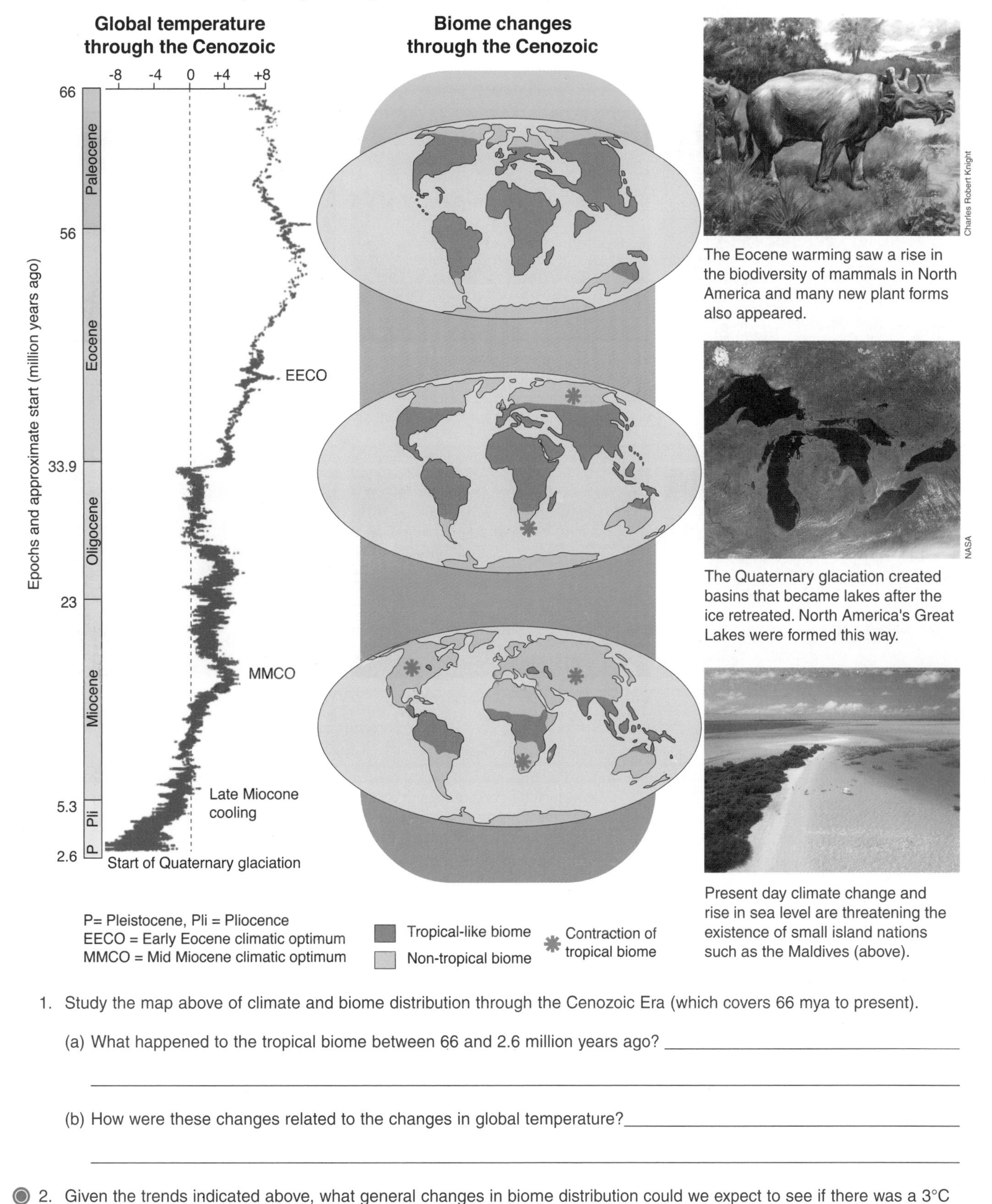

The Eocene warming saw a rise in the biodiversity of mammals in North America and many new plant forms also appeared.

The Quaternary glaciation created basins that became lakes after the ice retreated. North America's Great Lakes were formed this way.

Present day climate change and rise in sea level are threatening the existence of small island nations such as the Maldives (above).

1. Study the map above of climate and biome distribution through the Cenozoic Era (which covers 66 mya to present).

   (a) What happened to the tropical biome between 66 and 2.6 million years ago? ______________________

   ____

   (b) How were these changes related to the changes in global temperature? ______________________

   ____

2. Given the trends indicated above, what general changes in biome distribution could we expect to see if there was a 3°C to 5°C rise in global temperatures over the next 50-70 years?

____

____

ISBN: 978-1-98-856632-0

157 ➔ 155 ➔ ERT-1 1.B

12 Aquatic Biomes

Key Question: What are the characteristics of the major aquatic biomes and how are they distributed?

Water covers ~70% of Earth's surface, so aquatic biomes are a major component of the global environment. Aquatic biomes include all those environments that are dominated by water. These environments include deep oceans, shallow seas and reefs, swamps and estuaries, and rivers and lakes. Aquatic biomes include some of the most productive and the least productive ecosystems in the world (production being the amount of accumulated biomass). The characteristics of different aquatic ecosystems depend on where they occur on the globe and the local conditions that shape them.

Marine biomes
oceans, estuaries, and reefs

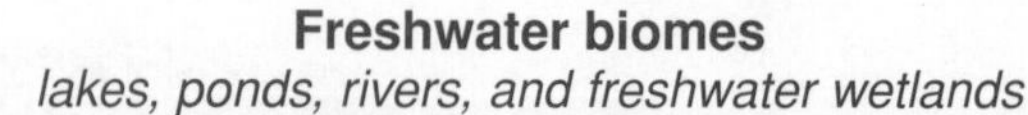

Freshwater biomes
lakes, ponds, rivers, and freshwater wetlands

The open oceans are characterized by saline (salty) waters, waves, and currents. Five oceanic divisions are recognized but they are all interconnected as one global ocean.

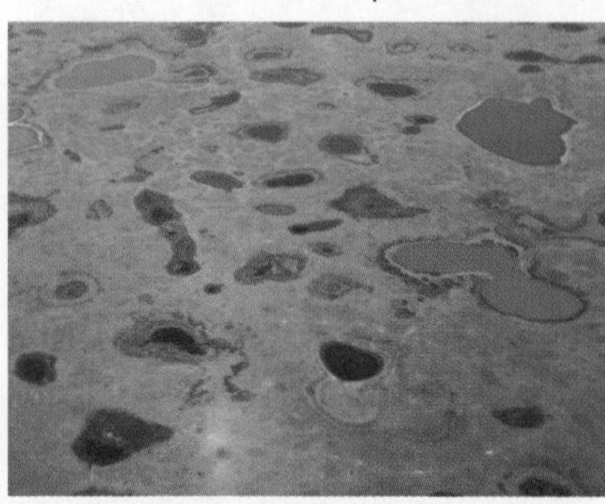

The prairie potholes of the midwest (USA) are shallow wetlands resulting from glaciation. Glaciation, tectonic events, and volcanic activity have formed the world's largest lakes.

Lakes are inland depressions containing standing water. Their distribution is not uniform but dependent on geology and geography. They are an important source of drinking water.

Estuaries are regions where fresh water of rivers meets tidal flows from the ocean.

Streams and rivers are characterized by continuously flowing water.

Wetlands include marshes, bogs, fens, and swamps. Bogs and fens have peaty soils.

Coral reefs occur in tropical and subtropical regions and are of biological (not geological) origin (they are made from living organisms).

- Aquatic biomes are broadly categorized as marine and freshwater. The marine biomes include coral reefs and estuaries, whereas the freshwater biomes include rivers, lakes and wetlands. Oceans cover more than 70% of the Earth's surface and contain 97% of the Earth's water. Less than 1% of the Earth's water is fresh water, an essential resource for plant and animal life.
- Temperature, salinity, tides, waves, and currents determine the characteristics and functioning of marine ecosystems. The most productive marine biomes are coral reefs, coastal waters, and estuaries and coastal marshes, because these are regions with high light and large nutrient fluxes.
- Freshwater biomes may be contained within a basin or flowing and are heavily influenced by geological formation, topography, and land use. Wetland systems are varied and often difficult to categorize. They are best described according to soil type, vegetation, and hydrology.

*Go to **BIOZONE's Resource Hub** for information on the distribution of aquatic biomes*

1. Describe the defining features of each of the following marine biomes:

   (a) Open oceans: ______________________

   (b) Estuaries: ______________________

   (c) Coral reefs: ______________________

2. What characteristic distinguishes rivers and streams from lakes and ponds? ______________________

____

ISBN: 978-1-98-856632-0

Characteristics of ocean ecosystems

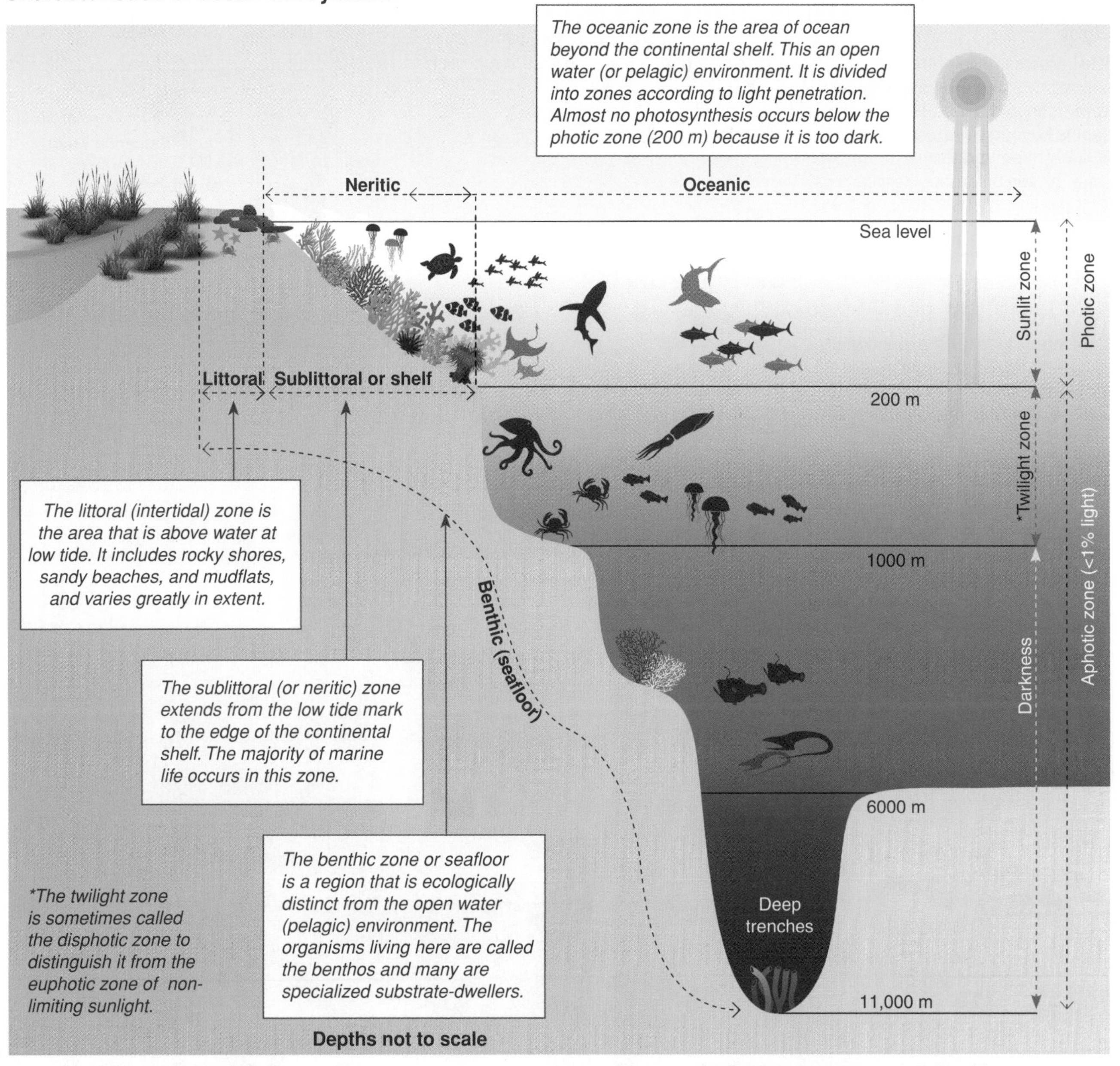

Temperature, salinity, and density

- Although the open ocean may appear to be quite uniform, the physical conditions vary considerably with depth. This feature, called **stratification**, is also a feature of freshwater systems provided they are deep enough.
- Most marine life is found where there is enough light for photosynthesis. Relatively few organisms are adapted to live in the dark at the immense pressures below 1000 m.
- Oceans overall are less productive than terrestrial systems, because so much of it is dark, but coastal waters, areas of upwelling, and reef ecosystems can be very productive. These zones of higher productivity are important sources of non-mineral marine resources such as fish.
- In mid-latitudes during summer and year-round in the tropics, warmer, less dense water overlies colder, denser water. Between these layers is a region of rapid temperature change called the thermocline. Salinity shows a similar gradient although it is more variable. In the tropics, evaporation can increase surface salinity, whereas at high latitudes, high precipitation rates can lower surface salinity.

Standard depth profiles for temperature, salinity and density (South Atlantic)

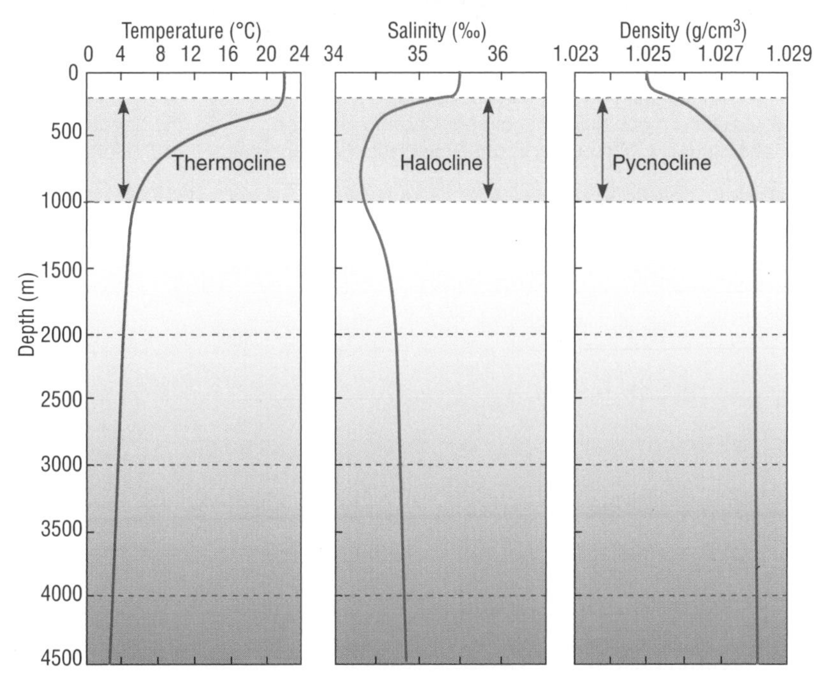

ISBN: 978-1-98-856632-0

Light

The vertical profile of the ocean is defined by light penetration. Here we have defined the aphotic zone as the depths beyond which less than 1% of sunlight penetrates (~200 m) but you may see different classifications for the photic and aphotic zones as these terms are not used uniformly. The 1% light level is the level below which there is insufficient light for photosynthesis.

Light intensity falls off exponentially with depth (right) but light quality (color) also changes with depth. In water, red light (longer wavelength) is absorbed quickly, leaving blue. However, water color is affected by particulates in the water. These include algae, which have pigments that absorb red and blue light (which are photosynthetically active wavelengths) and reflect green (which is not used in photosynthesis).

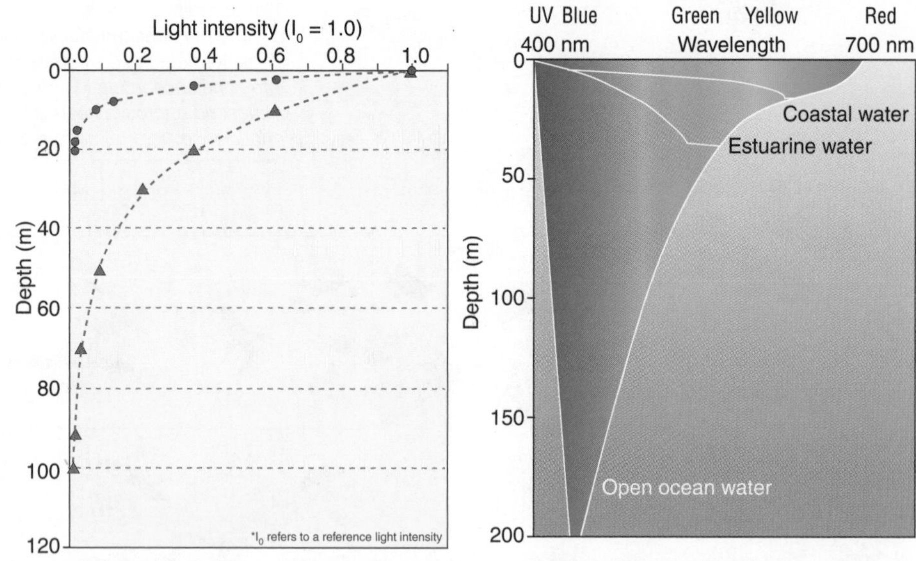

Light intensity declines exponentially with depth and most light is absorbed in the first 1 m. The depth of the 1% light level (the depth of the photic zone) determines whether we see the water as "blue" or "green".

Different waters get their colors from the mixture of pigments in algae, colored dissolved organic matter (CDOM), and minerals. More light is absorbed and scattered in productive coastal waters.

A person standing on the rocks at Casco bay in Maine would see a much different colored ocean to a person standing beside the ocean in the Greek island of Skopelos.

The contrast in color between the shallower, near shore waters and the deeper offshore waters is quite clear along the Big Sur coastline of California.

3. Explain why the salinity profiles of oceans often varies with location and climate: ______

4. (a) Explain what happens to light when it enters water: ______

(b) Describe factors that contribute to the different colors we see in natural water bodies: ______

ISBN: 978-1-98-856632-0

Trophic relationships and nutrient cycling in aquatic biomes

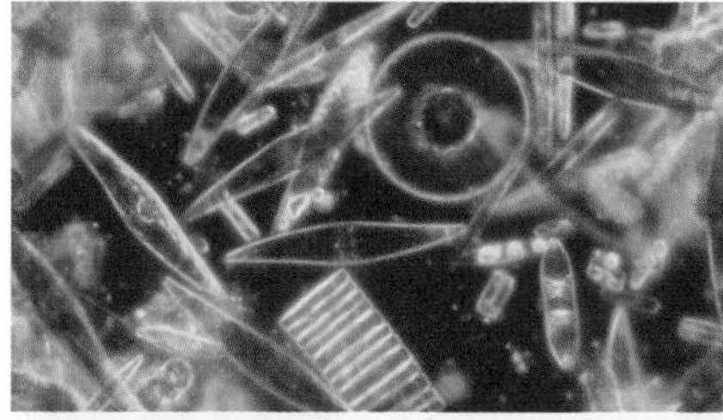

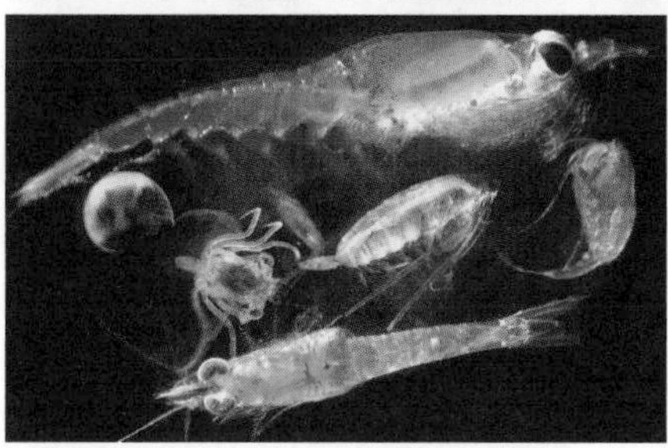

Lake Dora (Florida)

Phytoplankton, or algae, (top) are the ocean's producers. They support the ocean's primary consumers, the zooplankton (bottom). Plankton and their remains sink out of the photic zone and their nutrients return only slowly. A permanent thermocline in the tropics forms a barrier to nutrient return from deeper waters and contributes to the low productivity of tropical open oceans.

Coastal marshes, such as this one at Cape Cod on USA's east coast are highly productive ecosystems. Tidal flushing brings in new nutrients, sweeps out accumulated sulfides and metabolic wastes, and replaces anoxic water with oxygenated water. Algal and bacterial populations turn over rapidly and decomposition rates are high, so nutrient cycling is very efficient.

Lakes have well defined boundaries and their own internal systems of energy flow and nutrient cycling. However, they are strongly influenced by the nutrient inputs from the surrounding land. This makes them particular vulnerable to nutrient enrichment (eutrophication) as a result of activities such as agriculture and logging in the surrounding area. These lakes often suffer from extensive algal 'blooms' (above).

5. Explain why the majority of marine life is found in the neritic zone (sublittoral or continental shelf): ____________________

6. Explain how differences in the physical conditions in marine environments contribute to the differences in the global distribution of non-mineral resources (such as fish and shellfish):

7. Deepwater benthic communities are particularly vulnerable to exploitation by a fishing technique called deep sea trawling (bottom trawling). Nets are dragged along the seabed, or just above it, usually targeting just one high value species. Unwanted species are discarded. Much deep sea trawling occurs on **seamounts**, which support diverse deep water coral communities. The images right show trawled and untrawled seamounts at 1000 - 2000 m depth. Evidence from surveys indicates that recovery of these communities after trawling is poor. As a class, discuss what it is about the environment that makes recovery so poor.

Summarize your discussion on a separate sheet and attach it to this page.

Seamounts are undersea 'mountains', hundreds to thousands of meters below the surface. They are one of the most common marine environments and widely exploited.

CSIRO Marine Research cc 2.5

ISBN: 978-1-98-856632-0

13 Nutrient Cycles

Key Question: What processes drive the cycling of matter in Earth's ecosystems?

Nutrient cycles move and transfer chemical elements (e.g. carbon) within and between ecosystems. The cycling of these elements is called a nutrient cycle, or a biogeochemical cycle. The term biogeochemical means that **bio**logical, **geo**logical, and **chemical** processes are involved in the chemical transformations. Each biogeochemical cycle has one or more **reservoirs**, which are large, usually abiotic, stores of the chemical element and smaller, more active pools where the nutrient cycles between the biotic (living) and abiotic components of an ecosystem (see diagram below). Energy (ultimately from the Sun) drives the cycling of matter within and between systems. Matter is conserved throughout all these transformations, although it may pass from one ecosystem to another.

Tropical rainforest (Amazon)

Temperate woodland (Illinois)

Processes in a generalized biogeochemical cycle

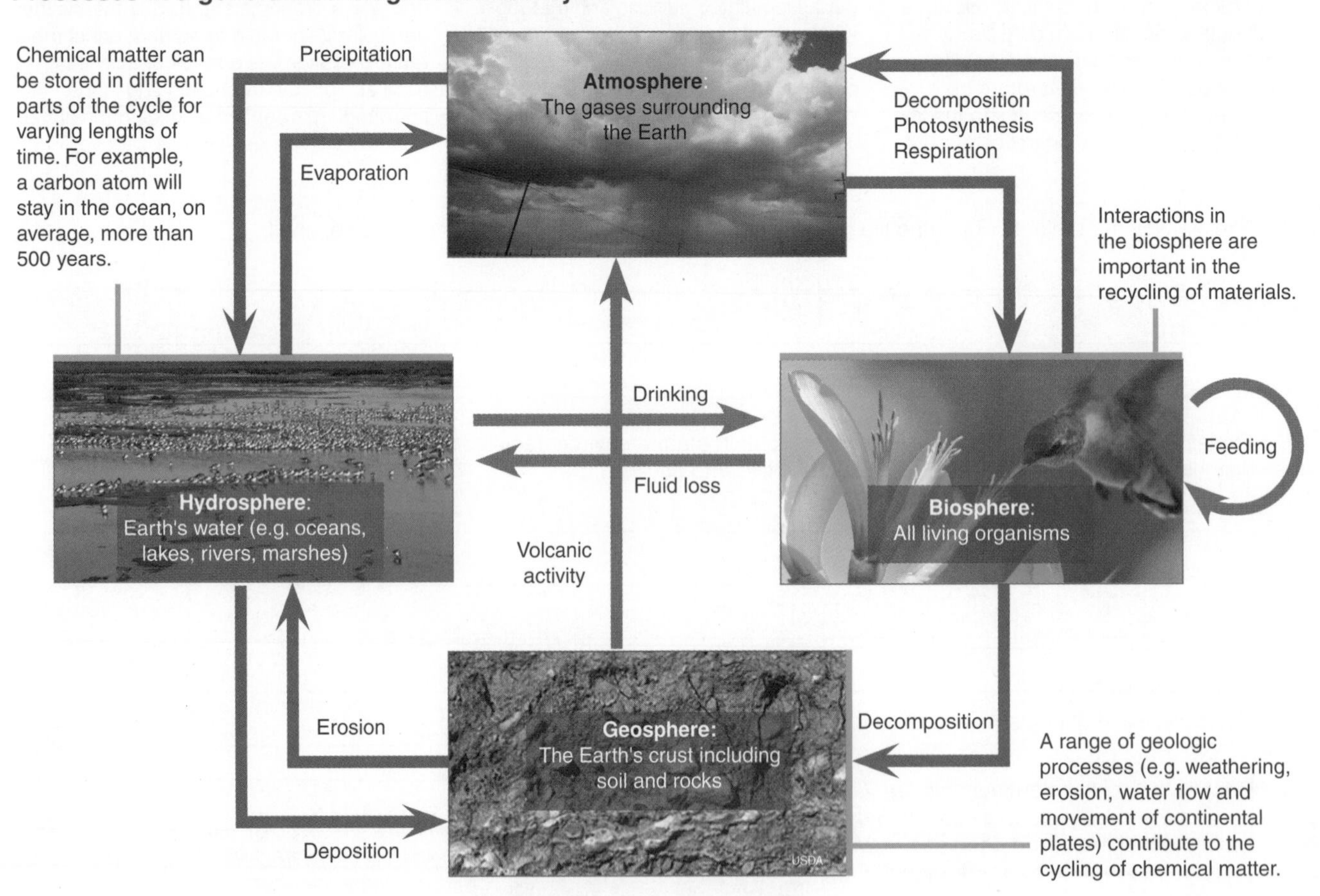

1. What is a nutrient cycle? ______________________________

____

____

2. Why do you think it is important that matter is cycled through an ecosystem? ______________________________

____

____

____

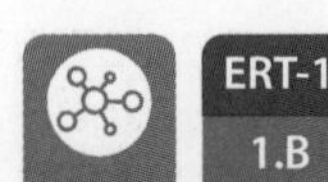

ISBN: 978-1-98-856632-0

14 The Carbon Cycle

Key Question: How does the cycling of carbon through the abiotic and biotic components of ecosystems make carbon continually available to organisms?

Carbon is an essential element of life and is incorporated into the organic molecules that make up living organisms. Large quantities of carbon are stored in **sinks**, which include the atmosphere as carbon dioxide gas (CO_2), the ocean as carbonate and bicarbonate, and rocks such as coal and limestone. Carbon cycles between the biotic and abiotic environment. Carbon dioxide is converted by autotrophs into carbohydrates via photosynthesis and returned to the atmosphere as CO_2 through respiration (**fluxes**). These fluxes can be measured. Some of the sinks and processes involved in the carbon cycle, together with the carbon fluxes, are shown below. Humans intervene in the carbon cycle through activities such as combustion and deforestation.

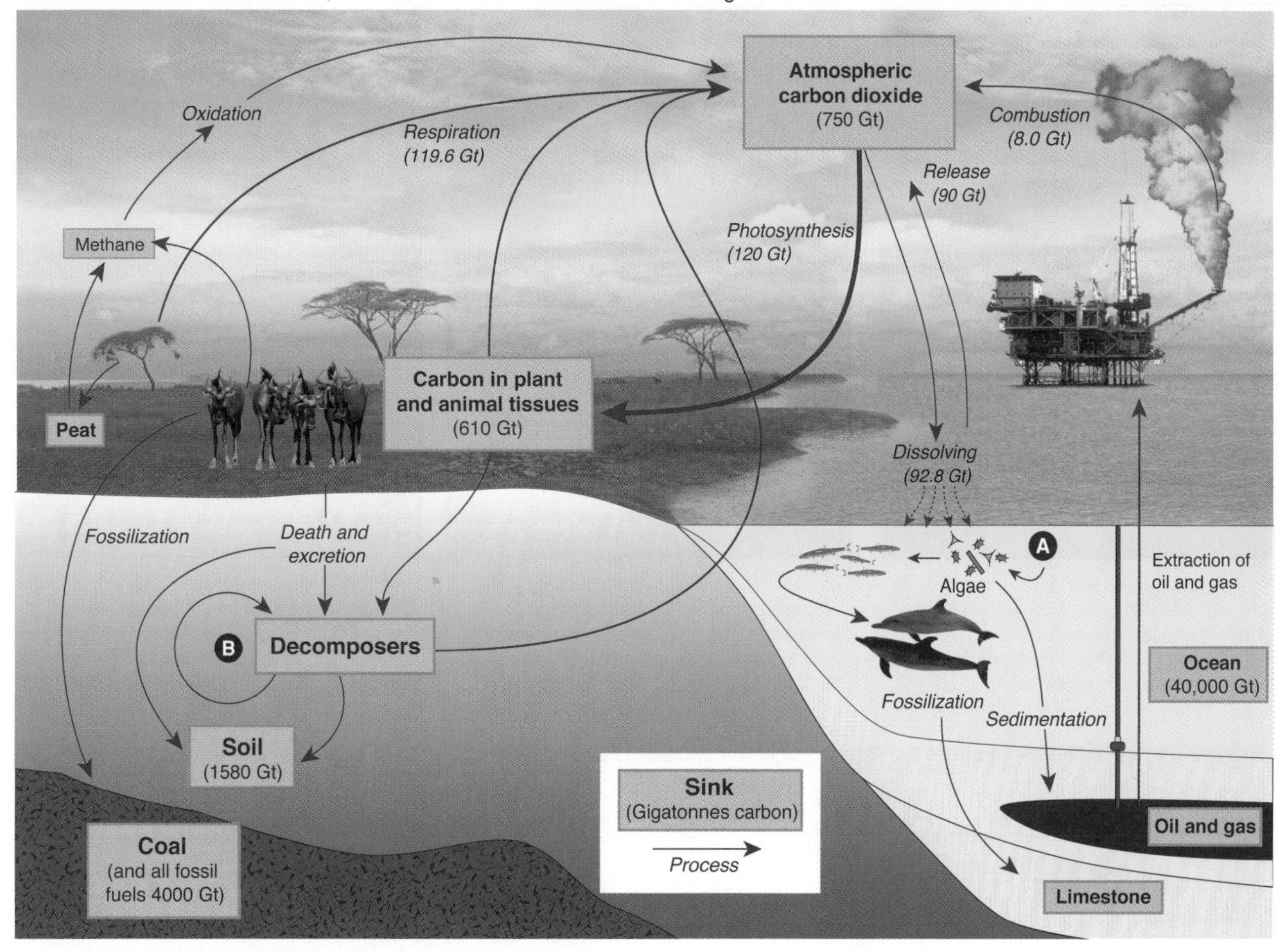

1. Add arrows and labels to the diagram above to show:

   (a) Dissolving of limestone by acid rain
   (b) Release of carbon from the marine food chain
   (c) Mining and burning of coal
   (d) Burning of plant material.

2. (a) Name the processes that release carbon into the atmosphere: ______

   (b) In what form is the carbon released? ______

3. Name the four geological reservoirs (sinks), in the diagram above, that can act as a source of carbon:

   (a) ______ (c) ______
   (b) ______ (d) ______

4. (a) Identify the process carried out by algae at point **A**: ______

   (b) Identify the process carried out by decomposers at **B**: ______

5. What would be the effect on carbon cycling if there were no decomposers present in an ecosystem? ______

ISBN: 978-1-98-856632-0

156 154

ERT-1 2.B

Carbon may be locked up in biotic or abiotic systems for long periods of time, e.g. in the wood of trees or in fossil fuels such as coal or oil. Human activity, e.g. extraction and large scale combustion of fossil fuels, has disturbed the balance of the carbon cycle.

Organisms break down organic material to release carbon. Fungi and decomposing bacteria break down dead plant matter in the leaf litter of forests. Termites, with the aid of symbiotic protozoans and bacteria in their guts, digest the cellulose of woody tissue.

Coal is formed from the remains of terrestrial plant material buried in shallow swamps and subsequently compacted under sediments to form a hard black material. Coal is composed primarily of carbon and is a widely used fuel source.

Oil and **natural gas** formed in the past when dead algae and zooplankton settled to the bottom of shallow seas and lakes. These remains were buried and compressed under layers of non-porous sediment.

Limestone is a type of sedimentary rock composed mostly of calcium carbonate. It forms when the shells of mollusks and other marine organisms with calcium carbonate ($CaCO_3$) skeletons become fossilized.

Peat (partly decayed organic material) forms when plant material is not fully decomposed due to acidic or anaerobic conditions. Peaty wetlands are an efficient carbon sink but are lost through oxidation when land is drained.

6. Describe the biological origin of the following geological deposits:

(a) Coal: ___

(b) Oil: ___

(c) Limestone: ___

(d) Peat: ___

7. Using examples, compare and contrast the amount of time carbon spends in its various reservoirs: ___

8. Explain the role of living organisms in the carbon cycle: ___

9. Accumulated reserves of carbon such as peat, coal, and oil represent a sink or natural diversion from the cycle. In natural circumstances, the carbon in these sinks eventually returns to the cycle through geological processes which return deposits to the surface for oxidation. Explain the effect of human activity on the amount of carbon stored in sinks:

___

ISBN: 978-1-98-856632-0

Fluxes in the biotic environment affect the carbon cycle

The balance of photosynthesizing and respiring organisms can affect the amount of CO_2 in the atmosphere. If the biomass of photosynthesizing organisms vastly outweighs that of respiring organisms, CO_2 will be removed from the atmosphere and the carbon will be stored as biomass. Respiration returns carbon to the atmosphere.

Photosynthesis and carbon

- Photosynthesis removes carbon from the atmosphere by fixing the carbon in CO_2 into carbohydrate molecules (e.g. glucose). Plants use the glucose to build structures such as wood.
- Respiration in living organisms returns some carbon to the atmosphere. If the amount or rate of carbon fixation exceeds that released in respiration then carbon will build up in the biosphere and be depleted in the atmosphere.

Respiration and carbon

- Cellular respiration breaks down glucose and releases carbon into the atmosphere as carbon dioxide.
- If the rate of carbon release is greater than that fixed by photosynthesis then carbon may accumulate in the atmosphere over time. Deforestation and the burning of fossil fuels have increased the amount of carbon in the atmosphere and depleted what was stored in the biosphere.

INVESTIGATION 1.1: Carbon cycling simulation

See appendix for equipment list.

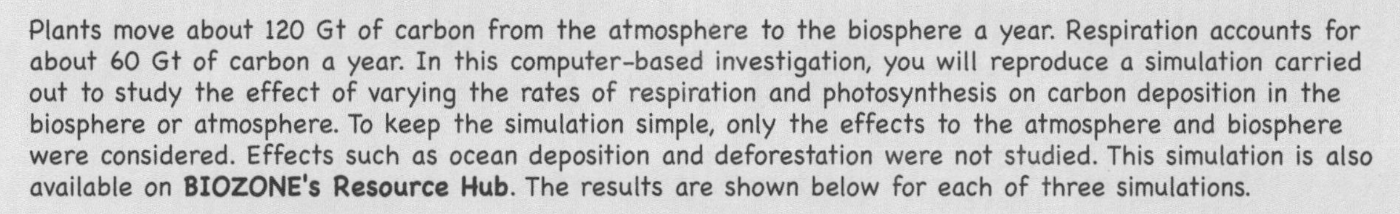

Plants move about 120 Gt of carbon from the atmosphere to the biosphere a year. Respiration accounts for about 60 Gt of carbon a year. In this computer-based investigation, you will reproduce a simulation carried out to study the effect of varying the rates of respiration and photosynthesis on carbon deposition in the biosphere or atmosphere. To keep the simulation simple, only the effects to the atmosphere and biosphere were considered. Effects such as ocean deposition and deforestation were not studied. This simulation is also available on **BIOZONE's Resource Hub**. The results are shown below for each of three simulations.

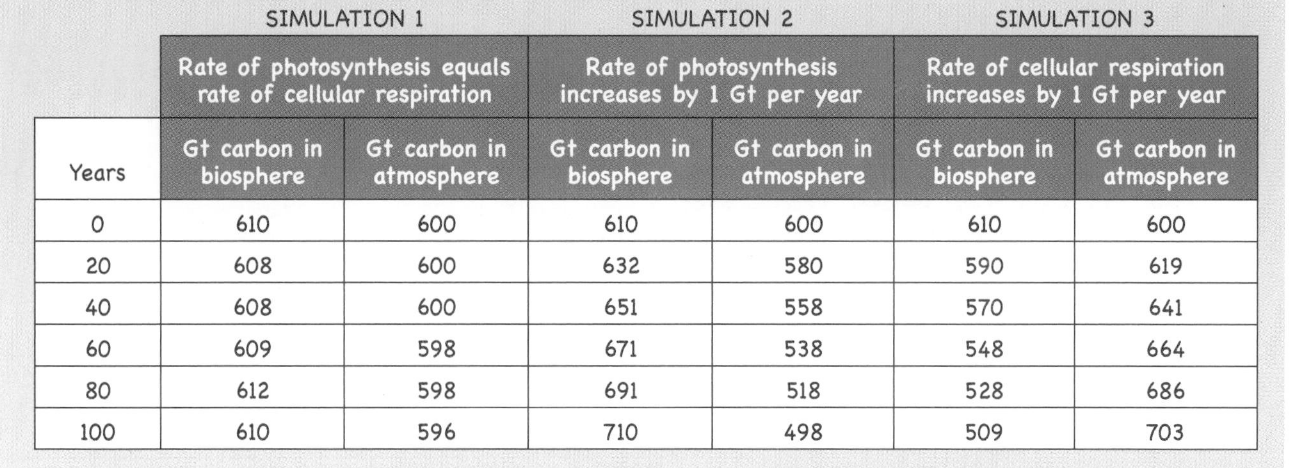

	SIMULATION 1: Rate of photosynthesis equals rate of cellular respiration		SIMULATION 2: Rate of photosynthesis increases by 1 Gt per year		SIMULATION 3: Rate of cellular respiration increases by 1 Gt per year	
Years	Gt carbon in biosphere	Gt carbon in atmosphere	Gt carbon in biosphere	Gt carbon in atmosphere	Gt carbon in biosphere	Gt carbon in atmosphere
0	610	600	610	600	610	600
20	608	600	632	580	590	619
40	608	600	651	558	570	641
60	609	598	671	538	548	664
80	612	598	691	518	528	686
100	610	596	710	498	509	703

1. Set up a spreadsheet in Microsoft Excel®, or similar program. Enter the data for the three simulations in columns as above. Select the data range including an appropriate header for each column of data.
2. From the menu choose < Insert < Chart XY scatter < Scatter with straight lines and markers. Right click on the graph and choose 'Select Data". You will have to choose Switch Row/Column. Click OK.
3. Right click on your plot to format your graph to add a graph title, axis titles, and a legend (key).

10. In your group, study the results of your simulation and discuss the effect of:
    (a) Increasing the rate of photosynthesis on atmospheric and biospheric carbon
    (b) Increasing the rate of cellular respiration on atmospheric and biospheric carbon.
    (c) Identify human activities with the same effects as increased respiration.
    Summarize your discussion and any notes on a separate sheet and attach it to this page.

ISBN: 978-1-98-856632-0

15 The Nitrogen Cycle

Key Question: What processes are involved in the cycling of nitrogen between the atmosphere and the biosphere?

Nitrogen is an essential element in living things. It is a component of photosynthetic pigments in plants, and part of proteins and nucleic acids in all organisms. Plants obtain their nitrogen from the soil or via symbioses, whereas consumers obtain their nitrogen from other organisms (e.g. by eating or via symbioses). The Earth's atmosphere is about 80% nitrogen gas (N_2), but molecular nitrogen is so stable that it is directly available only to those few organisms (all of them bacteria) that can fix it (capture and combine it into another molecule).

Bacteria play a crucial role in nitrogen cycling, transferring nitrogen between the biotic and abiotic environments through nitrogen fixation and other nitrogen transformations. Humans intervene in the nitrogen cycle by manufacture and application of nitrogen fertilizers. Manufacture of nitrogen fertilizer is an energy-intensive artificial nitrogen fixation process in which atmospheric nitrogen and hydrogen are combined under high temperature and pressure. This process (the Haber process) was responsible for the growth in intensive agriculture and is one of the largest contributors to a buildup of reactive nitrogen in the biosphere.

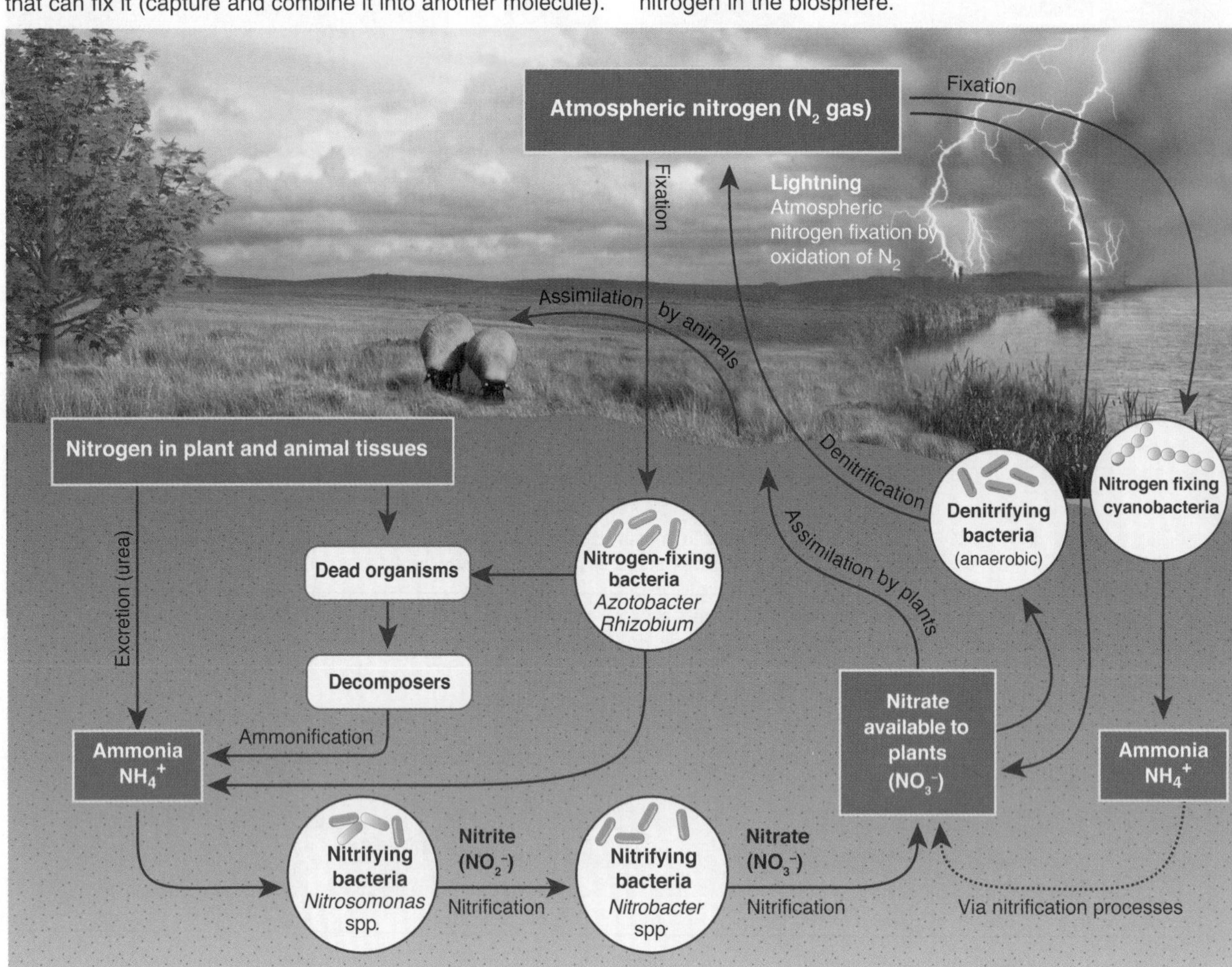

1. Use the diagram above to describe five instances in the nitrogen cycle where bacterial action is important. Include the name of each of the processes and the changes to the form of nitrogen involved:

(a) ______________________________

(b) ______________________________

(c) ______________________________

(d) ______________________________

(e) ______________________________

ERT-1
2.B

76

137

ISBN: 978-1-98-856632-0

Bacterial nitrogen fixation

Nitrogen fixation is a process by which molecular nitrogen is converted to ammonia, nitrites, or nitrates, which can be absorbed by plants and converted to protein and nucleic acids. Biological nitrogen fixation is carried out by various species of bacteria (including cyanobacteria), free living in the soil or water, or in symbioses with plants, protists, or lichen-forming fungi.

Nitrogen fixing symbioses in higher plants

- Root nodules are a root symbiosis between a higher plant and a bacterium. The bacteria fix atmospheric nitrogen and are extremely important to the nutrition of many plants, including the economically important legume family. Root nodules are extensions of the root tissue caused by entry of a bacterium. In legumes, this bacterium is *Rhizobium*. Other bacterial genera are involved in the root nodule symbioses in non-legumes.
- The bacteria in these symbioses live in the nodule where they fix atmospheric nitrogen and provide the plant with most, or all, of its nitrogen requirements. In return, they have access to a rich supply of carbohydrate. The fixation of atmospheric nitrogen to ammonia occurs within the nodule, using the enzyme nitrogenase. Nitrogenase is inhibited by oxygen and the nodule provides a low O_2 environment in which fixation can occur.

Above: Two examples of legume nodules caused by *Rhizobium*. Root nodules on the roots of vetch (left) and soybean (right).

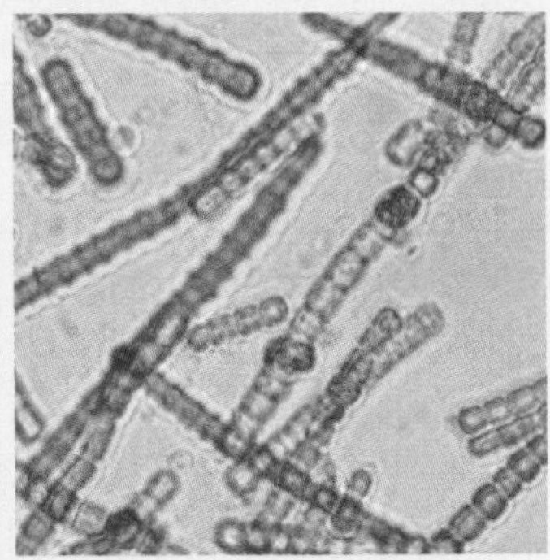

Above left: Nodules caused by the bacterium *Frankia* on roots of common alder. Above right: Nitrogen fixing cyanobacterium showing the heterocysts, which are specialized nitrogen fixing cells in the filament.

2. Describe three processes that fix atmospheric nitrogen:

(a) ______

(b) ______

(c) ______

3. What process releases nitrogen gas into the atmosphere? ______

4. What is the primary reservoir for nitrogen? ______

5. What form of nitrogen is most readily available to most plants? ______

6. Name one essential organic compound that plants need nitrogen for: ______

7. How do animals acquire the nitrogen they need? ______

8. Why might farmers plow a crop of legumes into the ground rather than harvest it? ______

9. Describe the ecological role of nitrogen-fixing symbioses in the nitrogen cycle. Use examples to illustrate your answer:

ISBN: 978-1-98-856632-0

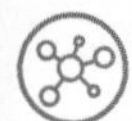

Human activity and nitrogen cycling

Nitrogen is often a limiting nutrient for plant and algal growth (as is phosphorus). A limiting nutrient is the one that is in shortest supply and therefore limits growth.

Application of nitrogen fertilizers at rates that exceed the ability of plants to use it leads to accumulation of nitrogen in the soil. This nitrogen can then leach (move down through the soil) into groundwater or run off into surface waters.

This extra nitrogen load is one of the causes of increased enrichment (eutrophication) of lakes and coastal waters so that algal blooms or mats are often seen at the surface (right). An increase in algal production also increases decomposer activity, depleting oxygen and leading to the death of fish and other aquatic organisms (far right). Anoxic bottom waters also cause the release of phosphorus from sediments, making enrichment worse.

The rate at which nitrates are added has increased faster than the rate at which nitrates are returned to the atmosphere. This has led to the widespread accumulation of nitrogen in the biosphere.

Global changes in nitrogen inputs and outputs between 1860 and 1995 in million tonne

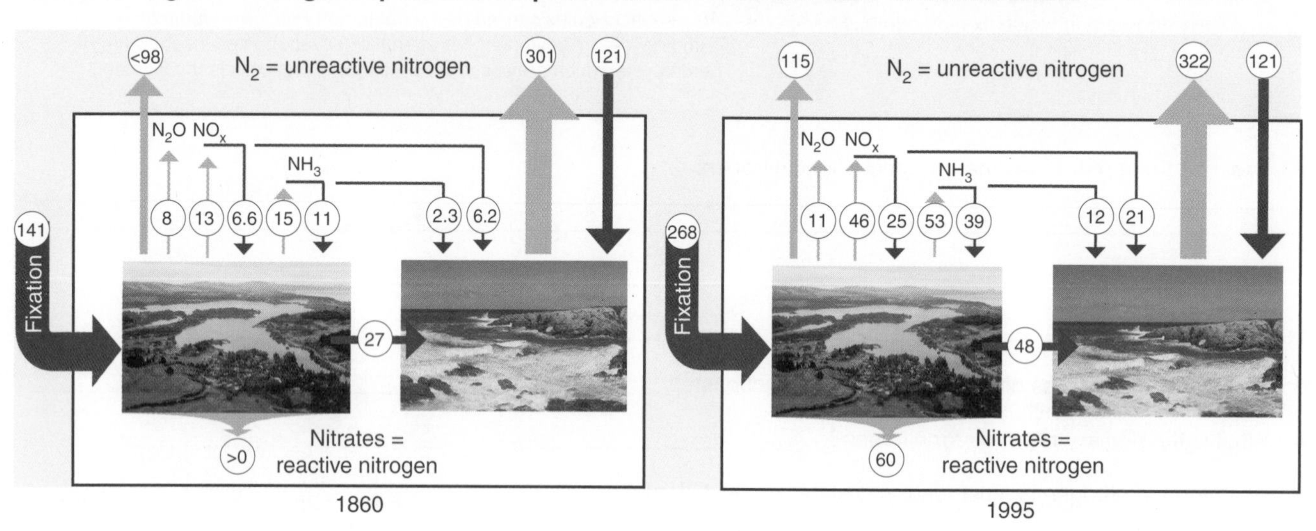

10. (a) How does excess nitrogen enter waterways? ______________________

(b) Describe one important effect of nitrogen pollution: ______________________

11. Using the quantitative models of nitrogen fluxes (1860 and 1995) above, calculate the increase in nitrogen deposition in the oceans from 1860 to 1995 and compare this to the increase in release of nitrogen from the oceans:

____

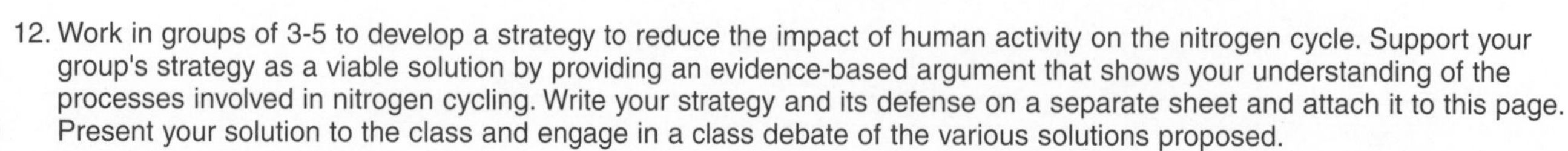

12. Work in groups of 3-5 to develop a strategy to reduce the impact of human activity on the nitrogen cycle. Support your group's strategy as a viable solution by providing an evidence-based argument that shows your understanding of the processes involved in nitrogen cycling. Write your strategy and its defense on a separate sheet and attach it to this page. Present your solution to the class and engage in a class debate of the various solutions proposed.

ISBN: 978-1-98-856632-0

16 The Phosphorus Cycle

Key Question: What are the major reservoirs of phosphorus in ecosystems and how is it made available to organisms?

Phosphorus is an essential component of genetic and energy systems of living organisms and an important limiting factor to productivity in ecosystems. Phosphorus cycling has no atmospheric component and return from the ocean to the land is very slow. Its main reservoirs are in rock and sediments and small losses from terrestrial systems by leaching are generally balanced by gains from weathering of rock. In both aquatic and terrestrial ecosystems, phosphorus is cycled through food webs. Sedimentation may lock phosphorus away although it can become available again through long term processes such as geological uplift. Some phosphorus returns to the land as guano (phosphate-rich manure) but this return is small relative to the phosphate transferred to the oceans each year by natural processes and human activity.

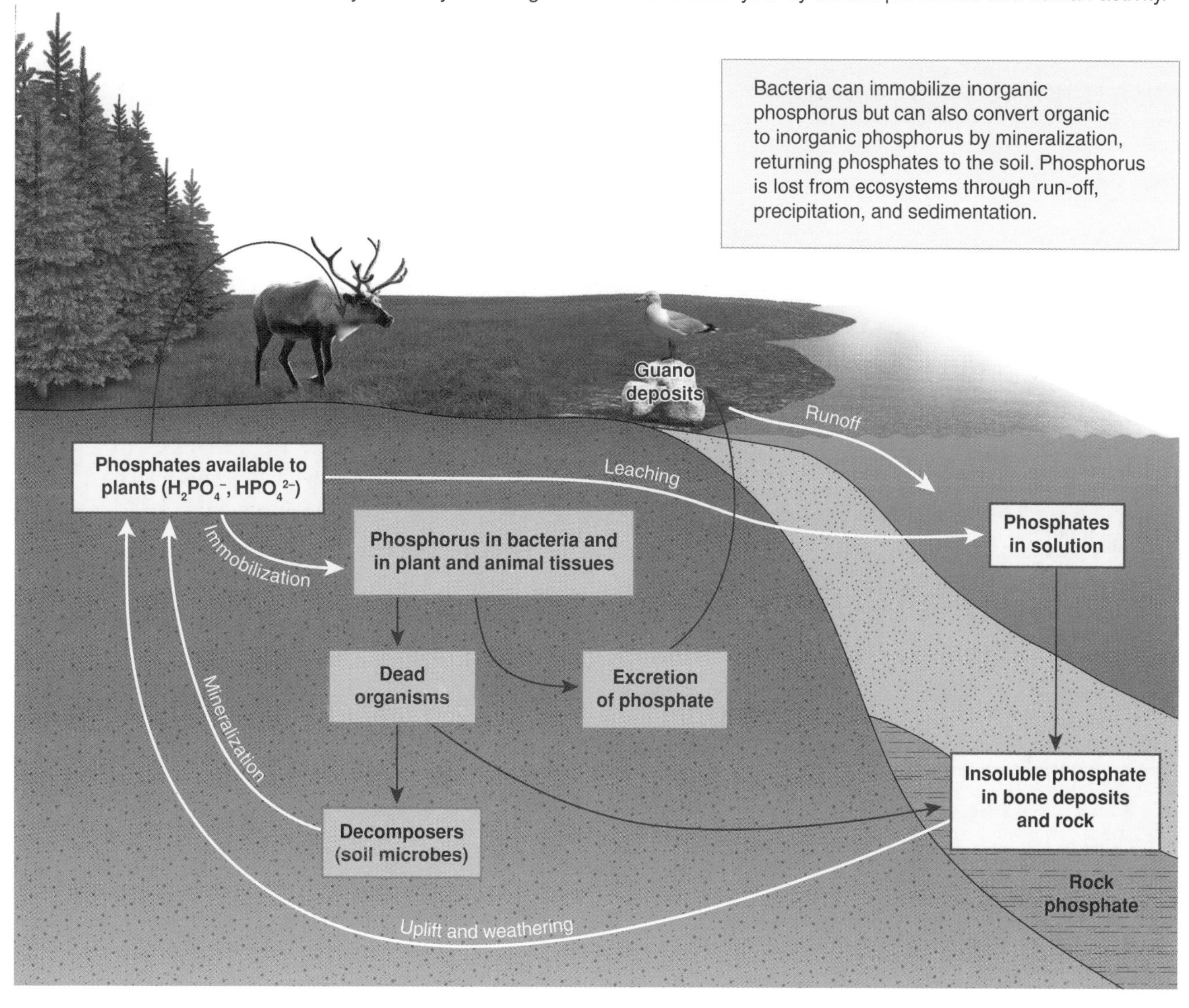

1. Identify the main reservoirs of phosphorus: ______

2. Explain why phosphorus is often a limiting factor in the productivity of ecosystems: ______

3. Identify two instances in the phosphorus cycle where bacteria are important and describe the transformations involved:

(a) ______

(b) ______

ISBN: 978-1-98-856632-0

17 The Hydrologic Cycle

Key Question: What processes move water between the oceans and the land in the hydrologic cycle?

Powered by energy from the Sun, the **hydrologic cycle**, collects, purifies, and distributes the Earth's fixed supply of water. The oceans are the Earth's largest reservoir of water with much smaller reservoirs in the ice caps and groundwater. Water constantly changes states between liquid, vapor, and ice as it moves through the biotic and abiotic components of ecosystems. Besides replenishing inland water supplies, rainwater causes erosion and transports dissolved nutrients within and among ecosystems. On a global scale, evaporation (conversion of liquid water to gaseous vapor) exceeds precipitation over the oceans. This results in a net movement of water vapor (carried by winds) over the land. On land, precipitation exceeds evaporation. Some of this precipitation becomes locked up in snow and ice but most forms surface and groundwater systems that flow back to the sea, completing the major part of the cycle. Over the sea, most of the water vapor is due to evaporation alone. However on land, about 90% of the vapor results from transpiration.

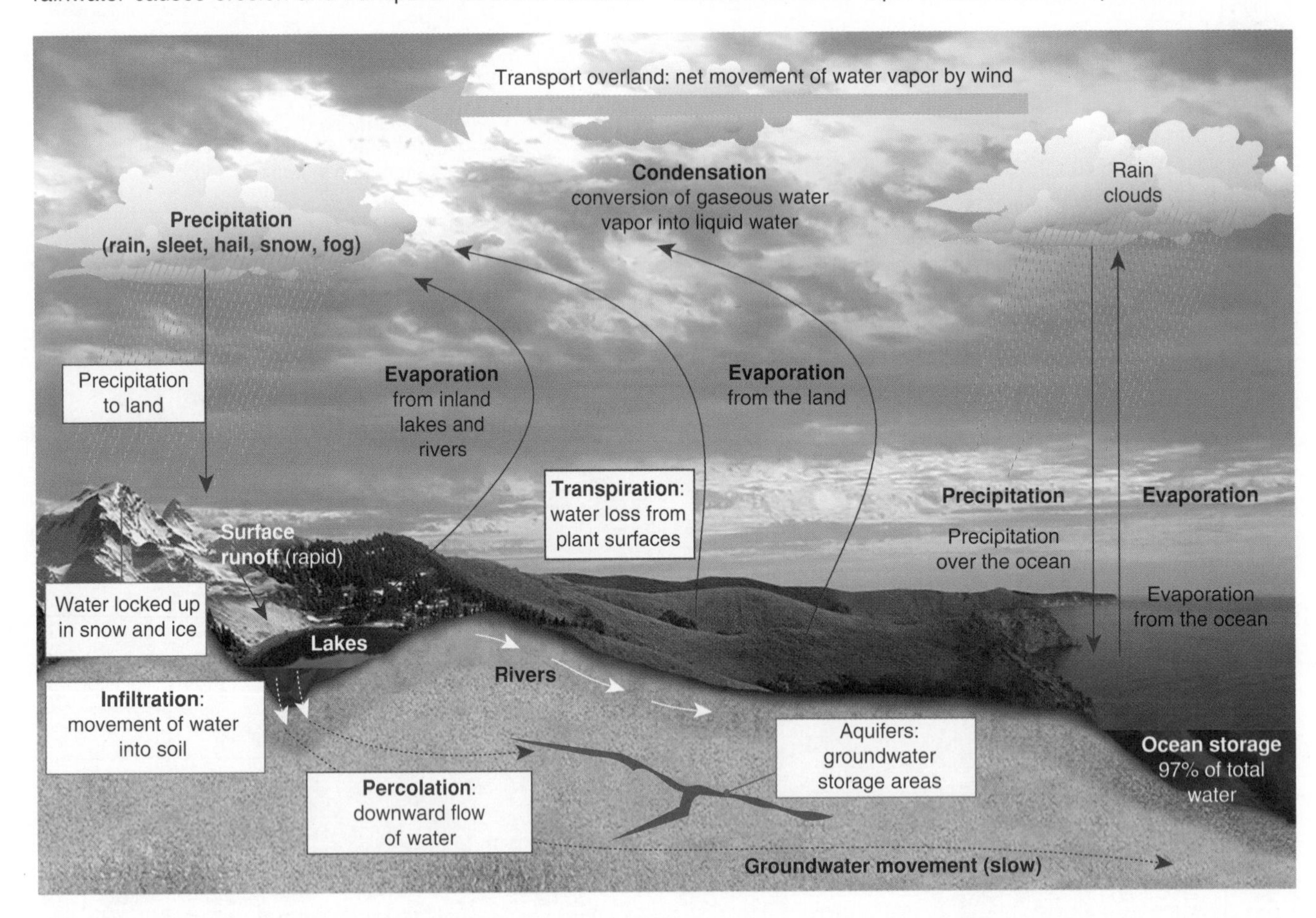

1. Identify the main reservoir for water on Earth: ______________________

2. Identify the main reservoirs for fresh water: ______________________

3. What is the ultimate source of energy for the processes involved in the hydrologic cycle?______________________

4. Describe what is involved in each of the following processes and its role in the hydrologic cycle:

   (a) Evaporation: ______________________

   (b) Precipitation: ______________________

   ____

   (c) Condensation: ______________________

   ____

   (d) Transpiration: ______________________

   ____

5. Identify two ways in which water returns to the oceans from the land:

   (a) ______________________ (b) ______________________

ISBN: 978-1-98-856632-0

18 Primary Productivity

Key Question: What is primary productivity, how does it differ from primary production, and why is it important?

What do we mean when we say that an ecosystem has a high (or low) productivity? The energy accumulated by plants or other producers in an ecosystem (or measured area) is called **primary production**. It is the first energy storage step in an ecosystem. All of the sunlight energy that is fixed as chemical energy is the **gross primary production** (**GPP**). However, some of this energy is required by the producers themselves for respiration. Subtracting respiration from GPP gives the **net primary production** (**NPP**). This represents the energy or biomass available to the primary consumers in the ecosystem. Note that 'production' refers to a quantity of material. **Productivity**, which is more meaningful in biological systems **is a rate**, usually expressed as grams or kJ per m^2 (or per m^3) per year. Having made that distinction, you will often see the terms used interchangeably because production values are usually given for a set time period.

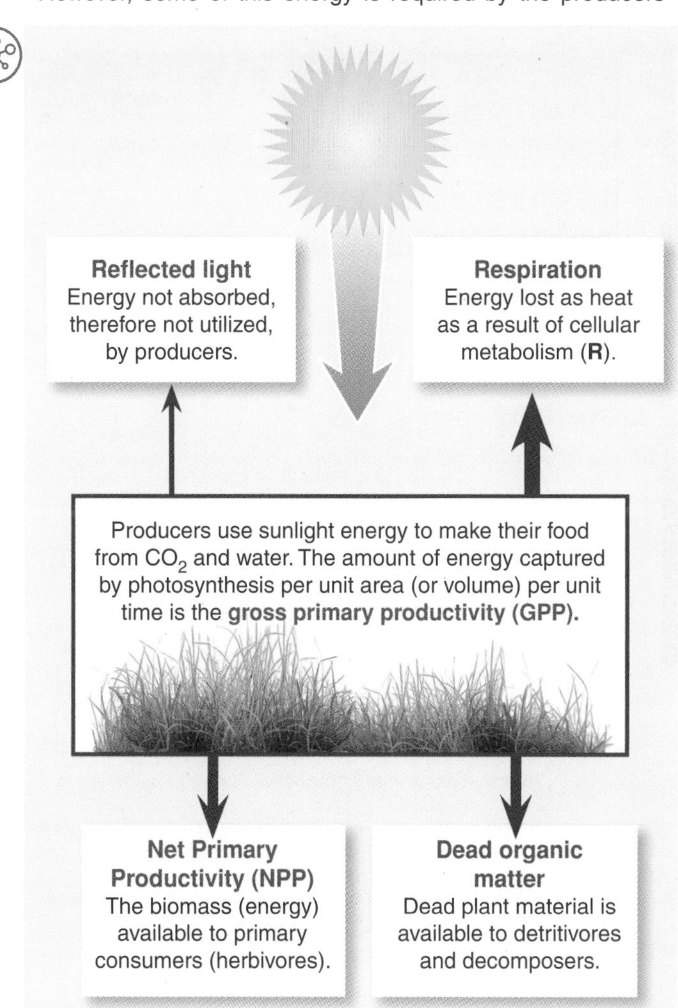

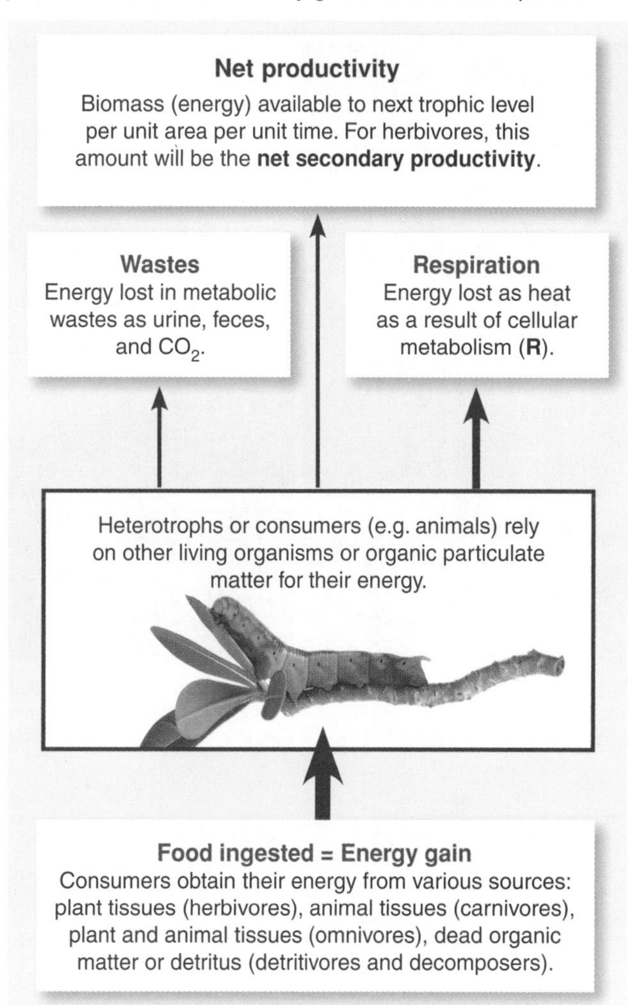

1. (a) Explain the difference between gross primary productivity (GPP) and net primary productivity (NPP): ______________

(b) Write a simple word equation to show how NPP is derived from GPP: ______________

(c) What factors do you think could influence the GPP of ecosystems? ______________

(d) Why do you think it is important to distinguish between GPP and NPP when studying the productivity of ecosystems?

ISBN: 978-1-98-856632-0

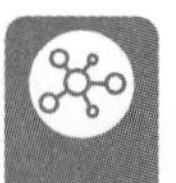

The productivity of ecosystems varies

- The energy entering ecosystems is fixed by producers at a rate that depends on limiting factors such as temperature and the availability of light, water, and nutrients such as nitrogen and phosphorus. This means that the gross primary productivity of ecosystems varies across the globe according to the local conditions.
- Producers convert the energy they capture into biomass. The biomass produced per area per unit time after respiratory needs are met is the net primary production. This will be the amount of energy (as biomass) available to the next trophic level.
- Globally, the least productive terrestrial ecosystems are those that are limited by heat energy and water. The most productive are those with high light and temperature, plenty of water, and non-limiting supplies of soil nitrogen. The primary productivity of oceans is lower overall than that of terrestrial ecosystems because the water reflects (or absorbs) much of the light energy before it reaches and is utilized by producers. Many regions of the open ocean are also low in nutrients.

Jan Kronsell CC3.0 SA

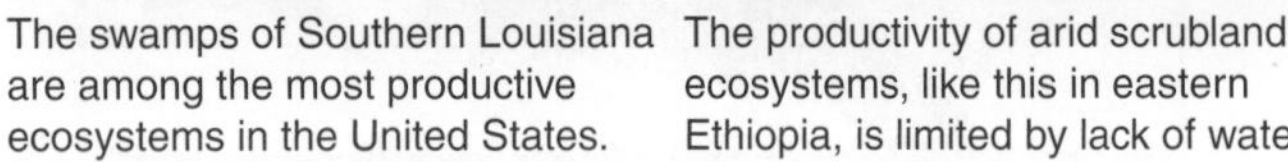

The swamps of Southern Louisiana are among the most productive ecosystems in the United States.

The productivity of arid scrubland ecosystems, like this in eastern Ethiopia, is limited by lack of water.

Ecosystem type

Estuaries
Swamps and marshes
Tropical rainforest
Temperate forest
Boreal forest
Savanna
Agricultural land
Woodland and shrubland
Temperate grassland
Lakes and streams
Continental shelf
Tundra
Open ocean
Desert scrub
Extreme desert

5 10 15 20 25 30 35 40 45 50

Average net primary productivity (x 1000 kJ/m²/yr)

2. Studying the ecosystem NPP graph above:

(a) Identify the three most productive ecosystems: ______

(b) What factors are likely to contribute to this high productivity? ______

(c) Why do deserts have low NPP? ______

(d) Why is primary productivity of the open ocean lower than that of most terrestrial ecosystems? ______

3. Estuaries and wetlands (including coastal wetlands) are among the most productive on Earth. Recall the characteristics of the aquatic biomes you looked at earlier and describe factors that contribute to the high productivity of these systems:

______

ISBN: 978-1-98-856632-0

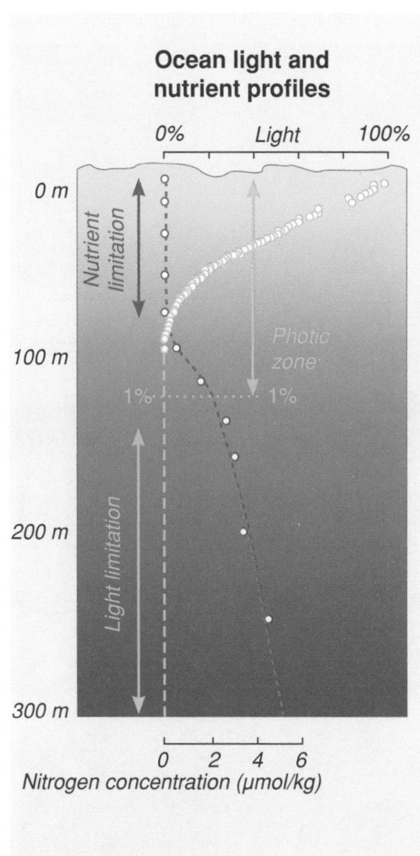

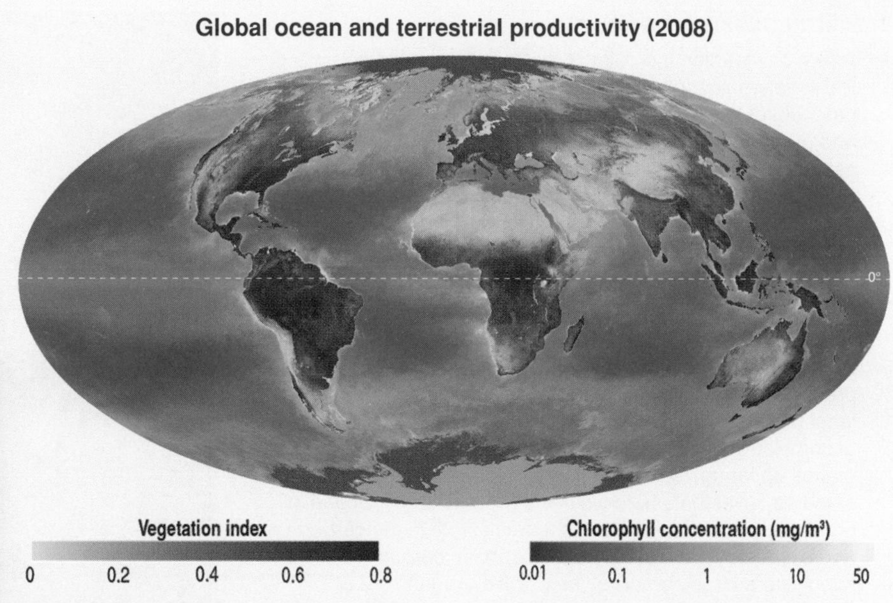

Above: Terrestrial vegetation and ocean chlorophyll concentrations can be used to estimate net productivity on land and in the oceans (this image shows a 2008 average). Chlorophyll is the pigment used to capture sunlight energy in photosynthesis so its concentration is a crude measure of the amount of algal photosynthesis occurring.
Left: Ocean productivity is limited by the availability of light and nutrients. Light declines with depth and nutrients are supplied slowly from deep waters and rapidly consumed by algae in the photic zone. Recall that only blue light penetrates below 100 m.

Profile data for subtropical waters collected by the Bermuda-Atlantic Time-series Station (July 2008) and made available by the Bermuda Institute of Ocean Sciences and redrawn in part. Figure above NASA.

4. Study the map showing terrestrial and ocean productivity (2008):

   (a) In general, where is ocean productivity the lowest? ______

   (b) In general, where is ocean productivity the highest? ______

5. (a) Are tropical open ocean waters generally more or less productive than temperate and polar waters? ______

   (b) Use what you have learned about ocean stratification in activity 12 to explain why: ______

6. Study the light and nutrient profiles above left and explain why maximum productivity occurs at around 90 m depth:

7. (a) The graph (right) shows primary productivity in the oceans. Describe and explain the shape of the curves:

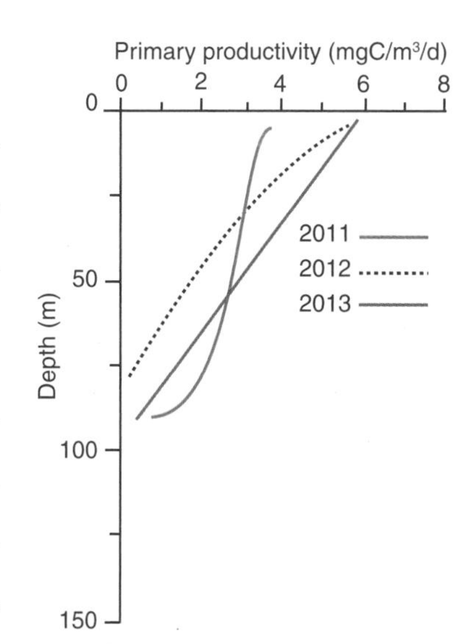

   (b) About 90% of all marine life lives in the photic zone (the depth to which light penetrates). Suggest why this is so:

ISBN: 978-1-98-856632-0

Tracking ocean productivity

- As we saw earlier, the color of the oceans (and lakes) on Earth varies according to water depth and the presence of particulates such as algae in the water column. In the oceans and other aquatic environments, primary productivity can be estimated by analyzing chlorophyll data using **remote sensing**. Such data are also used to track algal blooms and even identify the type of organisms responsible for the bloom based on the color information.
- Almost all photosynthesis in the oceans (99%) is carried out by phytoplankton (algae but also photosynthetic bacteria). Chemosynthesis is important in areas without light, such as the deep sea vents, but this is a tiny fraction of total primary production of the ocean. While the oceans are among the least productive ecosystems on Earth (in terms of carbon accumulated per unit volume per unit time), their sheer size makes up for this so that marine photosynthesis is about the same as terrestrial photosynthesis (~50 Gt C /yr). Ocean photosynthesis therefore plays a crucial role in the carbon and oxygen cycles, removing atmospheric carbon dioxide and supplying a large portion of the Earth's oxygen.
- Biomass does not accumulate in the ocean in the same way as on land because algae are continually sinking out the photic zone. This export of biomass contributes to the role of oceans as a carbon sink, removing carbon from the atmosphere.

Image right: Blooms of algae (mostly coccolithophores) near Alaska's Pribilof Islands (Sept. 22 2014) appear as milky green and light blue areas. Blooms increase in Spring, after winter ice cover retreats and nutrients are abundant near the surface.

NASA

Staying in the light

- Productivity in the ocean is a delicate balance between light and nutrients. Much phytoplankton biomass leaves the water column, but the rates of this biomass export are not uniform globally. In nutrient-poor tropical and subtropical water, grazing on small phytoplankton by microzooplankton is very efficient. Wastes are decomposed rapidly within the water column and there is very little net export. In nutrient-rich regions, larger phytoplankton dominate and grow rapidly, so much more accumulated biomass sinks out of the water column.
- Phytoplankton diversity varies globally too. Diatoms are the dominant producers in high latitude, coastal, and upwelling environments, whereas cyanobacteria (which are bacteria not algae) are important in nutrient-poor waters.
- Some phytoplankton, notably some dinoflagellates, combine photosynthesis with ingestion of prey. The dinoflagellates are also important as symbionts with corals. This symbiosis keeps the algae in the photic zone.
- Algae are not uniformly distributed through the water columns, but are adapted to different light intensities. What's more, some species, notably cyanobacteria, have various accessory pigments that absorb light of one color and emit light of another color. These color changes make more red light available for photosynthesis.

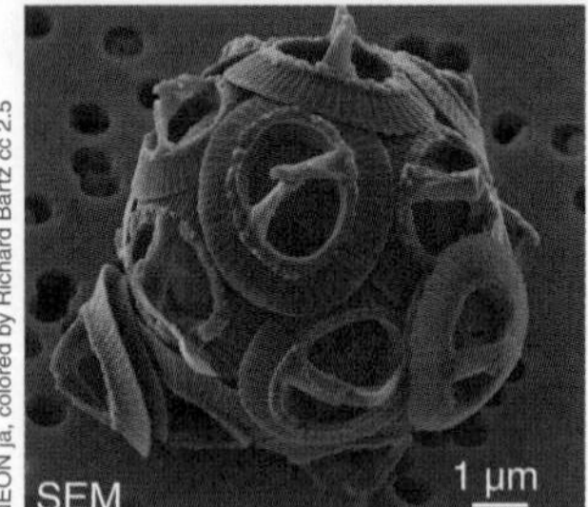

Coccolithophores are common bloom-forming algae, found in large numbers in the sunlit zone.

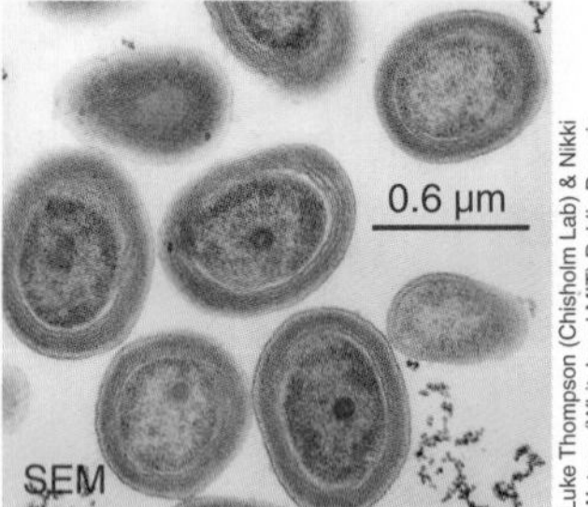

Cyanobacteria are part of the picoplankton (0.2-2 µm) and important in nutrient poor areas.

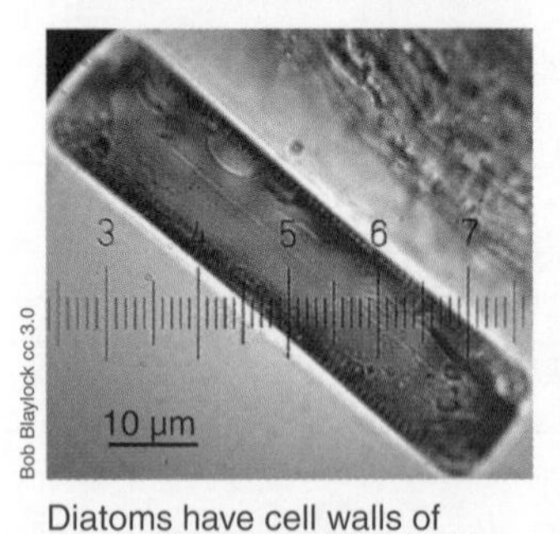

Diatoms have cell walls of silica. They predominate in high nutrient environments.

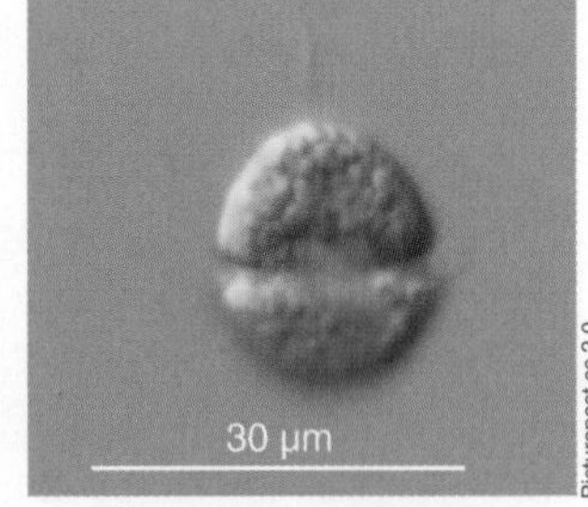

Dinoflagellates are important in ocean ecology as symbionts with corals and other animals.

8. (a) Explain how photosynthesis in aquatic environments is affected by light penetration: ____________________

(b) Explain some of the ways in which aquatic producers overcome limitations to photosynthesis: ____________________

ISBN: 978-1-98-856632-0

19 Measuring Primary Productivity

Key Question: How can we determine the gross and net primary productivity of an ecosystem?

Estimating ecosystem productivity is very problematic because It is technically difficult to measure the rates of photosynthesis and respiration directly. In terrestrial systems, plant biomass (dry weight) gives a good indication of the difference between GPP and respiration. In aquatic systems, productivity is often estimated indirectly from the quantities of oxygen released or carbon dioxide used in production (the light and dark bottle method). Although the method is useful, it cannot account for the respiration by bacteria and so may underestimate productivity.

Measuring productivity

Measuring gross primary productivity (GPP) can be difficult due to the effect of on-going respiration, which uses up some of the organic material produced (glucose) by photosynthesis. One method for measuring GPP is to measure the difference in production between plants kept in the dark and those in the light. A simple method for measuring GPP in aquatic systems, called the light and dark bottle method, is illustrated below. Other methods include radiocarbon tracer methods and chlorophyll concentration (see previous activity)

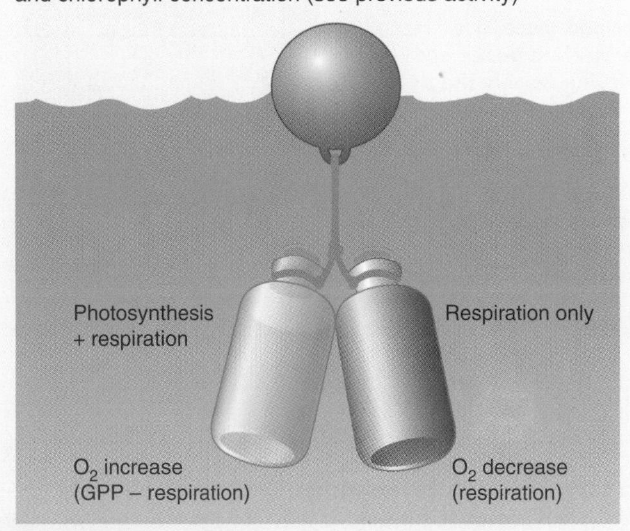

Two bottles are lowered into the ocean or lake to a specified depth, filled with water, and stoppered. One bottle is transparent, the other is opaque. The oxygen concentration of the water around the bottles is measured and the bottles are left for a specified amount of time. The algae (phytoplankton) in the transparent bottle will photosynthesize, increasing the O_2 concentration, and respire, using some of that O_2. The algae in the opaque bottle will only respire.

The final measured difference in O_2 between the bottles gives the amount of O_2 produced by the algae in the specified time (including that used for respiration). The amount of O_2 used allows us to determine the amount of glucose produced and therefore the GPP of the algae.

Estimating production using Leaf Area Index

Leaf Area Index or LAI is a measure of the total leaf area per unit ground area, for example, of a forest canopy or crop. It is a dimensionless quantity ($m^2 \div m^2$) that can be assessed directly or indirectly. LAI is directly related to the amount of light that can be intercepted by plants; the higher the LAI, the more light can be intercepted by the plants. LAI can therefore be used to predict primary production, evapotranspiration, and as a tool to evaluate crop growth. There is an inverse exponential relationship between LAI and primary production. As LAI increases, production increases exponentially, reaching a plateau after which further increases in LAI have no production benefit. This is largely due to the self shading that occurs in dense canopies.

Direct assessments of LAI are time consuming as all the leaves in a certain plot area must be collected and their areas calculated. The ratio of canopy area to sky in a forest can be used to estimate LAI but this method will underestimate LAI in dense canopies. LAI ranges from 0 (bare ground) to over 10 (dense conifer forests).

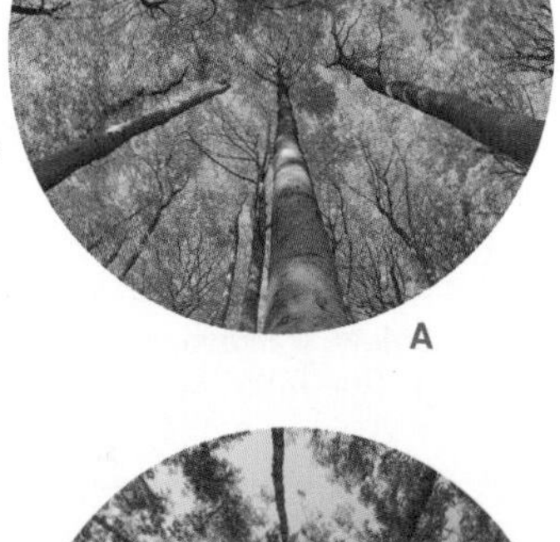

Images right: Hemispherical images of two temperate forest canopies. Note the differences in canopy coverage. At some point, increasing canopy density does not provide more production as upper plant leaves begin to shade leaves around and below them.

1. An experiment was carried out to measure the gross primary production of a lake. The lake was initially measured to have 8 mg O_2/L. A clear flask and an opaque flask were lowered into the lake, filled and stoppered. When the flasks were retrieved it was found the clear flask contained 10 mg O_2/L while the opaque contained 5 mg O_2/L.

   (a) How much O_2 was used (respired) in the opaque flask? ______________________

   (b) What is the net O_2 production in the clear flask? ______________________

   (c) What is the gross O_2 production in the system? ______________________

2. (a) Which of the canopy images shown above right, (A or B), would have the highest LAI? ______________________

   (b) Predict which will have the highest productivity and explain your answer: ______________________

   ____

   ____

ISBN: 978-1-98-856632-0

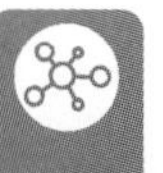

INVESTIGATION 1.2: Determining primary productivity in grass

See appendix for equipment list.

In this investigation, you will calculate the gross primary productivity of grass plots using wet and dry mass. Your teacher will provide plots (flats) of pre-prepared watered grass per group, sized approximately 20 x 40 cm. Divide your plot in half lengthwise, then into thirds to produce 6 plots. The two columns will be your replicates.

You will be provided with various light sources, fertilizer, and punches for aeration for your use so that you can select the conditions under which your plots will grow.

Replicate 1	Replicate 2
Starting plant mass (harvested at start)	Starting plant mass (harvested at start)
Foil covered. Grow 1 week	Foil covered. Grow 1 week
Uncovered. Grow 1 week	Uncovered. Grow 1 week

1. Record the area of each of your 6 plots here (they should be the same).

   ____

2. Measure grass length from soil to grass tips and trim with scissors if necessary to produce a sward of even height.
3. Remove the grass plants entirely from one plot in each column (**starting plant mass**). Brush gently to remove as much of the soil as possible from the plants then weigh the wet plant mass from each plot and record on the table below.
4. Place the plant material from each plot on newspaper and place in a drying oven at 65-70°C for 24-48 hours. You can use blotting paper and a plant press if you don't have a drying oven. After drying, weigh the dry mass of each plot and record on the table below.
5. Cover one plot from each column (replicate) with aluminum foil. Leave the remaining two plots uncovered.
6. Allow the four remaining plots to continue to grow for one week. It is your group's decision as to the growth conditions you choose for your grass (light regime, temperature, added nutrients, and aeration). Record these below:

   ____

   ____

   ____

7. After the one week of growth, describe the appearance of the grass in the uncovered plots in the space below. Remove the grass plants as in step 3. Weigh the plant material from each plot and record your results in the table below. Place the material from each plot on newspaper and place in the drying oven.

   ____

   ____

8. After the one week of growth, remove the foil from the covered plots. Describe the appearance of the grass below and then remove the grass plants as in step 3.

   ____

   ____

9. Weigh the wet mass of the foil covered plant material from each plot and record your results in the table below. Place the plant material from each plot on newspaper and place in the drying oven.
10. Allow all plant material from the covered and uncovered plots to dry completely as in step 4. Reweigh the plant material for both the covered and uncovered plots and record the dry weights in the table below.
11. Calculate a mean for the two replicates in your three conditions (start, uncovered, covered).

	Starting plant mass (time 0)				Uncovered plots (+ 1 week)				Covered plots (+ 1 week)			
	Wet mass (g)		Dry mass (g)		Wet mass (g)		Dry mass (g)		Wet mass (g)		Dry mass (g)	
	#1	#2	#1	#2	#1	#2	#1	#2	#1	#2	#1	#2
Mass (g)												
Mean (g)												

ISBN: 978-1-98-856632-0

3. Use the mean values (dry mass) you have recorded for your replicate plots to calculate the following. Be sure to include correct units for your answers:

   (a) Net primary productivity = Dry mass at time +1 week **uncovered** grass – Dry mass at time 0:

   (b) Respiration = Dry mass at time 0 – Dry mass at time +1 week **covered** grass:

   (c) Gross primary productivity = Net primary productivity + respiration:

4. Now make the same calculation using the mean values for wet mass. Include correct units for your answers:

   (a) Net primary productivity = Wet mass at time +1 week **uncovered** grass – Wet mass at time 0:

   (b) Respiration = Wet mass at time 0 – Wet mass at time +1 week **covered** grass:

   (c) Gross primary productivity = Net primary productivity + respiration:

5. Explain why you harvested the two plots at the start of the experiment:

6. What advantage was there in using replicate plots for each condition (start, covered, uncovered)?

7. (a) What do the foil covered plots represent?

   (b) You should have found that your covered plants lost mass. Why is this?

   (c) How would an increase in respiration rate affect your results for net primary productivity?

   (d) What factors might increase the respiration rate in your grass plots and how might you test this?

8. In your calculations, were the wet and dry mass results different? Which of the two calculations would provide you with a more accurate rate for gross productivity and why?

9. Compare your results with those of other groups in the class. Were they different and what could explain these differences? If you wish, create a column chart for the class results to compare gross primary productivity under the different growth conditions that groups used. Staple the plot to this page.

ISBN: 978-1-98-856632-0

20 Trophic Levels in Ecosystems

Key Question: What is a trophic level and how does energy and matter move between trophic levels in ecosystems?

Within ecosystems, organisms are assigned to trophic levels based on the way in which they obtain their energy. Producers or autotrophs manufacture their own food from simple inorganic substances. Most producers utilize sunlight as their energy source for this, but some use simple chemicals. The consumers rely directly or indirectly on producers for their energy. Ecosystems are not isolated from each other but connected through energy flows and biogeochemical cycles.

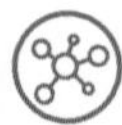

Trophic levels in ecosystems

The organisms in any ecosystem must obtain their energy (and a source of carbon) from somewhere. For plants and most other autotrophs (self-feeders), the energy source is the Sun and they make their own food by fixing carbon dioxide into organic compounds via the process of photosynthesis. Plants and other autotrophs are therefore called producers. All other organisms need to obtain their energy from other organisms and are consumers.

These feeding relationships can be considered in terms of trophic (feeding) levels. Trophic levels can be represented by numbers, with trophic level 1 being the producer level. Subsequent trophic levels are numbered according to how far the organism is along the chain of feeding connections. All organisms that obtain their energy in the same number of steps belong to the same trophic level.

Typically, there are four or five trophic levels in an ecosystem. This is determined by the energy lost at each transfer of energy.

First trophic level = primary producer: Green plants and the algae in the lake are primary producers, fixing atmospheric carbon dioxide into organic compounds using the energy of the Sun. In some deep sea ecosystems, the primary producers are chemosynthetic rather than photosynthetic organisms.

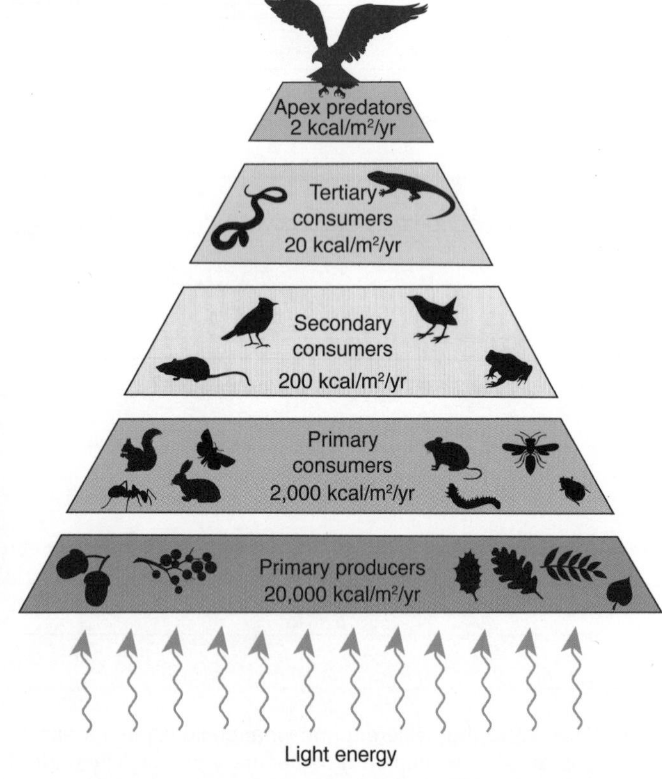

Second trophic level
The grasshopper eats organisms at the first trophic level so it is a primary consumer

Third trophic level
The frog eats organisms at the second trophic level so it is a secondary consumer.

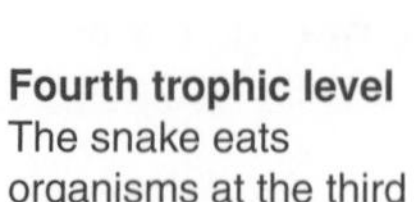

Fourth trophic level
The snake eats organisms at the third trophic level so it is a tertiary consumer.

Fifth trophic level
The hawk eats organisms at the fourth trophic level so it is a quaternary consumer or apex predator.

Note that any of these organisms may feed at other trophic levels.

1. The schematic above represents trophic levels in a generalized woodland ecosystem. The figures represent the energy stored as biomass at each level.
   (a) Label the tropic levels by adding numbers 1-5.
   (b) Add arrows and labels to the diagram to represent the energy lost as heat from each trophic level.
   (c) Add arrows and labels to represent the relationship between decomposers and trophic levels 1-5.

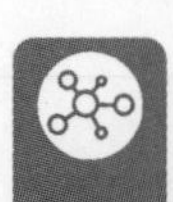

ISBN: 978-1-98-856632-0

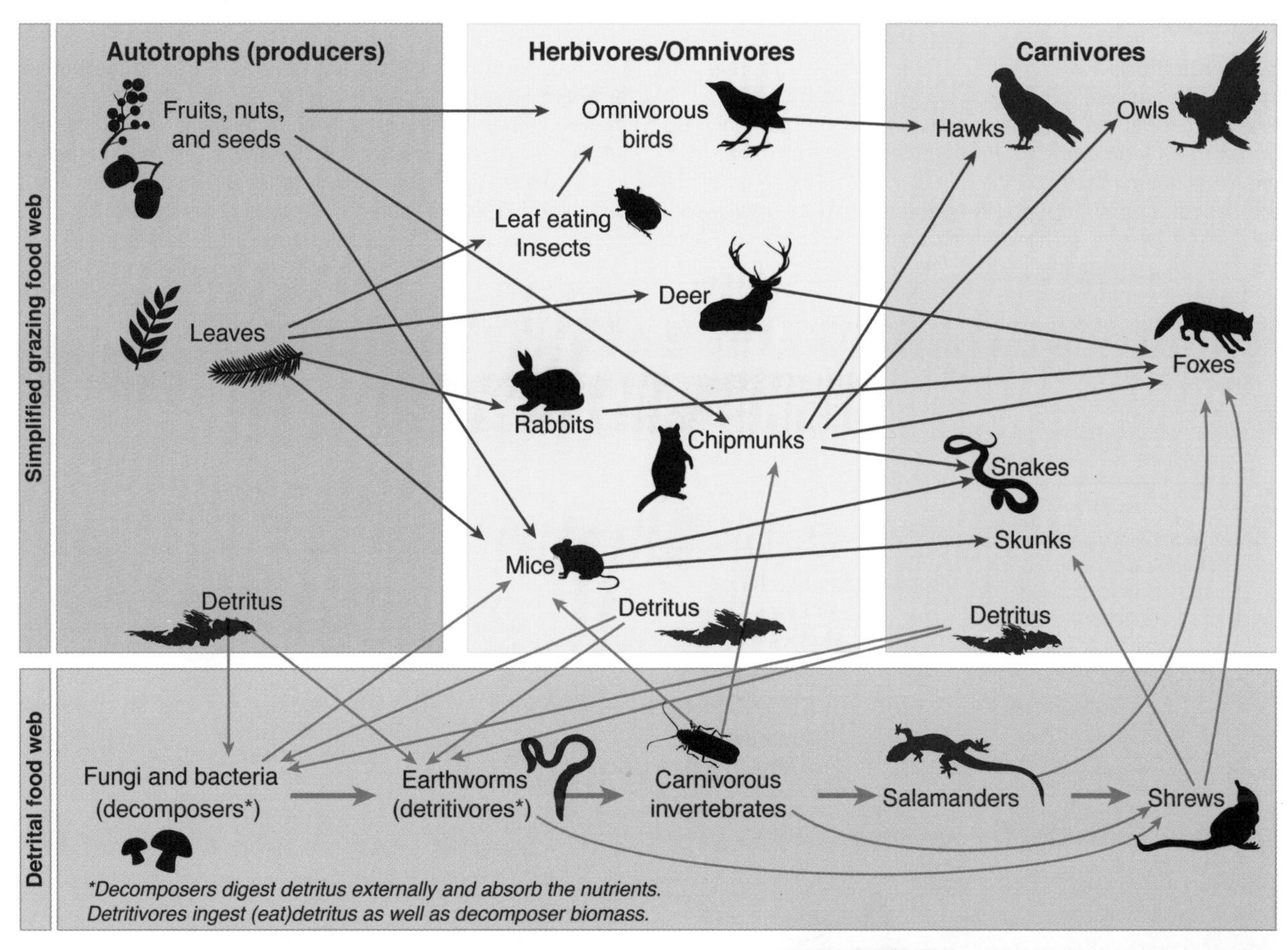

The energy transfers between living organisms are generally shown as a web of connected feeding relationships. Each arrow indicates a feeding interaction and points in the direction of the energy flow. At each of these interactions, energy is lost as heat. Within a single ecosystem, two general types of food webs interact. A **grazing food web** has photosynthetic organisms (e.g. plants) at its base, ultimately supporting all consumers (herbivores, omnivores, and carnivores). A **detrital food web** has a base of decomposers and detritivores that feed on decaying organic matter (dead organisms). All ecosystems require a way to recycle material from dead organisms, so most grazing food webs have an associated detrital food web.

Image right: Shrews connect detrital and grazing food webs.

2. Do decomposer organisms belong to a trophic level? Which trophic level would you assign them to? Justify your answer:

3. Use the diagram to explain how producers ultimately provide the energy to support grazing and detrital food webs:

4. Explain the role of detrital food webs in increasing the amount of energy available to consumers:

ISBN: 978-1-98-856632-0

21 Quantifying Energy Flow in an Ecosystem

Key Question: How much of the energy entering an ecosystem passes from one trophic level to the next?

Energy cannot be created or destroyed. It can only be transformed from one form (e.g. light energy) to another (e.g. chemical energy in the bonds of molecules). This means that the flow of energy through an ecosystem can be measured. Each time energy is transferred from one trophic level to the next (e.g. by eating), some energy is given out as heat to the environment as a result of cellular respiration. Living organisms cannot convert heat to other forms of energy, so this heat is effectively lost from the system and the amount of energy available to one trophic level is always less than the amount at the previous level. Potentially, we can account for the transfer of energy from its input (as solar radiation) to its release as heat from organisms, because energy is conserved. The percentage of energy transferred from one trophic level to the next is the **trophic efficiency**. It varies between 5% and 20% and measures the efficiency of energy transfer. An average figure of 10% trophic efficiency is often used. This is called the **ten percent rule**.

Energy flow through an ecosystem

NOTE
Numbers represent **kilojoules** of energy per square meter per year (kJ/m²/yr)

Energy absorbed from the previous trophic level
100
Energy lost as heat 65
Trophic level
15 Energy lost to detritus
20
Energy passed to the next trophic level

The energy available to each trophic level will always equal the amount entering that trophic level, minus total losses to that level (due to metabolic activity, death, excretion etc). Energy lost as heat will be lost from the ecosystem. Other losses become part of the detritus and may be used by other organisms in the ecosystem.

Sunlight falling on plant surfaces
7,000,000

Light absorbed by plants
1,700,000

A

Producers
87,400

50,450
(a)
22,950

Primary consumers
7,800
B
4,600
G
1600

Secondary consumers
1,330
(b)
Detritus
2,000
10,465
D
F
90
(c)
19,300
(d)

Tertiary consumers
55

Heat loss in metabolic activity

C
Decomposers and detritivores
19,200
E

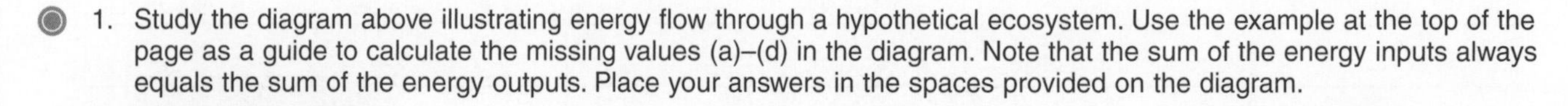

1. Study the diagram above illustrating energy flow through a hypothetical ecosystem. Use the example at the top of the page as a guide to calculate the missing values (a)–(d) in the diagram. Note that the sum of the energy inputs always equals the sum of the energy outputs. Place your answers in the spaces provided on the diagram.

ISBN: 978-1-98-856632-0

2. What is the original source of energy for this ecosystem? ____________

3. Identify the processes occurring at the points labelled **A – G** on the diagram:

A. ____________ E. ____________

B. ____________ F. ____________

C. ____________ G. ____________

D. ____________

4. (a) Calculate the percentage of light energy falling on the plants that is absorbed at point **A**:

Light absorbed by plants ÷ sunlight falling on plant surfaces x 100 = ____________

(b) What happens to the light energy that is not absorbed? ____________

5. (a) Calculate the percentage of light energy absorbed that is actually converted (fixed) into producer energy:

Producers ÷ light absorbed by plants x 100 = ____________

(b) How much light energy is absorbed but not fixed: ____________

(c) Account for the difference between the amount of energy absorbed and the amount actually fixed by producers:

6. Of the total amount of energy fixed by producers in this ecosystem (at point **A**) calculate:

(a) The total amount that ended up as metabolic waste heat (in kJ): ____________

(b) The percentage of the energy fixed that ended up as waste heat: ____________

7. (a) State the groups for which detritus is an energy source: ____________

(b) How could detritus be removed or added to an ecosystem? ____________

8. Under certain conditions, decomposition rates can be very low or even zero, allowing detritus to accumulate:

(a) From your knowledge of biological processes, what conditions might slow decomposition rates?

(b) What are the consequences of this lack of decomposer activity to the energy flow? ____________

(c) Add an additional arrow to the diagram on the previous page to illustrate your answer.

(d) Describe three examples of materials that have resulted from a lack of decomposer activity on detrital material:

9. The ten percent rule states that the total energy content of a trophic level in an ecosystem is only about one-tenth (or 10%) that of the preceding level. For each of the trophic levels in the diagram on the preceding page, determine the amount of energy passed on to the next trophic level as a percentage:

(a) Producer to primary consumer: ____________

(b) Primary consumer to secondary consumer: ____________

(c) Secondary consumer to tertiary consumer: ____________

(d) Which of these transfers is the most efficient? ____________

ISBN: 978-1-98-856632-0

22 Ecological Pyramids

Key Question: How are ecological pyramids used to represent the trophic structure of ecosystems? How do we represent the energy that flows through the decomposer level?

Ecological pyramids are graphical models showing the quantitative differences between trophic levels in an ecosystem. The trophic structure can be represented using energy, biomass, or numbers of organisms at each trophic level. The first trophic level is placed at the bottom of the pyramid and subsequent trophic levels are stacked on top in their 'feeding sequence'. Ecological pyramids provide a convenient quantitative model for the relationship between different trophic levels in an ecosystem.

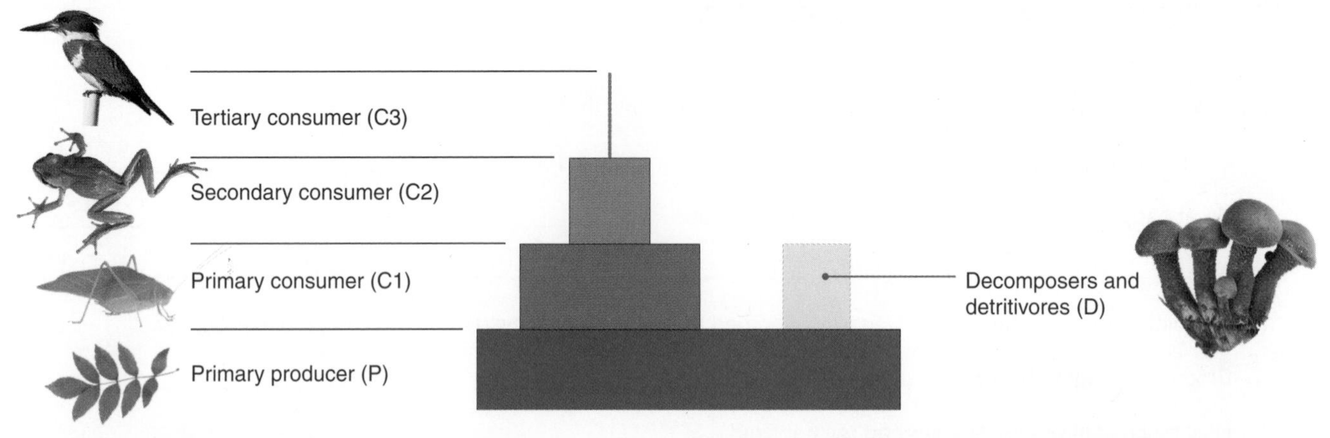

- The generalized ecological pyramid pictured above shows a conventional pyramid shape (often called **upright**), with a large number (or biomass) of producers forming the base for an increasingly smaller number (or biomass) of consumers.
- Decomposers are placed at the level of the primary consumers and off to the side. They may obtain energy from many different trophic levels and so do not fit into the conventional pyramid structure.
- For any particular ecosystem at any one time (e.g. the forest ecosystem below), the shape of this typical pyramid can vary greatly depending on whether the trophic relationships are expressed as numbers, biomass, or energy.

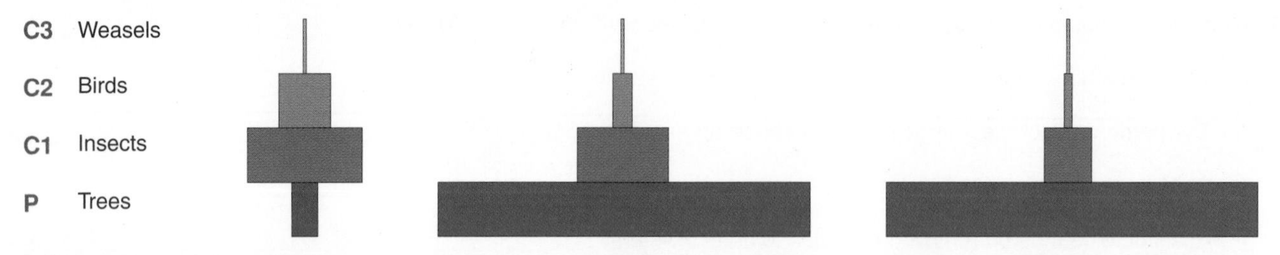

Numbers in a forest community

Pyramids of numbers display the number of organisms at each trophic level. Pyramids of numbers can be a pyramid shape or they can be inverted (above) if a small number of large organisms (e.g. trees) support the next trophic level.

Biomass in a forest community

Biomass pyramids measure the mass of biological material at each trophic level. Water content of organisms varies, so 'dry mass' is often used. Organism size is taken into account, allowing meaningful comparisons of different trophic levels.

Energy in a forest community

Pyramids of energy are often similar to biomass pyramids. The energy content at each trophic level is generally comparable to the biomass (i.e. similar amounts of dry biomass tend to have about the same energy content).

1. How do ecological pyramids provide a quantitative model of trophic structure in an ecosystem?

2. What is the advantage of using a biomass or energy pyramid rather than a pyramid of numbers to express the relationship between different trophic levels?

3. Explain why a pyramid of numbers can be inverted but a pyramid of energy can never be :

ISBN: 978-1-98-856632-0

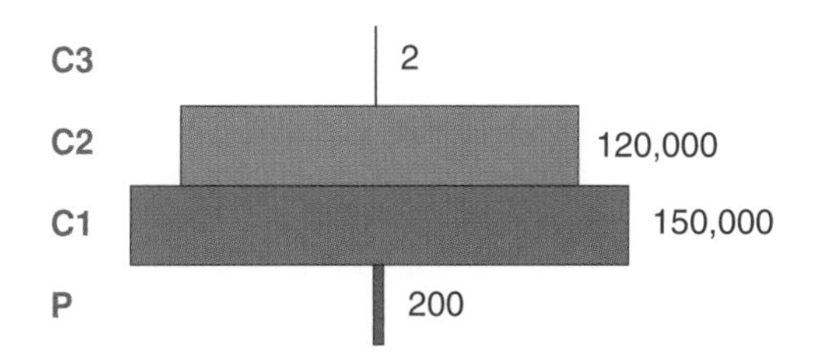

Pyramid of numbers: forest community

In a forest community, a few producers may support a large number of consumers (large trees can support many individual consumer organisms). The example above shows the numbers at each trophic level for an oak forest in England, in an area of 10 m^2.

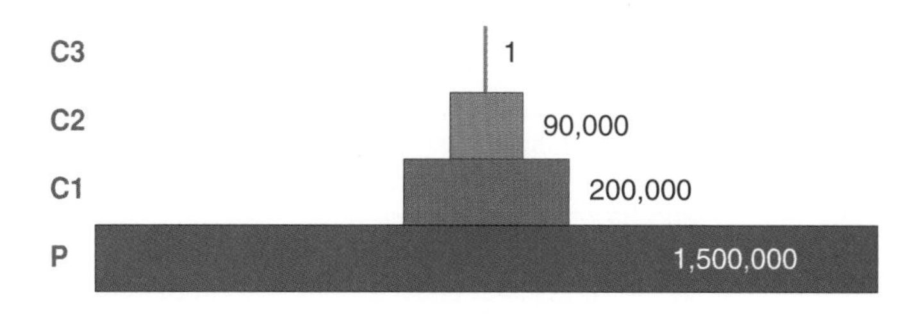

Pyramid of numbers: grassland community

In a grassland community, a large number of (small) producers support a much smaller number of consumers. Grass plants can support only a few individual consumer organisms and take time to recover from grazing pressure. The example above shows the numbers at each trophic level for a derelict grassland area (10 m^2) in Michigan, USA.

Pyramids for a plankton community

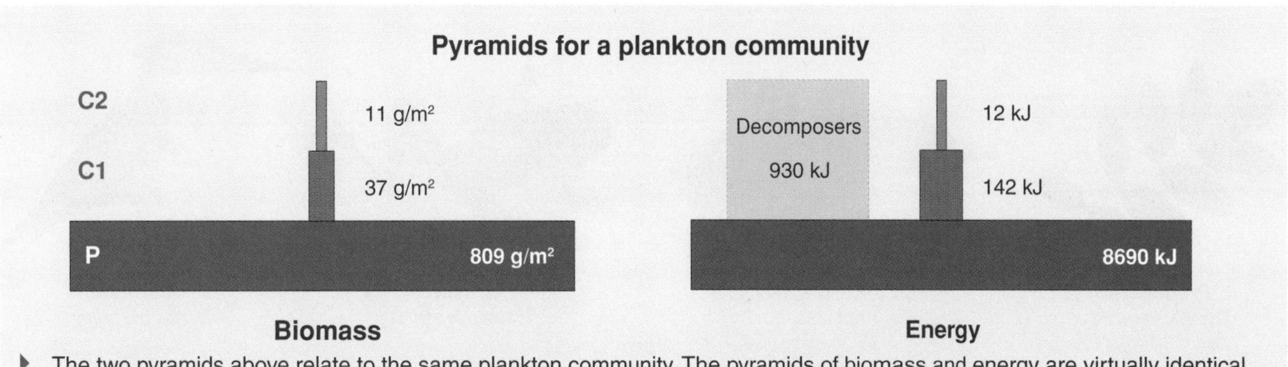

- The two pyramids above relate to the same plankton community. The pyramids of biomass and energy are virtually identical.
- A large biomass of producers supports a smaller biomass of consumers. The energy at each trophic level is reduced with each progressive stage in the food chain. As a general rule, a maximum of 10% of the energy is passed on to the next level in the food chain. The remaining energy is lost due to respiration, waste, and heat.

4. Determine the energy transfer between trophic levels in the plankton community example in the above diagram:

   (a) Between producers and the primary consumers: ______

   (b) Between the primary consumers and the secondary consumers: ______

   (c) Why is the amount of energy transferred from the producer level to primary consumers considerably less than the approximate 10% that commonly occurs in many other communities?

   ______

   ______

   (d) After the producers, which trophic group has the greatest energy content? ______

   (e) Give a likely explanation why this is the case: ______

   ______

   ______

   ______

An unusual biomass pyramid

The biomass pyramids of some ecosystems appear rather unusual with an inverted shape. The first trophic level has a lower biomass than the second level. What this pyramid does not show is the rate at which the producers (algae) are reproducing in order to support the larger biomass of consumers.

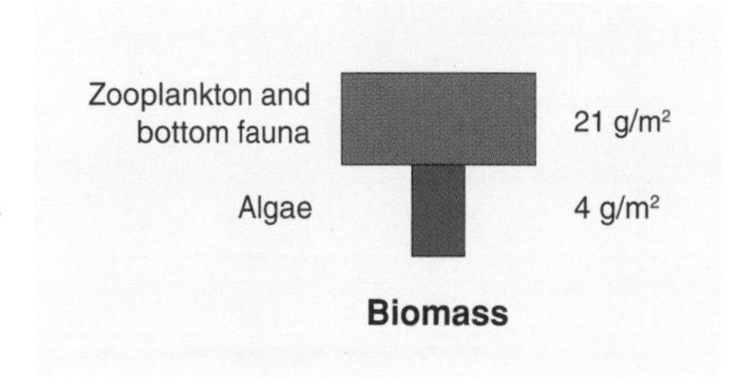

5. Give a possible explanation of how a small biomass of producers (algae) can support a larger biomass of consumers (zooplankton):

   ______

   ______

   ______

ISBN: 978-1-98-856632-0

23 Food Chains

Key Question: What do food chains tell us about the feeding relationships of organisms in an ecosystem?

As we have seen earlier, organisms in ecosystems interact by way of their feeding (trophic) relationships. These interactions can be shown most simply in a **food chain**, which illustrates how energy, in the form of food, passes from one organism (and one trophic level) to the next. Recall that only 5-20% of the energy at one trophic level is transferred to the next (the rest is lost as heat). For this reason, food chains usually have fewer than six links. An organism is assigned to a trophic level based on its position in the food chain, but they may occupy different trophic levels in different food chains or during different stages of their life. Arrows link the organisms in a food chain. Recall that the direction of the arrow shows the flow of energy through the trophic levels. Most food chains begin with a producer, which is eaten by a primary consumer (herbivore). Higher level consumers (carnivores and omnivores) eat other consumers.

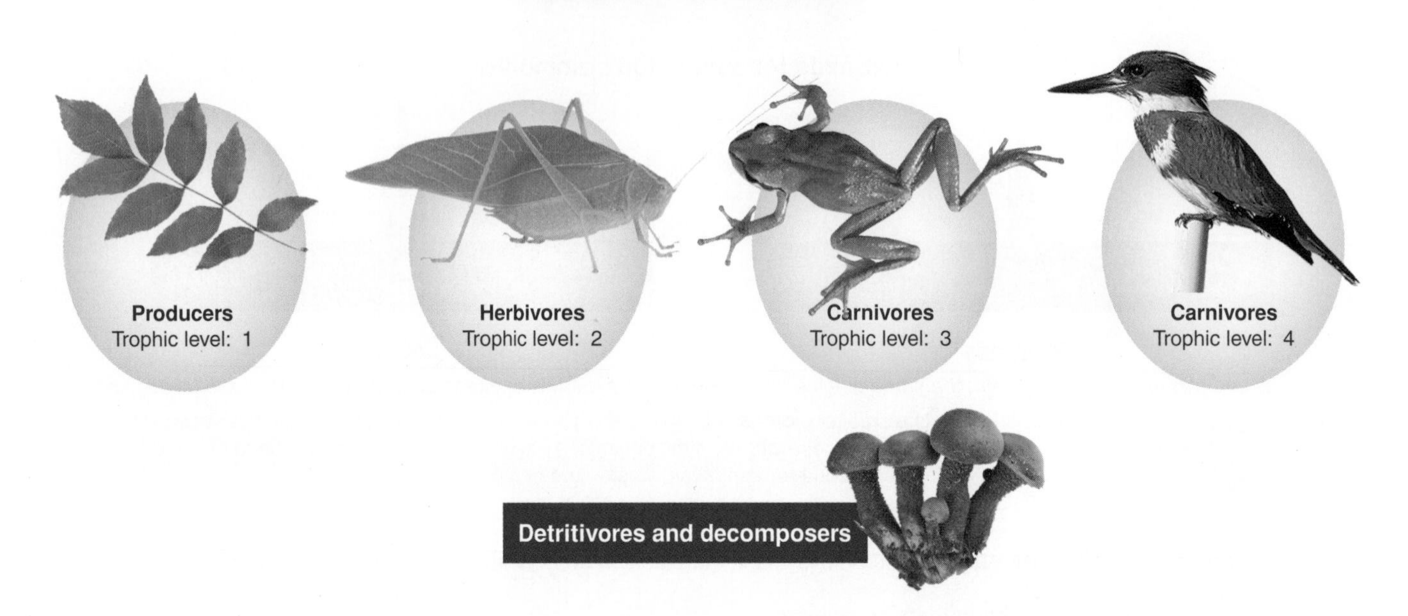

The diagram above represents the basic elements of a food chain. In the questions below, you are asked to add to the diagram the features that indicate the flow of energy through the community of organisms.

1. (a) State the original energy source for this food chain: ______

   (b) Draw arrows on the diagram above to show how the energy flows through the organisms in the food chain.

   (c) Label each of the arrows with the process that carries out this transfer of energy.

   (d) Draw arrows on the diagram to show how the energy is lost as heat by way of respiration.

2. (a) What happens to the amount of energy available to each successive trophic level in a food chain? ______

   (b) How does this limit the number of links in a food chain? ______

3. Discuss the trophic structure of ecosystems, including reference to food chains and trophic levels: ______

4. What could you infer about the trophic level(s) of the kingfisher if it was found to eat both leaf insects and frogs?

ISBN: 978-1-98-856632-0

24 Food Webs

Key Question: What determines the complexity of food webs and what is the effect of removing or adding a new species? Although feeding relationships can be shown as food chains, a more complex representation, or food web, more accurately represents the complexity of feeling relationships in a community. You encountered food webs in the earlier activity on trophic levels. Here you will examine a food web in more detail. Food webs recognize the different foods taken by organisms and the different trophic levels at which they feed. Species are assigned to trophic levels on the basis of their nutrition, with producers ultimately supporting all other (consumer) levels. Consumers are ranked according to the trophic level they occupy, although some may feed at several levels. A simplified food web for Lake Erie is shown below.

A simplified Great Lakes food web: Lake Erie (open water)

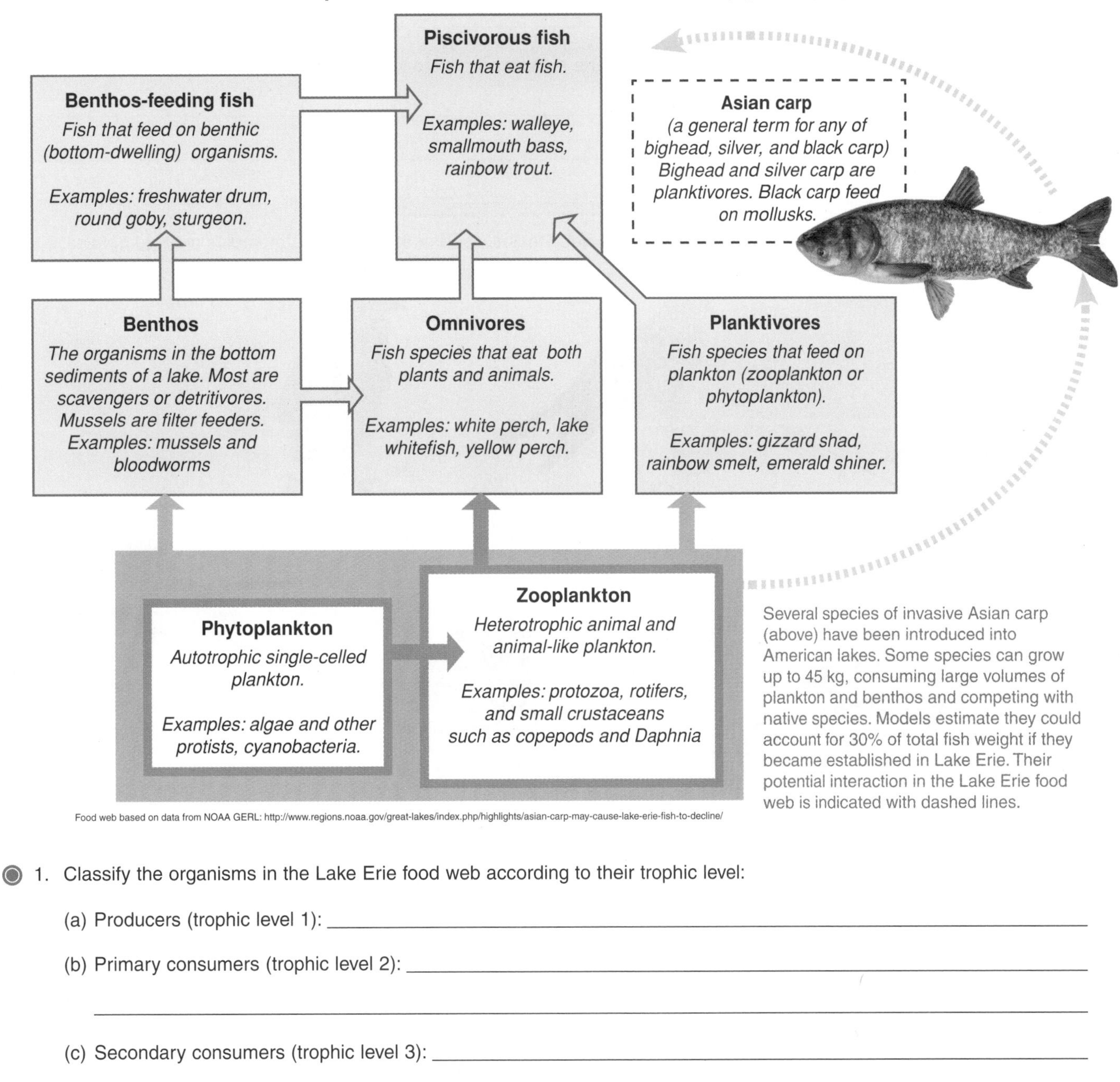

Food web based on data from NOAA GERL: http://www.regions.noaa.gov/great-lakes/index.php/highlights/asian-carp-may-cause-lake-erie-fish-to-decline/

Several species of invasive Asian carp (above) have been introduced into American lakes. Some species can grow up to 45 kg, consuming large volumes of plankton and benthos and competing with native species. Models estimate they could account for 30% of total fish weight if they became established in Lake Erie. Their potential interaction in the Lake Erie food web is indicated with dashed lines.

1. Classify the organisms in the Lake Erie food web according to their trophic level:

   (a) Producers (trophic level 1): ______

   (b) Primary consumers (trophic level 2): ______

   ______

   (c) Secondary consumers (trophic level 3): ______

   (d) Tertiary consumers (trophic level 4): ______

   (e) What trophic levels would Asian carp occupy in this food web? ______

2. (a) What organisms do Asian carp feed on? ______

   ______

   (b) What type of organisms would Asian carp potentially be a food source for? ______

3. Construct a food chain to represent the inclusion of Asian carp into Lake Erie: ______

______

ISBN: 978-1-98-856632-0

4. (a) What connection from Asian carp to a food source is not indicated on the food web diagram on the previous page:

 ____

 (b) Given your answer in (a), how could invasion by Asian carp affect efforts to restore populations of sturgeon, which were once an important fishery but are now near extinction?

 ____

 ____

 ____

5. Predict the potential effects on the food web of Lake Erie if Asian carp were to become established: _______________

 ____

 ____

 ____

6. The diagram below shows a simplified grassland food web. Decide whether the following statements are true or false:

 (a) The diagram shows two trophic levels: _______________

 (b) All the animals are consumers: _______________

 (c) The snake and the goshawk are at the same trophic level: _______________

 (d) The snake and the sparrow are at the same trophic level : _______________

 (e) The owl is both a secondary and a tertiary consumer: _______________

7. Predict a likely effect on this food web if owls were to become very rare in this ecosystem. Do you think the feeding relationships would stabilize? Explain your answer:

 ____

 ____

 ____

 ____

ISBN: 978-1-98-856632-0

25 Personal Progress Check

Answer the multiple choice questions that follow by circling the correct answer. Don't forget to read the question carefully!

1. A naturally occurring unit of organisms and their physical environment is called:
   (a) A biotic environment
   (b) A population
   (c) A community
   (d) An ecosystem

2. Which statement is true of a mutualistic relationship:
   (a) One species benefits and one is unharmed
   (b) One species benefits and one is harmed
   (c) Both species benefit
   (d) Both species are harmed

3. Direct competition for a finite resource is called:
   (a) Contest competition
   (b) Interspecific competition
   (c) Scramble competition
   (d) Territoriality

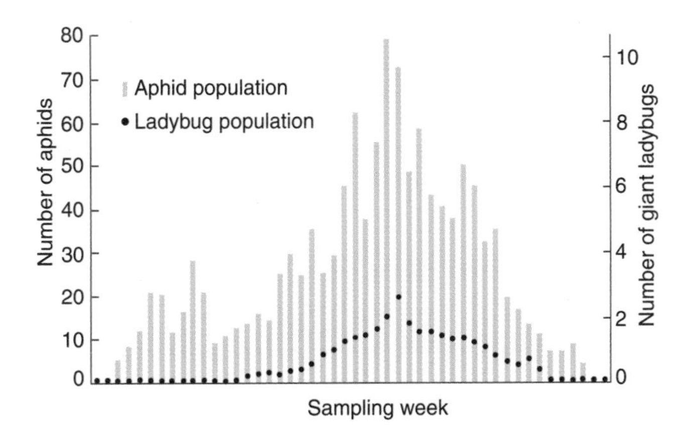

4. The graph above plots changes in numbers of a woolly aphid population and a ladybug population. The relationship between these species is:
   (a) The two species compete for a shared resource
   (b) Ladybugs are predators of aphids
   (c) Aphids are predators of ladybugs
   (d) Aphids depend on ladybugs for their survival

5. In an ecological interaction, commensalism can be represented as:
   (a) + –
   (b) – –
   (c) + 0
   (d) + +

6. Which of the following processes returns nitrogen to the atmosphere:
   (a) Nitrogen fixation by *Rhizobia*
   (b) Ammonification
   (c) Denitrification
   (d) Nitrification

7. Atmospheric circulation moves heat:
   (a) From the poles to the equator
   (b) Across mid latitudes
   (c) From the equator to the poles
   (d) From the Northern to the Southern Hemisphere

8. The four general climate-defined regions in each hemisphere are:
   (a) Polar, temperate, desert, tropical
   (b) Polar, cool temperate, warm temperate, equatorial
   (c) Cool temperate, warm temperate, tropical, desert
   (d) Polar, temperate, tropical, subtropical

9. Which of the following terrestrial biomes is found in equatorial latitudes with plentiful rainfall:
   (a) Taiga
   (b) Savanna
   (c) Tropical rainforest
   (d) Temperate rainforest

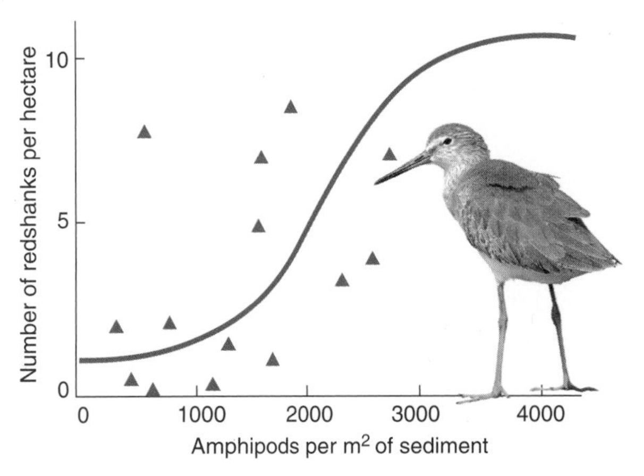

10. The graph above plots the number of redshanks (a wading bird) against its amphipod prey. The curve has been fitted to data (blue triangles). Which statement describes the behavior of this predator:
    (a) Redshanks feed faster at high prey densities
    (b) Redshanks don't feed at prey densities >3000/m^2
    (c) Redshanks are more dispersed in the environment when prey density is high
    (d) Redshanks aggregate to exploit patches of higher prey density

11. Which of the following is an example of a symbiosis:
    (a) A predator-prey interaction
    (b) A parasite-host relationship
    (c) A plant-herbivore interaction
    (d) Intraspecific resource competition

12. Resource partitioning is an adaptive response to:
    (a) Interspecific competition
    (b) Intraspecific competition
    (c) Prolonged periods of low food availability
    (d) Lack of producer biomass

ISBN: 978-1-98-856632-0

13. The majority of marine life occurs:
    (a) In the open ocean
    (b) In the neritic zone
    (c) In the benthic zone
    (d) In the coral reefs

14. Which of the following statements is not correct:
    (a) Pyramids of numbers can never be inverted.
    (b) Pyramids of energy can never be inverted.
    (c) Pyramids of energy and biomass are often a similar shape.
    (d) One producer organism can sometimes support a much greater number of consumers.

15. Which of the following statements about the open ocean biome is not correct:
    (a) The thermocline acts as a barrier to the mixing of deeper and surface waters.
    (b) Polar oceans have a poorly developed thermocline.
    (c) In polar regions, surface waters often have lower salinity than deeper waters.
    (d) In tropical regions, surface waters often have lower salinity than deeper waters.

16. When total photosynthesis exceeds total respiration:
    (a) Carbon will increase in the atmosphere
    (b) Carbon will increase in the biosphere
    (c) Average global temperatures will increase
    (d) The carbon in the atmosphere and biosphere will not change

17. Net primary productivity:
    (a) Determines the amount of energy available to primary consumers.
    (b) Is influenced by availability of water and nutrients.
    (c) Expresses a rate of biomass production per unit area or volume.
    (d) All of the above.

18. The different color of the two oceans above is primarily due to:
    (a) Differences in the depth of the water
    (b) Differences in the color of the seabed
    (c) Differences in particulate matter in the water
    (d) Differences in wave action

19. Phosphorus cycling is slow because:
    (a) Only a small number of animals make phosphate rich manure (guano).
    (b) There is no atmospheric component and phosphorus is returned to the land from the ocean via geological processes.
    (c) Phosphorus is immobilized for long periods in plant and animal tissues.
    (d) Humans remove too much phosphorus for agriculture.

20. In which of the following regions would you expect to find photosynthetic organisms?
    (a) The aphotic zone, the neritic zone, the oceanic zone, and the benthic zone
    (b) The pelagic zone, the aphotic zone, the neritic zone, and the oceanic zone
    (c) The photic zone, the deep trenches, the neritic zone, and the oceanic zone
    (d) The photic zone, the intertidal zone, the neritic zone, and the oceanic zone

21. Which of the following statements about light in aquatic ecosystems is not correct?
    (a) Light intensity falls off exponentially with depth and red light is absorbed first.
    (b) The 1% light level marks the point below which there is not enough light for photosynthesis.
    (c) Light intensity falls off exponentially with depth and red light passes furthest through the water column.
    (d) The depth of the 1% light level is important in determining the color of the water.

Questions 22-24 refer to the food web below:

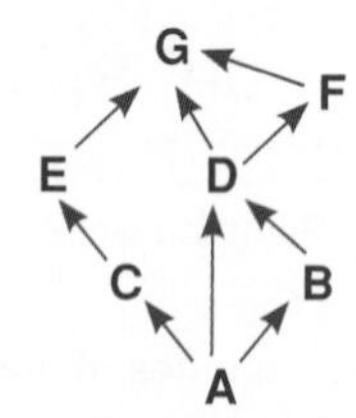

22. What flow correctly indicates the flow of energy?
    (a) DGF
    (b) ACE
    (c) ACD
    (d) BDC

23. Which two organisms are competing for food?
    (a) D and E
    (b) A and D
    (c) B and D
    (d) A and C

24. Organism B is:
    (a) A producer
    (b) A carnivore
    (c) A primary consumer
    (d) A secondary consumer

ISBN: 978-1-98-856632-0

25. The nutrient enrichment of inland and coastal waters is called eutrophication and it is increasingly a problem for water quality in environments that are modified by human activity. In the space below, analyze the problem of eutrophication and then propose a solution (or part solution) that will address the causes of eutrophication and mitigate its effects. You may wish to choose a specific example as a case study. Use the points identified in the table below to help you:

The problem	Your solution
Consider the proximate (immediate) and ultimate causes	Is it a permanent or temporary solution?
Explain the physical and biological effects of the enrichment	How much will it cost and over what time scale?
Explain the social and economic consequences of the enrichment	How will you measure its success as a solution?

(i) **Analysis of the problem**. You may attach photos if you wish. If you have used a specific case study include its details also. You may use more paper if you need to and attach it here:

(ii) **Your solution**. You may draw diagrams to illustrate your answer. Use more paper if you need to and attach it here:

ISBN: 978-1-98-856632-0

2. The Living World: Biodiversity

Developing understanding

Content: This unit explores the nature of biodiversity and its role in sustaining life on Earth. How do we quantify biodiversity and why are some species more important to maintaining diversity in ecosystems than others? The scale and impact of natural and human-induced disturbances to ecosystems is explored through case studies. This includes the role of succession in disturbed communities. Disturbance in ecosystems, whatever its causes, is common. The short and long term responses of organisms to disturbance forms the focus of the latter part of the unit.

Skills: This unit emphasizes skills in describing and explaining environmental concepts and processes in relation to biodiversity. Much of the material draws on case studies, so being able to describe and explain trends and patterns in data are important skills to practice. You will use these skills again in later chapters.

2.1 Introduction to biodiversity .... activities 26 - 29

☐ 1. Describe the components of biodiversity and the importance of each component. Use an example to explain the importance of biodiversity to life on Earth.

☐ 2. What is meant by ecosystem stability? Describe the difference between resilience and resistance and explain the role of each of these in determining how ecosystems respond to disturbance. Describe the relationship between ecosystem biodiversity and stability and explain the mechanisms by which this relationship is thought to operate.

☐ 3. Describe the effect of habitat loss on the diversity of ecosystems. Describe the differing responses of species to habitat loss (e.g. territorial species, interior specialists, generalists). Describe factors that make some species more vulnerable to habitat loss than others.

☐ 4. Describe ways in which biodiversity is quantified. Explain why it is important to recognize both species richness and species evenness in measures of biodiversity. Analyze data to evaluate the diversity of different communities.

2.2 Ecosystem services .... activity 30

☐ 5. Describe the four types of ecosystem services and provide examples of each. Describe the role of ecosystem services in supporting the human population and explain the connection between the diversity of ecosystems and their ability to continue to provide services.

☐ 6. Using an example, describe how human-induced changes to the environment can disrupt ecosystem services. Explain the economic and ecological impacts of these disruptions.

2.3 Island biogeography .... activity 31

☐ 7. Describe the principles of island biogeography. Describe the types of organisms that most easily colonize islands and explain the factors that affect both colonization rate and final island biodiversity.

☐ 8. Describe the role of island biogeography in the evolution of specialist species from a generalized mainland colonizer. Explain why the specialized nature of island biota increases its vulnerability to human impacts, including climate change, introduction of invasive species, deforestation, and pollution.

2.4 Ecological tolerance .... activity 32

☐ 9. Describe ecological tolerance and its application in environmental science. Understand that ecological tolerance can apply to individuals and to species and that tolerance can change seasonally or over an organism's lifetime. Explain how an understanding of tolerance range can help to explain the occurrence and distribution of species.

2.5 Natural ecosystem disruption ...... activities 33 - 34

☐ 10. Describe the types of natural disruption that affect ecosystems and identify them as periodic, episodic, or random. Earth system processes operate on a range of scales. Explain how scale, both in time (temporal) and in space (spatial), affects the impact of disruption and the ability of organisms to adapt to the changes.

☐ 11. Interpret data to describe how Earth's climate has changed over geological time and explain the different reasons for these changes. Describe the relationship between cycles of glacial expansion and retreat, and changes in sea level.

☐ 12. Describe the changes to habitats that can occur as a result of periodic or episodic environmental change. Interpret data to describe how organisms can respond to these changes by migration (seasonally or permanently). Predict how environmental changes occurring under projected climate change scenarios might affect the distribution and abundance of migratory species.

2.6 Adaptations .... activity 35

☐ 13. Describe what is meant by adaptation. Explain the role of the environment in selecting phenotypes that are most suited to the prevailing environment. Interpret data to show how species adapt to their environments over different time scales.

☐ 14. Describe why environmental change, particularly when it occurs rapidly, can threaten species survival. Which species are most vulnerable and why?

2.7 Ecological succession .... activities 36 - 39

☐ 15. Describe ecological succession, distinguishing between primary and secondary successions, their causes, and the time scale over which they occur. Interpret data relating to a case of primary succession to explain patterns of colonization and extinction.

☐ 16. Describe the effect of ecological succession on the diversity and structural complexity of ecosystems. Explain the role of pioneers and later seral species in succession. Describe situations where the progress of a succession can be suspended and the community returned to an earlier state.

☐ 17. Describe the role of keystone species in ecosystem structure and function. Interpret observational and experimental data to provide evidence for your explanations of the role of keystone species in ecosystem diversity.

☐ 18. Explain how indicator species are used in aquatic and terrestrial environments to evaluate environmental conditions, identify environmental deterioration, or monitor ecosystem recovery.

26 What is Biodiversity?

Key Question: What are the components of biodiversity and what is the role of biodiversity in sustaining life of Earth?

Biodiversity refers to the biological diversity present on Earth. It has several components (below), each of them equally important. Ecological theory suggests that all species in an ecosystem contribute in some way to ecosystem function. Therefore, species loss past a certain point is likely to have a detrimental effect on the functioning of the ecosystem and on its ability to resist change over time (its **stability**). Although many species still await discovery, we do know that the rate of species extinction is increasing. This loss of biodiversity has serious implications for the stability of many ecosystems.

The components of biodiversity

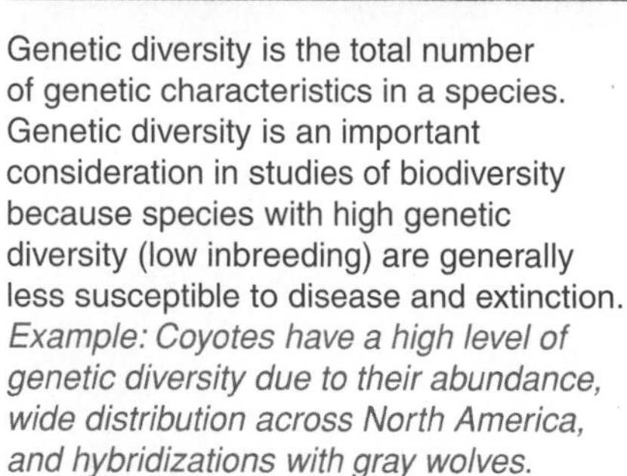

Genetic diversity is the total number of genetic characteristics in a species. Genetic diversity is an important consideration in studies of biodiversity because species with high genetic diversity (low inbreeding) are generally less susceptible to disease and extinction. *Example: Coyotes have a high level of genetic diversity due to their abundance, wide distribution across North America, and hybridizations with gray wolves.*

Species diversity is the number of different species (species richness) that are represented in a given community and their relative abundance (species evenness). High species diversity is associated with stable ecosystems and a large number of biotic interactions. *Example: The Raja Ampat Islands in Indonesia are considered the center of marine biodiversity. The region is home to 75% of all known species of hard corals.*

Habitat diversity describes the number of different habitats provided by a particular region. Habitat diversity is often described as heterogeneity and is associated with species diversity. More heterogeneous environments can support a larger number of species with different habitat needs. *Example: The tropical climate of the Raja Ampat Islands provides an enormous range of marine and terrestrial habitats. It is also relatively undisturbed by humans.*

Sea otters resting in Prince William Sound, Alaska. 40%[1] of this population died as a result of the Exxon Valdez oil spill in 1989.

[1] Garrott, R.A. *et. al.* (1993) Mortality of sea otters in Prince William Sound following the Exxon Valdex oil spill. Marine Mammal Science, 9(4). [2] Larson S.*et. al.* (2012) Genetic diversity and population parameters of sea otters, *Enhydra lutris*, before fur trade extirpation from 1741–1911. PLoS ONE 7(3).

The importance of genetic diversity

Sea otters are one of the smallest marine mammals, but superbly adapted to their marine life, where they feed on urchins and have an important role as a keystone species in coastal communities. The species, which was once numerous, was hunted almost to extinction for its fur. Most populations have recovered following a ban on hunting, conservation efforts, and relocations, and the species now occupies about two thirds of its former range.

Despite the apparent success of the population recovery, sea otters remain endangered. A primary reason for this is lack of genetic diversity. All existing populations have suffered at least one historic population bottleneck (severe reduction in genetic diversity) as a result of local extinctions during the fur trade period. A genetic study[2] comparing pre-fur trade and current populations found that modern populations have lost half the genetic diversity they once had. The California population is particularly impoverished as it descends from a single colony of only ~50 animals. This population, which was recovering, began to decline in the late 1990s and susceptibility to disease (particularly toxoplasmosis) appears to be the main factor in this. Sea otters still face significant threats, particularly from oil pollution, poaching, and conflicts with fisheries.

1. Describe the components of biodiversity, including the importance of each: ______________________

____

____

____

____

____

____

ISBN: 978-1-98-856632-0

38

ERT-2 1.A

VANISHING INSECTS: Why does biodiversity matter?

- Although they must often seem abundant to us, insect populations globally are in trouble. More than 40% of insect species are declining and a third are endangered. Just as concerning as this loss of diversity is the loss of insect biomass, which is falling by an estimated 2.5% a year.
- The cascading effect of insect loss threatens food chains globally. The causes are many and cumulative and include climate change, use of pesticides, and habitat loss.

A pair of blue tits may collect 100 insects a day to feed one chick

The winter moth caterpillar is an invasive species in the US but provides abundant food for birds.

The larvae of green lacewings feed on aphids and other soft bodied insect pests.

FIVE CRUCIAL INSECT ROLES

Insects have a central role in the ecosystem services humans rely on for survival. The decline in the numbers and diversity of insects has serious consequences for a sustainable future.

1: PROVIDERS

Insects are part of almost all food chains as prey for a wide range of other animals, including birds, bats, amphibians, and fish. Recent declines in many bird populations have been linked to scarcity of insect prey.

2: PEST CONTROLLERS

Predatory insects play a critical role in controlling the pest insects that threaten crops. They help to reduce pest control costs and increase yields, saving billions of dollars every year.

What may happen without insects:

1: *Species at higher trophic levels may decline in numbers and diversity.*

2: *Pests may increase, damaging crops and forests, and pesticide use may increase.*

2. (a) Describe the primary cause of the current lack of genetic diversity in modern sea otter populations: ______________

   ____

   ____

   (b) Describe the likely reason for the low genetic diversity in the California population: ______________

   ____

   (c) How might this be related to more recent declines in the California population? ______________

   ____

ISBN: 978-1-98-856632-0

Insect declines: how they're tracking

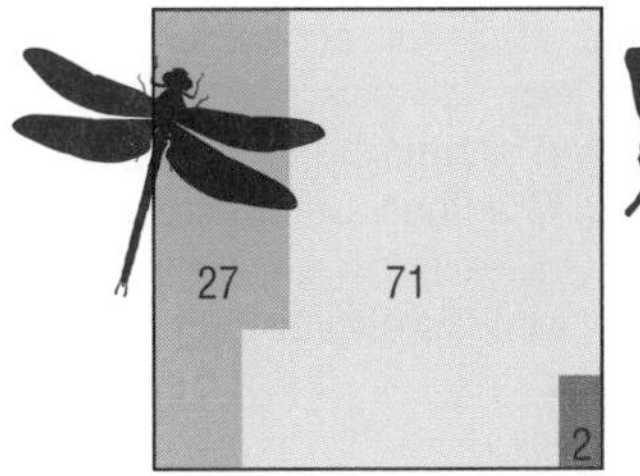

Dragonflies & damselflies

36
63
1

Butterflies and moths

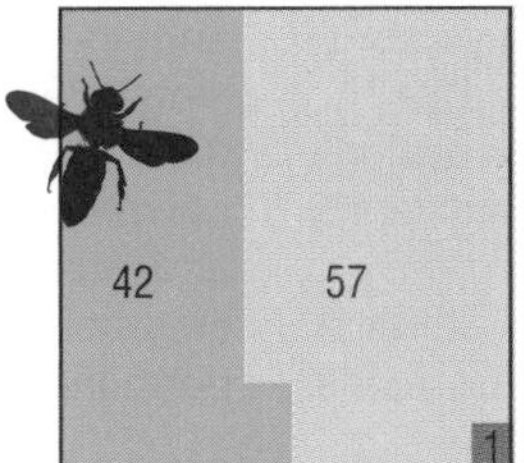

Bees, wasps, & ants

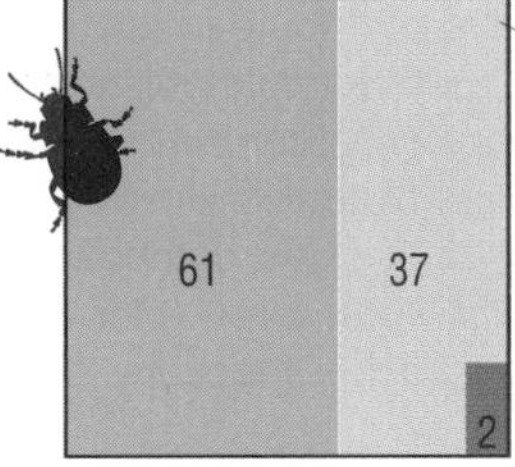

Beetles

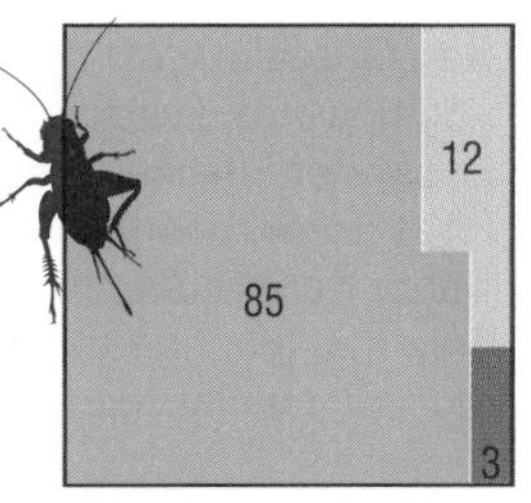

Grasshoppers & crickets

- % of species decreasing
- % of species stable
- % of species increasing

Species in the five major insect orders (above) have all declined in recent decades. Of the 2200 species tracked by the IUCN almost half are declining. These 2200 species represent just a tiny proportion of total insect biodiversity. Even with today's technological advancement, only 20% of insects species are even identified. We will not even know if they are lost.

Dung beetles process cattle dung in 23 months compared to the 28 it would take without them.

Bumblebees are important pollinators of both crops and wildflowers. A single bee can visit several thousand flowers a day.

One termite colony can excavate 0.2 tonnes of soil per year.

3: DECOMPOSERS

Insects that feed on wastes and dead material, such as dung, carrion, and dead plants, have an important role in nutrient cycles. Their activities release nutrients that would otherwise remain locked up for a considerable time.

Waste material would be recycled more slowly, hindering nutrient cycling.

4: POLLINATORS

Around 75% of crops benefit from insect pollination even if they do not completely depend on it. As the production of pollinator dependent crops increases, so too does our dependence on insect pollinators, which are declining.

Crops may reproduce poorly and some key food sources may be lost.

5: SOIL ENGINEERS

Termites and ants are an essential part of arid ecosystems. Their activities aerate hard ground, adding nutrients, improving soil structure, and allowing water to penetrate. They have even been used to rehabilitate regions affected by desertification.

Soils in arid regions may become barren, leading to crop failure and desertification.

3. Using insects as an example, explain the importance of biodiversity to ecosystem function and to human wellbeing:

ISBN: 978-1-98-856632-0

27 The Stability of Ecosystems

Key Question: What factors contribute to ecosystem stability and how are diversity and ecosystem stability related?

Ecosystem stability has long been a central principle in ecology. Ecosystems maintain a state of equilibrium and high diversity without continual change in species composition, although they may change over geological time. After a disturbance, the community recovers, species reoccupy their positions, and the equilibrium is restored. This state of ecosystem stability is closely linked to biodiversity. More diverse systems generally show greater stability over time although they may not recover quickly from disturbance. The loss of species and repeated large scale disturbances in a relatively short time period compromise the stability of ecosystems and can permanently change their characteristics.

Ecosystem stability (community equilibrium) can be viewed from two perspectives: **resistance**, the ability to resist disturbance and remain unchanged, and **resilience**, the ability to recover from external disturbances.

Communities most resistant to change typically have a large biotic structure (such as trees) with nutrients and energy stored in standing biomass. Forest communities tend to be relatively resistant, withstanding local disturbances such as temperature changes, insect outbreaks, and drought. However they have low resilience and are slow to recover from major disturbances such as logging or widespread fire.

Aquatic ecosystems, which lack large biomass stores are easily disturbed (low resistance) but tend to be highly resilient. The systems can be disturbed, e.g by pollutants or flooding, but will return to an equilibrium after the disturbance is removed.

Tropical rainforests, such as the Amazon, are amongst the highest diversity systems on Earth. These ecosystems are generally resistant to disturbance, but have little ability to recover once degraded.

Biodiversity and stability are connected and higher diversity systems are generally more stable. There are a number of mechanisms proposed for this relationship. In a hypothetical system (right), variation in community biomass over time is reduced relative to the variation in individual species, creating an overall community stability. The more species are contributing, the more the overall variations are reduced.

The biodiversity of ecosystems at low latitudes is generally higher than that at high latitudes, where climates are harsher, niches are broader, and systems may be dependent on a small number of key species.

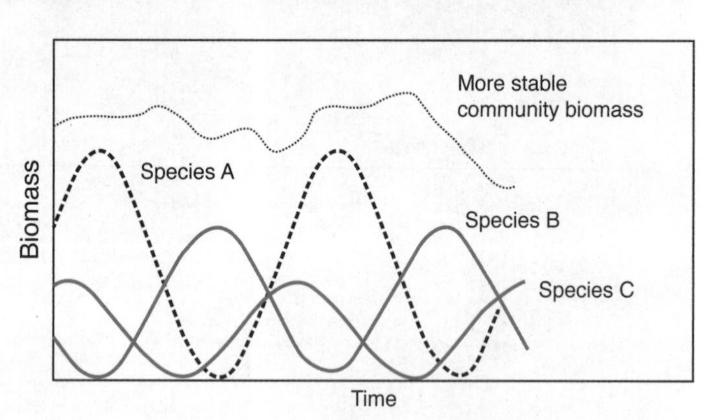

1. (a) What is meant by ecosystem stability? ______

______

______

(b) Describe the components of ecosystem stability and why each of these components is important: ______

______

______

2. (a) Describe the relationship between ecosystem stability and biodiversity: ______

______

______

(b) Describe possible reasons for this relationship. Use the graph above as evidence for your statement: ______

______

______

______

______

ISBN: 978-1-98-856632-0

Ecosystems are dynamic, constantly fluctuating between particular conditions. Most ecosystems, such as the spruce-fir forests of northern North America are resilient to relatively large scale and moderately frequent disturbances. However, major disturbances, such as large scale fires, climate changes, and volcanic eruptions can change the characteristics of the ecosystem.

Why are some systems stable and others are not?

Dolly Sods: an ecosystem forever changed

- Dolly Sods is a rocky high plateau area in the Allegheny Mountains of eastern West Virginia, USA. Originally the area was covered with spruce, hemlock, and black cherry. During the 1880s, logging began in the area and virtually all of the commercially viable trees were cut down. The logging caused the underlying humus and peat to dry out.
- Sparks from locomotives and campfires frequently set fire to this dry peat, producing fires that destroyed almost all the remaining forest. In some areas, the fires were so intense that they burnt everything right down to the bedrock, destroying seed banks. One fire during the 1930s destroyed over 100 km^2 of forest. The forests have never recovered. What was once a forested landscape is now mostly open meadow.

Right: The original dense forests of Dolly Sods have been replaced mostly by maple, birch, beech, and low growing scrub.

Equilibrium over time - spruce-fir forests

- A case study of ecosystem resilience is provided by the spruce-fir forest community in northern North America. Organisms in the community include the spruce budworm (right), and balsam fir, spruce, and birch trees. The community fluctuates between two extremes. During budworm outbreaks the environment favors the spruce and birch species, which are less susceptible to defoliation by spruce budworm. Between spruce budworm outbreaks, the environment favors the balsam fir, which outcompetes spruce and birch.
- The spruce-fir ecosystem is resilient even though some of the interacting components have low resistance.

Jerald E. Dewey, USDA Forest Service, Bugwood.org

1. Under certain environmental conditions, the spruce budworm population grows so rapidly it overwhelms the ability of predators and parasites to control it.
2. The budworm feeds on balsam fir (despite their name), killing many trees. The spruce and birch trees are left as the major species.
3. The budworm population collapses through lack of food.
4. Balsam fir saplings grow back in thick stands, eventually outcompeting the spruce and birch. Evidence suggests these cycles have been occurring for possibly thousands of years.

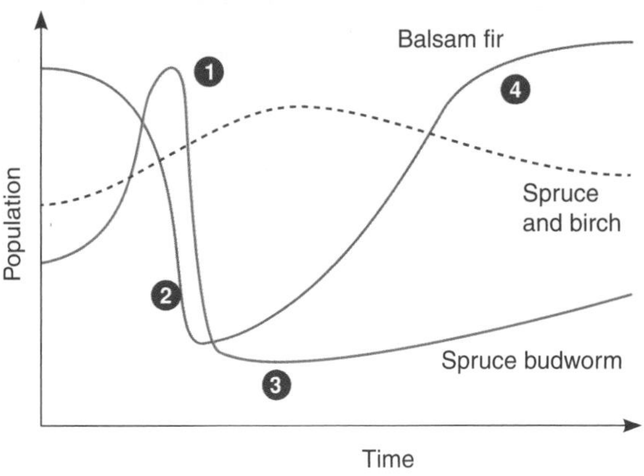

3. (a) Describe the large scale ecosystem change that occurred at Dolly Sods: ____________________

____

(b) What caused this change in the ecosystem? ____________________

(c) Explain why the ecosystem has not been able to recover quickly after the change: ____________________

____

____

4. In what way is the spruce-fir-budworm system resilient in the long term, despite fluctuations? ____________________

____

____

____

____

ISBN: 978-1-98-856632-0

28 Effect of Habitat Loss on Ecosystems

Key Question: What are causes and consequences of habitat loss and fragmentation?

The impact of humans on the Earth's systems is undeniable. Over the past few decades, scientists have documented a pattern of population decline in more and more plant and animal species. Habitat loss is the leading cause of these population declines globally. Humans cut and burn forest, clear land for agriculture, dam rivers, and drain wetlands leaving the resident species with no place to go. Species with restricted ranges are particularly vulnerable.

Species vulnerability to habitat loss

Resident species

- Wherever humans have settled, they have cleared land, built cities, and dammed rivers, altering and often destroying the natural landscape that existed before their arrival. For many species, the loss of habitat is the major causative factor in population decline. As populations decline, lack of genetic diversity creates increasing vulnerability to inbreeding and disease. Endemics (those species found only in one place) are at particular risk of extinction when habitat is lost.
- The loss and fragmentation of habitat reduces 'interior' habitat and creates more edge environments, where one type of environment meets another. This affects species differently. Some species are particularly area sensitive, and are specialist interior dwellers relying on the environmental conditions characteristic of interior habitats and away from the changes associated with boundary environments. These species are much more vulnerable to habitat loss than more generalist species, which are less affected by habitat patchiness. Specialist species therefore tend to be the first to disappear when habitats become degraded or disappear.
- Studies of forest birds provide evidence of these habitat preferences. As habitat size increases, the probability of finding interior species increases. Some species are insensitive to habitat area. These species are probably the least vulnerable to habitat loss, all other factors being equal.
- Habitat loss also disproportionately affects species with large range requirements such as predators with a large territories (e.g. brown bears, cougars, and wolves).

Habitat responses in different forest bird species
(±95% confidence intervals as dotted lines)

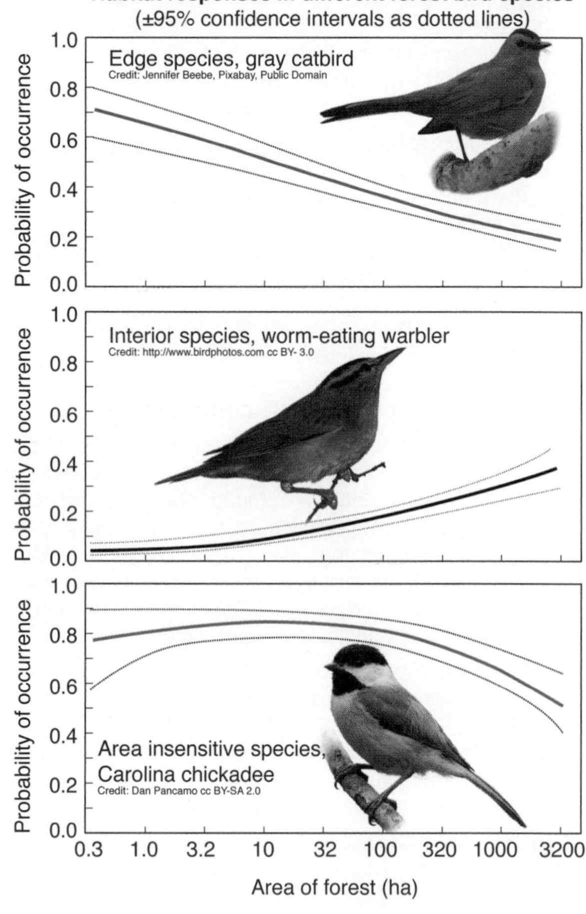

1. (a) Describe some of the causes of habitat loss: ____________________

   (b) Describe the consequences of habitat loss to wild populations of plants and animals: ____________________

2. Using evidence from above, explain why some species are more vulnerable to habitat loss than others: ____________________

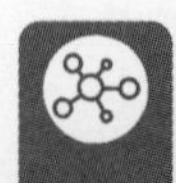
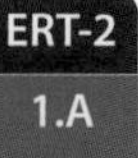

ISBN: 978-1-98-856632-0

Migrant species

Migrants face particular challenges if habitat loss affects one or both of their habitats. Habitat loss may be the result of habitat destruction, as is the case of the cerulean warbler below. Habitat can also be lost if animals cannot reach it, as in the case of salmonids. Salmonids are anadromous, leaving their natal streams as young smolt and returning to spawn after growing at sea.

The cerulean warbler – from abundant to near threatened

- The cerulean warbler has shown a steady decline in its breeding population since the 1960s (below) and it is now one of the rarest Neotropical migrant songbirds. It requires structurally diverse forests with a well developed canopy and is regarded as area sensitive because of its preference for forest interiors. It is threatened by loss of pristine forest in its South American wintering range and by mountaintop mining and logging in its North American breeding grounds.

Decline in the breeding population of cerulean warbler (1966-2011)

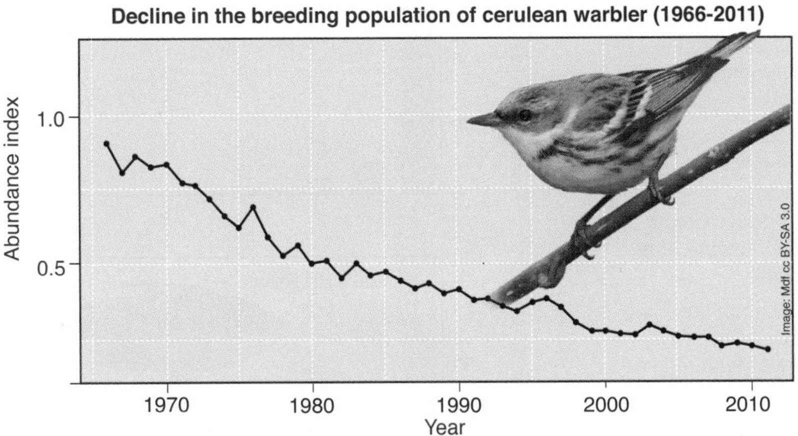

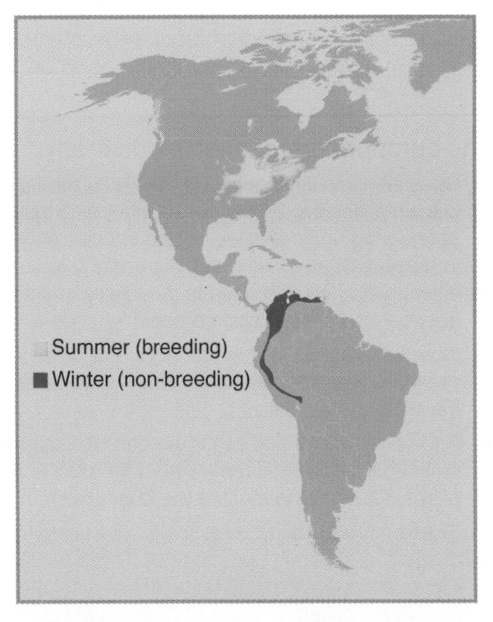

The sad salmonid story

- When we think of habitat loss, we often think of deforestation or loss of wetland habitat, but habitat loss and fragmentation also occurs when a species can no longer access critical parts of the habitat required for it to complete its life cycle. North America has a diverse freshwater fish fauna, yet between 1898 and 2006 a total of 39 species and 18 subspecies have become extinct in North America, a rate that is hundreds of times the natural background rate of extinction.
- Salmonids and other anadromous fish species are particularly at risk. In the United States, there are approximately 75,000 dams impounding around 17% of the nation's rivers. Dams restrict the upstream movement of adults to spawning (breeding) areas. Dams also delay the moment of smolts to the sea, a journey they must complete within 15 days in order to make the adjustments needed to move from fresh to salt water.
- The massive Grand Coulee Dam was built without any fish passage facilities and cut off from the sea nearly 2000 km of salmon spawning grounds on the upper Columbia. It is estimated that 30-50% of the original spawning habitat on the Colombia Basin is now either submerged under reservoirs or blocked by dams with inadequate bypass facilities. Only 214 of the original 400+ salmon and steelhead trout stocks of the US Pacific coast now remain. Of these, 169 populations are at high or moderate risk of extinction.

3. Describe factors that contribute to the vulnerability of the cerulean warbler population: ______

4. (a) Explain how the construction of dams results in a loss of upstream habitat for migratory fishes: ______

   (b) Explain why migratory fish are particular vulnerable to extinction in the United States: ______

ISBN: 978-1-98-856632-0

29 Measuring Biodiversity

Key Question: How do we quantify the diversity of ecological communities and why are measures of diversity important?

An important consideration when studying ecological communities, especially those threatened by habitat losses or other stressors, is to be able to quantify the diversity present. Data is collected from ecosystems by sampling, and the methods used to do this depend on the species of interest and their distribution, the habitat and topography, and the time and resources available. Species diversity is defined by the both the number of species (richness) and their relative abundance (evenness). These two measures are often combined into a mathematical index of diversity, which allows different communities to be compared meaningfully or changes in community diversity to be evaluated over time.

The components of species diversity

- Species diversity is defined not only by the number of species present (the species richness, S) but also by the relative abundance of those species (the species evenness). Both are important. Species richness is a crude measure of community diversity but we also need to be able to quantify the relative abundance of the species present.
- Species evenness is highest when the proportions of all species are the same and decreases as the proportions of species become less similar.
- Species richness and evenness can be illustrated using column plots against species rank, where the rank is defined by the order of species from the most to the least abundant (right).
- These methods allow us to make a visual comparison of the diversity of different communities. These two components (species richness and evenness) are also often incorporated into one value, called an index of diversity (Appendix 1).

Right: Patterns of diversity for two fish communities in Trinidad. In the Cat's Hill River, the most dominant species (the two spot tetra) made up 28% of the total catch. In contrast, the most dominant species in the Innis River represented 76% of the sample.

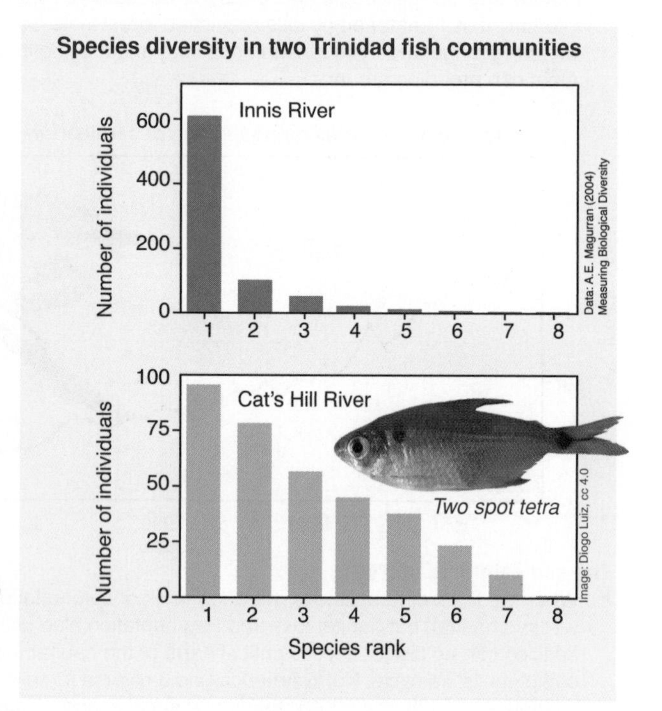

1. Examine the diversity data for the two fish assemblages above:

   (a) What is the species richness (S) of the rivers? ____________

   (b) Which river has the greatest species evenness? ____________

   (c) Which community has the greatest diversity overall? ____________

2. Describe the importance of considering the relative abundance of species as well as the number of species when quantifying the diversity of an ecosystem:

   ____

   ____

   ____

3. Students used quadrats to sample three sites in a stream. They recorded the species found and the number of individuals per m^2 at each site. Their results are shown in Table 1.

   (a) Determine the species richness at each site:

   i) Site 1: ____________

   ii) Site 2: ____________

   iii) Site 3: ____________

   (b) Rank the sites in terms of their species evenness:

   ____

   (c) Which is the most abundant species in the stream?

   ____

   (d) Which site has the lowest species diversity? ____________

Table 1. Sample of freshwater stream invertebrates

Common name	Site 1 (no./m^2)	Site 2 (no./m^2)	Site 3 (no./m^2)
Freshwater shrimp	20	67	5
Freshwater mite	15	0	0
Flat mayfly	21	23	0
Bighead stonefly	18	12	2
Blackfly	40	78	100
Bloodworm	22	21	43

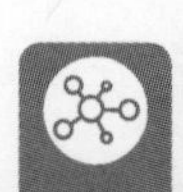
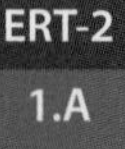

ISBN: 978-1-98-856632-0

The table right provides data on the number of individuals in two hardwood forest stands with different aspect in WV. Totals have been provided.

4. Complete the columns for relative abundance. The first values in each columns have been provided. Species rank (most to least common) is given in brackets after the number.

5. Using the relative abundance values expressed as proportions (e.g. 0.475) plot the data on the semi-log grid provided below. The first two points are plotted for you. This type of plot is called a **rank-abundance diagram**.

6. How does the slope of the rank-abundance curve vary with increasing species evenness and why?

Table 2. Diversity of two second-growth forest stands in West Virginia

	NE facing stand		SW facing stand	
Species	Number of individuals (rank)	Relative abundance (% of total)	Number of individuals (rank)	Relative abundance (% of total)
Sugar maple	191 (1)	47.5	172 (2)	22.9
Sweet buckeye	100 (2)		0	
American beech	22 (3)		197 (1)	
White ash	19 (4)		16 (9)	
Laurel	19 (5)		0	
Shagbark hickory	13 (6)		0	
Sycamore	13 (7)		0	
Box elder	13 (8)		0	
Black cherry	3 (9)		0	
Yellow poplar	3 (10)		0	
Pignut hickory	3 (11)		22 (8)	
Basswood	3 (12)		0	
Red maple	0		113 (3)	
White oak	0		81 (4)	
Flowering dogwood	0		75 (5)	
Red oak	0		38 (6)	
Hornbeam	0		28 (7)	
Pitch pine	0		9 (10)	
Totals	**402**	**100%**	**751**	**100%**

Activity developed using data from Gilliam *et al* (2014) *Variation in vegetation and microbial linkages with slope aspect in a montane temperate hardwood forest*. Ecosphere 5(5):66.

7. Compare the diversity of these two forest stands. Are they very different? Make your comparisons in terms of both species richness and evenness:

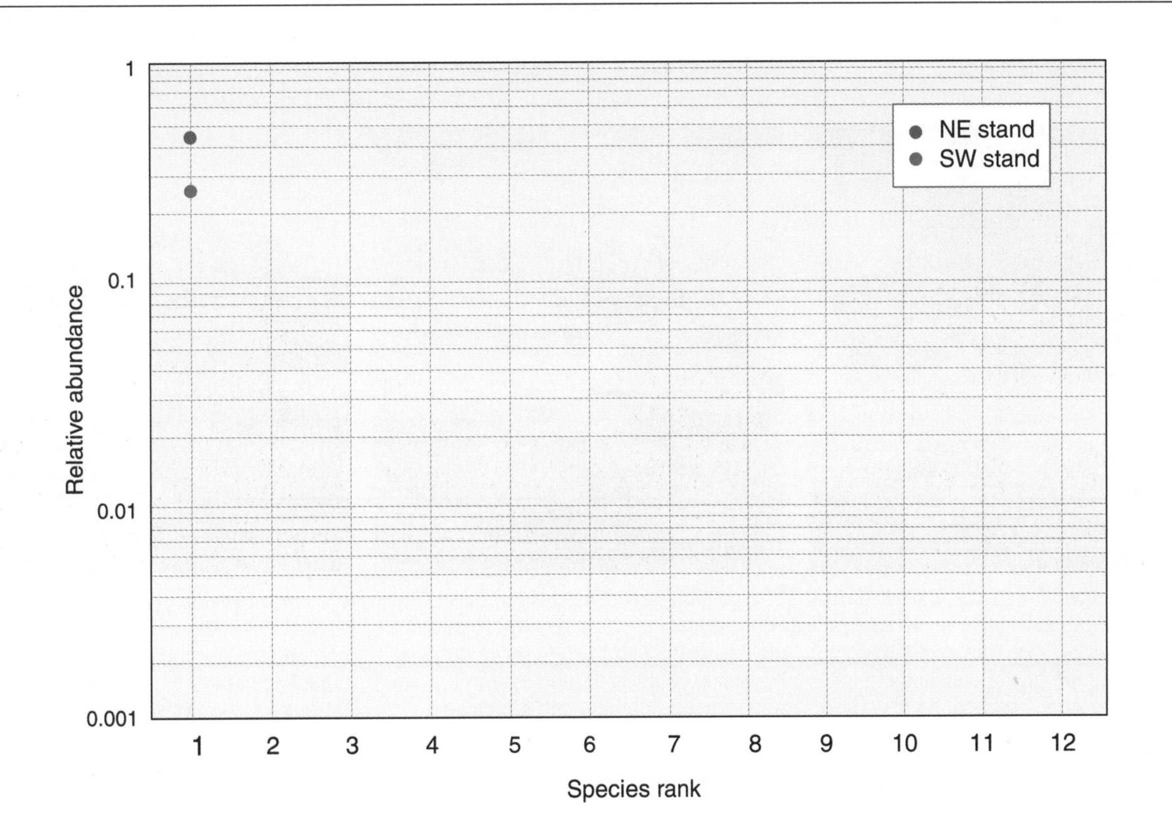

ISBN: 978-1-98-856632-0

30 Ecosystem Services

Key Question: What are ecosystem services, what do they provide, and why do we need them?

Humans depend on Earth's ecosystems for the services they provide. These ecosystem services include resources such as food and fuel, as well as processes such as purification of the air and water. Biologically diverse and resilient ecosystems that are managed in a sustainable way are better able to provide the ecosystem services on which we depend. The UN has identified four categories of ecosystem services: supporting, provisioning, regulating, and cultural.

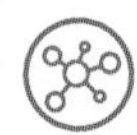

Services required for the functioning of all other ecosystem services such as nutrient cycling, pollination, soil formation, and seed dispersal.

Products obtained directly from ecosystems for basic human needs such as food, water, minerals, shelter, and fuel.

SUPPORTING
PROVISIONING
REGULATING
CULTURAL

Ecosystem services

Pollination
Nutrient cycling
Soil formation
Photosynthesis
Biodiversity
Habitat
Stewardship
Esthetics
Recreation
Education
Clean air
Carbon storage
Flood control
Pure water
Temperature control
Food
Lumber and fuel
Fish
Clean water

Non-material benefits obtained from ecosystems. Cultural and provisioning services are closely linked. Ecosystems can define a way of life for many.

The benefits obtained from the regulation of ecosystem processes, including climate regulation and purification of air and water.

Healthy, biodiverse ecosystems are crucial to maintaining provisioning services. Brazil nuts, for example, are harvested only from the wild. The tree grows only in the pristine forests of the Amazon because disturbed forest lacks the pollinating insects it needs to fruit. Logging, burning, and overharvest seriously threaten supplies of the nut.

The cultural services provided by ecosystems include the esthetic values we associate with pristine environments. For many cultures though, cultural and provisioning services are closely intertwined. For example, for small scale fishing communities, fishing provides food but it is also a way of life.

Barataria Preserve, Mississippi River delta region, Louisiana

Wetlands provide critical regulating services including water purification, flood control, and carbon storage. At the same time, key habitat services are provided by wetland biodiversity. Wetlands are threatened globally as they are drained for agriculture, yet the services they provide cannot be easily replaced.

ISBN: 978-1-98-856632-0

Climate change and ecosystem services

Current and future climate change will affect human populations both directly and indirectly as ecosystems lose their ability to provide the services that humans rely on. One of the clearest ways to illustrate this is to examine the effect of glacier recession in the tropics and its effect on the current and future hydrologic resources.

Case study: Glaciers in the Cordillera Blanca

- The Cordillera Blanca ('white range") in Peru extends for 200 km NW and once included 722 individual glaciers. It is the most extensive tropical ice-covered mountain range in the world. Snowmelt from the Cordillera Blanca provides part of northern Peru with a year round supply of water and 5% of Peru's power comes from a hydroelectric plant in the Santa River valley, which runs parallel to the range to the west.
- A 22% reduction in glacier area occurred across the range between 1970 and 2003, and a further 17% loss occurred between 2003 and 2010. Based on satellite imagery, only 485 glaciers remain.
- The glaciers that feed the tributaries of the Santa River regulate seasonal stream flows. Communities of the Cordillera Blanca depend on access to water. Water supplies can increase temporarily as a result of meltwater produced as glaciers retreat, but these increases decline as glacier mass decreases.
- Rapid melting creates unstable high elevation lakes and expands the volume of those already present.
- Hydrological adjustments are causing a contraction in high altitude wetlands, which are important in maintaining stable stream flows, regulating evapotranspiration cycles, and supporting pastures. There has been an increase in daily variation in temperature, with warmer dry-season days and colder nights. These changes are threatening agricultural production for subsistence farmers.
- Rapid ice loss is increasing the likelihood of disaster events, such as the 1941 flood caused by overflow of Lake Palcacocha (top right). The lake's volume has increased more than 30 fold since 1970, due largely to the retreat of an adjacent glacier. It now presents a serious flood hazard to the city of Huaraz.

A temperature rise of 0.5-0.8°C has seen more than 30% of Peru's ice caps vanish in the last 40 years. The Cordillera Blanca's glaciers have retreated substantially, as have many in the Andes, and many have disappeared.

1. Explain why ecosystem services are important to humans: ______________________

____

____

____

2. Explain the relationship between climate change and glacial retreat in the Cordillera Blanca and the changes in ecosystem services provided in the region:

____

____

____

____

____

____

____

____

____

ISBN: 978-1-98-856632-0

31 Island Biogeography

Key Question: What factors determine the diversity of islands and why are island species usually specialists?

We have explored what biodiversity is, but what factors determine the biodiversity of an ecosystem? Biodiversity tends to increase with habitat size, environmental variation (as with variation in topography and microclimate), and latitude. Island biogeography is a branch of science that seeks to explain the ecological relationships and spatial patterns of biodiversity on islands. Islands have some of the characteristics of habitats that have become fragmented in that they are small and vulnerable to disturbance and species loss. However, they are often centers of diversity with a high proportion of endemic species (species found nowhere else). Island biogeography theory makes predictions about island biodiversity based on island size and distance from a source area (below). These predictions have largely been supported by observational and experimental data and appear to apply to fragmented habitats also.

Factors determining diversity on islands

Island biogeography is a fascinating area of study. Why are island species often found nowhere else? Why are some taxa (groups of organisms) overrepresented, whereas others are underrepresented? Why do they often show rapid rates of evolution? What determines the biodiversity present in land areas of different sizes? These questions are central to island biogeography theory, which supposes that species disperse from a source area to islands of different sizes and distances away. The size of the island and distance from the source allow us to predict how many species will be present as a result of random dispersal (see figures A and B below).

Island biogeography theory can help predict the diversity of both island habitats and isolated ecosystems such as mountaintops, oases, seamounts, and forest fragments.

However, a large number of factors influence the final diversity of an island, including whether or not the island is continental or oceanic (right) and the length of time the island has been isolated. Oceanic islands typically have more impoverished biota than continental islands (see table below).

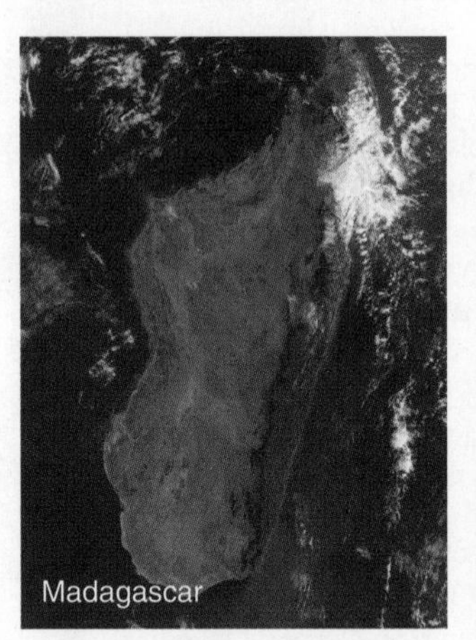

Continental islands formed as part of a continent and then became isolated from the main land mass, e.g. Madagascar, which lies off the coast of East Africa separated ~ 100 mya.

Images: NASA

Oceanic islands are volcanic islands of fairly recent origin. These include the Galápagos islands, Hawaiian islands, the Aleutians, and Tristan da Cunha in the mid Atlantic.

Factors affecting final biota
Degree of isolation (distance from diversity source area, usually mainland)
Length of time of isolation
Size of island
Climate (tropical/polar, arid/humid)
Location relative to ocean currents
Initial plant and animal composition
Species composition of earliest arrivals (if always isolated)
Serendipity (chance arrivals)

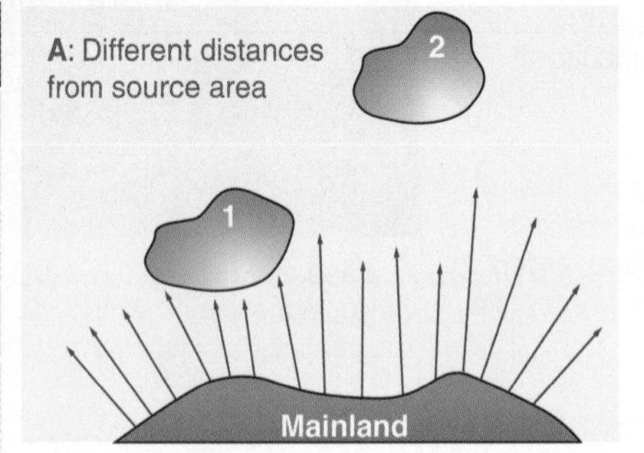

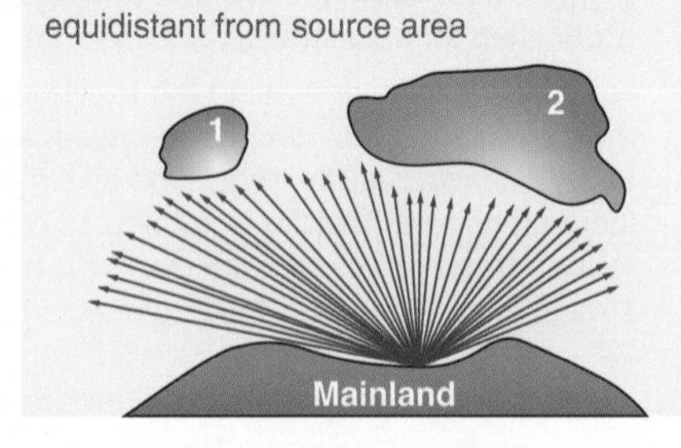

Island biogeography theory makes two general predictions about factors affecting species richness. These are illustrated in the schematic above. However other factors can be important also (table left), especially the amount of time an island has been isolated.

1. Islands close to a source area (mainland) will have a more species than similar sized islands that are further away (in **A**, island 1 receives more random dispersals).
2. Larger islands will have more species than smaller islands located at similar distances from the source area (in **B**, island 2 receives more random dispersals).

1. Describe how each of the following might affect the diversity and vulnerability of the biota found on an oceanic island:

(a) Island area: ______________________________

____

____

____

(b) Distance from a continental land mass: ______________________________

____

____

____

ISBN: 978-1-98-856632-0

Islands have unique biota

Islands globally are characterized by high endemism (species found nowhere else) and a high proportion of specialist species. Island residents often become flightless or grow to very large sizes in the absence of predation. Islands, because of their smaller size, have more limited resources, so colonizing species typically become specialized (through evolution) to exploit a narrow resource range, partitioning the resource base so that competition is minimized. This pattern of evolution, called adaptive radiation, is a feature of the biota of the Galápagos (below). Once specialists, these species are vulnerable to invasions of generalist species.

putneymark cc BY-SA 2.0

Matthew Field www.photography.mattfield.com CC 3.0

The flightless cormorant (above) is one of a number of bird species that lost the power of flight after becoming an island resident. Giant tortoises, such as the 11 subspecies remaining on the Galápagos today (center) were, until relatively recently, characteristic of many islands in the Indian Ocean including the Seychelles archipelago, Reunion, Mauritius, Farquhar, and Diego Rodriguez. These were almost completely exterminated by early Western sailors, although a small population remains on the island of Aldabra. Another feature of oceanic islands is the rapid evolution of colonizing species into different specialist forms. The three species of Galápagos iguana almost certainly arose, through speciation, from a hardy traveler from the South American mainland. The marine iguana (above with endemic blue-footed boobies) is the only iguana that feeds at sea. The two species of land iguana (not pictured) feed on cacti, which are numerous. One of these (the pink iguana) was identified as a separate species only in 2009.

Island diversity: extinction vs immigrations

- The predictions of island biogeography theory (opposite page) are largely supported by observational (right) and experimental data*.
- The number of species present on an island can be seen as a balance between species arrivals and species extinctions. Distance largely determines the rate of arrivals, while island size is an important factor in extinction rate. However, this does not account for speciation occurring on islands (e.g. as on the Galápagos and Hawaiian islands).
- It follows then that species richness on near, large islands is greater than that on distant, small islands. Small islands are much more vulnerable to the impact of human activities.
- For oceanic islands where colonists must arrive by air, water, or wind, organisms with high dispersal capabilities, such as plants and birds, are overrepresented in the biota.

*Simberlof and Wilson (1970). Experimental zoogeography of islands: a two-year record of colonization. Ecology 51: 934-937. This experiment involved removing the arthropod fauna of six mangrove islands in the Florida Keys by fumigation and then studying recolonization. See BIOZONE's Resource Hub for an account of this.

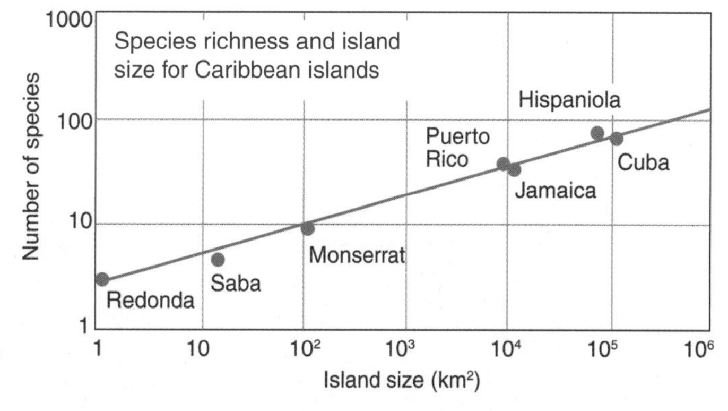

Total number of species of amphibians and reptiles on seven islands in the Caribbean. Based on 1957 data reported in MacArthur & Wilson (1967), so numbers are not current.

2. (a) Explain why island communities typically have a large number of specialist (as opposed to generalist) species:

(b) Explain why this makes island species vulnerable to habitat loss and the effects of invasive species. What factors might increase their vulnerability?

ISBN: 978-1-98-856632-0

32 Ecological Tolerance

Key Question: What is ecological tolerance and how does tolerance range affect individuals and populations?

The survival, growth, and reproduction of individual organisms and populations depend on the availability of essential environmental factors, such as (depending on the species) specific nutrients, light, and temperature. In any environment, individuals (and species) will be able to function within a certain range of environmental conditions. This is the tolerance range, often represented as a bell shaped tolerance curve (below). Tolerance curves are broad for some organisms and much narrower for others, and tolerance may shift seasonally and for different life stages. An understanding of tolerance range is useful in explaining species distributions and understanding their response to factors such as pollution.

Abiotic factors and ecological tolerance

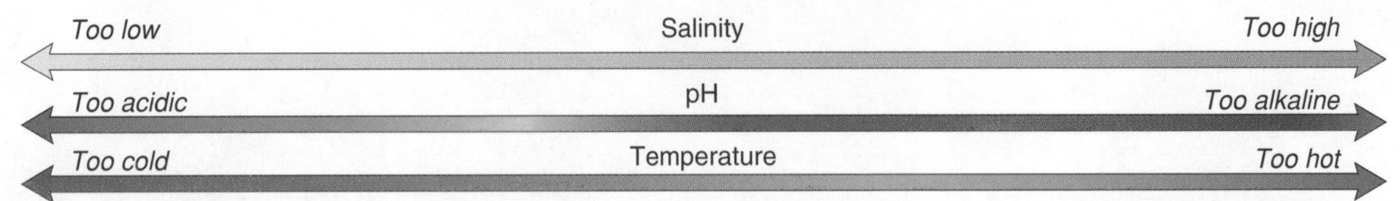

The law of tolerances states that "*for each abiotic factor, a species population (or organism) has a tolerance range within which it can survive. Toward the extremes of this range, that abiotic factor tends to limit the organism's ability to survive*".

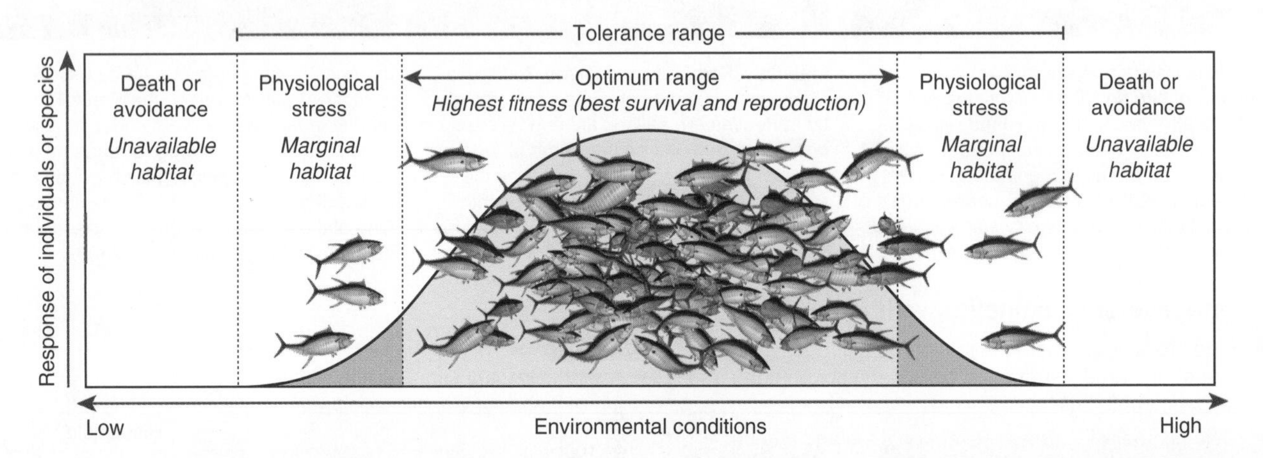

Some species (e.g. the zander) tolerate a wider range of temperatures than others (e.g. salmonids). Even within a species, tolerance can change seasonally as individuals acclimatize to slowly changing conditions, e.g. from winter to summer.

Tolerance for a particular environmental factor can be broad for some life stages and very narrow for others. Adult Atlantic blue crabs for example survive in a wide range of salinities, but eggs and larvae survive only in salinities above 23 ppt.

Tolerance range can explain species distribution. A mature tree may grow outside its natural range but its seedlings may not survive. The Colorado pinyon pine for example cannot survive mean winter temperatures below –10°C.

1. What is ecological tolerance? ______________________

2. Explain the role of ecological tolerance in determining species distribution and as a tool scientists can use to detect changes in the environment:

ISBN: 978-1-98-856632-0

33 Natural Ecosystem Changes

Key Question: What are the agents of natural ecosystem change and how do these changes vary in scale?

Ecosystems are dynamic systems, and natural disruptions are common. Environmental changes come from three sources: the biosphere, geological forces (crustal movements and plate tectonics), and cosmic forces (the movement of the Moon around the Earth and the Earth and planets around the Sun). All these can cause cycles, steady states, and directional changes (trends) in the environment. Many of these disruptions, e.g. seasonal changes and tidal movements, are periodic in occurrence and allow organisms to adapt to the predictable changes. Others, such as volcanic eruptions, are episodic and largely unpredictable. Ecosystem changes also occur over very different scales of time and space, from large scale geological and climate changes to short term localized changes to weather (below).

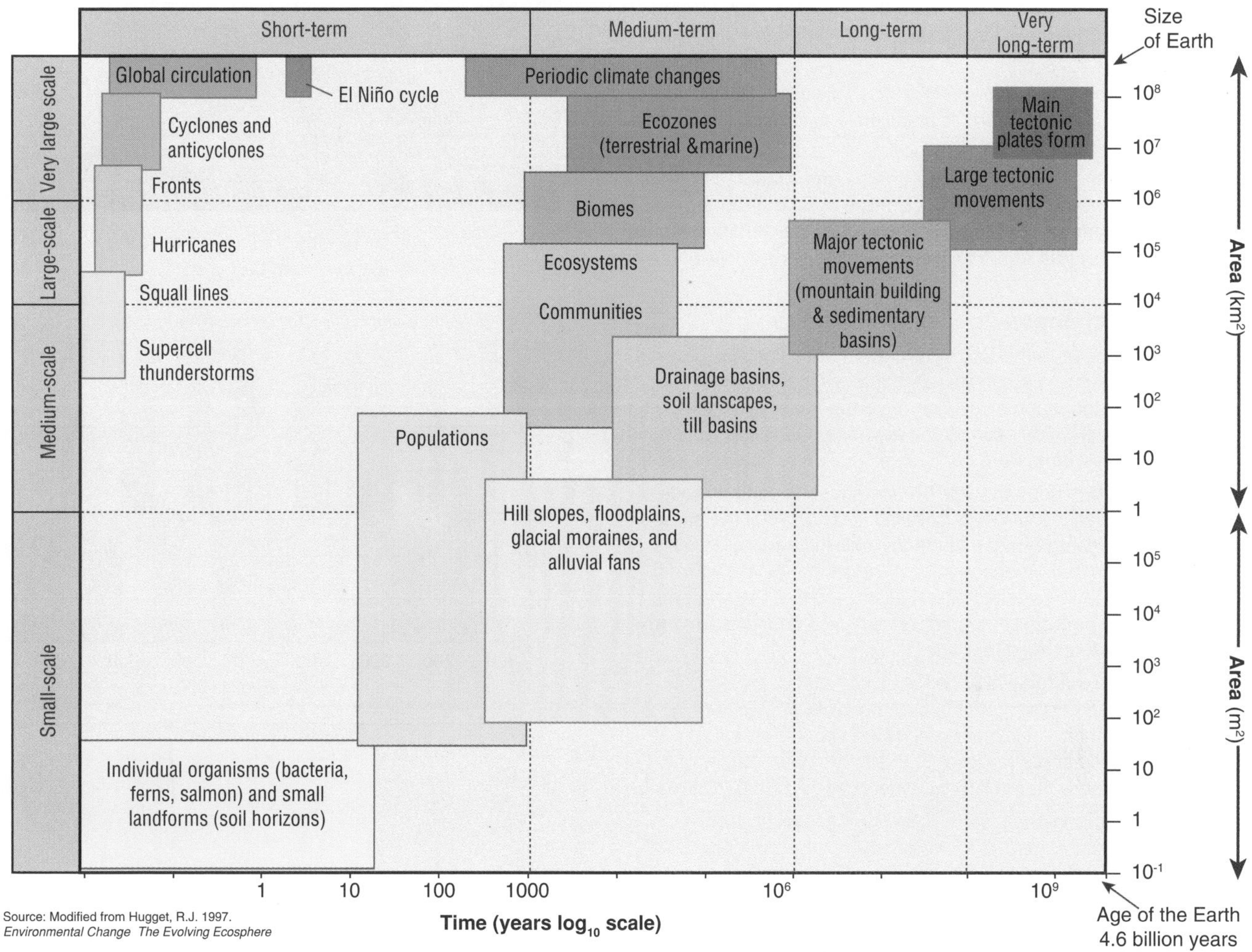

Above: Large scale natural changes occurring over millennia are responsible for the formation of landscapes and their associated biological communities. Some short term periodic changes, such as tidal fluxes, influence local environmental patterns. Others, e.g. seasons, can cause larger scale environmental changes such as the advance and retreat of the polar sea-ice every winter and summer. Environmental trends such as climate cooling can cause long term changes in communities, especially if they occur rapidly.

Cycles of glacial and interglacial conditions during the last 2-3 million years are largely the result of an interplay between astronomical cycles and atmospheric CO_2 concentrations.

Volcanic eruptions can be very sudden. They vary in scale, from small to massive explosions. Large eruptions can alter regional or global weather and devastate widespread areas of landscape.

Tropical cyclones are rapidly rotating storm systems. They are named (hurricane, typhoon etc) according to their location and strength and can cause considerable disruption to ecosystems.

ISBN: 978-1-98-856632-0

158 157 155 72 ERT-2 5.A

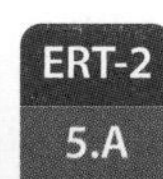
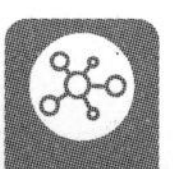

Episodic events can disrupt ecosystems

- Large volcanic eruptions can affect ecosystems, and alter local and global climate by releasing flows of ash and gas and blasting ash and aerosols into the atmosphere.
- A well documented example of this is the eruption of Mount Pinatubo, located on the island of Luzon in the Philippines. Eruptions began on June 3 1991, after almost 500 years with almost no activity. On June 15, after many large explosions, Mount Pinatubo entered its final eruptive phase, blasting 10 km^3 of ash 34 km into the atmosphere and producing high-speed avalanches of hot ash and gas. The Earth's climate was severely affected by Pinatubo's eruption. Over the course of the eruption, some 17 million tonnes of SO_2 and 10 km^3 of ash were released into the atmosphere. The ash caused an almost 10% reduction in sunlight reaching the Earth's surface over the following year, and global temperatures dropped by 0.5°C over the following 2-3 years. Ozone levels reached some of their lowest recorded levels.
- Similarly, the eruption of El Chichon in Mexico, 1982, lowered the global temperature by 0.5°C over two years, emitting about half the SO_2 volume of Pinatubo.
- In the 1800s, the eruptions of Tambora and Krakatau in Indonesia affected climate as far away as Europe and North America. Effects included early snow falls and cold wet weather. 1816, the year after the Tambora eruption, was called the year without summer.

The eruption column of Mount Pinatubo on June 12, 1991, three days before the final eruption phase.

Long term changes on Earth: Ice ages

- Some changes to the Earth happen on such vast time scales that they are not perceivable to humans. Changes may take place over thousands to million of years. Some changes occur in cycles (periodic), such as the advance and retreat of ice sheets, while others are continuous, such as continental drift.
- The Earth has gone through five ice ages, i.e. long periods of time when large ice sheets covered large parts of the globe. The latest ice age began about 2.7 million years ago and is still ongoing. Within an ice age, there are periods of warmer climate conditions called interglacials, such as the present. The cooler periods of time are called glacials. These tend to last longer than the interglacials.
- The current interglacial began about 12,000 years ago. Antarctic ice cores (right) confirm the cycle of glacials (blue) and interglacials (yellow) as ice sheets advanced and retreated. Ice cores reveal a lot of climate data, reaching depths of more than 3 km and extending back 800,000 years.
- Sea level changes on Earth have been associated with advances and retreat of ice sheets (bottom right). Sea levels fall and land is exposed when ice sheets expand. They then rise when the ice retreats as glacial melt enters the oceans.

  The figure right shows how sea levels have changed over the last 4 glacial cycles. When sea level is low (more negative) more water is locked up in ice sheets.

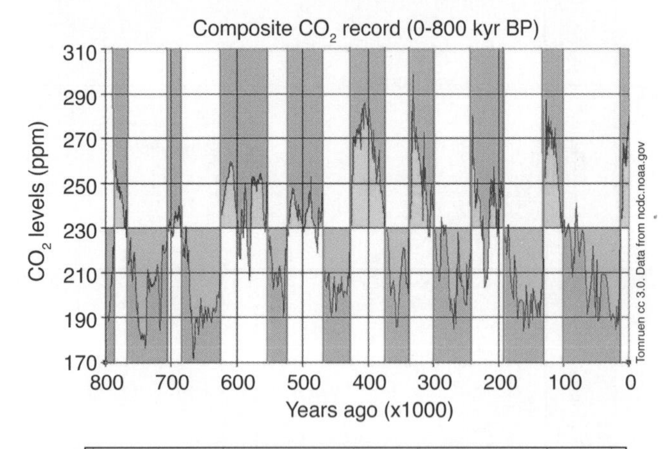

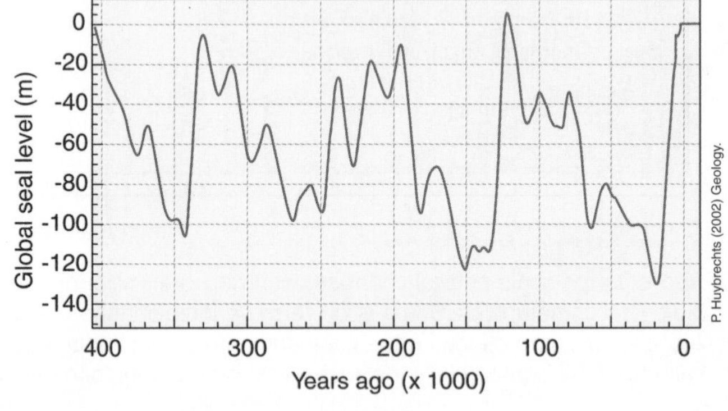

1. Study the diagram on the previous page showing the extent and time scale of environmental change:

   (a) Identify the geologic event occurring on the largest temporal and spatial scale: ______

   (b) Identify two very large scale events that take a relatively short amount of time to occur: ______

   ______

   (c) How long does it take for a soil landscape to form? ______

2. Describe how volcanic eruptions can affect local ecosystems and the wider climate: ______

   ______

   ______

   ______

ISBN: 978-1-98-856632-0

The ice sheets that covered much of the Northern Hemisphere during the last glacial began to retreat about 20,000 years ago. As they melted, the flood of fresh water into the oceans shut down ocean currents, causing warming in the Southern Hemisphere. Release of CO_2 from the seas warmed the planet, melting continental ice sheets and creating the current climate.

There may be several periods of warming (interglacials) and cooling (glacials) within an ice age. It is not fully understood what causes these changes, but they may be due to changes in carbon dioxide and methane in the atmosphere, changes in solar output, and changes in Earth's orbit.

In North America during the last glaciation, ice covered all of Canada and extended south as far as the Upper Midwest, Idaho, Montana, and Washington. Evidence of this glaciation includes the grooves and U-shaped valleys formed as the glaciers advanced and retreated.

What's happening now?

Ice sheets, sea levels, and climate change

- Global sea levels rose by approximately 120 m in the years after the last glacial and remained stable until the late 19th century. During the 20th century, global average sea level rise has been estimated at ~3.3 mm per year. Depending on carbon emissions, sea level is expected to rise by up to 130 cm by 2100, relative to 2000 (National Climate Assessment). Melting ice sheets and glaciers have the most potential to significantly contribute to rising sea levels. Worse case scenarios would involve a large Antarctic contribution.
- Data to 2006 (right) indicate the significant contribution of small glaciers and ice caps to sea level rise. Ice melt is not uniform either. Ice sheets in Canada, for example, are melting at an unprecedented rate and sea levels in parts of Atlantic Canada are projected to rise even higher than the global average this century. As more ice is lost surfaces become less reflective, which means more sunlight is being absorbed, which leads to more melting.
- Glaciers can lose ice via surface melt or by calving from the glacier edge. Prior to 2005, ice loss in the Queen Elizabeth Islands was shared almost equally between the two (48% and 52% respectively). As a result of warming, 90% of ice lost is now a result of surface melt.

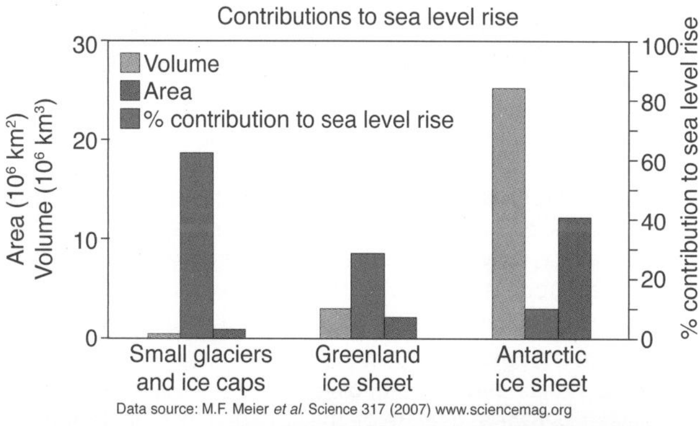

Image: Agassiz ice cap, Queen Elizabeth Islands, Canada.

3. Using the data opposite, describe the climate and sea level changes during the latest (current) ice age:

4. Sea level is expected to rise even more quickly by the end of this century. Use the data plotted above to explain why worse-case scenarios (greatest) sea level rise involve a large contribution from the Antarctic ice sheet:

ISBN: 978-1-98-856632-0

34 Responding to Environmental Change

Key Question: How do organisms respond to natural short-term and longer-term changes in their environment?

Organisms globally have life histories and patterns of behavior that have evolved over millennia to maximize survival and reproductive success. One of the biggest challenges animals face is finding enough food, particularly during seasons when food is scarce (commonly winter). Some overwinter in place by entering a period of hibernation but many others migrate every year between summer feeding grounds and overwintering habitats. These migrations can cover thousands of kilometers. Long distance bird migrants may even cross from one side of the globe to the other.

Migration in barren-ground caribou, *Rangifer tarandus groenlandicus*

Barren-ground caribou bulls in Denali National Park, Alaska. Caribou feed on lichen but climate changes threaten their access to it.

- The barren-ground caribou is a subspecies of caribou found mainly in the Canadian territories of Nunavut and the Northwest Territories, and in West Greenland. This subspecies has the longest migration of any terrestrial mammal, traveling up to 1200 km in a season between summer grazing lands in the Arctic tundra, where the young are born, and overwintering areas in the taiga (boreal forest) to the south. Despite being widespread and numerous overall, most caribou herds are experiencing declines and several genetically distinct populations are endangered.
- Climate changes represent the biggest threat to the species because there is an increasing mismatch between when the animals arrive at their summer breeding grounds and the period of maximum food availability. Caribou have evolved to match time of calving with what used to be the time of maximum lichen abundance. However, this is shifting to earlier in the season, before the caribou arrive. This leads to starvation, poor calf survival, and high mortality. Coupled to this, precipitation as freezing rain, rather than snow, creates ice layers in winter feeding grounds, preventing access to lichen and leading to malnutrition and starvation.
- Warmer temperatures have also resulted in white tailed deer expanding their range. Deer carry a parasitic brain worm that kills caribou but not deer. Herds already under stress through poor nutrition are particularly at risk.

1. Describe the survival benefits of a seasonal migration in an animal such as caribou: ________________

2. Look at the graph right.

   (a) Describe the relationship between increasing July (summer) temperature and cow (female) mortality:

   (b) Based on the information given above, give possible reasons for this relationship:

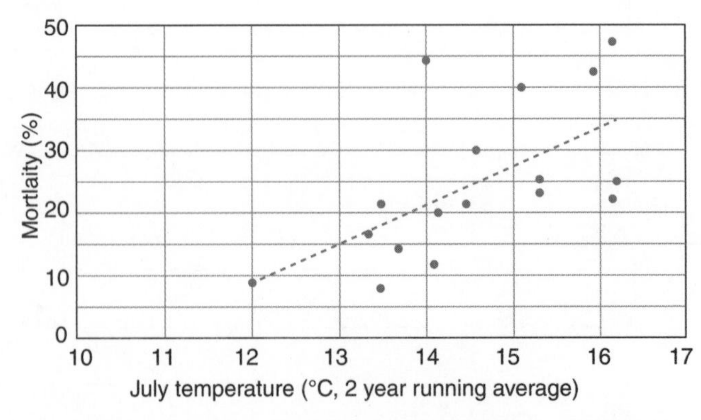

Relationship between Canada caribou adult cow mortality and the 2 year running average of mean daily July temperature 1997-2015. Data as reported in arctic.noaa.gov (2018)

3. Seasonal migration is a successful strategy that has evolved because it increases survival and the chances of successful reproduction. Explain why the barren-ground caribou are at risk from a warming climate:

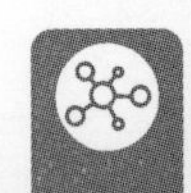
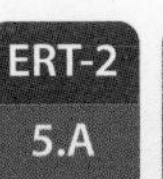

ERT-2
5.A

158

164

ISBN: 978-1-98-856632-0

Climate change and migratory shifts

A great many US bird species migrate variable distances between summer and winter ranges as part of their normal behavioral response to seasonal changes. These migrations allow them to take advantage of seasonally variable food resources. Records of the winter migrations of 17 US bird species (The National Audubon Society) show northern shifts in their winter destinations. These shifts may expose them to new threats and different food bases and provide indicators for how species may increase or decrease their range as climate warms.

Change in winter destination over 40 years, 17 US bird species

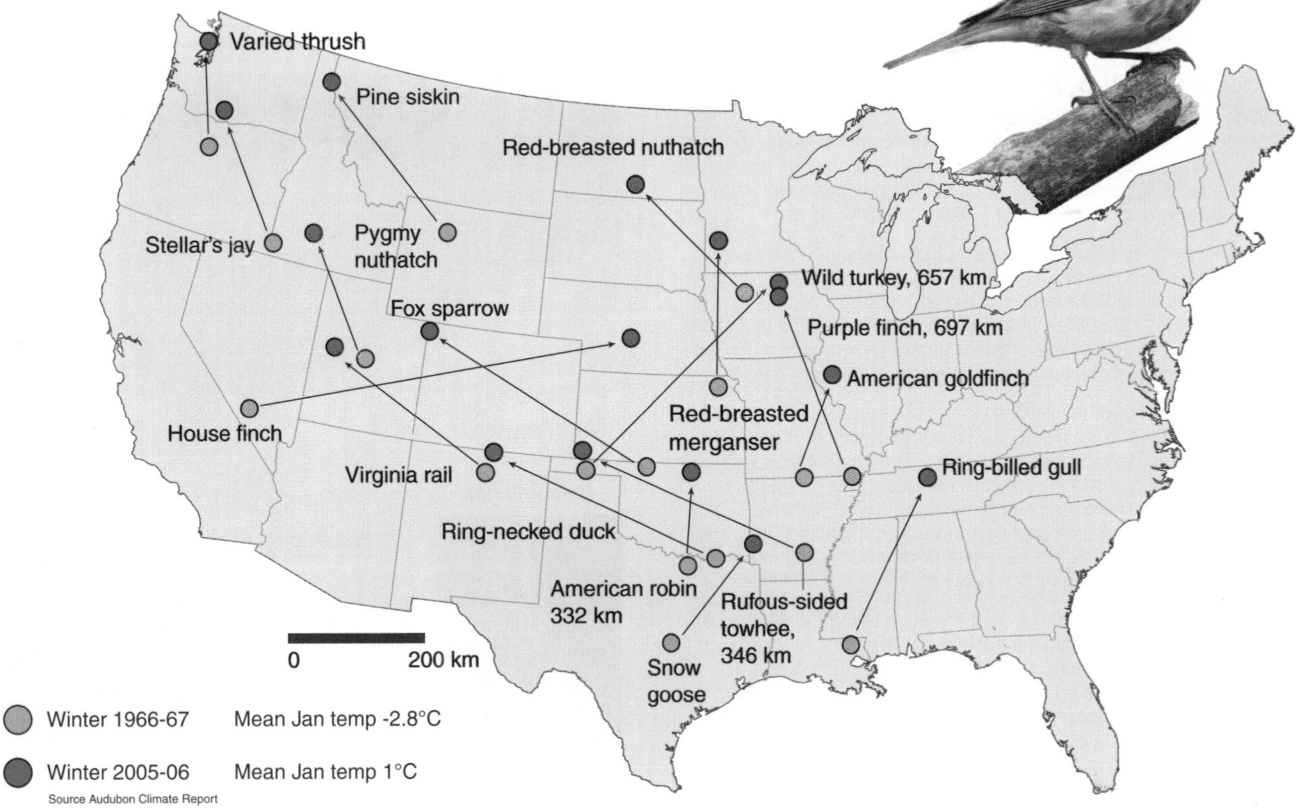

Study the map above showing the change in winter destinations of 17 bird species in the US between 1966-67 (average January temperature -2.8°C) and 2005-06 (average January temperature 1°C).

4. (a) What does the map show? ______________________________

(b) What is the most likely reason for this? ______________________________

(c) What is the likely outcome for these bird populations of a predicted further 1.5°C increase in temperature?

____

5. What is the likely outcome for the habitable range of Arctic resident bird species under the predicted warmer climate?

____

6. Under a predicted climate change of +1.5°C or more by 2100 (relative to the 1980–1999 average), what would you predict for the ranges of:

(a) Low altitude adapted species? ______________________________

(b) High altitude adapted species? ______________________________

ISBN: 978-1-98-856632-0

35 Adaptation and Environmental Change

Key Question: How do organisms adapt to their environment? Adaptation describes the genetic response of populations to their environment over time. The phenotype (observable characteristics) of organisms is a product of their genetic makeup and the influences of environment. Individuals with phenotypes most suited to the prevailing environment will have better survival and produce more offspring, and so their genes will become more common. Individuals with less favorable phenotypes will have poorer success and their genes will have a lower representation in subsequent generations. In this way, the environment selects the genes that will become more common. This process of adaptation by natural selection proceeds at varying rates. Rapid environmental change can act as a powerful selection pressure for genetic change in a population, providing the species has the capacity to adapt. An inability to adapt invariably creates a high risk of extinction.

Genes and environment: who survives where?

- When we look at the diversity around us, it is clear that organisms are well adapted to their environments. In many populations of animals, coat coloration is one obvious phenotypic character. The genetic basis of coat color has been well studied in populations of oldfield mice in Florida, USA.
- Oldfield mice are found in two distinct habitats in Florida. In inland (mainland) areas, which are vegetated with dark, loamy soil, and in coastal sand dunes, which have little vegetation and brilliant white sand. Mice in these different habitats have distinct coat-colors. Mainland mice have a darker brown coat, whereas beach mice, such as the one pictured right, are very pale.
- Researchers hypothesized that these rodents rely on camouflage to avoid detection by predators. Two phenotypes for coat color are common; dark and light (or white). Their hypothesis was tested and supported in an experiment using clay models painted to resemble beach and mainland forms. Relative predation rates on dark and light models in mainland (top right) and beach (bottom right) habitats are shown in a column graph. Column color is matched to model color.
- Genetic studies have shown that the mice along the Gulf coast form one genetically distinct population, whereas the mainland mice and the mice along the Atlantic coast form a separate, less defined genetic group. The genetic data indicate that light colored fur must have evolved independently in the Gulf coast and Atlantic coast populations.
- Genetic analysis also shows that the genes responsible for the light fur are different in the two groups. The light color in the Gulf coast populations is the result of mutation in the MC1R gene and all the Gulf coast beach mice probably arose from a few founding individuals. The light color in the Atlantic coast beach mice has several different genetic causes. Lighter fur provides a survival advantage in beach habitats, so pale mice are more common there, regardless of the genetic mechanism by which the light color arises.

Alabama beach mouse

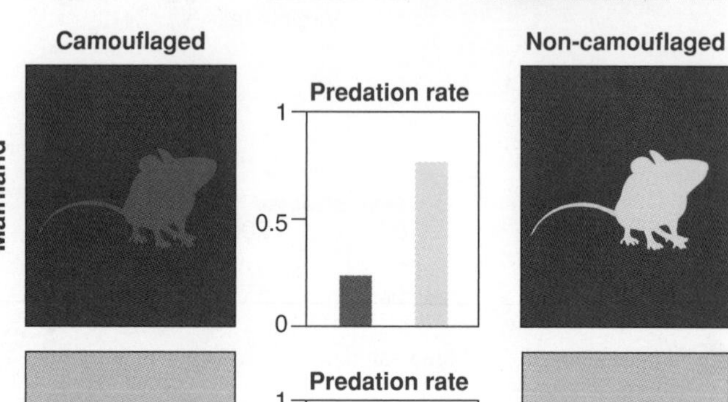

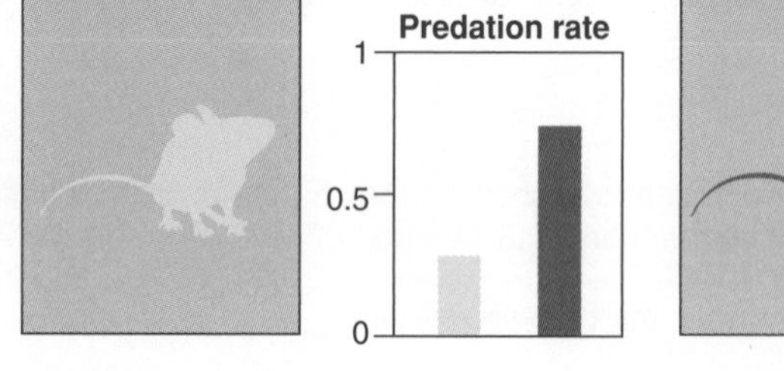

1. In the example of the oldfield mice above:

   (a) Where are darker colored mice found? ______________________

   (b) Where are lighter colored mice found? ______________________

2. Using the experimental evidence presented above, describe the role of predation as a selective agent for coat color adaptation in oldfield mice:

   ____

3. Describe the evidence that light colored fur has evolved independently in Gulf coast and Atlantic coast populations:

   ____

ISBN: 978-1-98-856632-0

Rapid adaptation in pasture grasses

- A well documented example of how environmental change can drive genetic change in populations is found in the grass browntop (*Agrostis capillaris*) growing on pasture and contaminated soil around a copper mine site. Tolerant plants were those able to grow on the contaminated mine soil whereas non-tolerant plants were less able to grow on the mine soil and had reduced fitness (survival and reproduction). Tolerant plants had reduced fitness when growing on uncontaminated soil.
- Flowering stages were used to calculate the number of days plants at each transect site were reproductively isolated (when they could not interbreed). Tolerant and not tolerant plants were genetically distinct, with a hybrid zone between. Similar results were obtained for sweet vernal growing on a zinc and lead mining site (also in Wales).

Drws-y-Coed mine (Wales) Browntop (*Agrostis capillaris*)

Contaminated soil

Mine

Contaminated pasture

Pasture

1 2 3 4 5 6 7 8

Transect sites

Thomas McNeilly *et al Heredity* 1968

Dam below Drws-y-Coed copper mine

- About 25% of the tolerant plant population flowered earlier than non-tolerant plants, preventing interbreeding between the populations.
- These flowering differences were verified as genetic by removing plants to a controlled environment where the difference in flowering was still observed.

Flowering isolation in browntop

Isolation time (days)	Tolerant			Intermediate	Non-tolerant	
Year \ Site	2	3	4	5	6	7
1964	6.09	5.96	12.17	7.95	0	3.23
1965	3.73	4.86	8.49	7.85	0	2.79

4. Describe the evidence for the adaptation of browntop grass to soil contamination by copper: ______________________

5. Explain how tolerant and intolerant grasses have become genetically isolated: ______________________

6. How was the difference in flowering time between tolerant and non-tolerant plants confirmed to be genetically influenced rather than environmentally influenced?

7. The North American pika is a thermally sensitive, cold-adapted specialist species found in the mountains of western North America. In the southern extent of their range they are usually found above 2500 m. Pika are very sensitive to high temperatures and will die if exposed to temperatures above 25.5°C for even a few hours. Their strategies for avoiding thermal stress are largely behavioral and they seek out cool microclimates to avoid high temperatures. A survey in 2014-2015 found widespread evidence of a decrease in range, shifting to higher altitude, and local extinction. Suggest why climate warming threatens pika populations and why biologists are worried for their future:

ISBN: 978-1-98-856632-0

36 Primary Succession

Key Question: What is primary succession and what are the community changes that characterize it?

Ecological succession is a natural process of continuous, sequential change in an ecological community. It usually occurs in response to a disturbance and is the result of the dynamic interactions between biotic and abiotic factors over time. Earlier communities modify the physical environment, making it more favorable for the species that will make up later communities. Over time, a succession may result in a stable, mature, or climax, community, although this is not always the case. Succession occurring where there is no pre-existing vegetation or soil is called **primary succession**.

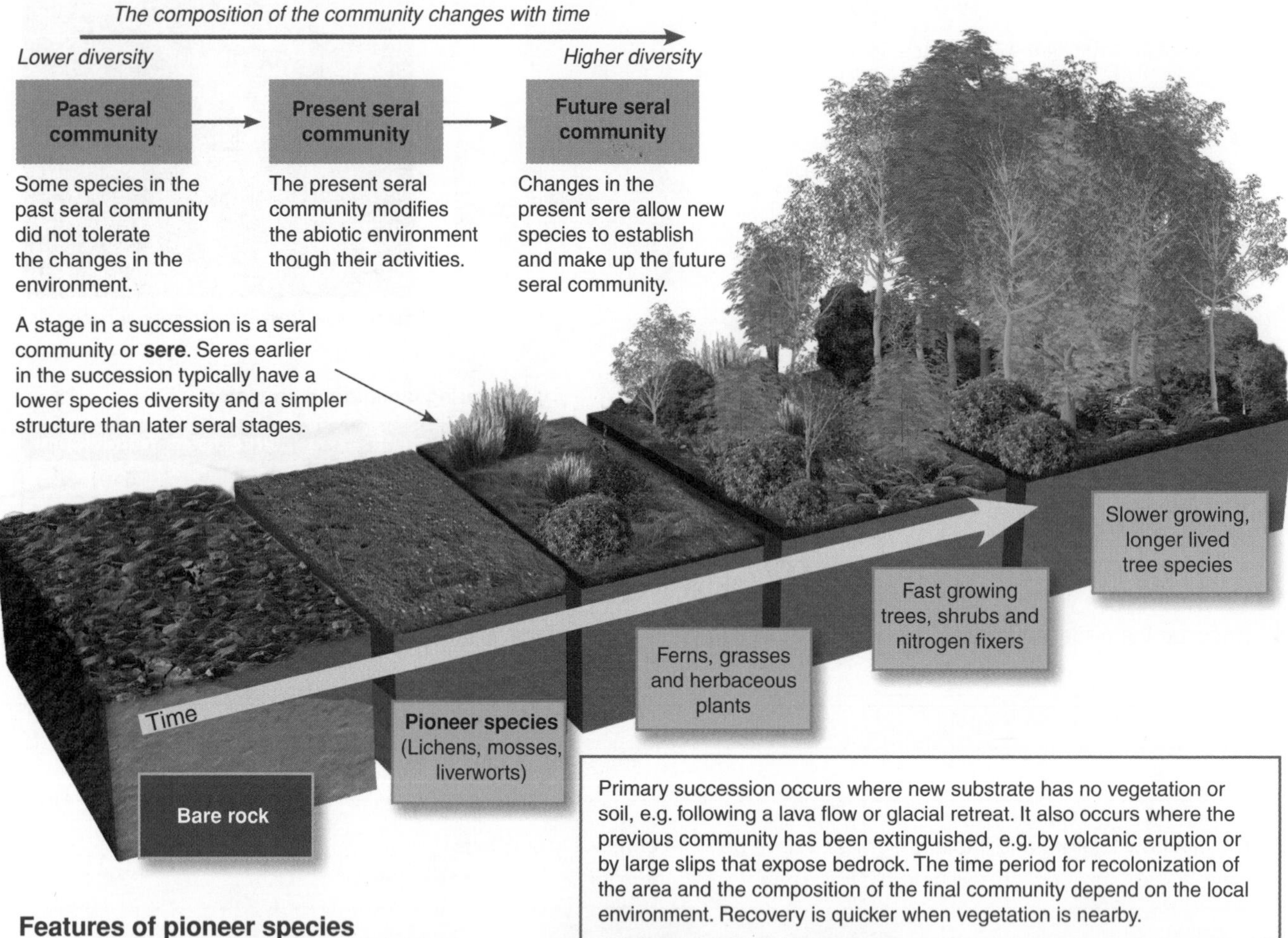

Primary succession occurs where new substrate has no vegetation or soil, e.g. following a lava flow or glacial retreat. It also occurs where the previous community has been extinguished, e.g. by volcanic eruption or by large slips that expose bedrock. The time period for recolonization of the area and the composition of the final community depend on the local environment. Recovery is quicker when vegetation is nearby.

Features of pioneer species

The earliest pioneer species are microorganisms (e.g. cyanobacteria) and simple photosynthetic plants and algae. They are able to survive on exposed substrates lacking in nutrients and make their own food using sunlight energy. Even at this level, ecological associations are important. Lichens, which are important pioneers, are a symbiosis between fungi and algae. Associations between mosses and cyanobacteria (which can fix nitrogen) are also important. Pioneers begin the process of soil formation by breaking down the substrate and adding organic matter through their own death and decay. Their growth therefore creates a more favorable environment for vascular plant growth.

Note the vascular plants establishing in the crevices where soil is forming.

Associations between mosses and cyanobacteria provides mosses with nitrogen.

1. Describe situations in which a primary succession is likely to occur: ______

2. (a) Identify pioneers during the colonization of bare rock: ______

   (b) Describe two important roles of the species that are early colonizers of bare slopes: ______

ISBN: 978-1-98-856632-0

Surtsey: A case study in primary succession

Surtsey Island is a volcanic island lying 33 km off the southern coast of Iceland. The island was formed over four years from 1963 to 1967 when a submarine volcano 130 m below the ocean surface built up an island that initially reached 174 m above sea level and covered 2.7 km^2. Erosion has since reduced the island to around 150 m above sea level and 1.4 km^2.

As an entirely new island, Surtsey was able to provide researchers with an ideal environment to study primary succession in detail. The colonization of the island by plants and animals has been recorded since the island's formation. The first vascular plant there (sea rocket) was discovered in 1965, two years before the eruptions on the island ended. Since then, 69 plant species have colonized the island and there are a number of established seabird colonies.

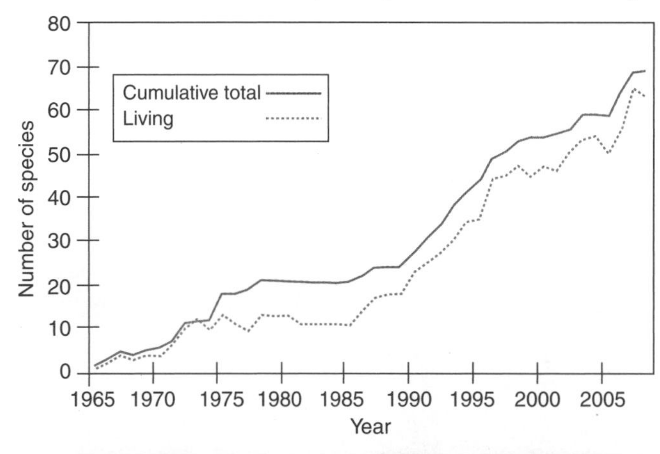

Sea rocket

H. peploides

P. annua

S. phylicifolia

The first stage of colonization on Surtsey was dominated by shore plants colonizing the northern shores, brought by ocean currents. The most successful of these was *Honckenya peploides*, which established on tephra sand and gravel flats. It set seed in 1971 and subsequently spread across the island. This initial colonization by shore plants was followed by a lag phase with few new colonizers. A number of new plant species arrived after a gull colony became established at the southern end of the island.

Populations of plants within or near the gull colony expanded rapidly to about 3 ha, while populations outside the colony remained low but stable. Grasses such as *Poa annua* formed extensive patches of vegetation. After this rapid increase in plant diversity, the arrival of new colonizers again slowed. A third wave of colonizers began to establish following this slower phase and soil organic matter increased markedly. The first bushy plants established in 1998, with the arrival of willow *Salix phylicifolia*.

3. Explain why Surtsey provided ideal conditions for studying primary succession: ______

4. Explain why the first colonizing plants established in the north of the island, but later colonizers established in the south.

5. There are three distinct phases on Surtsey where species richness increased rapidly.

   (a) Label on the graph the three phases of rapid increase in species richness on Surtsey.

   (b) Label the two lag phases where species richness increased slowly.

6. A gull colony established on the island in 1985. What was the effect on this on the number of plant species on the island?

7. Why is the living number of plant species on the island less than the cumulative number colonizing the island?

ISBN: 978-1-98-856632-0

37 Secondary Succession

Key Question: What are the features of secondary successions and what events cause them?

Secondary succession occurs when land is cleared of vegetation (e.g. after a fire or tree fall). Soil and seed stocks are not lost and root stocks are often undamaged. As a result, the succession tends to proceed more rapidly than is the case with primary succession, although the time scale depends on the species involved, soil composition, and climate. Secondary successions may occur over a wide area (as after a forest fire), or in smaller areas where abandoned farmland has been left to regenerate or single trees have fallen (a phenomenon called gap regeneration).

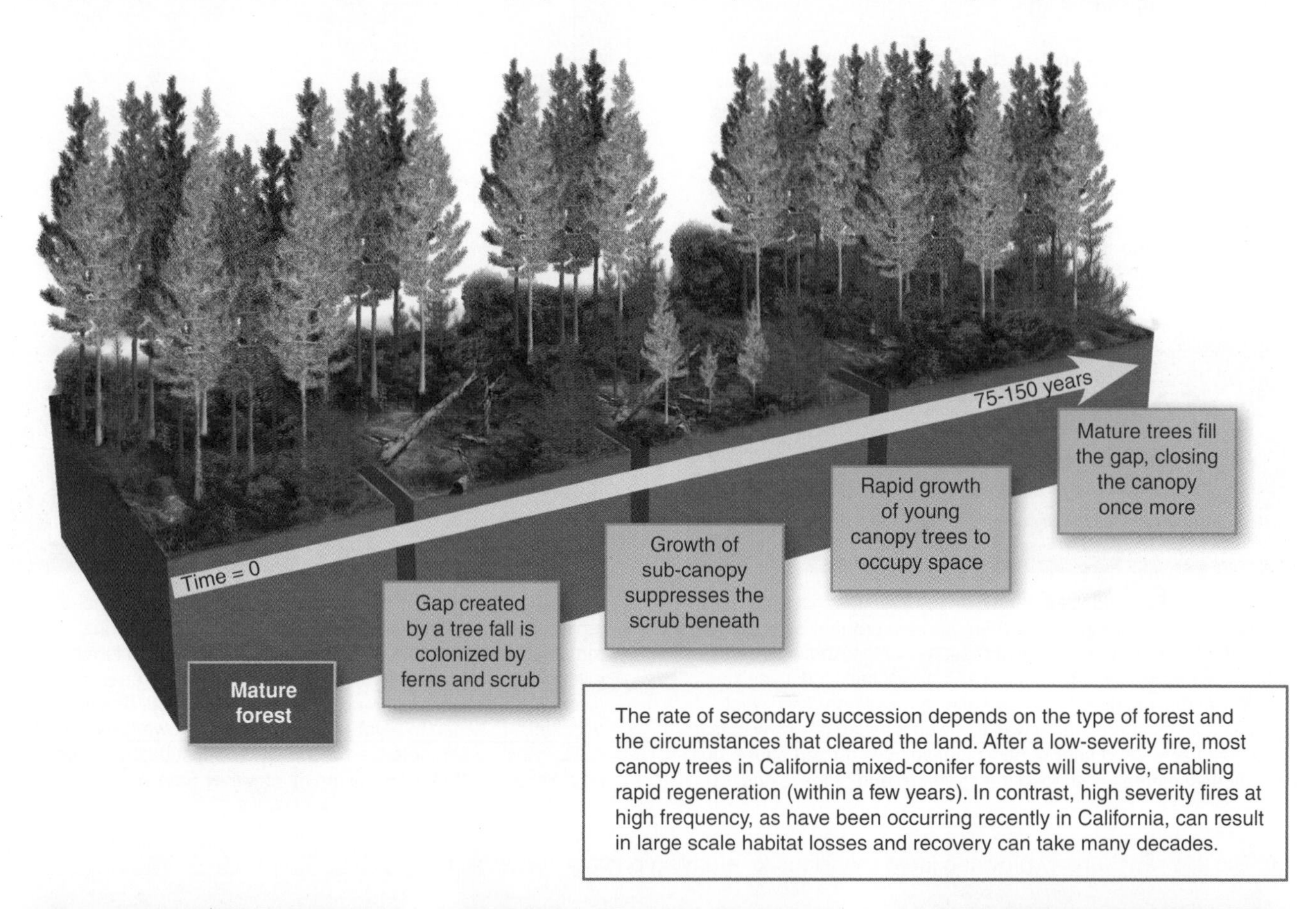

The rate of secondary succession depends on the type of forest and the circumstances that cleared the land. After a low-severity fire, most canopy trees in California mixed-conifer forests will survive, enabling rapid regeneration (within a few years). In contrast, high severity fires at high frequency, as have been occurring recently in California, can result in large scale habitat losses and recovery can take many decades.

The progression of a succession depends on many factors. The rate of growth of the various plants involved is important. Plants in some climax communities grow to full height within decades (e.g. eucalypt forests) while in other communities (e.g. cold boreal forests) recovery may take many decades or even centuries.

The intensity of the clearance of the land and community can play a role in secondary succession. Low intensity fire may remove smaller grasses and shrubs while leaving the larger trees relatively intact, whereas high intensity fires canopy fires may completely remove all vegetation. Clear felling tends to affect larger trees more than undergrowth.

Succession can be suspended by frequent disturbances, so that "climax" communities never develop. Californian forest are adapted to fire intervals of 10-20 years and species respond to frequent fires by rapid regeneration. Fireweed (above) is one of the first colonizers after fire, along with nitrogen-fixing, fast growing and fire tolerant lupines.

1. Why does a secondary succession proceed more rapidly than a primary succession?

2. What factors can influence the time scale of a secondary succession?

ISBN: 978-1-98-856632-0

38 Keystone Species

Key Question: What are keystone species and why do they have a disproportionate effect on ecosystem processes?

Every species has a functional role in an ecosystem (its niche), but some have a much bigger effect on ecosystem processes and stability than their abundance would suggest because their activities are crucial to the way the ecosystem as a whole functions. These species are called keystone species. They are often top (apex) predators, or have a critical role in seed dispersal or nutrient cycling. The loss of a keystone species can have a large and rapid impact on the structure and function of an ecosystem, changing the balance of relationships and leading to instability. This has important implications for the management of threatened ecosystems because many keystone species are endangered.

Why are keystone species important?

The term keystone species comes from the analogy of the keystone in a true arch. An archway is supported by a series of stones, the central one being the **keystone**. If the keystone is removed, the arch collapses.

The idea of the keystone species was first hypothesized in 1969 by Robert Paine. He determined through experimentation that the ochre starfish (*Pisaster)*, a predator in rocky shore communities, had a role in maintaining community diversity. When the starfish were removed, their prey species increased, crowding out algae and reducing species richness in the area from 15 to 8.

Yellowstone wolves run down a bull elk

Return of gray wolves to Yellowstone

- Gray wolves are a top predators in North American ecosystems, yet federal extermination programs in the late 1800s-early 1900s reduced them to near extinction in the US, including in the Yellowstone National Park (YNP) where National Park status did not protect them.
- Once the wolves were gone, numbers of elk (their primary prey) increased and the deciduous vegetation became severely overgrazed. This had a number of consequences. Without wolves, coyotes also increased, and the numbers of pronghorn antelope (coyote prey) then declined. Beavers became largely absent.
- In 1974, the gray wolf was declared endangered under the Endangered Species Act (1973) and in 1995 its reintroduction to the park began. Since that time, wolf numbers in the park have grown, elk have declined and shifted into less favorable habitats, deciduous vegetation has recovered, beavers have returned, and the coyote population has stabilized at a lower level.

Figures, right, show some of the ecological changes recorded in YNP following the 1995/1996 reintroduction of gray wolves. Individual plots show numbers of wolves (A), elk (B), and beaver (C), together with vegetation changes. Aspen heights recorded in areas with downed logs, which regenerate somewhat faster than areas without downed logs. Dashed lines represent time periods with at least 1 year of missing data.

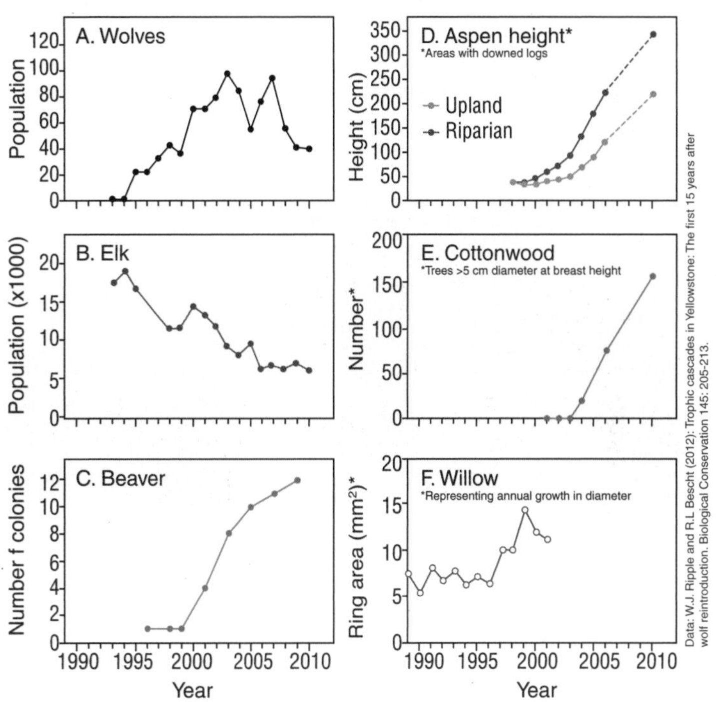

1. Use the figures (A-F) above to discuss the evidence for the role of gray wolves as a keystone species:

ISBN: 978-1-98-856632-0

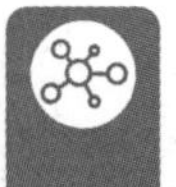

Sea otters as keystone species

- Sometimes the significant keystone effects of a species are evident when a species declines rapidly to the point of near extinction. This is illustrated by the sea otter example described below.
- Sea otters live along the Northern Pacific coasts and had been hunted for hundreds of years for their fur. Extensive commercial hunting between 1741 and 1911 reduced the global population to fewer than 2000 animals.
- The drop in sea otter numbers had a significant effect on local marine environments. Sea otters feed on shellfish, particularly sea urchins, and keep their populations in check. Sea urchins eat kelp, on which many marine species depend for food and habitat. Without the sea otters, sea urchin numbers increased and the kelp forests were destroyed or severely reduced.
- Sea otters have been protected since 1911 and reintroduced throughout much of their original range. The most secure populations are now in Russia.

Sea otter feeding on a sea urchin

matt knoth cc BY 2.0

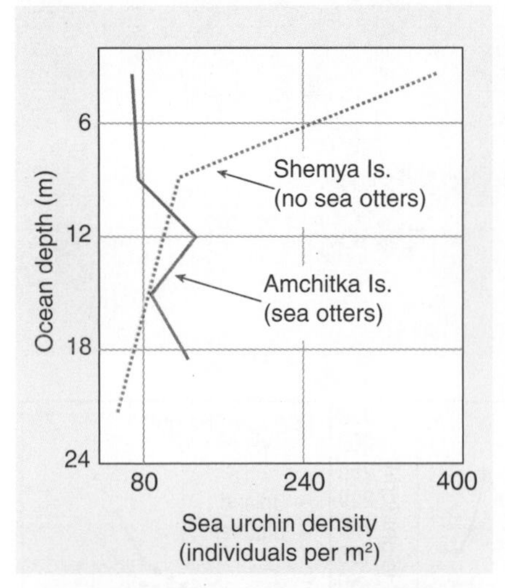

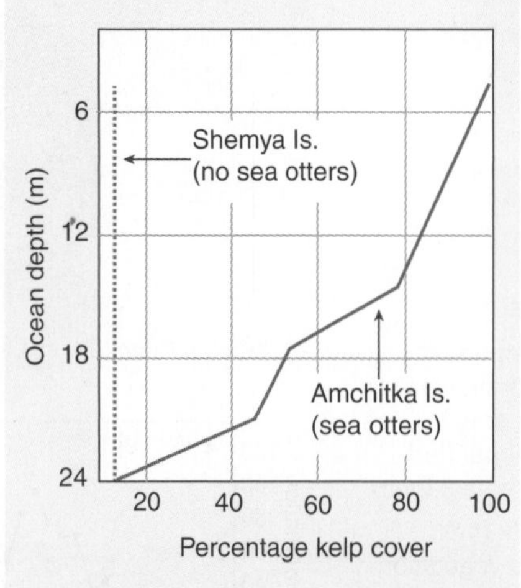

Sea otters are critical to the functioning of North Pacific coastal ecosystems. Their widespread decline, including many local extinctions, was associated with sea urchin increases and widespread disappearance of the kelp forests (above left). In the Aleutian Island group, most islands experienced local extinctions of sea otters. This provided the opportunity to record the ecology of coastal systems with and without sea otters (Palmisano and Estes 1976).

The effect can be seen on Shemya and Amchitka Islands. Where sea otters are absent, there are large numbers of sea urchins and almost no kelp. Sea otters began recolonizing Shemya in the 1990s and the kelp has since recovered.

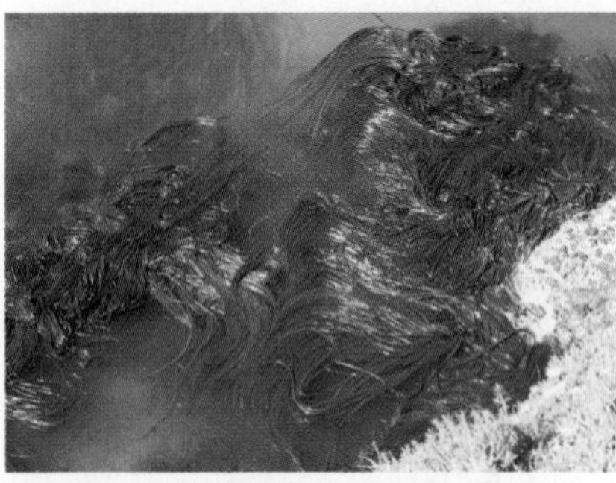

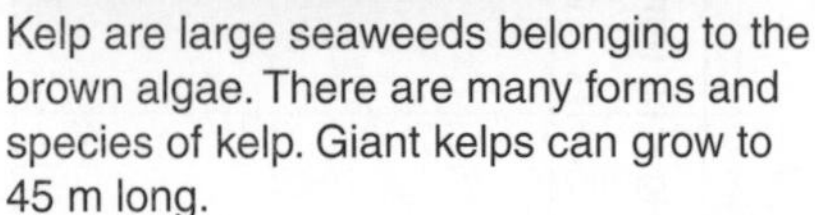

Kelp are large seaweeds belonging to the brown algae. There are many forms and species of kelp. Giant kelps can grow to 45 m long.

In much the same way that forests on land provide diverse habitats for terrestrial species, kelps provide habitat, food, and shelter for a variety of marine animals.

Urchin barren

NPS

Sea urchins kill kelp by eating the holdfast that secures the kelp to the seabed. Unchecked urchin populations can quickly turn a kelp forest into an **urchin barren**.

2. (a) What effect do sea otters have on sea urchin numbers? ______________________________

____

(b) What effect do sea urchins have on kelp cover? ______________________________

____

(c) What evidence is there that the sea otter is a keystone species in these Northern Pacific coastal ecosystems?

____

____

____

____

____

____

ISBN: 978-1-98-856632-0

39 Indicator Species and Environmental Health

Key Question: How can diversity be used to quantify changes in ecosystems and assess environmental health?

Environmental scientists often use the presence or absence of particular species, called indicator species, to evaluate the status of an ecosystem and determine if it is changing (deteriorating or recovering). Indicator species can be any type of organism, and different organisms are used for different purposes. Mosses, lichens, aquatic invertebrates, birds, and amphibians are common indicator organisms. Typically, indicator species are associated with particular environmental conditions, their biology is well known, and their presence or absence therefore provides information about factors in the environment, including pollution levels, salinity, temperature, and nutrient or food availability.

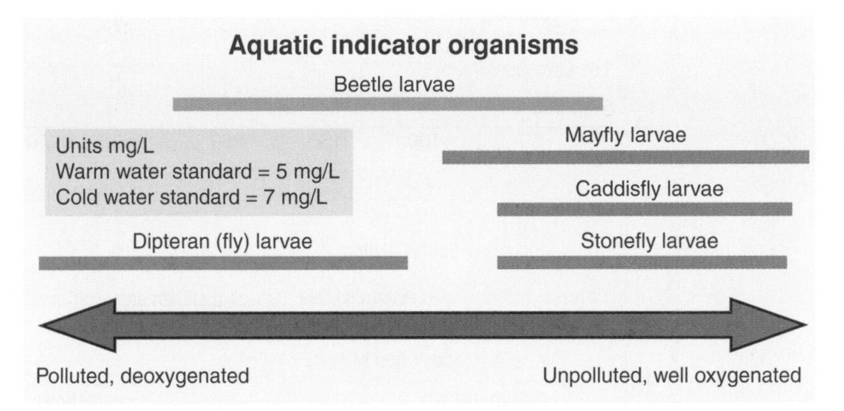

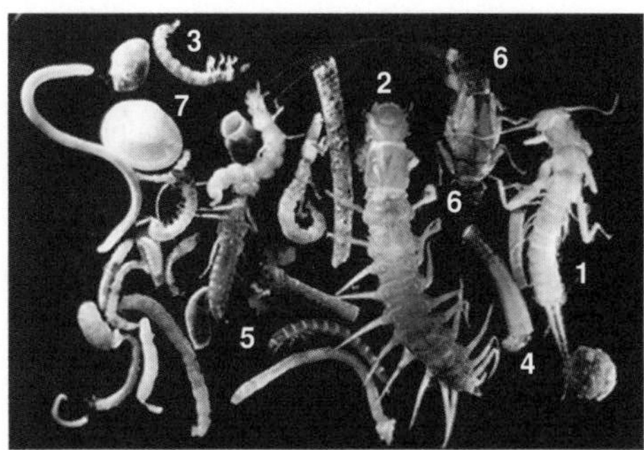

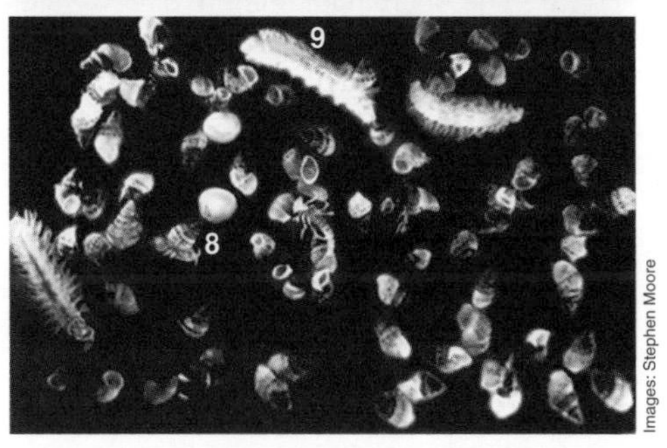

Taxa: Stonefly larva (1), alderfly larva (2), caddisfly larva (3)(4), beetle larva (5) dragonfly larva (6), mollusk (7)(8), dipteran larva (9).

Aquatic invertebrates are widely used to monitor the health of rivers and streams, to evaluate changes in hydrology (such as the effect of fresh water extractions), and to track recovery from point source pollution events (such as effluent discharges). Certain taxa are characteristic of environmental conditions associated with either clean water or polluted water. The larvae of mayflies, stoneflies, alderflies, and caddisflies are all clean water indicators, and will disappear if oxygen levels fall (low oxygen indicates a high load of organic pollution).

The images right show typical high diversity (top) and low diversity (bottom) assemblages. In aquatic systems, the absence of a single indicator species is generally less informative than the overall community composition. A diverse assemblage of sensitive species is indicative of high water quality .

Terrestrial indicator organisms

Mosses and lichens are sensitive indicators of pollution levels, particularly acid rain and heavy metals. A study of heavy metal concentrations in splendid feather moss (*Hylocomium splendens*) growing either side of a mining haul road in northwest Alaska showed a pattern of heavy metal deposition to the north and south of the road. The deposition was unrelated to heavy metal concentrations in the subsurface soil, which was also tested.

Feather moss is a sensitive indicator of environmental change. Both climate warming and increased nutrient deposition have a negative effect on its growth.

Figure: Levels of aluminum (Al), zinc (Zn), lead (Pb), and cadmium (Cd) north and south of the DeLong Mountain Regional Transportation System (DMTS) haul road corridor

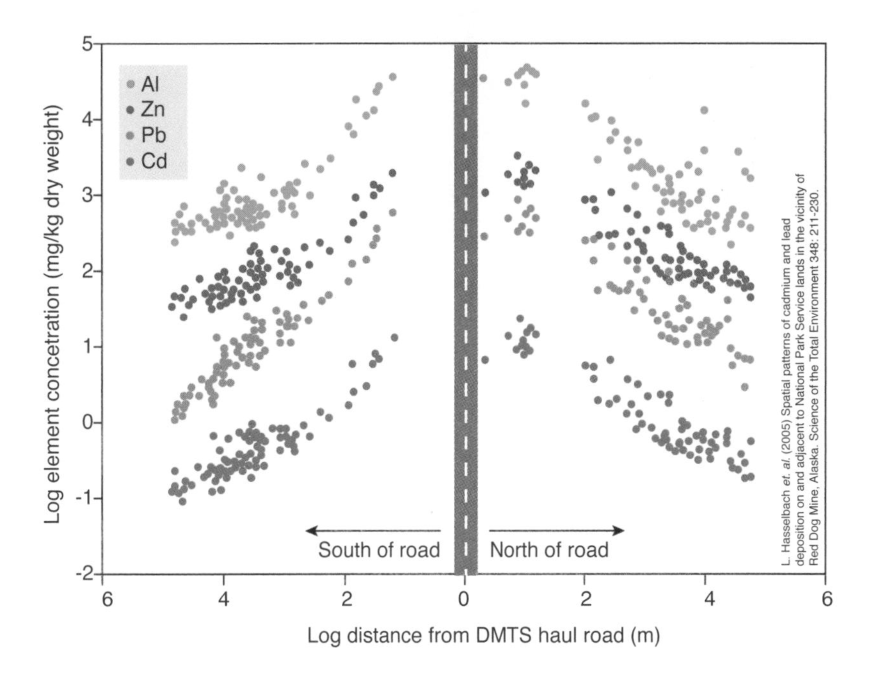

1. Use the scatter plot above to explain what the feather moss heavy metal levels indicate about pollution from the road:

ISBN: 978-1-98-856632-0

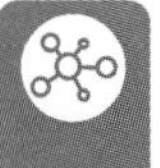

40 Personal Progress Check

Answer the multiple choice questions that follow by circling the correct answer. Don't forget to read the question carefully!

1. The most important component of biodiversity is:
   (a) Species diversity
   (b) Genetic diversity
   (c) Habitat diversity
   (d) All of the above

2. Low genetic diversity is characteristic of:
   (a) Populations with a wide distribution
   (b) Populations that have experienced bottleneck events in their history
   (c) Endemic species
   (d) Coastal populations

3. Ecosystem resilience refers to:
   (a) The unchanging nature of ecosystems over time
   (b) The ability to recover from external disturbances
   (c) Ecosystems with high diversity
   (d) A steady state of community biomass

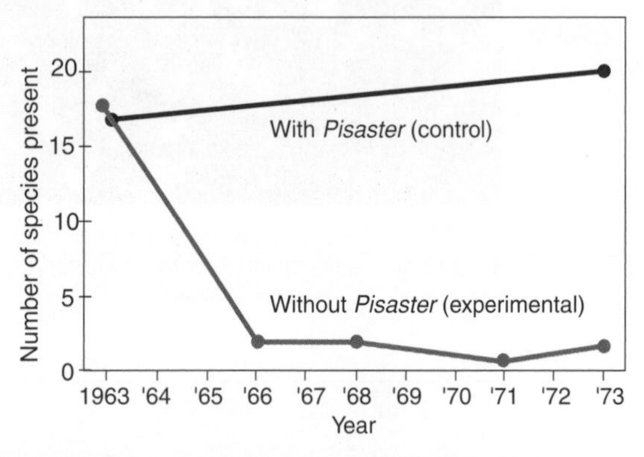

Questions 4 and 5 refer to the graph above, which shows the results of the experimental removal of the starfish *Pisaster* from a region of an ecosystem:

4. The graph shows that:
   (a) *Pisaster* causes a decline in species richness
   (b) Species richness declines when *Pisaster* is removed
   (c) *Pisaster* is a predator.
   (d) There is a maximum of 20 species in this ecosystem

5. The results of this experiment indicate that:
   (a) The presence of *Pisaster* has no effect of community diversity
   (b) The ecosystem has high diversity
   (c) The ecosystem has low diversity
   (d) *Pisaster* is a keystone species

6. Habitat loss has a disproportionate effect on:
   (a) Endemic species
   (b) Specialist species
   (c) Species with large territories
   (d) All of the above

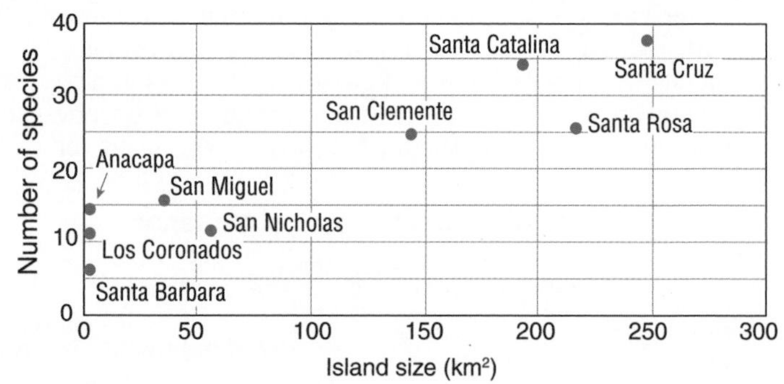

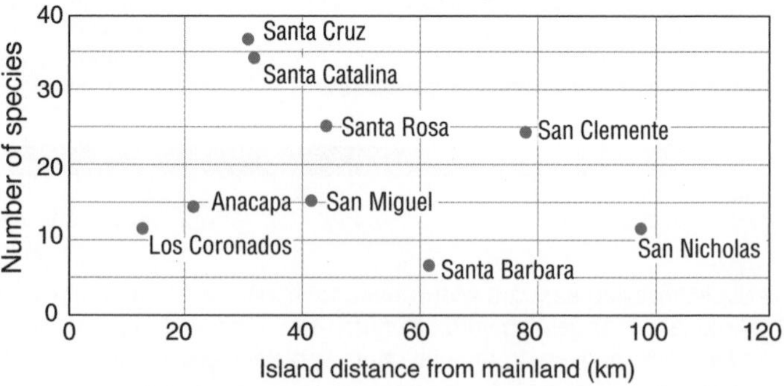

Questions 7 and 8 refer to the graphs above, which show species richness on various islands in the Gulf of California

7. The graphs indicate that:
   (a) Large islands most distant from the mainland have the highest species diversity.
   (b) Small islands most distant from the mainland have the highest species diversity.
   (c) Large islands close to the mainland have the highest species diversity.
   (d) Small islands close to the mainland have the highest species diversity.

8. The data in the graphs provide supporting evidence for:
   (a) Island endemism
   (b) Island biogeography theory
   (c) Mainland dispersal theory
   (d) The richness of island biota

9. Products obtained directly from ecosystems for basic human needs are known as:
   (a) Regulating services
   (b) Provisioning services
   (c) Cultural services
   (d) Supporting services

10. Air and water purification are examples of:
   (a) Regulating ecosystem services
   (b) Provisioning ecosystem services
   (c) Cultural ecosystem services
   (d) Supporting ecosystem services

ISBN: 978-1-98-856632-0

11. The seasons and the tidal changes are examples of:

(a) Random events
(b) Periodic events
(c) Episodic events
(d) None of the above

12. Which of the following statements is not correct:

(a) Sea levels rise following glacial retreats.
(b) Sea levels rise during glacial periods.
(c) Increased levels of carbon dioxide are associated with rising sea levels.
(d) A fall in sea level can create land bridges between continents.

13. Migratory species can suffer heavy mortality if:

(a) Their migration to summer feeding grounds does not coincide with maximum food abundance.
(b) Climate change alters the distribution of their predators.
(c) Migration routes are fragmented by human-induced changes to the landscape.
(d) All of the above.

14. Adaptation is best described as:

(a) A genetic response of populations that increases survival and reproduction.
(b) A response of individuals that increases their individual survival and reproduction.
(c) A feature of a species that can't be changed.
(d) None of the above.

15. Ecological succession on an area that lacks any vegetation or soil is called:

(a) Secondary succession.
(b) Gap regeneration.
(c) Primary succession.
(d) Deflected succession.

16. Secondary successions typically:

(a) Result in a higher diversity ecosystem than primary successions.
(b) Progress more slowly than primary successions.
(c) Progress more rapidly than primary successions.
(d) Will never restore the original community.

17. Which of the following statements about ecological successions is not true?

(a) Ecological successions can be suspended by frequent disturbances such as fire.
(b) Ecological successions are always the result of human activities in the natural environment.
(c) Ecological successions proceed at different rates dependent on the local environment and colonizing species.
(d) Ecological successions can occur over vastly different spatial scales.

Cumulative dispersal routes of vascular plants to Surtsey

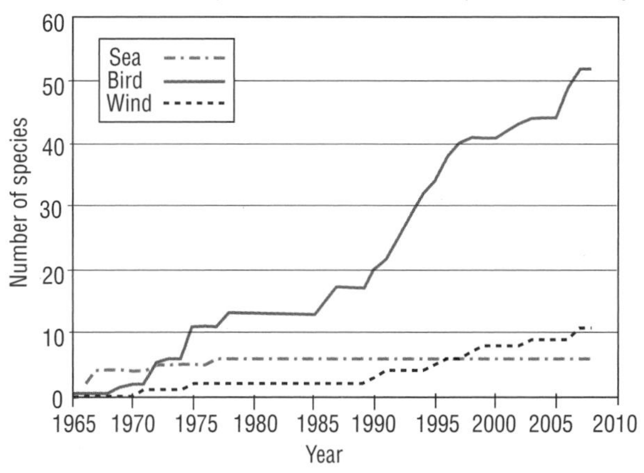

Questions 18 and 19 refer to the graph above showing the dispersal routes of plants to newly formed Surtsey Island on the southern coast of Iceland.

18. Which of the following statements about Surtsey's colonization by plants is true:

(a) Most plants arrived at the island by sea
(b) Most plants arrived at the island by wind
(c) Birds brought most of the colonizing plants to the island
(d) The most rapid period of plant colonization was between 1975 and 1985.

19. A gull colony established on the island in 1985. What was the effect of this?

(a) They ate the seeds of the colonizing plants.
(b) The rate of vascular plant colonization increased.
(c) The rate of plant colonization by sea fell
(d) It became windier on the island.

Numbers of different invertebrate species at four sites in a stream (per m^2 of stream bed sampled)

Species	Site 1	Site 2	Site 3	Site 4
Mayfly larva	0	8	4	0
Stonefly larva	0	4	4	0
Caddis larva	0	6	2	0
Beetle larva	1	4	6	2
Bloodworm	14	0	2	8
Snail	0	2	4	4
Blackfly larva	2	1	4	5

Questions 20 and 21 refer to the table above recording the invertebrate diversity at 4 sites in a stream that had suffered a moderate effluent spill 2 weeks before sampling.

20. What site is most likely to be closest to the spill?

(a) Site 1
(b) Site 2
(c) Site 3
(d) Site 4

21. Which sequence represents the position of the sites from the closest to the furthest from the spill?

(a) $1 \rightarrow 2 \rightarrow 3 \rightarrow 4$
(b) $1 \rightarrow 4 \rightarrow 3 \rightarrow 2$
(c) $2 \rightarrow 3 \rightarrow 4 \rightarrow 1$
(d) $1 \rightarrow 3 \rightarrow 4 \rightarrow 2$

ISBN: 978-1-98-856632-0

22. Your task in this question is to design an experiment to investigate the effect of habitat area on the species richness of invertebrates found in unmowed areas of habitat in your school surrounds. The areas should be relatively uniform (both unmowed areas of pasture) because you are to assess the effect of habitat fragmentation on diversity. Some guidelines on sampling are provided in **Appendix 1: "Assessing invertebrate diversity"** at the end of this book. For this task, the aims, constraints, and guidelines are provided below.

    Aim: To assess the effect the habitat size on invertebrate diversity.
    Constraints: You must evaluate diversity in similar habitats varying predominantly in size. We recommend areas of 1600 m^2 (40 x 40 m) and 225 m^2 (15 x 15 m). You can decide how you will sample this area and be prepared to justify your decision taking into account the resources you might have to carry out your sampling (including time).
    Guidelines: Decide how you will separate your unmowed sample areas. Consider ways to assess diversity and different methods for capturing arthropods, including flying insects (see Appendix 1). How often will you sample your plots and will you return the organisms you capture to the area?

    Record your experimental design below, including any notes on data collection, recording, and analysis. Attach photographs of your sites and of the organisms you capture.

NEED HELP?
see Appendix 1

ISBN: 978-1-98-856632-0

3. Populations

Developing understanding

Content: This unit explores the responses of different types of organisms to factors that affect their populations, including responses to habitat changes. Organisms with different life history strategies (r- vs K-selected species) show different population responses in terms of growth, survivorship, and longevity. We will examine the factors affecting population growth, including the availability of resources and the significance of carrying capacity. The projections of global human population growth and the importance of demographic transition conclude the unit.

Skills: This unit emphasizes skills in analyzing trends and patterns in data. The analysis of population data will help you understand how data can clearly illustrate environmental concepts such as carrying capacity. Analyzing population growth, age structure diagrams, and survivorship curves will also help you to develop skills in predicting patterns and trends.

3.1 Generalist and specialist species ...... activity 41

☐ 1. Explain what is meant by demography. Describe what demographic analysis can tell us about the attributes of populations, such as their age structure, growth, and fertility.

☐ 2. Describe the differences between specialist and generalist species. Explain why generalist species often tend to be colonizers of disturbed habitats.

3.2 K- and r-selected species .... activity 42

☐ 3. Identify the differences between *r*-selected and K-selected species. Include reference to body size, reproductive strategy, lifespan, and the role of competition. Explain how *r* and K strategies represent a continuum and many species may show attributes of both strategies.

☐ 4. Explain what is meant by biotic potential and compare the biotic potential of *r*- and K-strategists and what it means for their life history. Describe the relationship between biotic potential and the rate of population growth.

☐ 5. Explain why K-selected species are typically more adversely affected by disturbances. Explain why most invasive species tend to be *r*-selected organisms.

3.3 Survivorship curves .... activities 43 - 46

☐ 6. Explain what a survivorship curve displays about the attributes of a population. Construct survivorship curves from life table data and interpret the curves with reference to Type I, II, or II patterns of survivorship. Describe how survivorship curves differ for *r*- and K-selected species.

☐ 7. Use historical data to construct a survivorship curve for a human population and explain any patterns or trends in the data. Interpret data to describe how life expectancy can vary in different human populations and explain the reasons for any differences you observe.

3.4 Carrying capacity .... activities 47 - 48

☐ 8. Describe carrying capacity and explain how it places limits on population growth and size. Interpret data to describe what happens when a population exceeds carrying capacity and explain the population response.

3.5 Population growth and resource availability .... activities 49 - 52

☐ 9. Describe exponential and logistic population growth and relate these growth curves to the availability of resources and the biotic potential of the organisms involved. Describe how population growth is limited by the limited resources of the environment, especially space and food.

☐ 10. Explain how an abundance of resources usually results in an increase in the rate of population growth and describe the density-dependent effect of resource limitation as resources become depleted. Explain the effect of a long term or permanent depletion in resources on population growth and explain how the effects are mediated through higher mortality or reduced fertility.

☐ 11. Distinguish between density-dependent and density-independent factors in populations and explain how they act to alter population growth and size.

3.6 Age structure diagrams .... activity 53

☐ 12. Explain age structure diagrams. Interpret age structure diagrams for different populations to determine if a population is declining, stable, or expanding. Understand the term population momentum and use it to explain why a population will continue to expand even if population fertility declines (as is true for the human population currently).

3.7 Total fertility rate .... activities 46, 54 - 55

☐ 13. Explain factors that affect total fertility rate (TFR) in human populations, including the age at which women have their first child, education for females, and access to family planning and contraception. Relate fertility rate to population stability and describe what happens to population growth if fertility declines to sub-replacement levels..

☐ 14. Describe factors that affect infant mortality. Explain how changes in these factors can lead to changes in infant mortality over time. What is the effect of declining infant mortality on total fertility rate?

3.8 Human population dynamics ...... activities 54 - 55

☐ 15. Describe human population growth over the last 100-200 years (regionally and globally). Explain the factors that determine whether the population is growing or declining and describe current trends in human population growth. Use the rule of 70 to predict population doubling rate in human populations in exponential growth.

☐ 16. Describe the environmental problems associated with rapid population growth, including lack of resources or their inadequate distribution. Describe the role of density-dependent and density-independent factors in human population dynamics, recognizing that their effects are often interrelated if natural disasters result in population displacement, lack of resources, and disease.

3.9 Demographic transition .... activity 56

☐ 17. Explain demographic transition and its effects on population growth. Describe the four stage demographic transition model and important features of each stage.

41 Features of Populations

Key Question: What are the attributes of populations and what distinguishes specialist and generalist species?

The statistical study of populations is called demography. Demographers are concerned about population attributes that can be measured or calculated to provide information about the population. Such attributes include aspects of population composition, distribution and abundance, and dynamics (below). It is also useful to understand the characteristics of a species in terms of its resource needs, i.e. is it a generalist or a specialist? This information, when used in conjunction with an understanding of population dynamics, can help to evaluate a population's risk of extinction.

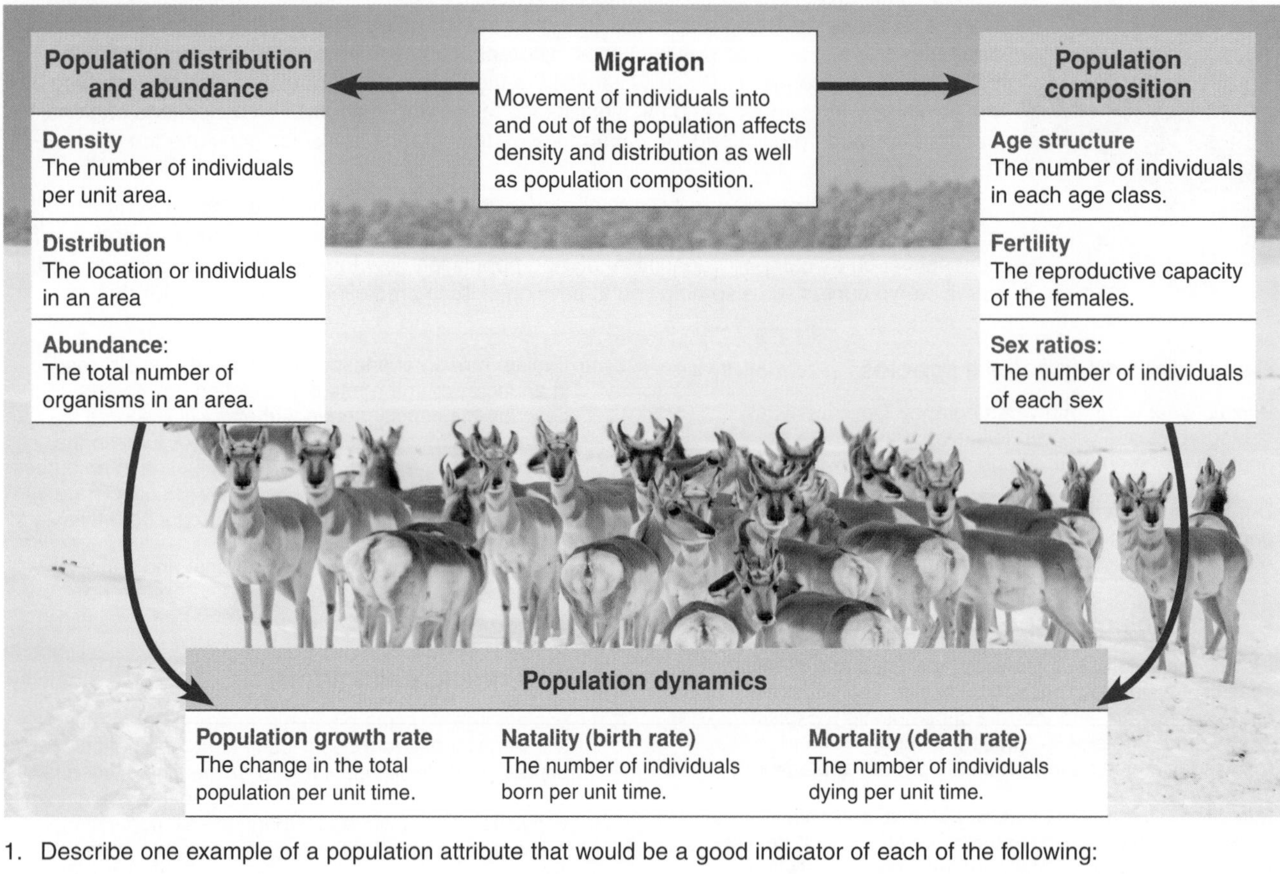

1. Describe one example of a population attribute that would be a good indicator of each of the following:

   (a) Whether the population is increasing or decreasing: ______

   (b) The ability of the environment to support the population: ______

2. (a) Identify the population attributes that can be measured directly from the population: ______

   (b) Identify the population attributes that must be calculated from the data collected: ______

3. Explain the value of population sampling for each of the following situations:

   (a) Conservation of a population of an endangered species: ______

   (b) Management of a fish stock: ______

ISBN: 978-1-98-856632-0

Generalist vs specialist species

- Population management requires information not only about the dynamics of the population in question, but also the biological characteristics of the species as a whole. Organisms can be broadly categorized as generalists or specialists. Generalists thrive in a wide range of habitats and are able to exploit a wide range of resources in order to meet their requirements. Specialists on the other hand have specific, narrow resource needs in terms of habitat and food.
- Organisms do not generally fit neatly into one or other of these categories. Specialists and generalists exist along a continuum from highly specialized to broadly-generalist species. Even within a single taxon, such as butterflies (below), we can recognize specialists and generalists based on aspects of their life history and feeding preferences.

	Generalists	Specialists
Ecological niche	Broad	Narrow
Ecological tolerance	Tolerant of a wide range of environments	Narrow tolerance (specialized needs)
Extinction risk	Low	High
Resource use	Exploits a wide range of resources	Uses a specific and narrow set of resources
Response to disturbance	Tolerant of disturbance, high resilience	Poor tolerance of disturbance, low resilience
Environment	Changing conditions	Stable conditions
Examples	Raccoons, coyotes, white-tailed deer, bobcat	Pandas, Venus fly-trap, Canada lynx, koala

- In a study of butterfly community structure, the proportions of specialist and generalist species were determined for habitats with varying amounts of human disturbance. Species were classified as generalists or specialists on the basis of larval diet breadth and number of generations per year. Specialists had one generation per year and a narrow range of host plants. A number of species were intermediate in their strategy (images below).
- Generalists had a wide and continuous distribution and were often the dominant species, whereas specialists were restricted and fragmented in their distribution and were generally rare.

Generalist: Common grass yellow. Many generations per year. Wide food base.

Intermediate: Red Helen. Two generations per year. Wide food base.

Specialist: Orange hairstreak. One generation per year. Feeds only on oak.

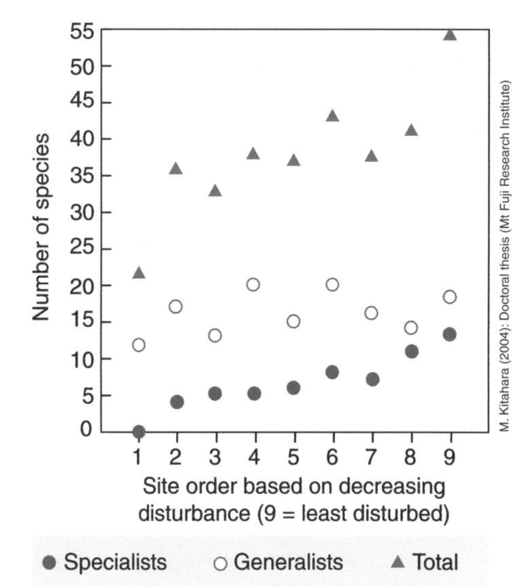

Above: Number of specialist and generalist butterfly species against habitat disturbance. Totals include species classed as intermediate.

4. Examine the scatter plot of butterfly species richness above right. Describe the pattern in the data for:

   (a) Total species richness: ______________________

   (b) Number of generalist species: ______________________

   (c) Number of specialist species: ______________________

5. Explain this pattern in terms of the characteristics of generalist and specialist species outlined in the table above:

____

____

____

____

ISBN: 978-1-98-856632-0

42 r-Selected and K-Selected Species

Key Question: What are the characteristics of *r*-selected and K-selected species and what do these terms mean?

The maximum rate at which a population can grow is called its **biotic potential** (*r*) It is a measure of reproductive capacity and is assigned a value that is specific to the organism involved. Species with high biotic potentials are called *r*-selected species. Their life history strategy is to maximize reproduction at an early age and many are generalists in unpredictable environments. In contrast, K-selected species have lower biotic potentials and exist as specialists at or near the carrying capacity of the environment (K). Their life history strategy is to maximize competitive ability over a longer life.

Rodents are r-strategists

r- and K selection and life history strategy

- Organisms can be grouped according to how they allocate their resources to growth and reproduction. A suite of characteristics are correlated with species that are either "*r*-selected" or "K-selected".
- **K = the carrying capacity of the environment**. This is the number of individuals that the environment can support indefinitely.
- **r = biotic potential**. This is the potential of the species to increase in number. Different species have different biotic potentials as part of their biology. You will learn more about these terms later in this chapter as they are important in models of population growth.
- In reality, species exist along an ***r*-K continuum** and may show some r-selected and some K-selected traits. Their life history reflects the strategy that results in highest fitness in the prevailing environment.

Large primates are K-strategists

	***r*-selected**	**K-selected**
Climate	Variable and/or unpredictable	Fairly constant and/or predictable
Mortality	Density independent	Density dependent
Population size	Highly variable. Often below carrying capacity.	Fairly constant in time. Close to carrying capacity.
Competition	Variable, often lax. Generalist niche.	Usually keen. Specialist niche.
Selection favors	Rapid development, early reproduction, small body size, single reproduction (annual).	Longer development, delayed reproduction, larger body size, repeated reproduction.
Length of life	Short (often less than one year)	Longer (greater than one year)
Examples	Insects, mice, annual plants, oysters, algae	Elephants, gorillas, beech trees, tortoises

Flexible strategists

- Small species with rapid reproductive rates, such as mice, are generally categorized as *r*-strategists, and long-lived slow growing species, such as elephants, are considered to be K-strategists. However, under certain conditions, individuals may shift towards one or other strategy.
- Meadow voles (also called field mice) are typically an r-selected species. In meadow voles, the average lifespan is less than one month because of high juvenile mortality and they typically show large cycles (fluctuations) in populations numbers. However, beach voles on Muskeget Island (MA), a closely related species, do not show large population cycles and exhibit attributes of K-selected organisms, such as larger size, later age at maturation, stable populations, and low reproductive output.
- Muskeget Island lacks mammalian predators, which normally prey on voles during dispersal phases. The absence of mammalian predators has seen a shift in the strategy towards maintaining a more stable population of longer-lived individuals.

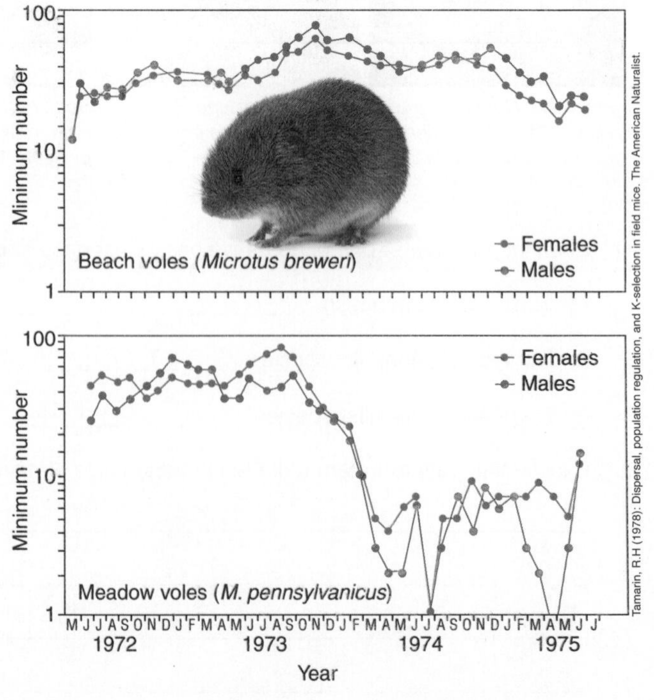

Figures: Seasonal population variation in beach voles on Muskeget Island (top) and mainland meadow vole (bottom).

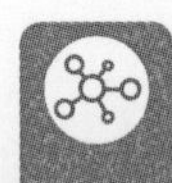

ISBN: 978-1-98-856632-0

r-selected species are colonizers in ecological successions

- The characteristics of *r*-selected species mean that they typically dominate in early successional communities. As the succession develops over time, these early colonizers are replaced by species with more K-selected traits. In a mature community, K-selected species are relatively more common, although moderate disturbances as occur naturally in all communities allow colonizing (pioneer) species to maintain a presence.
- Scientists followed the succession of plant species on Mt. St. Helens, Washington, following its eruption in 1980. They observed the typical pattern of increasing species richness in the years following the eruption, with a steady decline in pioneer (*r*-selected) species, such as fireweed and hairy catsear (below left), and an increase in larger, shrubby mat forming species such as partridgefoot (below right).

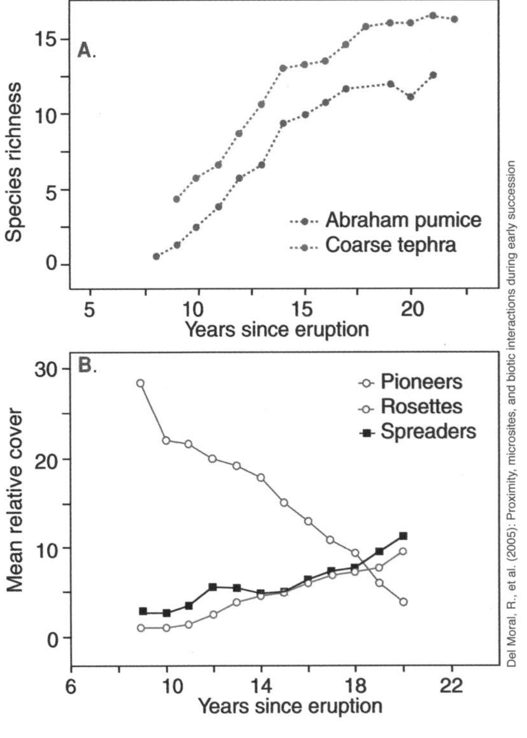

Above: **A**. Change in species richness at two sites on Mt. St. Helens. Trends were similar for other sites sampled. **B**. Relative cover of three types of species from the Abraham site.

1. Compare the pattern of population fluctuation in the beach voles and meadow voles on the opposite page: ______________

2. How does the population data from the study of vole populations provide evidence for an r-K continuum?

3. Describe features of *r*-selected organisms that explain their role as early pioneers in ecological successions:

4. (a) Describe the pattern of plant diversity (species richness) on Mt. St. Helens in the years following the eruption:

   (b) Describe the change in plant types following the eruption: ______________

   (c) Based on the traits of *r*- and K-strategists, provide an explanation for the pattern observed in the data:

ISBN: 978-1-98-856632-0

43 Survivorship Curves

Key Question: What are survivorship curves and what do they tell us about an organism's life history strategy?

A survivorship curve is a graph showing age-specific mortality. It is obtained by plotting the number of individuals of a particular age against time. Survivorship curves are standardized to start at 1000 and, as the population ages, the number of survivors progressively declines. The shape of a survivorship curve thus shows graphically at which life stages the highest mortality occurs. Survivorship curves in many populations fall into one of three hypothetical patterns (below). The late loss (Type I) curve is typical of populations in which individuals tend to live out their physiological life span. Such species are typically K-strategists. In contrast, r-selected organisms suffer most mortality in early life stages (a Type III curve). They compensate by producing vast numbers of offspring. In Type II populations, mortality is evenly spread across all life stages.

Hypothetical survivorship curves

Type I: Late loss

Mortality is very low for young and throughout most of adult life. Mortality increases rapidly in old age. **Examples**: Humans (in developed countries) and other large mammals (e.g. big cats, elephants).

Type II: Constant loss

Mortality is relatively constant through all life stages (no one age is more susceptible than another). **Examples**: Some invertebrates, some birds, some annual plants, some lizards, and many rodents.

Type III: Early loss

Mortality is very high during early life stages, followed by a low death rate for the few individuals reaching adulthood. **Examples**: Many fish (not mouth brooders), frogs, most plants, and most marine invertebrates (e.g. oysters, barnacles).

These curves are conceptual models only, against which real life curves can be compared. Many species exhibit a mix of two of the three basic types.

Graph of age specific survival

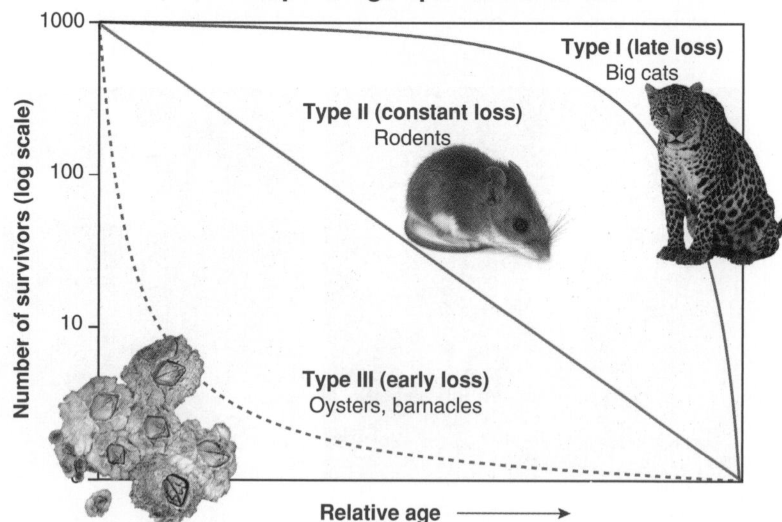

Three basic types of survivorship curves and representative organisms.

Elephants have a close matriarchal society and a long period of parental care. Elephants are long-lived and females usually produce just one calf.

Rodents are well known for their large litters and prolific breeding capacity. Individuals are lost from the population at a more or less constant rate.

Despite vigilant parental care, many birds suffer high juvenile losses (Type III). For those surviving to adulthood, deaths occur at a constant rate.

1. Based on the survivorship curves presented above, what age groups suffer the highest mortality in:

   (a) A Type I curve: ______________________

   (b) A Type II curve: ______________________

   (c) A Type III curve: ______________________

2. (a) Identify the survivorship curve typical of an *r*-selected species: ______________________

   (b) Identify the survivorship curve typical of a K-selected species: ______________________

3. Discuss the following statement: "There is no standard survivorship curve for a given species. The curve depicts the nature of a population at a particular time and place and under certain environmental conditions.":

____

____

____

ISBN: 978-1-98-856632-0

44 Life Tables and Survivorship

Key Question: How can life tables be used as a tool for analyzing populations dynamics?

Life tables, such as those shown below, provide a summary of mortality for a population (usually for a group of individuals of the same age or cohort). The basic data are just the number (or proportion) of individuals remaining alive at successive sampling times (the survivorship or l_x). Life tables represent the data collected from real populations, so they are an important tool when analyzing changes in populations over time. They can tell us what age groups in a population suffer the most mortality and can provide information about life span and population age structure. The survivorship (l_x) column of a basic life table is used to derive a survivorship curve. In this activity, we will look at data from real populations to draw conclusions about the general statements made about survivorship curves earlier (opposite).

Age in years (x)	No. alive each year (N_x)	Proportion surviving at the start of age x (l_x)	Proportion dying between x and x +1 (d_x)	Mortality (q_x)
0	142	1.000	0.563	0.563
1	62	0.437	0.198	0.452
2	34	0.239	0.098	0.412
3	20	0.141	0.035	0.250
4	15	0.106	0.028	0.267
5	11	0.078	0.036	0.454
6	6	0.042	0.028	0.667
7	2	0.014	0.0	0.000
8	2	0.014	0.014	1.000
9	0	0.0	0.0	–

Life table (left) and survivorship curve (below) for a population of the barnacle *Balanus*

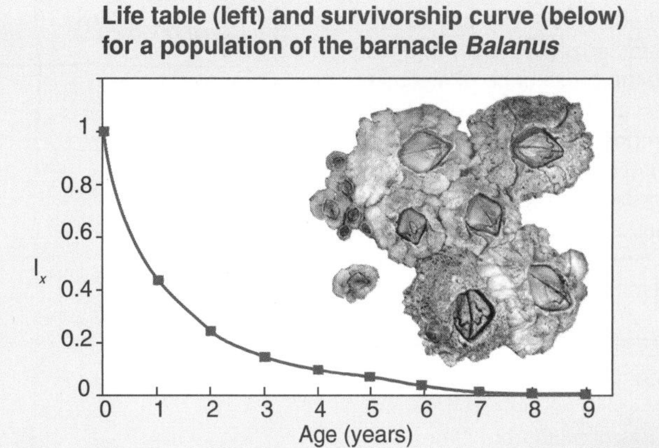

Life table for female elk, Northern Yellowstone National Park

x	l_x	d_x	q_x
0	1000	323	0.323
1	677	13	0.019
2	664	2	0.003
3	662	2	0.003
4	660	4	0.006
5	656	4	0.006
6	652	9	0.014
7	643	3	0.005
8	640	3	0.005
9	637	9	0.014
10	628	7	0.001
11	621	12	0.019
12	609	13	0.021
13	596	41	0.069
14	555	34	0.061
15	521	20	0.038
16	501	59	0.118
17	442	75	0.170
18	367	93	0.253
19	274	82	0.299
20	192	57	0.297
21+	135	135	1.000

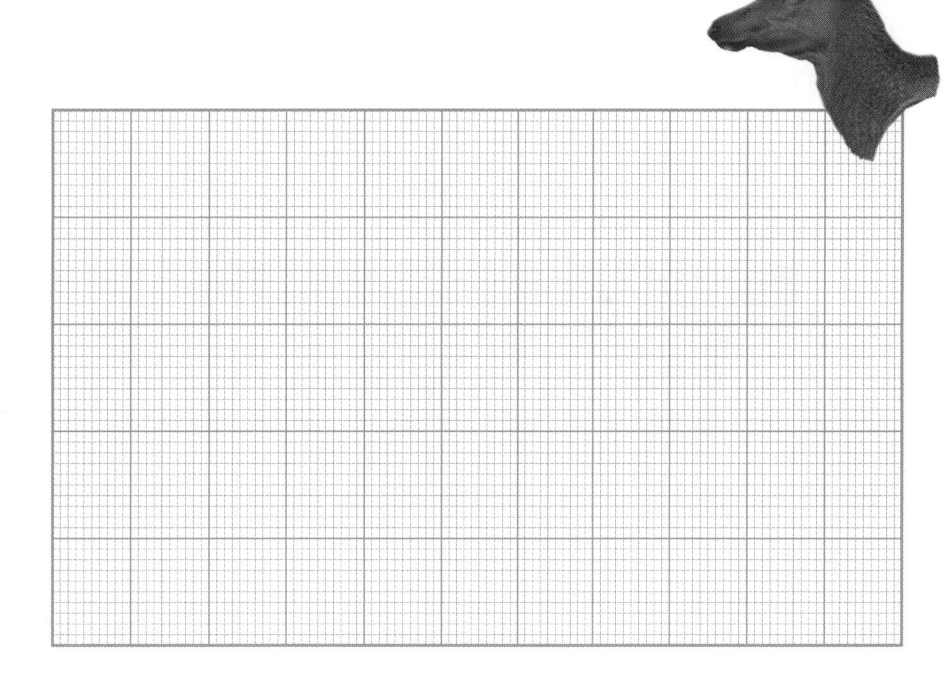

1. Based on the *Balanus* data, identify the type of survivorship curve for this animal: ______________________

2. (a) Using the grid, plot a survivorship curve for elk hinds (above) based on the life table data provided:

   (b) Describe the survivorship curve for these large mammals: ______________________

   ____

3. Do the life table data above support the general statements made about survivorship curves opposite? Explain:

   ____

   ____

ISBN: 978-1-98-856632-0

45 Modeling Human Survivorship

Key Question: How can historical data be used to examine changes in human survivorship?

Cemeteries are an excellent place to study changes in human demographics. Data collected from headstones can be used to calculate death rates and produce survivorship curves. It is also possible to compare survivorship curves over different periods and see how certain factors (e.g. war or advancements in medicine) have altered survivorship.

Death data males and females

The data (right) represents age of death data for males and females collected over two different time periods; pre-1950 and post 1950. The pre-1950s was characterized by two world wars, and the prevalence of diseases such as polio and tuberculosis. The post 1950s have also seen global conflict, but to a lesser degree than the pre-1950 period. Many advances in medicine (e.g. vaccines) and technology have been made during this time.

The data used in this exercise has been collected from the online records of several cemeteries across five different states in the United States to provide representative data.

Pre-1950						Post 1950					
Males age at death			Females age at death			Males age at death			Females age at death		
81	89	71	9	43	1	80	60	64	92	87	87
40	31	27	76	64	84	81	71	41	46	76	82
54	10	64	0	67	68	79	62	76	44	63	80
70	42	0	78	42	58	81	63	17	70	33	90
75	1	41	69	39	19	8	83	40	80	99	85
64	5	77	6	4	24	30	31	79	71	76	63
45	0	21	46	18	62	88	78	74	88	92	58
22	24	1	60	71	52	90	56	46	65	96	89
71	70	75	84	2	29	84	86	71	51	65	56
62	39	50	75	63	8	64	80	90	80	54	86

Data source: http://www.interment.net/us/index.htm

1. Complete the following table using the cemetery data provided. The males pre-1950 data have been completed for you.
   (a) In the number of deaths column, record the number of deaths for each age category.
   (b) Calculate the survivorship for each age category. For each column, enter the total number of individuals in the study (30) in the 0-9 age survivorship cell. This is the survivorship for the 0-9 age group. Subtract the number of deaths at age 0-9 from the survivorship value at age 0-9. This is the survivorship at the 10-19 age category. To calculate the survivorship for age 20-29, subtract the number of deaths at the age 10-19 age category from the survivorship value for age 10-19. Continue until you have completed the column.

	Males pre-1950		Females pre-1950		Males post 1950		Females post 1950	
Age	No. of deaths	Survivorship	No. of deaths	Survivorship	No. of deaths	Survivorship	No. of deaths	Survivorship
0-9	5	30						
10-19	1	25						
20-29	4	24						
30-39	2	20						
40-49	4	18						
50-59	2	14						
60-69	3	12						
70-79	7	9						
80-89	2	2						
90-99	0	0						
Total	30							

2. (a) On a separate piece of graph paper, construct a graph to compare the survivorship curves for each category. Staple the graph into this workbook once you have completed the activity.
   (b) What conclusions can you make about survivorship before 1950 and after 1950? ______________________
   (c) What factors might cause these differences? ______________________

ISBN: 978-1-98-856632-0

46 Life Expectancy

Key Question: What is life expectancy and why does it vary? Life expectancy is the average number of years of life remaining at any given age and changes as an individual ages. For example, in the US, a human has a life expectancy of around 78 years at birth. However, a 66 year old has a life expectancy of around 16 years meaning they should live to the age of 82. In human societies, life expectancy depends on sex and on variable socio-economic factors such as public health and level of poverty. Countries where war, famine, or disease are common invariably have low life expectancies.

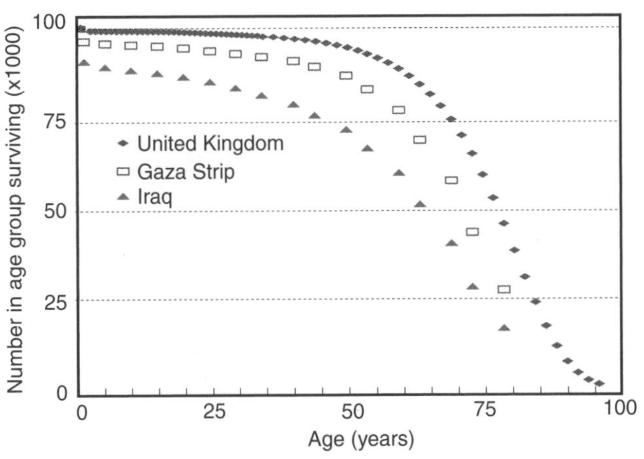

Human populations typically exhibit Type I survivorship. However, average life expectancy can vary greatly between developed and developing nations. The average life expectancy can be estimated from the survivorship curves above as being the age at which 50% of individuals are still alive.

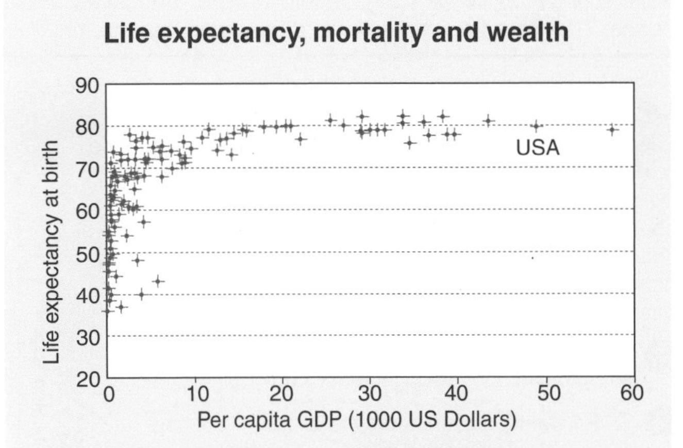

Life expectancy is linked to many factors but in human society there is a close correlation between life expectancy and a country's per capita gross domestic product (GDP). Those countries with high GDP can be expected to have citizens with long life expectancies.

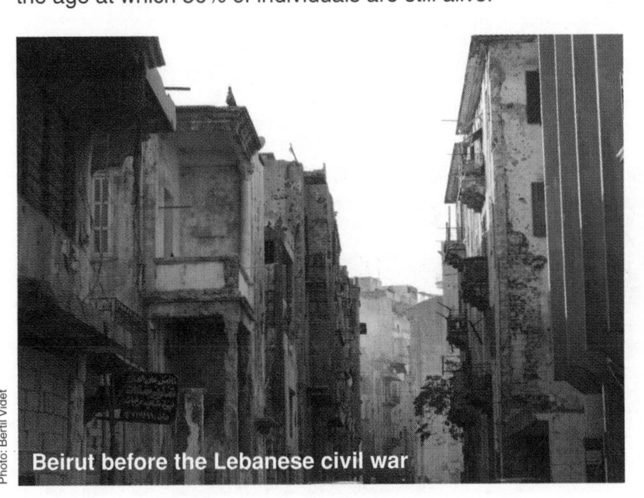

War, civil instability, poor infrastructure, and poverty can greatly reduce life expectancy. Life expectancy in stable, industrialized nations, e.g. Japan, can be around 80 at birth, while war-torn, poor, or developing nations may have life expectancies as low as 39 at birth, e.g. Swaziland.

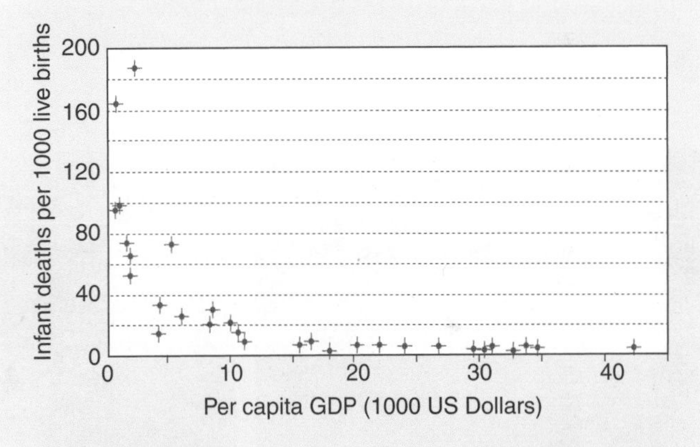

In developed nations, the infant mortality rate (IMR) is low because of better standards of living and access to medicine. People in developing countries often lack access to medical care and the IMR can be high, especially where there are high rates of endemic disease. However, populations in developing countries often have high birth rates so that population growth rates remain high despite a high IMR.

Life expectancy and survivorship of a population are closely linked to the wealth of the country they live in:

1. (a) Describe the relationship between a country's per capita GDP and life expectancy of its citizens: ____________________

   (b) Explain why IMR might be linked to a nation's wealth: ____________________

   (c) Identify some factors that lower life expectancy and survivorship of a country: ____________________

2. Explain why life expectancy changes as one ages: ____________________

3. Estimate average life expectancy for: (a) United Kingdom: ________ (b) Gaza Strip: ________ (c) Iraq: ________

ISBN: 978-1-98-856632-0

47 Carrying Capacity

Key Question: What is carrying capacity and why is it important in studies of populations?

An ecosystem's carrying capacity, i.e. the size of population that the available resources can sustain indefinitely, is limited by the ecosystem's resources. Factors affecting carrying capacity (population limiting factors) can be biotic (e.g. food supply) or abiotic (e.g. water, climate, and available space). The carrying capacity is determined by the most limiting factor and can change over time (e.g. as a result of environmental changes). A population at below carrying capacity, will increase because resources are not limiting. As the population approaches its carrying capacity (or exceeds it) resources become limiting and environmental resistance increases, decreasing population growth. An understanding of carrying capacity is important to explaining population fluctuations and patterns of population growth.

Limiting factors and carrying capacity

Limiting factors are factors that limit the growth, abundance, or distribution of an organism or a population. Which factor is limiting and its effect may change over time. Ultimately, changes in limiting factors (such as water or food) operate by changing a habitat's carrying capacity. The graph right shows how the carrying capacity of a steppe environment varies based on changes to biotic and abiotic limiting factors.

1. A small number of steppe voles move into an area of steppe. The population increases quickly.
2. The population overshoots the carrying capacity.
3. Large numbers damage the environment and food becomes limiting. The carrying capacity falls.
4. The population stabilizes at the new carrying capacity.
5. The steppe experiences a drought and carrying capacity is reduced.
6. The drought breaks and carrying capacity rises to a stable, but lower level because of drought damage.

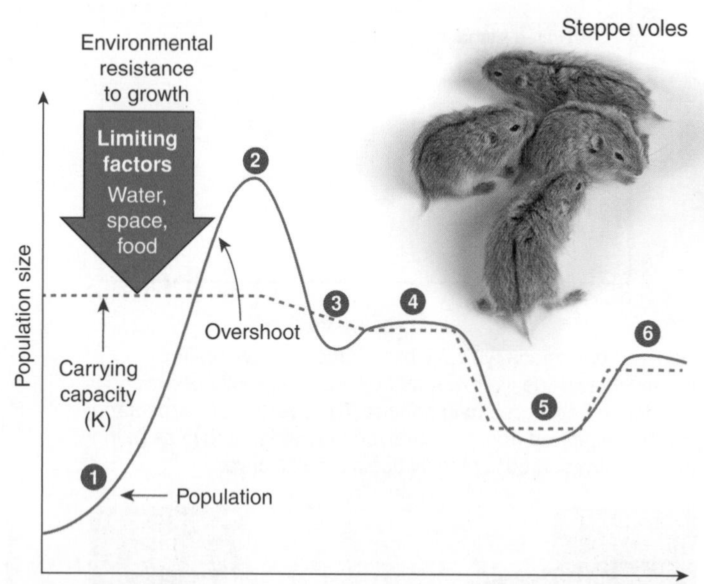

Large wildfires, especially when they occur with high frequency, can severely reduce the carrying capacity of ecosystems, especially if recovery is slowed by climatic factors such as drought.

Temporary increases in carrying capacity (increase in food supplies) can result in rapid population increases, especially in *r*-selected species. When carrying capacity is exceeded, many will die.

Water is a critical limiting factor in many ecosystems. Droughts, especially over several years, can reduce the ecosystem's carrying capacity and result in large losses of crops, wildlife, and livestock.

1. Explain how changes in limiting factors alter carrying capacity? ____________________

____

____

2. What limiting factors have changed at points 3, 5, and 6 in the graph above, and how have they changed?

(a) 3: ____________________

(b) 5: ____________________

(c) 6: ____________________

3. Explain what the scenario above illustrates about carrying capacity: ____________________

____

____

ISBN: 978-1-98-856632-0

48 A Case Study in Carrying Capacity

Key Question: What evidence do we have for the carrying capacity of ecosystems?

The introduction of wolves to Coronation Island, Alaska, was a classic example of an experiment that failed in its aims but revealed a lot about the carrying capacity of ecosystems. Coronation Island is a small island and includes 78 km^2 of wilderness area. In 1960, the Alaska Department of Fish and Game released two breeding pairs of wolves onto the island. Their aim was to control the sitka black-tailed deer, which had been overgrazing the land. They had expected the wolves would control the deer and the ecosystem would recover. What happened was entirely different.

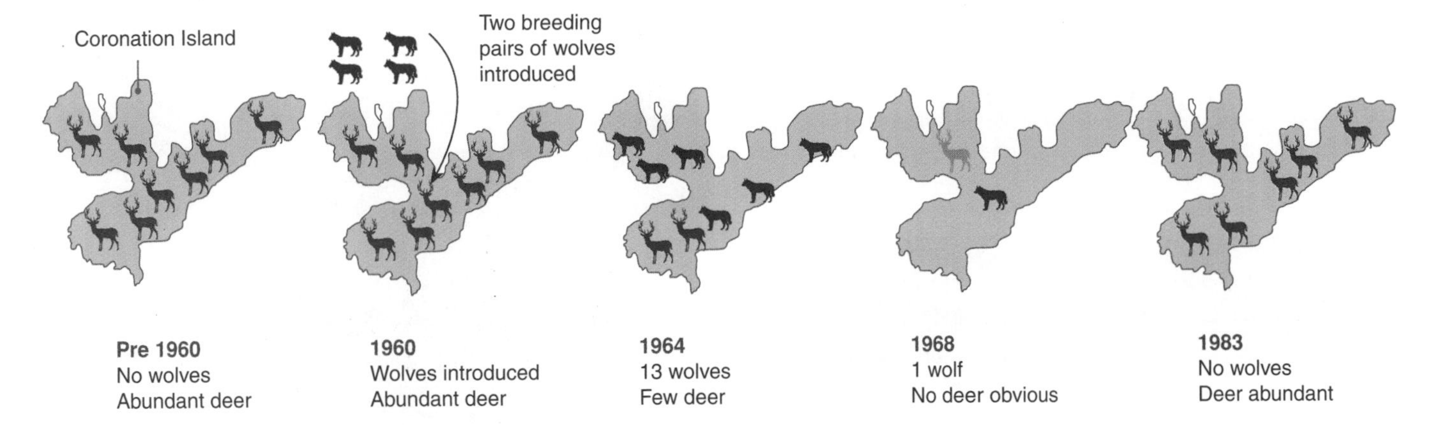

The experiment and its results

Introduction of the wolves in 1960 initially appeared to have the desired effect. The wolves preyed on the abundant deer and bred successfully. Deer numbers fell dramatically (right). However, within a few years the deer numbers completely crashed. The wolves ran out of food (deer) and began eating each other. Within 8 years of the wolves being introduced, only one wolf remained on the island. By 1983, wolves were absent and the deer were once again abundant.

What went wrong?

- The study showed Coronation Island was too small to sustain both wolf and deer populations.
- The deer could not easily find refuge from the wolves, so their numbers were quickly reduced.
- Reproductive rates in the deer may have been low because of poor forage following years of overgrazing. When wolves were introduced, predation and low reproductive rates, caused deer to decline.
- The deer were the only food source for the wolves. When deer became scarce the wolves lacked other prey and resorted to cannibalism.

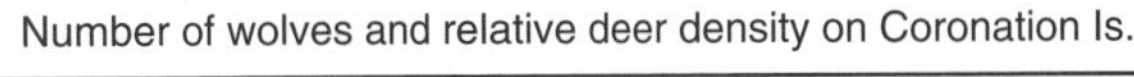

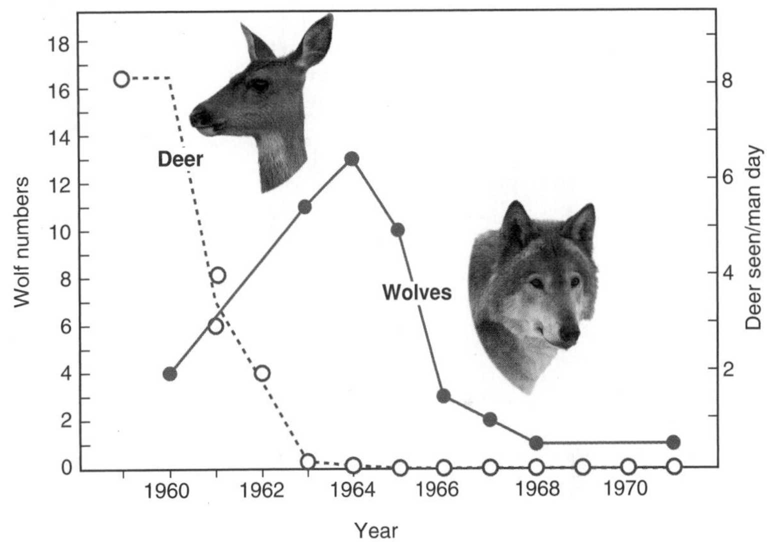

Above: Following the introduction of wolves to Coronation Island, deer numbers were reduced to the point they were rarely seen.

Data: The introduction, increase, and demise of wolves on Coronation Island, Alaska, David R. Klein (chapter in "The Ecology and Conservation of Wolves in a Changing World, Canadian Circumpolar Institute).

1. Why was the introduction of wolves to Coronation island considered a failure in terms of its aims? ________________

2. What factors contributed to the observed results? ________________

3. What did the results tell ecologists about the carrying capacity of this ecosystem? ________________

ISBN: 978-1-98-856632-0

49 Population Growth

Key Question: What factors are responsible for changes in population number?

The number of individuals in a population (N) is calculated by knowing the gains and losses to the population. Births, deaths, immigrations (movements into the population) and emigrations (movements out of the population) are events that together determine the number of individuals in a population. Scientists usually measure the rate of these events, which are influenced by the resources available and the biotic potential, which varies among species.

Births, deaths, immigration (movements into the population) and emigration (movements out of the population) are events that determine the population size. Population growth depends on the number of individuals added to the population from births and immigration, minus the number lost through deaths and emigration. This is expressed as:

Population growth =
(Births + Immigration) – (Deaths + Emigration)
(B + I) – (D + E)

The difference between immigration and emigration gives net migration. Ecologists usually measure the **rate** of these events. These rates are influenced by limiting factors in the environment (such as availability of food, water, or habitat) and by the characteristics of the organisms themselves (their biotic potential or natural capacity to increase, *r*).

Rates in population studies are commonly expressed in one of two ways:

- **Numbers per unit time**, e.g. 20,150 live births per year. The birth rate is termed the natality, whereas the death rate is the mortality.
- **Per capita rate** (number per head of population), e.g. 122 live births per 1000 individuals per year (12.2%).

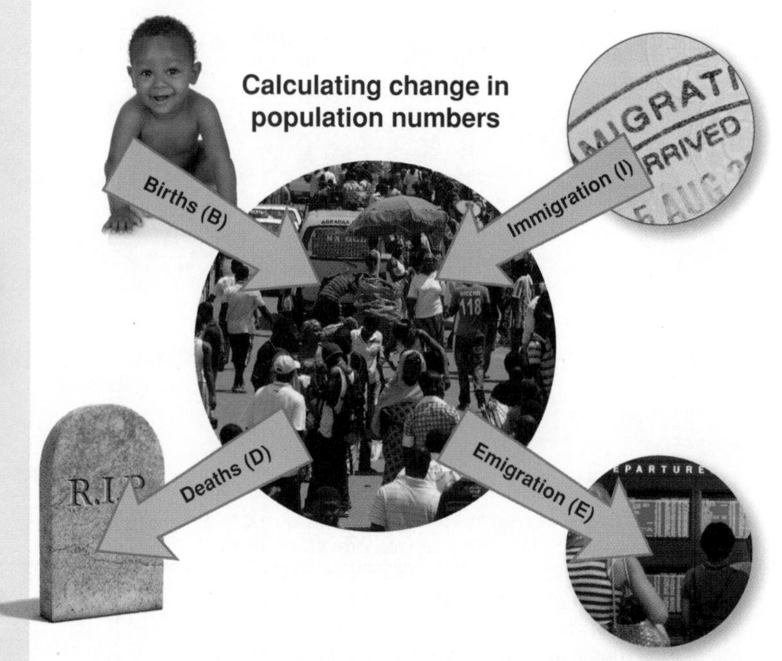

The human population is estimated to peak at around 9 billion by 2050 as a result of multiple factors, including falling birth rates. Humans have the technology and production efficiency to solve many resource problems and so might appear exempt from the direct influence of limiting factors. However, declining availability of water and land for food production are limiting factors likely to constrain population growth, at least regionally.

1. Define the following terms used to describe changes in population numbers:

(a) Death rate (mortality): ______

(b) Birth rate (natality): ______

(c) Net migration rate: ______

2. Explain how the concept of limiting factors applies to population biology: ______

3. Using the terms, B, D, I, and E (above), construct equations to express the following:

(a) A population in equilibrium: ______

(b) A declining population: ______

(c) An increasing population: ______

4. A population started with a total number of 100 individuals. Over the following year, population data were collected. Calculate birth rates, death rates, net migration rate, and rate of population change for the data below (as percentages):

(a) Births = 14: Birth rate = ______

(b) Net migration = +2: Net migration rate = ______

(c) Deaths = 20: Death rate = ______

(d) Rate of population change = ______

(e) State whether the population is increasing or declining: ______

ISBN: 978-1-98-856632-0

50 Patterns of Population Growth

Key Question: What do exponential and logistic patterns of growth look like and how does carrying capacity limit the maximum population size that can be sustained?

Population growth is the change in a population's numbers over time (dN/dt or ΔN/Δt). It is regulated by the carrying capacity (K), which is the maximum number the environment can sustain. Population growth falls into two main patterns: exponential or logistic. Both can be defined mathematically. **Exponential growth** occurs when resources are essentially unlimited and produces a J shaped curve on a linear scale. **Logistic growth** begins exponentially, but slows as the population approaches carrying capacity.

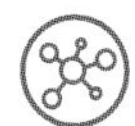

Exponential growth

Recall the relationship between the factors determining population growth. If we want to compare populations of different sizes, it is useful to express population parameters such as rates of birth, death, and population growth on a **per capita** (per individual) basis.

The maximum per capita rate of population increase under ideal conditions (or **biotic potential**) is called r_{max}. We can calculate this using a simple equation (in words to the right, below):

r_{max} = B – D / N

r_{max} = Births – Deaths ÷ Population number

Exponential growth (right) is then expressed as:

$dN/dt = r_{max}N$

Population growth rate at time t = per capita rate of increase X population number

Exponential growth is **density independent** because per capita birth and death rates do not depend on the population size. It is a typical pattern of population growth when a few individuals enter a new area with unlimited resources, but it is rarely sustained.

The biotic potential (recall this is the r_{max}) is constant for any one species. However, in natural populations, the per capita rate of increase (*r*) is usually lower than the r_{max} because resource limitation slows population growth. Organisms will show exponential growth if *r* is positive and constant so the equation is often given simply as **dN/dt = *r*N** (right).

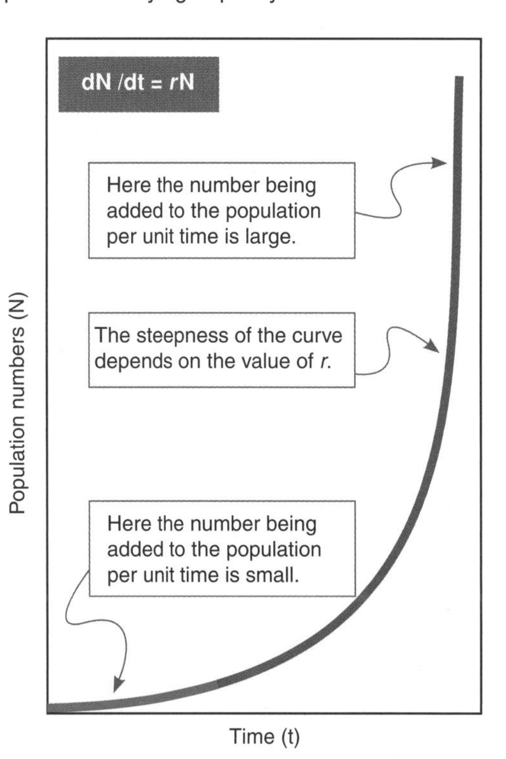

Exponential curve: Note the lag (red) and exponential (blue) phases of the curve.

Recall that gray wolves were hunted almost to extinction in many parts of North America. In the 1980s, following their protection under law, packs began to repopulate parts of the US from Canada. The table below records the wolf population in Montana 1979-1995. Gray wolves were removed from the endangered species list in 2011 and hunting has since recommenced.

Gray wolf population in Montana			
Year	Population	Year	Population
1979	5	1997	52
1981	5	1999	75
1983	9	2001	125
1985	20	2003	190
1987	15	2005	252
1989	16	2007	420
1991	38	2009	525
1993	52	2011	651
1995	60	2013	620
		2014	552

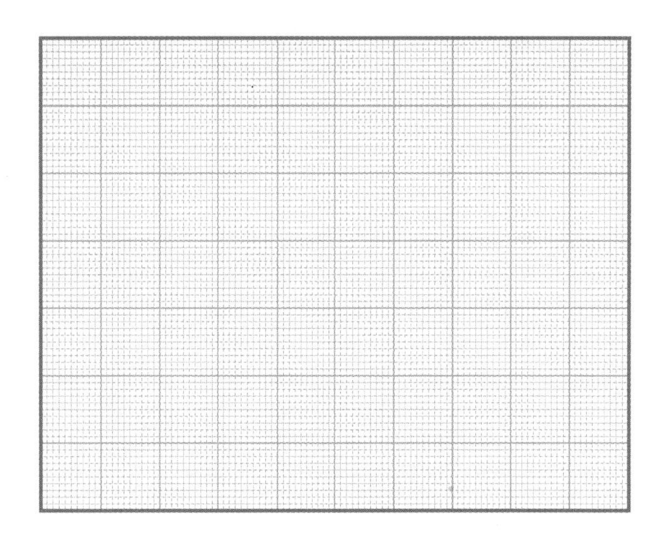

1. Produce a line graph of the gray wolf population on the grid above:
2. What would explain the lag in population growth before 1999? ______
3. Explain why wolves showed this pattern of population growth: ______

ISBN: 978-1-98-856632-0

47 ← 42 ← ERT-3 6.B

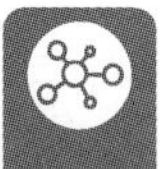

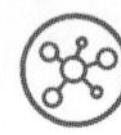

Logistic growth

Populations do not generally continue to grow unchecked. Their numbers generally stabilize around a maximum that can be supported by the environment. This maximum number is called the carrying capacity (K). As the population number approaches K, the resources required for continued growth become limiting and there is increasing environmental resistance to further expansion. As a result, the rate of population growth slows. If the change in numbers is plotted over time, the curve is S shaped (sigmoidal), and the pattern of growth is called logistic. Logistic growth is typical of populations that live at or near carrying capacity and per capita birth and death rates are affected by population size (**density dependent**). Logistic growth is expressed as: **dN/dt = rN(K−N/K)**.

- Under the logistic growth model, dN/dt = rN is multiplied by the proportion of K that is left unused.
- As the population increases (N approaches K), the proportion of K available decreases and individuals find it difficult to find or utilize space and resources.
- The rate of population increase slows as population size approaches carrying capacity.
- Often, there is a lag between depletion of resources and the population's response to that depletion. This can cause the population to overshoot K before declining again in response to lack of resources. In time, populations usually stabilize around K.

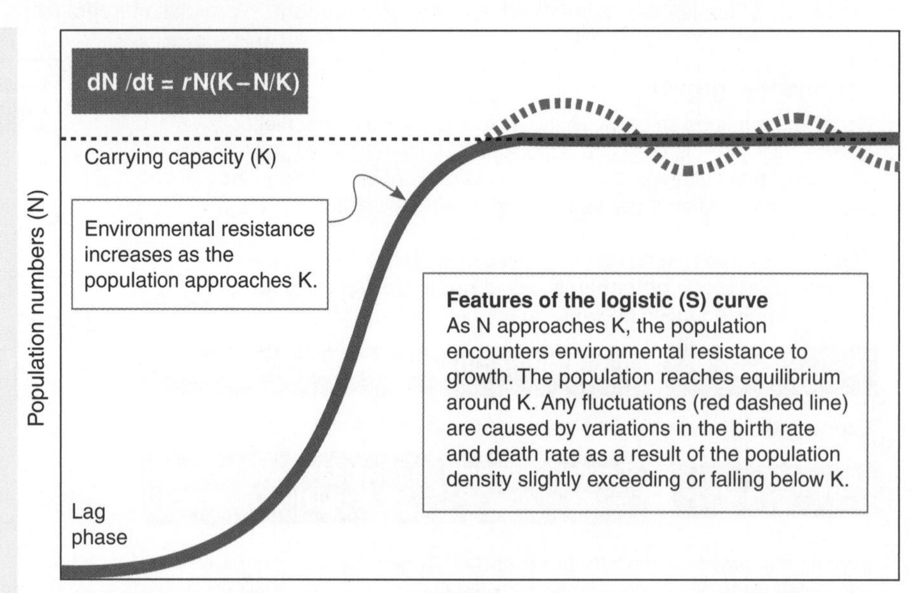

Population growth, West Virginia			
Year	Population	Year	Population
1800	78,592	1900	958,800
1810	105,469	1910	1,221,119
1820	136,808	1920	1,463,701
1830	176,924	1930	1,729,205
1840	224,537	1940	1,901,974
1850	308,313	1950	2,005,552
1860	376,688	1960	1,860,421
1870	442,014	1970	1,744,237
1880	618,457	1980	1,949,644
1890	762,794	1990	1,793,477

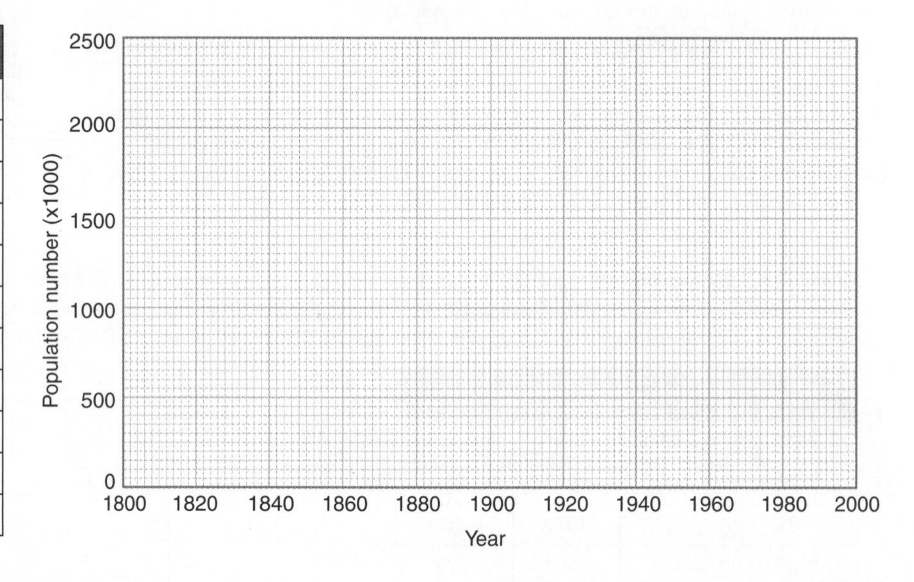

4. Census information provides a good test of the predictions of population growth models. The table of data above records census data for the human population of West Virginia 1800-1990.

   (a) Based on what you know so far, what sort of curve would you predict for a new settlement of humans? Explain:

   ___

   ___

   (b) Plot the data on the grid provided. The axes have been labeled to help you.

   (c) Did the plotted curve agree with your predictions? ___

5. Use mathematical reasoning to explain the differences between exponential and logistic growth: ___

   ___

   ___

   ___

ISBN: 978-1-98-856632-0

51 Modeling Population Growth

Key Question: How can a computer model help us to understand the factors affecting logistic growth?

Plotting a logistic growth curve on a spreadsheet can help in understanding logistic growth and the factors that affect population growth rate. In this exercise, you will create your own spreadsheet model of logistic growth for a hypothetical population of 2, where *r* is 0.15 and K 100. You can use Microsoft Excel or an equivalent spreadsheet program.

INVESTIGATION 3.1: Creating a model of logistic growth

See appendix for equipment list.

1. In cells A1 to F1, add the headings r, t(period), N, K, K-N/K, and dN/dt, as shown in the image below.

	A	B	C	D	E	F	G
1	r	t (period)	N	K	K-N/K	dN/dt	
2	0.15	0	2	100	=($D$2-C2)/$D$2	=$A$2*C2*E2	
3		=B2+1	=C2+F2				
4							
5							
6							
7							
8							

Population at t_1 = population at t_0 + dN/dt (the amount of population change over 1 time period)

2. In cell A2, type 0.15, the value for r.
3. In cell B2, type 0.
4. In cell C2, type 2 (the initial population number).
5. In cell D2, type 100 (the carrying capacity).
6. In cell E2, type =($D$2-C2)/$D$2. This term, K-N/K, is the fraction of the carrying capacity that has not yet been "used up."
7. In cell F2, type =$A$2*C2*E2. This is the change in population number described by the logistic equation **rN(K-N/K)**.
8. In cell B3, type =B2+1. In cell C3, type =C2+F2. Shift-select cells B3 and C3 and fill down.
9. Shift-select cells E2 and F2 and fill down to about 60 time periods. The cells will automatically calculate (the first few are shown below).

	A	B	C	D	E	F	G
1	r	t (period)	N	K	K-N/K	dN/dt	
2	0.15	0	2.00	100	0.98	0.29	
3		1	2.29		0.98	0.34	
4		2	2.63		0.97	0.38	
5		3	3.01				
6							

10. When your time series is complete, select the data in columns B (time) and C (Numbers) and choose < **Insert** < **Chart** < **XY scatter** to create a plot of dN/dt.
11. Under **Chart Design** in the menu, you can choose **Add Chart Element** to add axis labels and a title.

1. Describe the shape of the curve you have plotted: ______________________________

2. Around which time period does the curve on the spreadsheet above begin to flatten out? ____________

3. Use the logistic equation and mathematical reasoning to explain the changes in population growth rate (dN/dt):

____

____

____

____

____

____

ISBN: 978-1-98-856632-0

52 Populations and Resources

Key Question: How does the availability of resources influence population growth?

The **size** of populations can be altered by factors that may or may not be influenced by population density (i.e. density dependent vs density independent). However, population **growth** is regulated primarily by factors that alter the rates of births and/or deaths. These regulatory factors, such as competition for food, have a proportionately greater effect at higher population densities. Density-independent factors, such as natural disasters, can severely limit growth, e.g. by increasing death rates. Both density-dependent and density independent factors can alter the availability of resources and so directly or indirectly limit population growth and size.

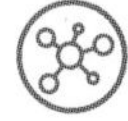

Density-dependent and density-independent factors in populations

Density dependent factors in populations

- The effect of these on population growth is influenced by population density.
- They are most important at high population densities.
- Tend to be biotic factors such as competition and predation.
- Usually self regulating (negative feedback).
- **Alters resource availability through density-mediated effects.**

Density independent regulating factors

- The effect of these on population growth is independent of population density.
- Tend to be abiotic factors such as natural disasters (droughts, floods, and wildfires).
- May limit growth but do not regulate it, as regulation implies feedback.
- **Resource availability altered independently of the population density.**

Density-dependent and density-independent factors can alter the availability of resources

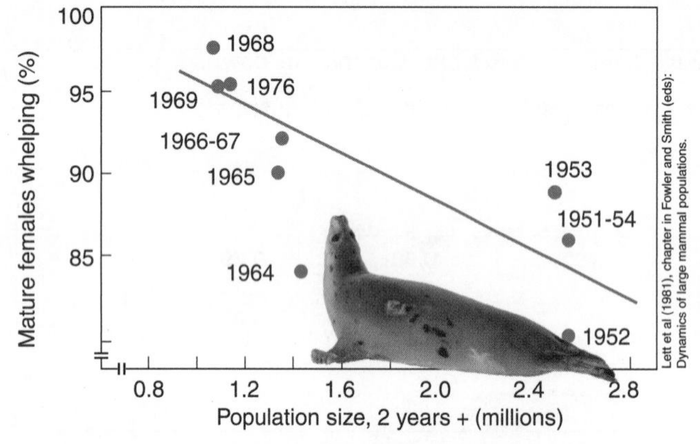

In mammals, there is a strong relationship between population density, population fertility, and population growth. For example, fertility in harp seals (above), as measured by the number of females breeding, is density dependent (above). Fertility declines were recorded at higher densities when the population was more resource limited. This decline slows population growth.

Density-independent factors can act indirectly on population growth. Climatic events can be unpredictable. A cold spring may kill oak flowers and cause the acorn crop to fail. Squirrels, which depend on plentiful acorns, may then starve the following winter. The proximate cause of starvation is the density of squirrels and lack of food, but the ultimate cause was climate related.

1. Explain how each of the following can influence the population growth through changes to resource availability:

   (a) Density dependent factors: ______________________________

   ____

   ____

   ____

   (b) Density independent factors: ______________________________

   ____

   ____

   ____

ISBN: 978-1-98-856632-0

Population regulation in pronghorn antelope

- The Coronation Island example earlier in the chapter showed how biotic factors can influence population numbers. Abiotic factors are also important in regulating population growth and size. Drought (lower than average rainfall) is one such factor and can persist for many years.
- During the late 90s and early 2000s drought occurred in Arizona and New Mexico. Researchers studied the effect of the drought on the ecosystem. In particular, they wanted to know how populations were affected by changes to habitat and availability of food and water. One of the aspects they investigated was how drought affected the survival rate of pronghorn fawns in Arizona. Their results are shown in the table below right.

Pronghorn fawn

Antelope_aka_Pronghorns.jpg: Larry Lamsa CC2.0

2. Plot the tabulated rainfall and fawn survival data on the grid below.

3. (a) Describe the plot for rainfall over time: ____________________

____

____

(b) Describe the fawn survival rate over time: ____________________

____

(c) Describe the relationship between rainfall and fawn survival:

____

____

____

Year	Rainfall (cm)	Fawns surviving to December per 100 females
1995	11	12
1996	3	0
1997	4	0
1998	19	32
1999	6	0
2000	5	15
2001	15	78
2002	2	9

Data after Bright, J., and J. Hervert. (2005). Adult and fawn mortality of Sonoran pronghorn Wildlife Society Bulletin, 33(1):43-50 pp.

(d) Explain why rainfall might be correlated with fluctuations in pronghorn fawn survival and predict the effects of these fluctuations on population growth:

____

____

____

____

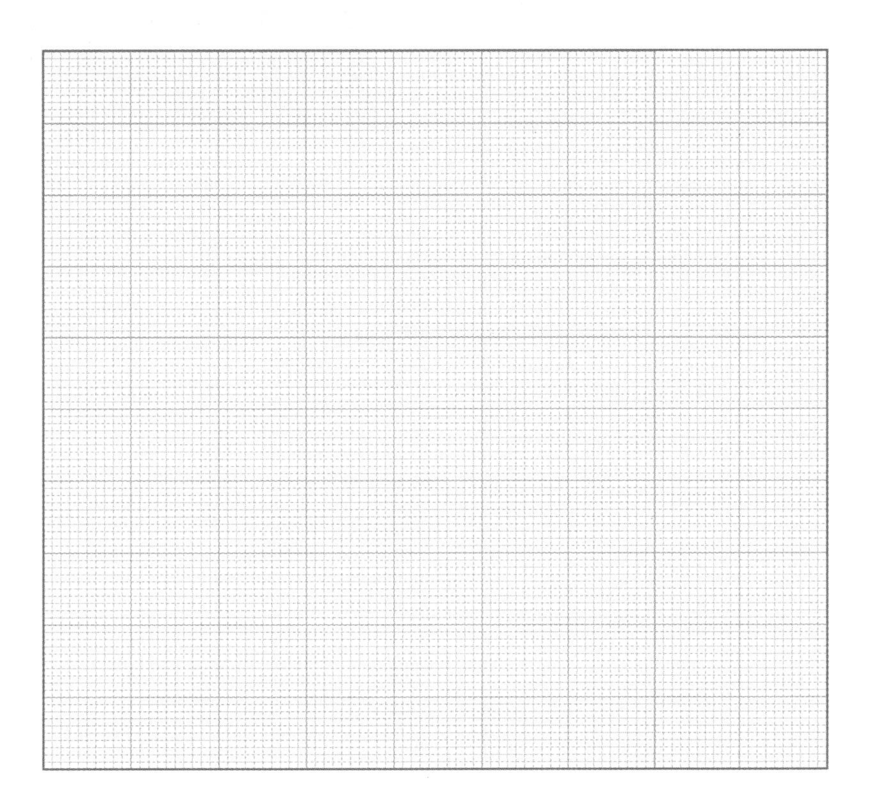

ISBN: 978-1-98-856632-0

53 Population Age Structure

Key Question: What do population age diagrams tell us about the growth and sustainability of populations?

The age structure of a population refers to the relative proportion of individuals in each age group in the population. The age structure of populations can be categorized according to specific age groups (e.g. years), or by other measures such as life stage (egg, larvae, pupae) or size class (height or diameter in plants). Population growth is strongly influenced by age structure. Population age structures are represented as diagrams (or pyramids), in which the proportions of individuals in each age class are plotted with the youngest individuals at the diagram's base. The number of individuals moving from one age class to the next influences the age structure of the population from year to year. The loss of an age class (e.g. through over-harvesting) can profoundly affect a population's ability to sustain itself.

Age structures in animal populations

Population growth is strongly influenced by age structure. A population with a high proportion of reproductive and pre-reproductive aged individuals has a much greater potential for population growth than one that is dominated by older individuals. These theoretical age pyramids show how growing populations are characterized by a high ratio of young (white bar) to adult age classes (blue bars). Aging populations with poor production are typically dominated by older individuals.

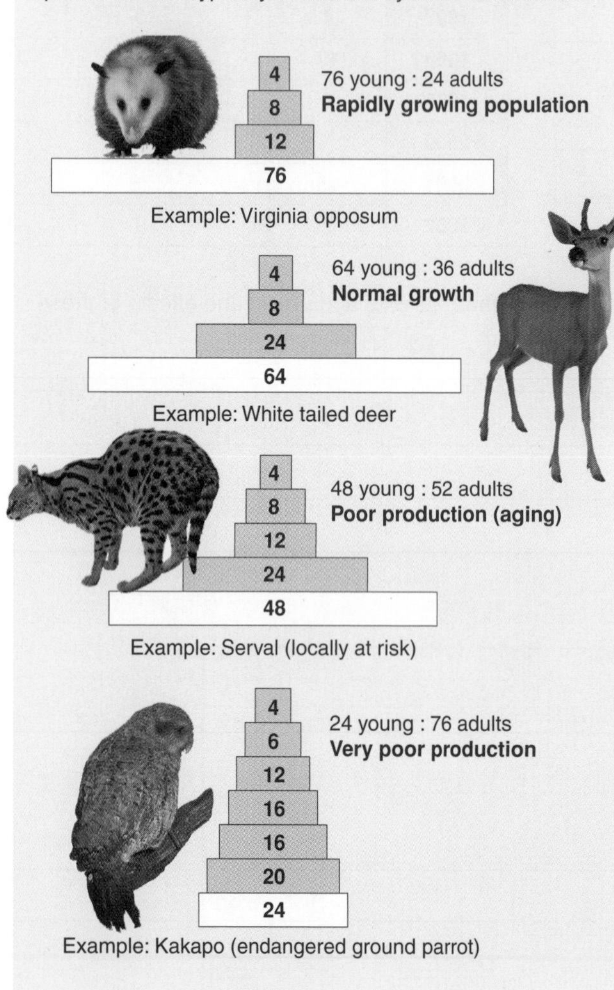

Age structures in human populations

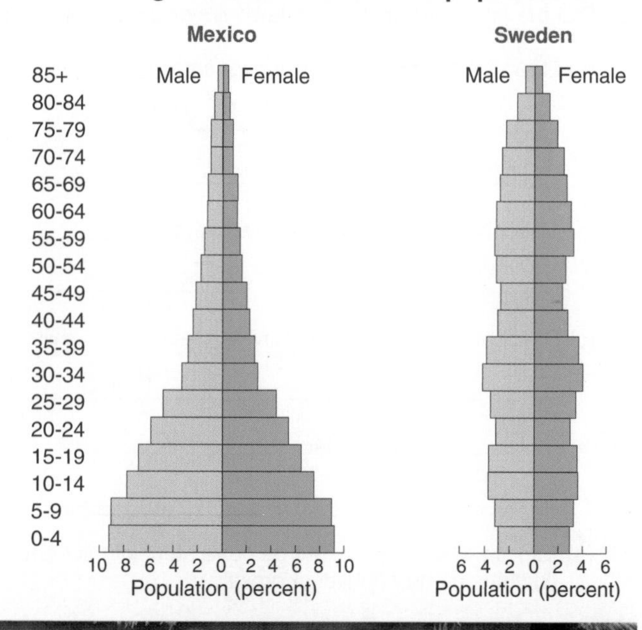

Most of the growth in human populations in recent years has been in the developing countries in Africa, Asia, and Central and South America. This is reflected in their age structure. A large proportion of the population is made up of individuals younger than 15 years (age pyramid above, left). Even if each has fewer children, the population will continue to increase for many years (a phenomenon known as **population momentum**). Compare this to the stable age structure of Sweden. In projections of human population growth for the rest of this century, Africa will be the only world region still with strong population growth.

1. For the theoretical age pyramids above left:

(a) Determine the approximate ratio of young to adults in a rapidly increasing population: ______________________

(b) Explain how the age structure diagram for a population can provide information about the population's growth rate:

____

____

____

____

ISBN: 978-1-98-856632-0

Age structure can be a tool in managing fisheries

Analysis of a population's age structure can help in its management because it can indicate where most of the mortality occurs and whether or not reproductive individuals are being replaced. The age structure of plant and animal populations can be assessed through an analysis of size which is often related to age in a predictable way.

The graphs below show the age structure of a hypothetical fish population under different fishing pressures. The age structure of the population is determined by analyzing the fish catch to determine the frequency of fish in each size (age) class.

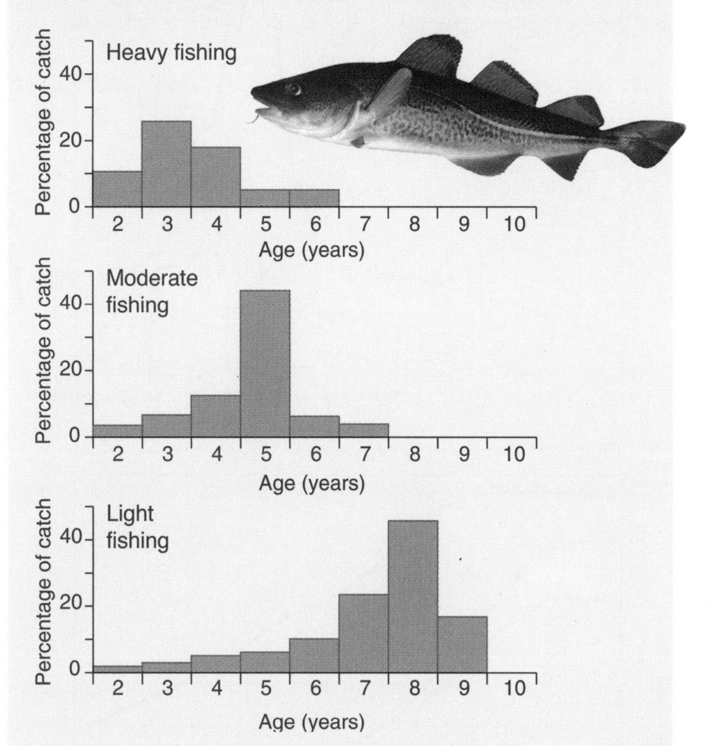

Age structure can reveal the history of a population

Examining a population's age structure from year to year can detect how the population might ne affected by stressors in the environment, such as drought or disease.

In Galápagos finches, reproductive activity and breeding success are determined by rainfall, which governs food supplies. In 1982, rainfall on the island of Daphne Major was minimal and in 1983 reproduction in the cactus ground finch failed. 1983 was an El Niño year, rainfall was heavy, and reproduction was very successful. The changes in age classes for males and females for the breeding years 1983 and 1984 are shown below.

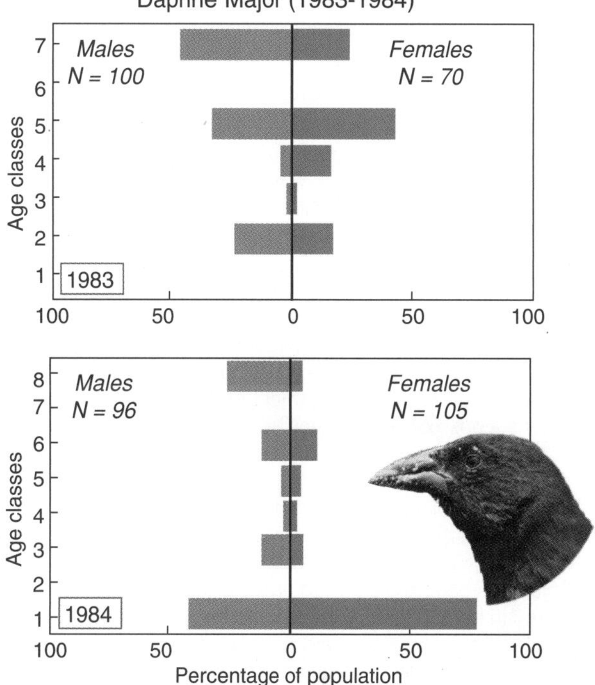

2. Why are changes in population age structure alone not necessarily a reliable predictor of population trends?

3. Why is the population of Mexico likely to continue to increase rapidly even if the rate of population growth slows?

4. With reference to the data above left,explain why is it important to know the age structure of a harvested population:

5. Answer the following with reference to the population age data presented for the cactus ground finch on Daphne Major:

   (a) What was effect of the 1982 drought on the age structure of the population in 1983?

   (b) How can you tell from the data that 1983's birds had good breeding success?

   (c) Describe what the data reveals about the population growth rate in:

   1983: ______ 1984: ______

ISBN: 978-1-98-856632-0

54 World Population Growth

Key Question: What are the trends in world population growth and what factors predominate in projections?

For most of human history, humans have not been very numerous compared to other species. It took all of human history to reach a population of 1 billion in 1803, but little more than 150 years to reach 3 billion in 1960. The world's population, now at 7.8 billion, is growing at just over 1% but this rate of growth is projected to decline (below). World population increase carries important environmental consequences, particularly when it is associated with increasing urbanization. Global population growth rates are declining however and the world population is moving towards stabilization.

World population trends

The graphs (right) illustrate some of the important current trends in human population dynamics. Estimates of population growth are always uncertain and political, social, and environmental changes all combine to affect population growth. However, for the first time in modern human history, the world's population is expected to virtually stop growing.

Falling fertility

The slowing of population growth is due largely to falling global fertility rates. The global total fertility rate (TFR) is expected to be 1.9 births per woman by 2100, down from the current 2.5 births per woman. This decline is associated with education of women, postponement of marriage, and access to contraception. The rate is projected to fall below the replacement fertility rate (2.1 births per woman) by 2070. The replacement fertility rate is the number of births per woman needed to maintain a population's size. Projections of population growth are complicated by the fact that countries with sub-replacement fertility may continue to grow because of immigration, population momentum, increased life expectancy, and lower infant mortality.

The world's median age is expected to increase to 42 in 2100, up from the current 31 and almost double what it was in 1950. From 2073, there are projected to be more people ages 65 and older than under age 15. This is the first time in human history this will be the case. Contributing factors to the rise in the median age are the increase in life expectancy and falling fertility rates.

Africa is the only world region projected to have strong population growth for the rest of this century. Six countries are projected to account for more than half of the world's population growth through to the end of this century, and five are in Africa (Nigeria, the Democratic Republic of the Congo, Tanzania, Ethiopia and Angola). The sixth country is Pakistan. Lagos (below) is the most populous state in Nigeria and one of the fastest growing cities in the world. Nigeria is a lower middle-income economy but over 89 million of its more than 200 million people live in poverty.

Figure 1: World population and growth rate

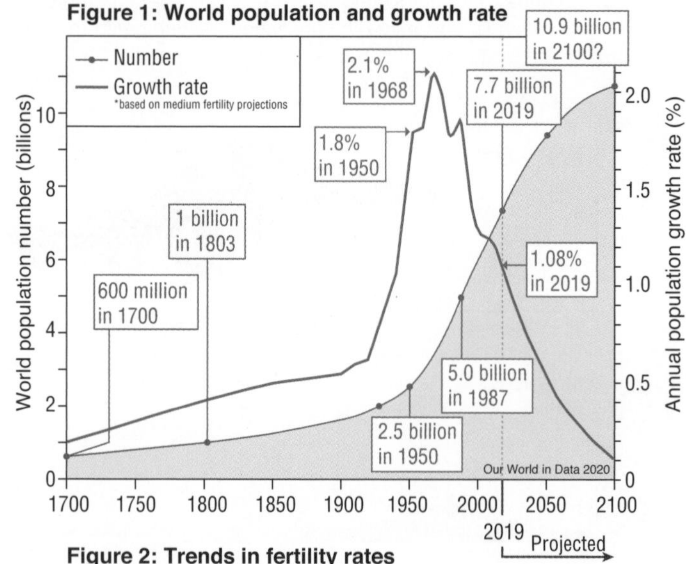

Figure 2: Trends in fertility rates

Children born per woman

0 1 2 3 4 5 6 7

1950 1960 1970 1980 1990 2000 2010 2020 2030 2040 2050

← Projected →

UN Population Division

Figure 3: Progress towards population stabilization

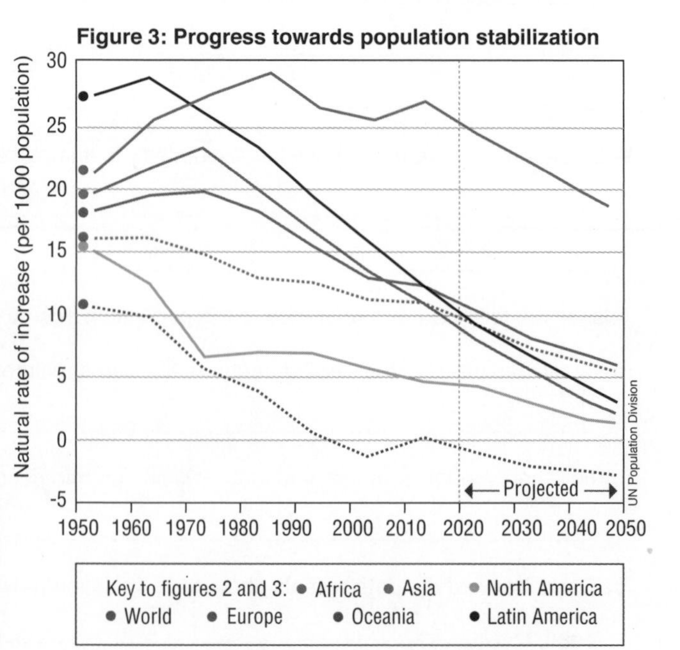

ISBN: 978-1-98-856632-0

Year	Developed nations (billions)	Developing nations (billions)
1950	0.8	1.7
1960	0.9	2.1
1970	1.0	2.7
1980	1.1	3.4
1990	1.1	4.2
2000	1.2	4.9
2010	1.2	5.7
2020	1.3	6.5
2030	1.3	7.3
2040	1.3	7.9
2050	1.3	8.4

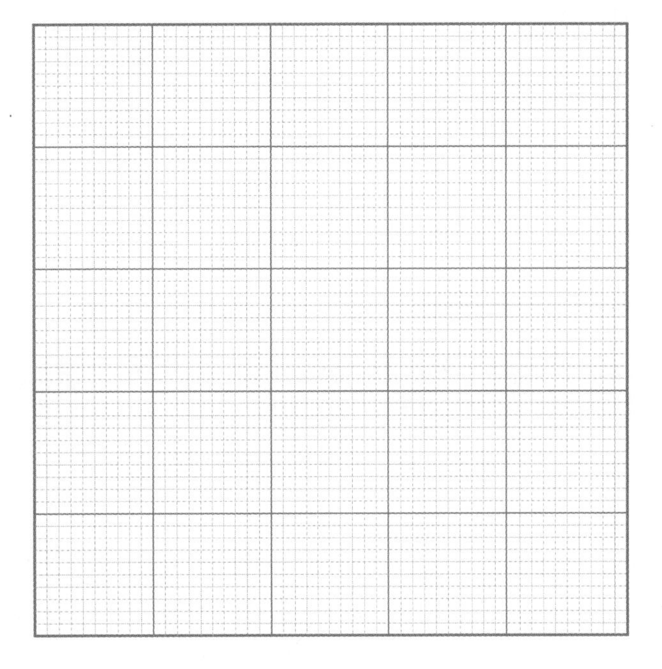

The world population has grown exponentially following advances in medicine and food production (Figure 1, left). The numbers above show how this growth is apportioned between developed and developing nations.

For a population in exponential growth, the **rule of 70** (below) is a simple way to approximate population doubling time. As the growth rate for humans is given in years, the calculated doubling time is also in years.
70 ÷ % growth rate = population doubling time

1. (a) Plot a graph population numbers for developed and developing nations on the grid above.

   (b) Compare the pattern of growth in developing and developed nations: ______

2. (a) Use the rule of 70 to calculate the doubling time of the human population based on the growth rate in 1950 (Fig. 1): ______

   (b) How good was this approximation of doubling time for humans during this period in history: ______

   (c) Now use the rule of 70 to calculate the doubling time of the human population based on the growth rate in 2019: ______

   (d) Does this approximation of doubling time agree with current projections of world population size? Explain: ______

3. Describe one environmental problem associated with the continued high population growth rate projected for Africa: ______

ISBN: 978-1-98-856632-0

55 Factors Affecting Human Population Dynamics

Key Question: What factors are currently affecting the growth and stability of the world's nations?

Human population growth is affected by the same density-dependent and density independent factors that affect all populations. Disease and lack of resources are important proximate causes, but the ultimate causes are varied and complex. They include conflict and events associated with climate change, such as crop failures and natural disasters.

Challenges to human sustainability

The human population faces a large number of challenges in the coming decades. As described earlier, global fertility rates are falling to sub-replacement levels in many countries. However, the developing nations (where most population growth is projected to occur) are those where a large proportion of the population live with severe food insecurity (without reliable access to sufficient food). Widespread famines, such as those in Asia and Europe last century are rare today, but the increasing impact of climate change and political conflicts make food insecurity an increasing concern. Populations displaced by conflict, such as the population of Syria, are at particular risk, and their displacement places pressure on the infrastructure of those countries that take them in. When civil unrest coincides with natural disasters such as drought (as is occurring in Syria) the effects on the population can be devastating. In Yemen, the 2020 humanitarian crisis has 80% of its 24 million people in need of aid.

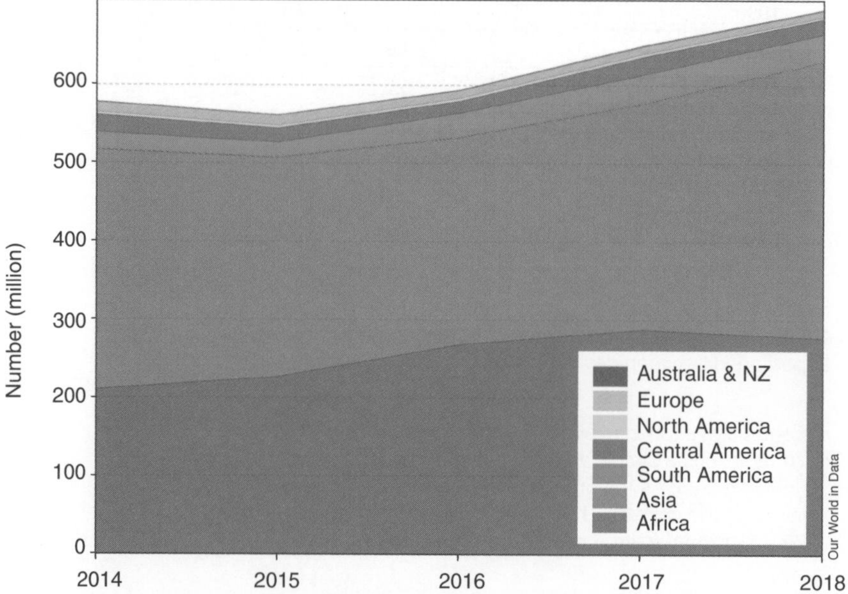

Food insecurity 2014-2018. This does not include the current food emergencies affecting Yemen, South Sudan, Somalia, Nigeria, and Ethiopia.

Slums are densely populated urban areas inhabited mainly by the impoverished. Around 33% of the urban population in the developing world live in slums like Kibera (Nairobi, Kenya) the largest urban slum in Africa. Lack of access to clean water and sanitation are major problems in slums.

Natural disasters such as floods and droughts can cause the displacement of thousands of people. Jakarta in Indonesia suffers frequent floods. The 2007 flood displaced half a million people and floods early in 2020 (above) displaced thousands. Disease outbreaks often follow floods.

Regional conflicts can cause the death and mass migration of thousands of people. The Syrian civil war coincided with one of the most intense droughts on record. 3.8 million Syrians have been made refugees and 10.9 million, or almost half the population, have been displaced.

1. Discuss some of the challenges facing the human population as it continues to grow. In your answer, consider which regions of the world will contribute to most of the projected increase in the human population:

ISBN: 978-1-98-856632-0

56 Demographic Transition

Key Question: What demographic changes occur as human populations move from developing to developed societies?

Human populations through time have undergone demographic shifts related to societal changes and economic development. The demographic transition model (DTM) was developed in 1929 to explain the transformation of countries from high birth rates and high death rates to low birth rates and low death rates as part of their economic development from a developing to a developed (post-industrial) economy. The original DTM recognized four stages, but more recently, as some nations enter a stage of sub-replacement fertility, a fifth stage has been proposed. Each stage of the transition reflects the changes in birth and death rates observed in human societies over the last 200 years. Most developed countries are beyond stage three of the model and the majority of developing countries are in stage two or stage three. The model was based on the changes seen in Europe, so these countries follow the DTM relatively well. Many developing countries have moved into stage three. The exceptions include some poor countries, mainly in sub-Saharan Africa and some Middle Eastern countries, which are affected by poverty, poor government policy, or civil strife.

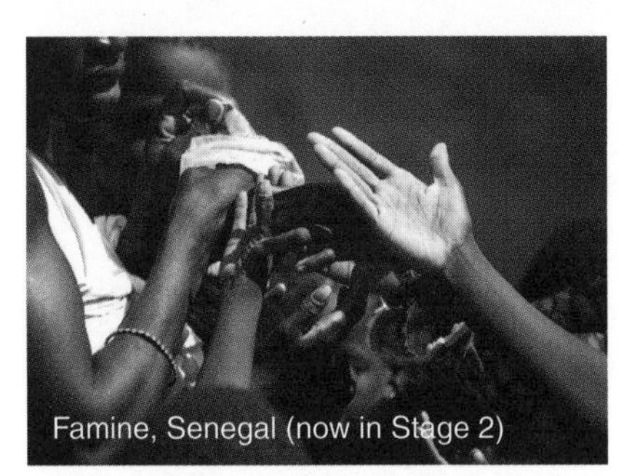

Stage 1: Birth and death rates are balanced but high as a result of starvation and disease.

Stage 2: Improvement in food supplies and public health result in reduced death rates and birth rates are high.

Stage 3 moves the population towards stability through a decline in the birth rate, as in this city in Malaysia.

Stage 4: Birth and death rates are both low and the total population is high and stable. Argentina is in Stage 4.

The demographic transition model

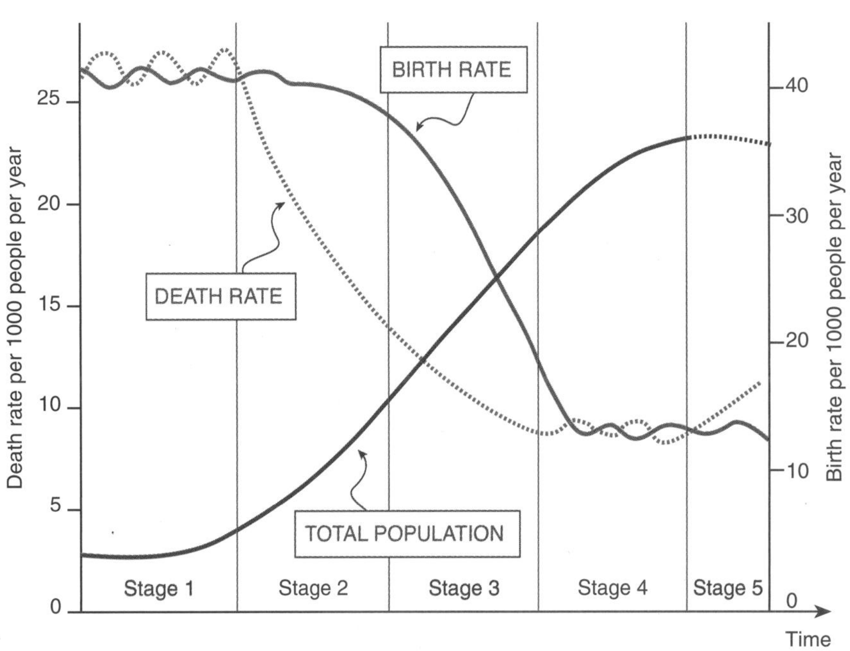

- **Stage 1 (high stationary)**: A balance between birth and death rates as was true of all populations until the late 18th century. Children are important contributors to the household economy. Losses as a result of starvation and disease are high. Population growth is typically very slow in this stage, because it is constrained by the available food supply. Unless the society develops new technologies to increase food production, any fluctuations in birth rates are quickly matched by death rates. Today there are no countries still in Stage 1.
- **Stage 2 (early expanding)**: Rapid population expansion as a result of high birth rates and a decline in death rates. The changes leading to this stage in Europe were initiated in the Agricultural Revolution of the 18th century but have been more rapid in developing countries since then. Stage 2 is associated with more reliable food supplies and improvements in public health. Countries in Stage 2 include much of Sub-Saharan Africa, Iraq, Nauru, and Yemen.
- **Stage 3 (late expanding)**: The population moves towards stability through a decline in the birth rate. This stage is associated with increasing urbanization and a decreased reliance on children as a source of family wealth. Low infant mortality allows women to have fewer children. Family planning in nations such as Malaysia (left) has been instrumental in their move to Stage 3.
- **Stage 4 (low stationary)**: Birth and death rates are both low and the total population is high and stable. The population ages and in some cases fertility is below replacement. Stage 4 of the DTM is viewed as an ideal placement for a country because total population growth is gradual. Examples of countries in Stage 4 of demographic transition are Argentina, Australia, Canada, China, Brazil, most of Europe, Singapore, South Korea, and the U.S.
- **Stage 5 (declining)**: This stage represents countries that have undergone the economic transition from manufacturing based industries into service and information based industries and the population reproduces well below replacement levels. Countries in Stage 5 include the United Kingdom, Germany, and Japan. Stage 5 models are largely theoretical because population outcomes can be heavily influenced by immigration.

ISBN: 978-1-98-856632-0

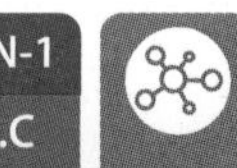

1. Each of the first four stages of the DTM is associated with a particular age structure. The diagrams below show structures for three of the five stages. They are not in order.

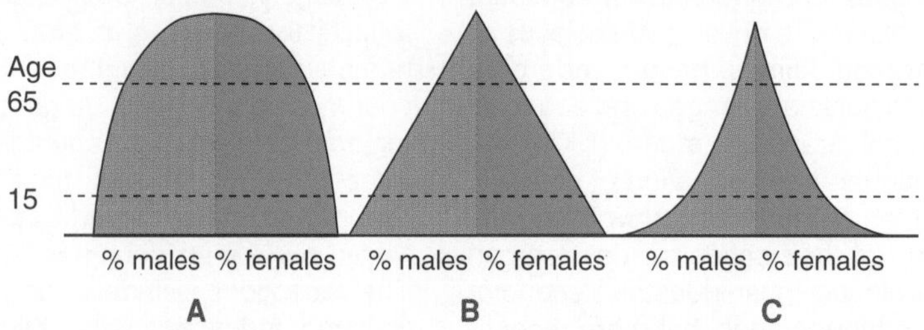

(a) Identify which of the diagrams corresponds to Stage 1 of the DTM and explain your choice:

(b) Identify which of the diagrams corresponds to Stage 3 of the DTM and explain your choice:

2. Suggest why it might become less important to have a large number of children in more economically developed nations:

3. Among births there is a slightly higher male birth rate than female birth rate (a ratio of about 1.1: 1). What effect does this have on the replacement birth rate (i.e. the number of births per female required to maintain a stable population).

4. Describe factors that might delay the demographic transition of some countries from Stage 2 to Stage 3:

5. In many countries, the government pays a benefit (superannuation) to retired citizens. In others, there is no government help for people who are elderly and cannot work, or are retired. Explain why both of these systems require a large population of younger workers and cannot be supported by declining populations where young people are the minority.

6. It might be expected that wealthy countries would have high birth rates because wealthy families can support more children. However this is not the pattern seen in most developed countries. Suggest some reasons why this might be so:

ISBN: 978-1-98-856632-0

57 Personal Progress Check

Answer the multiple choice questions that follow by circling the correct answer. Don't forget to read the question carefully!

1. The fertility of a population is defined as:
   (a) The reproductive capacity of the females
   (b) The number of individuals of each sex
   (c) The number of individuals born per unit time
   (d) The change in the total population per unit time

2. Which of the following is true of a specialist species:
   (a) Narrow niche, low risk of extinction
   (b) Broad niche, high risk of extinction
   (c) Narrow niche, high risk of extinction
   (d) Broad niche, low risk of extinction

3. The following are likely to be pioneer species in an ecological succession:
   (a) Specialists and *r*-selected species
   (b) Specialists and K-selected species
   (c) Generalists and K-selected species
   (d) Generalists and *r*-selected species

4. Which of the following is not true of K-selected species:
   (a) Population regulation is usually density independent
   (b) Population size tends to be stable over time.
   (c) Reproductive rate is slower
   (d) Population regulation is usually density dependent

5. A typical sequence of species succession in a primary succession is:
   (a) K-strategists > intermediate strategists > *r*-strategists
   (b) *r*-strategists > intermediate strategists > K-strategists
   (c) *r*-strategists > K-strategists > intermediate strategists
   (d) There is no typical pattern of species replacement

6. A Type I (late loss) survivorship is typical of:
   (a) *r*-selected organisms
   (b) Marine invertebrates
   (c) Rodents
   (d) K-selected organisms

7. An age structure diagram can provide information on:
   (a) The proportion of young in the population
   (b) Whether reproduction has been successful
   (c) Whether a population is increasing or decreasing
   (d) All of the above

8. Carrying capacity is defined as:
   (a) The maximum number of individuals an ecosystem can support indefinitely.
   (b) The maximum number of individuals an ecosystem can support for a brief period.
   (c) A measure of ecosystem quality.
   (d) A measure determining logistic growth.

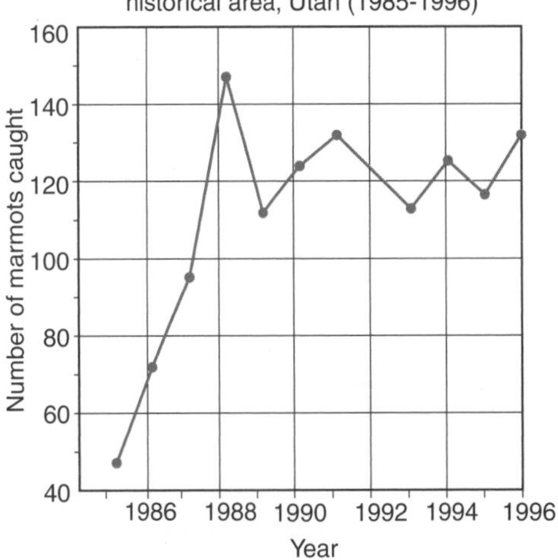

Question 9 refers to the graph above, which shows changes in a marmot population in Utah.

9. The graph indicates that:
   (a) The carrying capacity for this population is ~150 marmots.
   (b) The carrying capacity for this population has been increasing over time.
   (c) The carrying capacity for this population is ~120 marmots.
   (d) The ecosystem was not able to support this population of marmots.

10. An example of a density independent limiting factor is:
   (a) A decrease in water due to drought
   (b) The amount of available space
   (c) The amount of available food
   (d) The availability of mates

11. The equation for determining population growth is:
   (a) (B + E) + (D – I)
   (b) (B + D) – (I + E)
   (c) (B + I) – (D + E)
   (d) (B + I) + (D – E)

12. In a population in equilibrium:
   (a) (B + I) = (D + E)
   (b) (B + I) < (D + E)
   (c) (B + D) = (I + E)
   (d) (B + I) > (D + E)

ISBN: 978-1-98-856632-0

13. A population's growth rate is determined by births, deaths,
    (a) immigration, and emigration.
    (b) migration, and biotic potential.
    (c) immigration, and biotic potential.
    (d) immigration, and number of females.

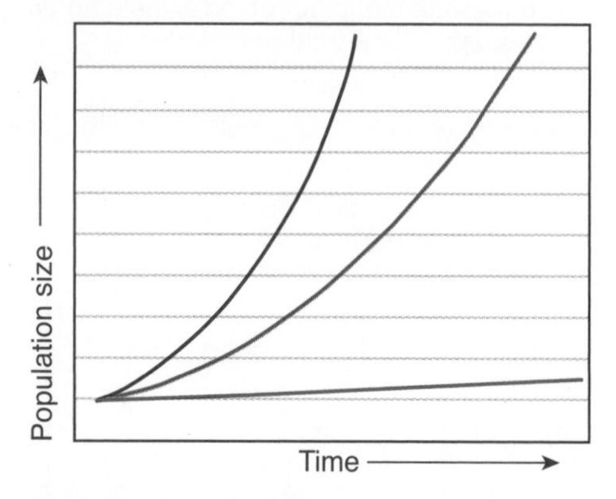

14. The plots above represent:
    (a) Logistic growth in species with different biotic potentials.
    (b) Exponential growth in species with different biotic potentials.
    (c) Logistic growth in species at different carrying capacities.
    (d) Exponential growth in species at different carrying capacities.

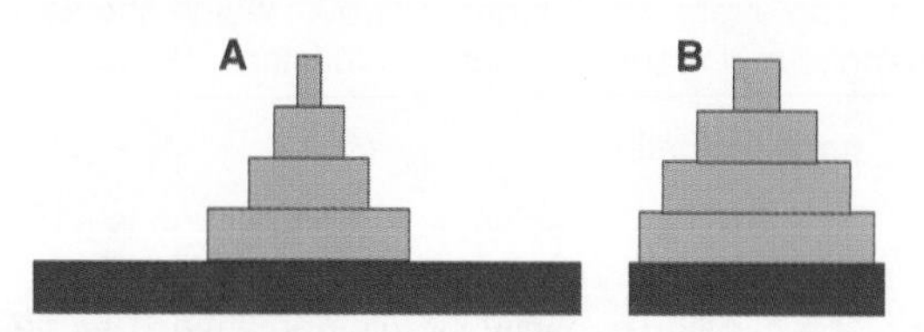

15. The diagrams above depict the age structure of two populations (A and B). The dark bars represent young individuals. Which statement is correct:
    (a) Population A is stable and population B is growing slowly.
    (b) Population A is expanding and population B is probably declining.
    (c) Population A is expanding rapidly and population B shows normal growth.
    (d) Population A is stable and population B is probably declining.

16. The rule of 70 is a simple way to approximate:
    (a) The number of years until a population will collapse.
    (b) Population growth rate
    (c) Population doubling time
    (d) None of the above

17. If a population of 10,000 is growing at 2% per year:
    (a) It will go extinct.
    (b) It will take 35 years to double.
    (c) It will take 140 years to double.
    (d) It will increase to 20,000 in 2 years.

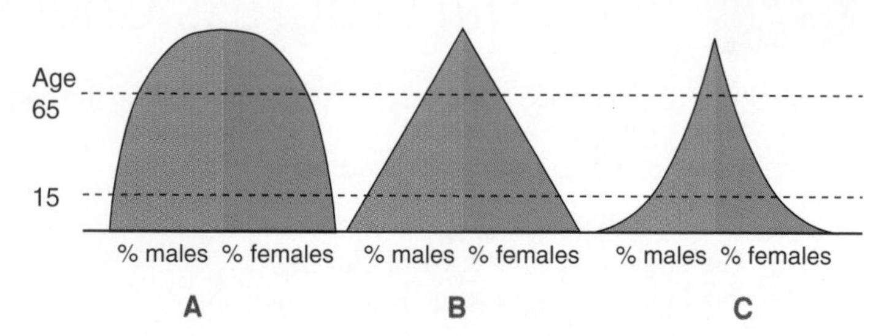

Questions 18 - 20 refer to the diagrams above:

18. In the Demographic Transition Model (DTM), diagram A represents:
    (a) Stage 1 of the DTM
    (b) Stage 2 of the DTM
    (c) Stage 3 of the DTM
    (d) Stage 4 of the DTM

19. In the Demographic Transition Model (DTM), diagram B represents:
    (a) Stage 1 of the DTM
    (b) Stage 2 of the DTM
    (c) Stage 3 of the DTM
    (d) Stage 4 of the DTM

20. A life table provides information that:
    (a) Gives a picture of a population's mortality and survival.
    (b) An indication of which age classes suffer the highest mortality in a population.
    (c) Allows prediction of population growth.
    (d) All of the above.

21. The region(s) projected to account for most of the global increase in the human population to 2100 are:
    (a) Africa
    (b) Asia
    (c) Africa and Asia
    (d) Latin America

22. The decline in global human fertility is the result of:
    (a) Better education for women
    (b) Aging populations and lower child mortality
    (c) Demographic transition
    (d) All of the above

23. A proposed stage 5 in demographic transition is characterized by:
    (a) High mortality
    (b) Sub-replacement fertility
    (c) Low population numbers
    (d) All of the above

24. Density-dependent regulation of populations:
    (a) Involves negative feedback
    (b) Operates through changing birth or death rates
    (c) Is important for populations near carrying capacity
    (d) All of the above

ISBN: 978-1-98-856632-0

Management of sea otter population recovery in Washington state

The data below documents aspects of sea otter population dynamics along the coast of Washington State, where the endangered sea otter has been reintroduced after populations became locally extinct following hunting (see activity 38). The populations along the coast of the US Pacific Northwest are closely monitored, but recovery of populations has not been uniform and the dynamics of the recovering populations are variable. What researchers have found is that the sea otter "population" is not one uniform population. Sea otters have small home ranges and limited dispersal and their populations are regulated locally because of variations in their sea urchin prey and high site fidelity in females (they return to a previously occupied place). There are no viable estimates of carrying capacity and regulating factors vary among sub-populations. Peripheral populations, which are near the outer boundary of the geographic range and often isolated from the central population, suffer high mortality from shark bites. In the center of the range, food supplies have been boosted by a recent increase in sea urchins. Fig. 1 is a schematic showing how populations are in different demographic stages. Black circles represent relative densities. Fig. 2 shows how population trends vary between three subpopulations on the Washington coast.

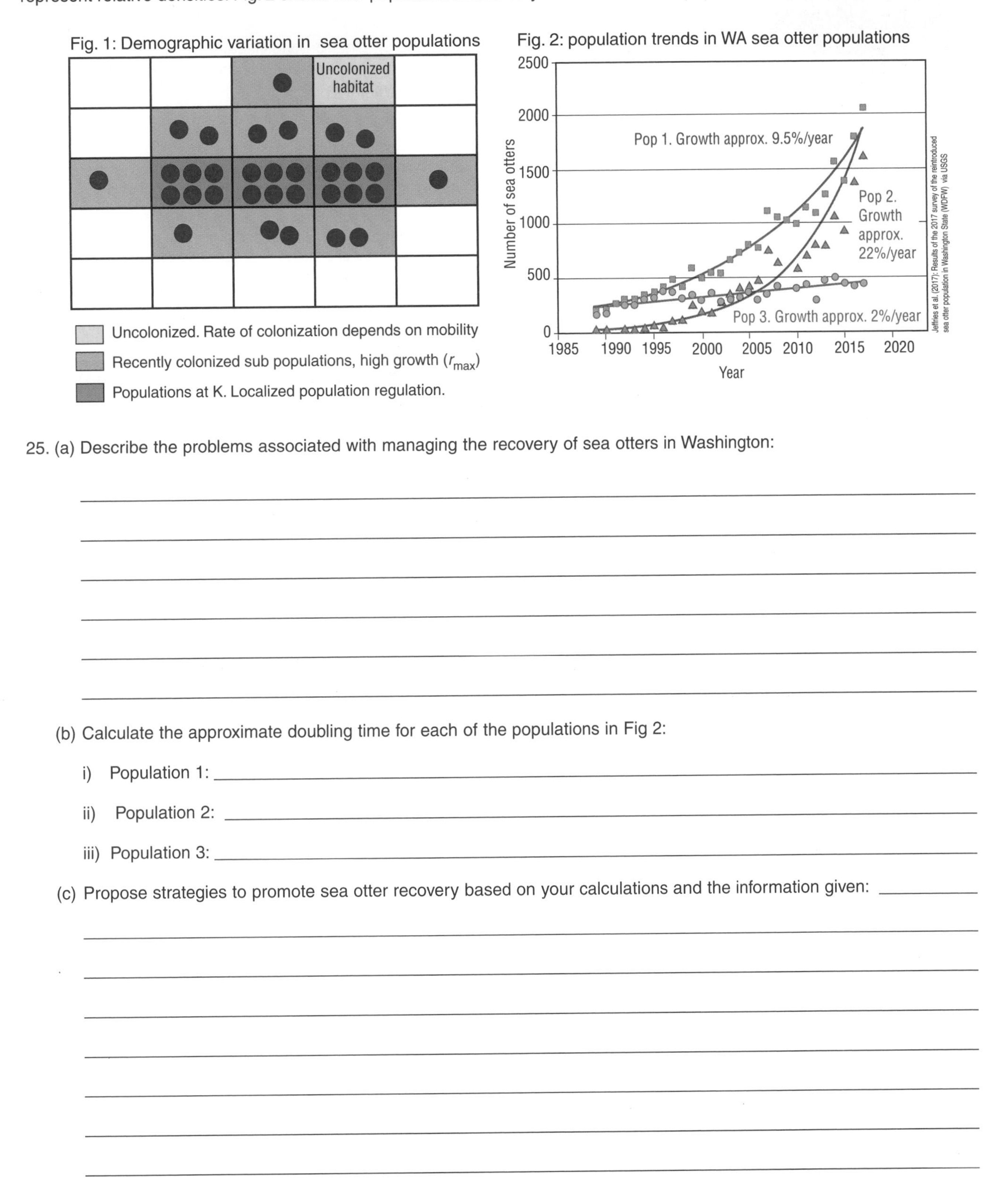

25. (a) Describe the problems associated with managing the recovery of sea otters in Washington:

(b) Calculate the approximate doubling time for each of the populations in Fig 2:

i) Population 1:

ii) Population 2:

iii) Population 3:

(c) Propose strategies to promote sea otter recovery based on your calculations and the information given:

ISBN: 978-1-98-856632-0

4. Earth Systems and Resources

Developing understanding

Content: This unit explores Earth systems and the resources that support life, including the geological changes that occur at the boundaries of tectonic plates, the geological structures that result from these changes, soil, the atmosphere, and the role of the Sun's energy in the Earth's climate systems.

Skills: This unit emphasizes skills in analyzing and interpreting visual models and representations of Earth processes. Through analysis and interpretation you will develop an ability to explain relationships between Earth systems.

4.1 Plate tectonics .... activities 58 - 61

☐ 1. Describe the basic structure of the Earth and relate its internal structure and composition to the processes that we see occurring at the Earth's surface.

☐ 2. Describe the geological changes and events occurring at different types of plate boundaries. Include reference to convergent boundaries, divergent boundaries, and transform boundaries. Describe the geological features associated with each of these types of boundary and their characteristics.

☐ 3. Explain how the theory of plate tectonics accounts for plate movement. Use maps showing the global distribution of plate boundaries to determine the location of volcanoes, island arcs, earthquakes, hotspots, and faults. Interpret data from active plate boundaries to visualize plate movements and explain the events occurring there, including earthquakes and volcanoes.

4.2 Soil formation and erosion .... activities 62 - 64

☐ 4. Describe the characteristics and formation of soil. Explain how soils are categorized by horizons based on their composition and organic material. Discuss the influence of the parent rock type and climate on soil type.

☐ 5. Explain how soils can be eroded by wind or water. Describe feedback mechanisms operating in the loss of soil and explain the role of riparian vegetation in reducing soil loss and maintaining high water quality.

4.3 Soil composition and properties .... activity 65

☐ 6. Describe similarities and differences in the properties of different soil types. These properties include water holding capacity, which (in turn) is influenced by particle size and composition. Explain how the properties of a soil affect soil productivity and fertility.

☐ 7. Use a soil texture triangle to identify and compare soil types based on their percentage of clay, silt, and sand.

4.4 Earth's atmosphere .... activity 66

☐ 8. Describe the structure and composition of the Earth's atmosphere, including the relative abundance of the major gases. Identify the layers of the atmosphere and describe the basis for how they are determined.

4.5 Global wind patterns .... activity 67

☐ 9. Explain the causes of the Earth's patterns of atmospheric circulation, including reference to the differential heating of the atmosphere and the rotation of the Earth itself. Describe the Coriolis effect and explain its cause. Use the tricellular model to describe patterns of atmospheric circulation and explain global climate patterns.

4.6 Watersheds .... activity 68

☐ 10. Explain what is meant by a watershed (also called a catchment or drainage basin). Identify the characteristics used to describe watersheds. Describe how these characteristics vary and explain their role in shaping the drainage system and the water it carries. Explain the different scales at which we can identify watersheds and describe the characteristics of different watersheds using maps and photographs.

4.7 Solar radiation & the seasons ...... activities 69 - 70

☐ 11. Identify the Earth's main source of energy. Describe how the amount of insolation depends on season and latitude.

☐ 12. Describe the relationship between the angle of the Sun's rays and the intensity of solar radiation. Explain how this relationship accounts for the differences in the solar radiation received per unit area between the equator and the poles. Investigate this for yourself using a flashlight angled to illuminate graph paper. Recall that it is the difference in solar energy received at different latitudes that drives atmospheric circulation.

☐ 13. Using illustrations or diagrams, explain the cause of the Earth's seasons. Explain why the daylight hours and the solar radiation received at a particular location on the Earth's surface vary with the seasons.

4.8 Earth's geography and climate .... activity 71

☐ 14. Most of the Earth's atmospheric processes are driven by input of energy from the Sun but weather and climate are also affected by geological and geographic factors. Describe some of these influences, including the occurrence of rain shadows and the effect of ocean currents on the weather and climate of coastal regions.

4.9 El Niño and La Niña .... activity 72

☐ 15. El Niño and La Niña are phenomena associated with changing ocean surface temperatures in the Pacific Ocean. They are part of a larger phenomenon called the El Niño-Southern Oscillation (ENSO). El Niño and La Niña are considered the ocean part of ENSO, while the Southern Oscillation is its atmospheric changes. Describe the environmental changes and effects that result from El Niño and La Niña events, including global changes to rainfall, wind, and patterns of ocean temperature and circulation.

☐ 16. Interpret diagrams of El Niño and La Niña climate cycles to account for the contrasting effects of ENSO on different geographic locations.

58 The Structure of the Earth

Key Question: What is the internal structure of the Earth? The Earth has five main layers. These are organized based on density. The most dense materials are at the center, whereas the least dense materials make up the outer layer.

Crust: Between 5 and 70 km thick. Density about 3 g/cm^3. Divided into seven large tectonic plates and a number of smaller ones.

Upper mantle: Solid layer about 400 km thick with a transition layer between the upper and lower mantle of about 300 km. The temperature reaches about 1000°C.

Lower mantle: Approximately 2000 km thick, extending to about 3000 km below the surface. Like the upper mantle it is solid but behaves like a viscous liquid with convection currents and mantle plumes slowly moving the mantle material about.

Inner core: Solid. The temperature at the core is between 5500°C and 6000°C. The core is made of mostly iron and nickel and is about 1200 km in diameter. The density of the core is about 12 g/cm^3.

Outer core: Liquid. The movement of the outer core acts like a dynamo, an electric generator, and produces Earth's magnetic field. Made mostly of iron and nickel the outer core is 2200 km thick and reaches 4000°C.

Evidence for the Earth's structure comes from many different sources. One is the timing of seismic waves produced by earthquakes. Evidence from these waves shows that the outer core must be liquid.

The Earth's magnetic field also indicates the outer core is liquid and surrounds a solid iron/nickel inner core. Evidence from magnetic minerals shows the magnetic field reverses polarity every few million years.

The Earth is geologically active due to the residual heat from its formation. This heat causes mantle movements which move the crustal plates about, resulting in earthquakes and mountain building.

1. Why does the Earth have different internal layers? the difference in density & properties of the Earths materials forms different internal layers

2. Identify whether each of the following is liquid or solid:

   (a) Mantle: solid (b) Outer core liquid (c) Inner core solid

3. What produces the Earth's magnetic field? Movement of the outer core produces the Earths magnetic field

ISBN: 978-1-98-856632-0

59 Plate Boundaries

Key Question: What is the evidence for tectonic plates and what happens where they meet?

The Earth's crust is broken up into seven large, continent-sized tectonic plates and about a dozen smaller plates. Evidence of these plates can be seen in many places around the Earth, but some of the best evidence is found on the seabed. The tectonic plates meet at plate boundaries. The characteristics of the boundaries are determined by the direction the meeting plates are moving and the type of geological material the plates are made of.

Volcanoes and earthquakes

- The Pacific rim is a very geologically active area. By mapping the areas of geological activity we can identify the edges of the Pacific plate. The maps below show the location of volcanoes and earthquakes. These appear to be located in specific locations.

Major earthquakes in the Pacific

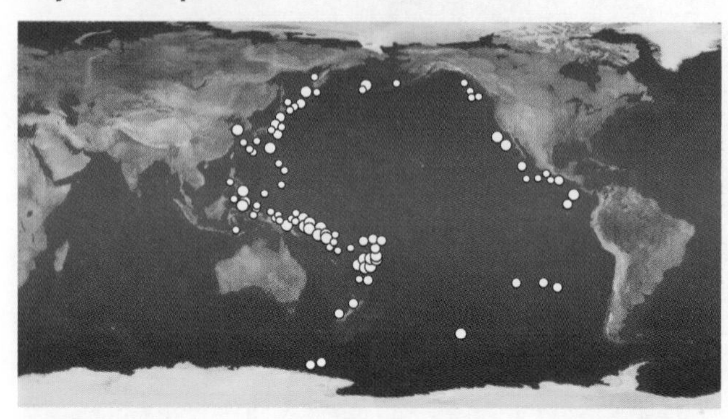

Volcanoes around the Pacific

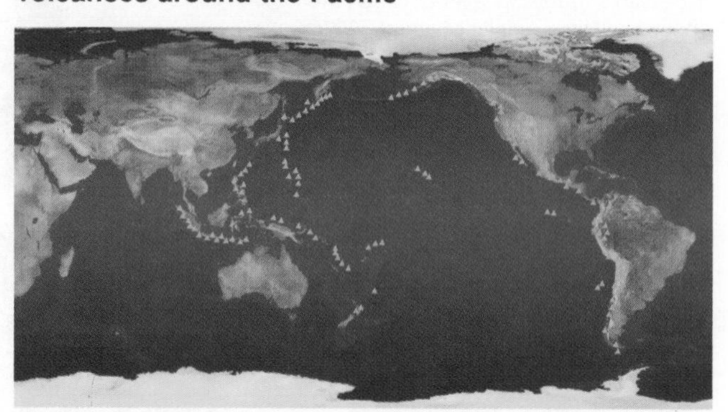

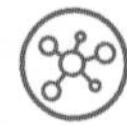

On the land

- Some areas on land show dramatic geological formations related to the movement of the land. At these formations, the movement of the land on one side of the formation is often quite different from the movement on the other side of the formation.

1. (a) The San Andreas fault line runs for about 1300 km through California. The data below and on the next page are from two GPS tracking stations, one on each side of the fault line. Station P284 is west of the fault. Station P294 is east of the fault. The data shows the total movement of the fault north (positive) or south (negative), and west (positive) or east (negative) from a reference point (0, set when the data tracking began). Plot the movement for the data from each tracking station. Include a key to distinguish N-S and E-W movements.

Station P284 west of San Andreas fault

Time period	Date	Movement north/south (mm)	Movement east/west (mm)
1	7/02/05	0	0
2	7/07/05	12.78	13
3	7/02/06	31.91	27.32
4	7/07/06	44.33	39.29
5	7/02/07	63.94	55.27
6	7/07/07	77.55	67.17
7	7/02/08	99.89	80.53
8	7/07/08	109.83	91.48
9	7/02/09	127.89	109.68
10	7/07/09	141.56	120.05
11	7/02/10	163.07	132.05
12	7/06/10	174.51	142.61
13	7/10/10	184.36	152.82
14	7/02/11	195.95	160.41
15	7/06/11	206.39	168.7
16	7/10/11	217.56	179.58
17	7/02/12	228.12	187.3
18	7/06/12	239.15	196.56
19	7/10/12	249.89	206.52
20	7/02/13	259.55	215.35

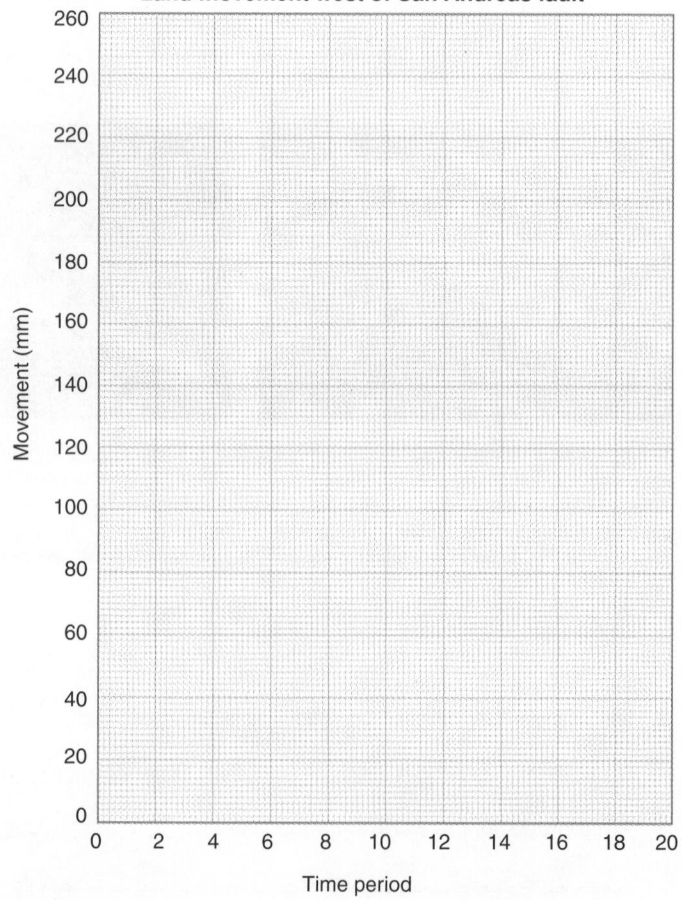

ISBN: 978-1-98-856632-0

Station P294 east of San Andreas fault

Time period	Date	Movement north/south (mm)	Movement east/west (mm)
1	18/05/06	0	0
2	18/11/06	5.73	4.22
3	18/05/07	12.09	9.32
4	18/11/07	18.4	13.47
5	18/05/08	24.83	16.87
6	18/11/08	31.92	21.54
7	18/05/09	38.77	25.85
8	18/11/09	44.88	29.44
9	18/05/10	51.86	33.01
10	18/11/10	59.04	38.08
11	18/05/11	66.02	44.11
12	18/11/11	72.45	48.23
13	18/05/12	79.31	49.6
14	18/11/12	81.14	53.45
15	18/05/13	92.13	59.07
16	18/11/13	99.63	62.69
17	18/05/14	107.92	68.23
18	18/11/14	115.01	72.44
19	18/05/15	122.76	77.47
20	18/11/15	129.36	82.29

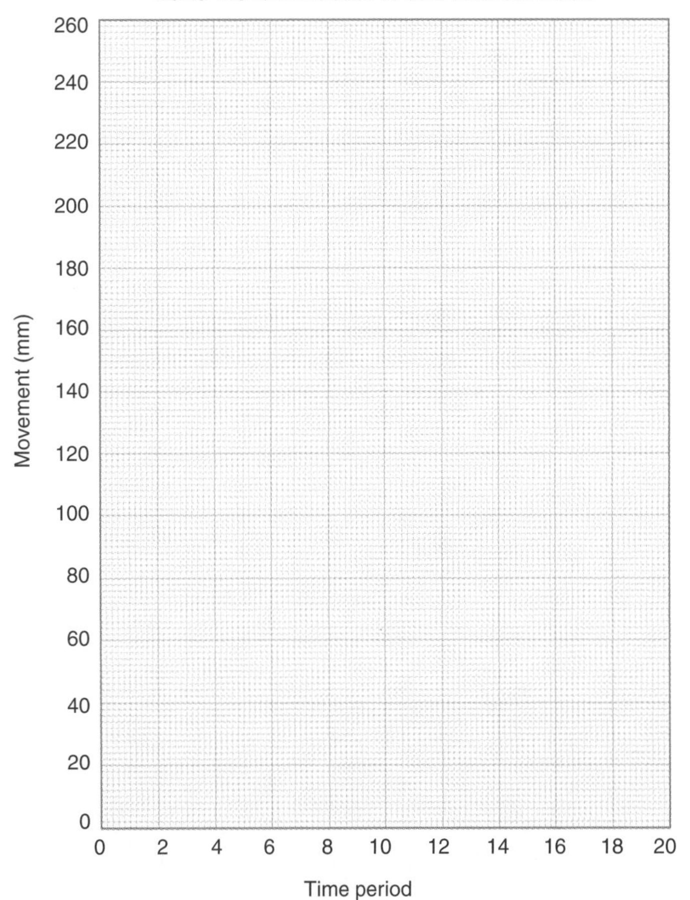

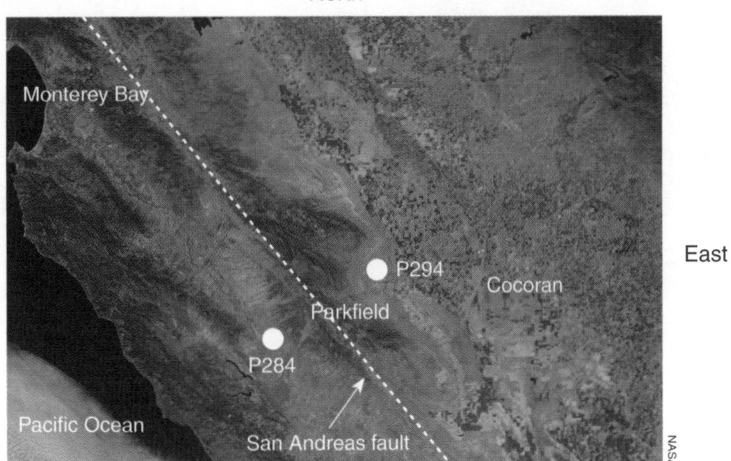

(b) What is the direction of movement of the land at station P284? NW

(c) What is the direction of the movement of the land at station P294? NW

(d) In terms of relative movement (i.e. one side of the fault compared with the other) what is the movement of the land in the west compared to the east?

(e) The San Andreas fault is the boundary between the North American plate and the Pacific plate. It is a **transform boundary**. From the information above, define the term *transform boundary*:

Where meeting plates slide past each other

ISBN: 978-1-98-856632-0

Plate boundaries

- Plate boundaries are marked by well-defined zones of seismic and volcanic activity. Plate growth occurs at **divergent boundaries** along sea floor spreading ridges (e.g. the Mid-Atlantic Ridge and the Red Sea) whereas plate attrition (decrease) occurs at **convergent boundaries** marked by deep ocean trenches and subduction zones. Divergent and convergent zones make up approximately 80% of plate boundaries. The remaining 20% are called **transform boundaries**, where two plates slide past one another with no significant change in the size of either plate.

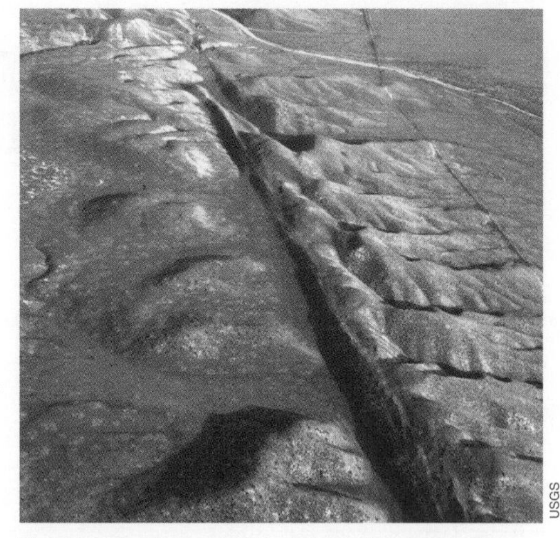

The San Andreas Fault is a transform boundary running for over 1300 km through California.

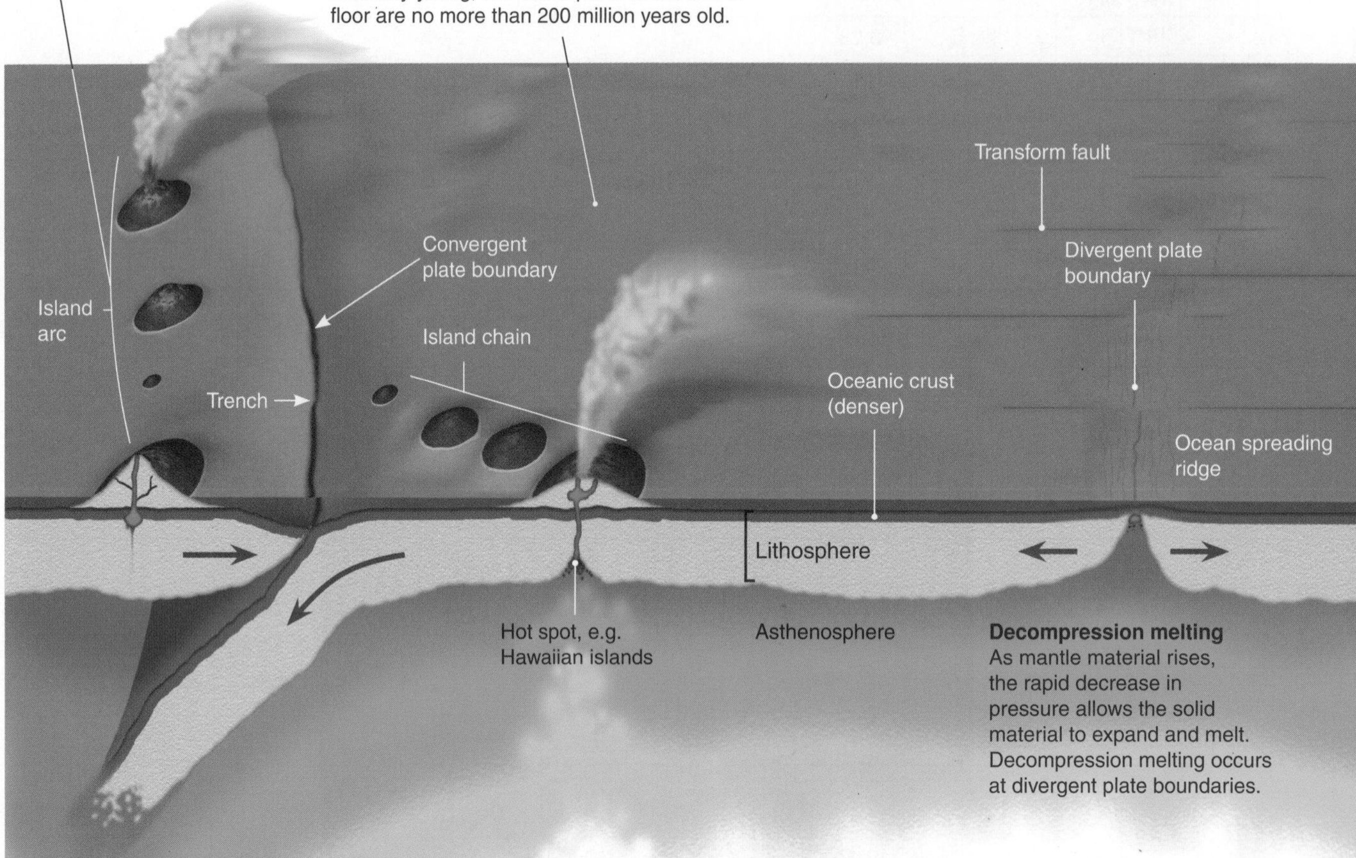

2. Describe what is happening at each of the following plate boundaries and identify an example in each case:

(a) Convergent plate boundary: plate boundaries move towards each other. Convergence of continental & oceanic form volcanoes. Convergence of continentals form mountains

(b) Divergent plate boundary: Plate boundaries are moving away from each other

(c) Transform plate boundary: Move past each other

ISBN: 978-1-98-856632-0

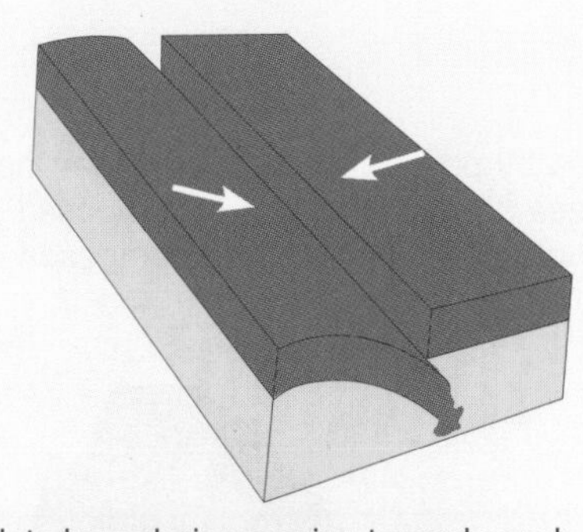

Plate boundaries moving towards each other are called **convergent plate boundaries**. Where oceanic crust and continental crust meet, the denser oceanic crust will travel under the continental crust, creating a subduction zone. Volcanoes form along the continental border of a subduction zone. When continental crusts collide, huge mountain ranges such as the Himalayas can form.

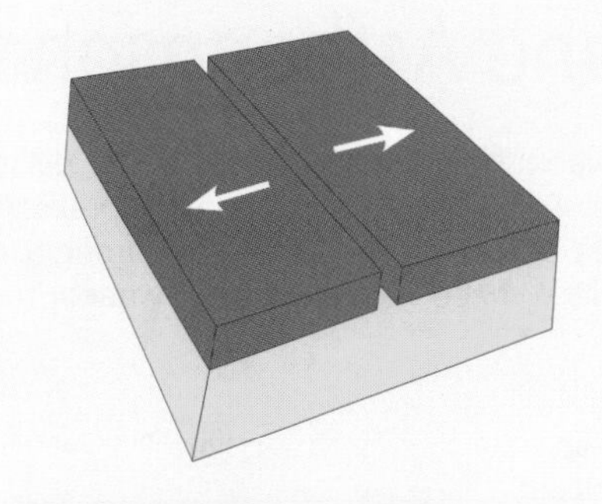

Divergent plate boundaries form where the tectonic plates are moving away from each other. These are commonly found along the mid ocean ridges, but occasionally are seen on land, as in the Great Rift Valley and Iceland. Divergent boundaries are also known as constructive boundaries as they produce new crust from the upwelling of magma.

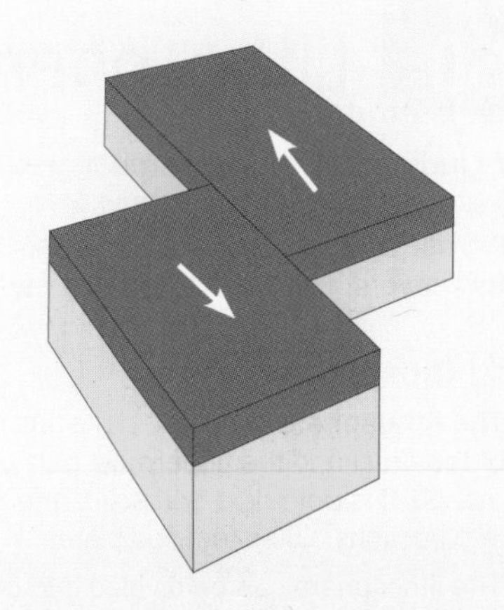

Transform boundaries are formed when the tectonic plates are moving past each other. Crust is neither formed nor destroyed. Examples include the San Andreas Fault in California and the Alpine Fault in New Zealand.

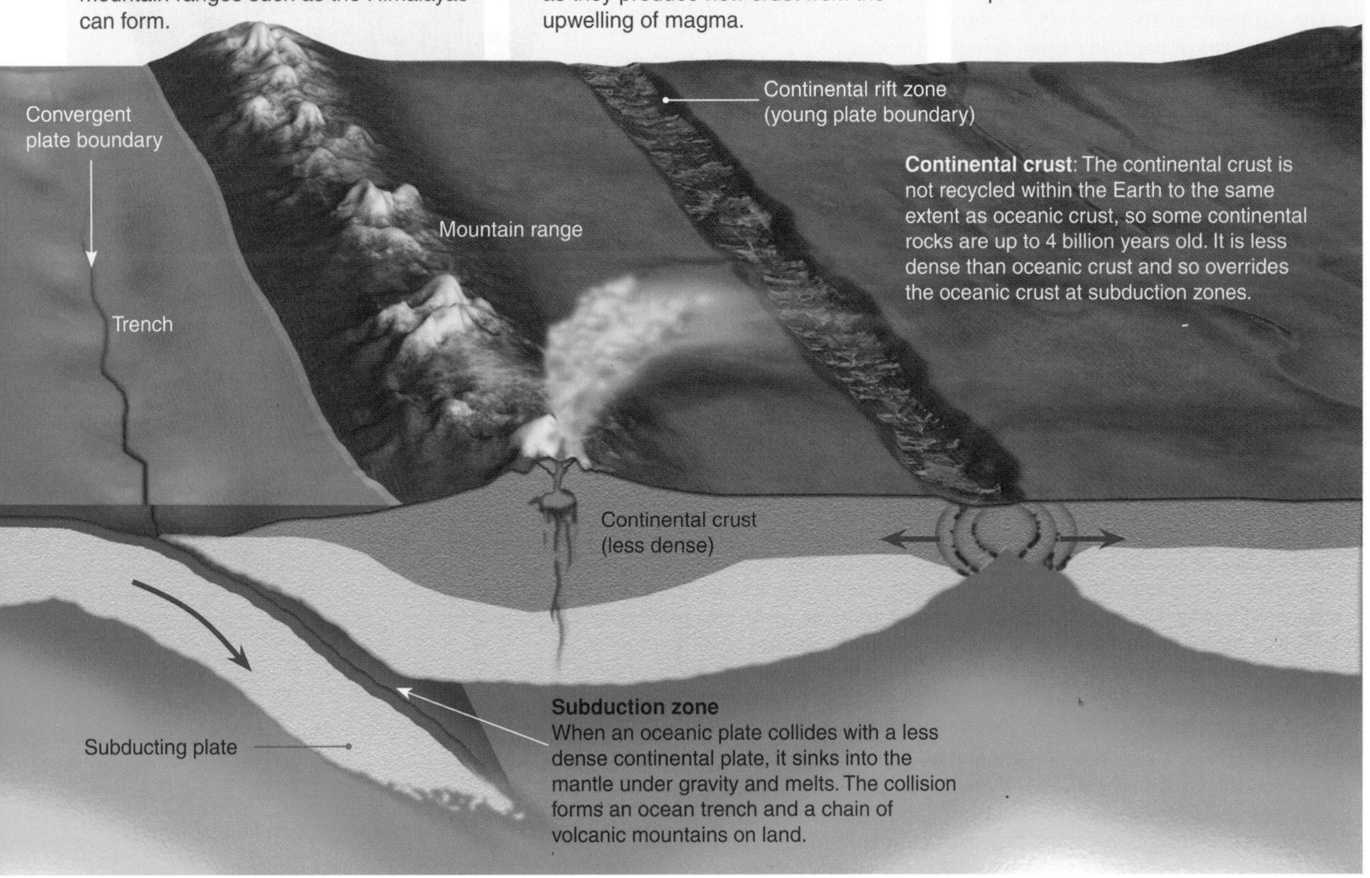

3. Identify the type of plate boundary at which each of the following occurs:

(a) Mountain building: Convergent (c) Creation of new ocean floor: Divergent

(b) Subduction: Convergent (d) Island arc: Convergent

4. Use the information represented visually above to:

(a) Explain why the oceanic crust subducts under the continental crust in a subduction zone: Oceanic crust is more dense

(b) What causes volcanoes to form along the continental plate boundary of a subduction zone? ____________

ISBN: 978-1-98-856632-0

60 Lithosphere and Asthenosphere

Key Question: How do we distinguish between the different layers of the Earth?

The crust and the upper part of the mantle are chemically distinct layers. However there are layers within these layers that can be distinguished by physical properties rather than chemical properties. These are the lithosphere, composed of cooler, stronger rocks, and the asthenosphere composed of hotter, weaker rocks.

The lithosphere

- The **lithosphere** (*lithos* = "stone") is made up of the crust and the uppermost part of the upper mantle. It is both rigid and solid, and broken up into sections called tectonic plates.
- The lithosphere can be divided into continental lithosphere, which contains relatively light minerals, and oceanic lithosphere, which contains much denser minerals. The lithosphere ranges from 400 km thick over the continents to 70 km thick in the oceans.

The asthenosphere

- The **asthenosphere** (*asthenes* = "weak") lies below the lithosphere. This layer of rock is viscous and plastic (semi-fluid) in its behavior. It changes through plastic deformation, slowly moving about and so allowing for movement of the tectonic plates above.
- The asthenosphere is relatively thin, around 100 km thick. The boundary between the lithosphere and asthenosphere is thermal. The lithosphere conducts heat out to the surface whereas the asthenosphere retains its heat.

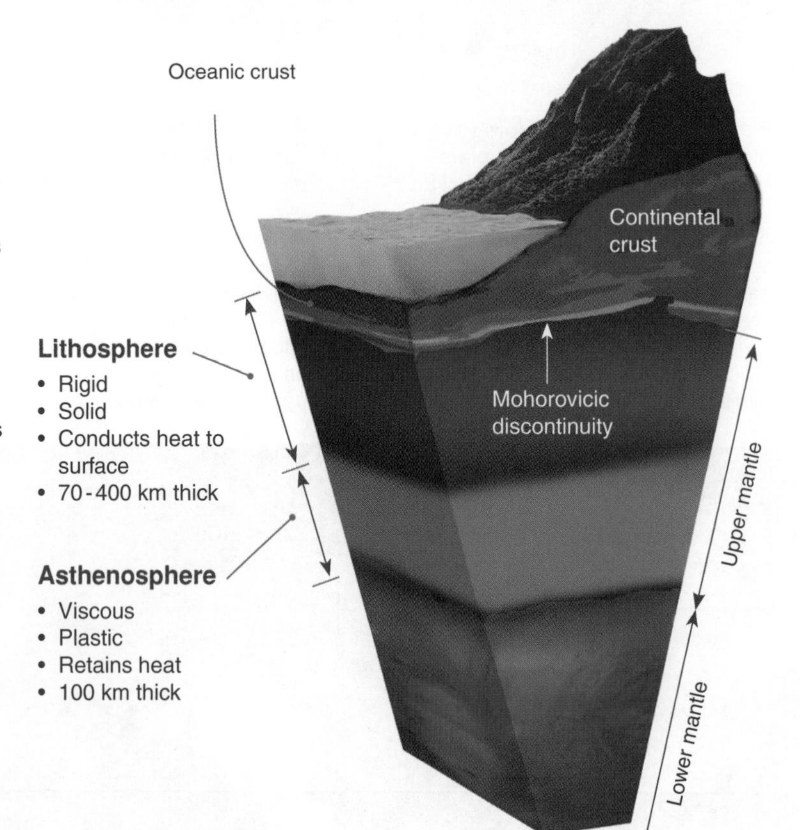

How do we know?

- The Mohorovicic discontinuity marks the boundary between the crust and the mantle. It was discovered by Andrija Mohorovicic in 1909 while he was studying seismic waves from an earthquake near Zargreb, Croatia. Mohorovicic noticed that the seismographs 200 km or more away from the earthquake epicenter were reading the seismic waves as arriving earlier that he expected. He realized that this was because the waves were traveling through a denser layer of material and so speeding up, arriving earlier than if they traveled through material that was of uniform density. Because this change in speed happened at a specific distance from the epicenter, the change in material must have been very sudden.
- The lithosphere - asthenosphere boundary can also be detected by measuring seismic waves. In a recent experiment in New Zealand, geologists exploded charges of TNT to produce ground waves and measured their echoes. This revealed the lithosphere-asthenosphere boundary is a thin jelly-like layer of rock.

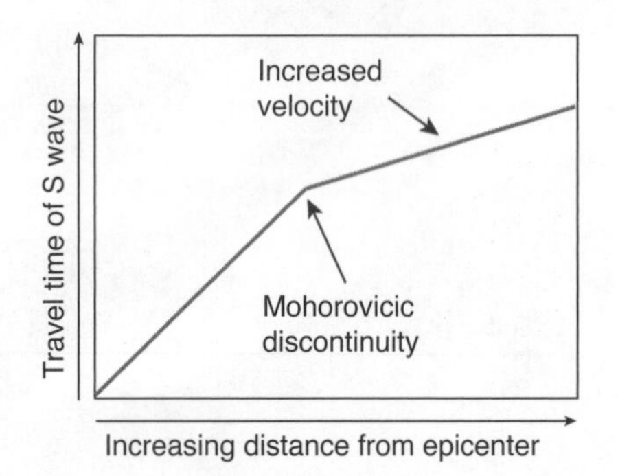

1. (a) Describe the structure of the lithosphere: Made up of crust & upper mantle, Solid & rigid & divided up into tectonic plates

   (b) Describe the structure of the asthenosphere: Below lithosphere, it is solid & viscous making it move slowly

2. Describe the general method that scientists use to study the interior of the Earth: Scientists study the speed of seismic waves

ISBN: 978-1-98-856632-0

61 Plate Tectonics

Key Question: How does the theory of plate tectonics explain plate movement?

Evidence from earthquakes, volcanoes, and land formations has helped formulate the theory of plate tectonics, which describes the large scale movement of the Earth's crustal plates. The key principle of the theory is that the rigid plates are able to ride on the fluid-like underlying asthenosphere. The energy for this movement comes from dissipation of heat from the mantle. It is the movement of the plates that produces phenomena such as earthquakes and volcanism.

Subduction zones

- The lowest points on the Earth's surface are in the ocean trenches. The Mariana Trench is the deepest of these trenches at 10,994 meters below sea level, an area called Challenger Deep. The Mariana Trench is located east of Guam in the Western Pacific. Humans first reached Challenger Deep in 1960.
- Many ocean trenches are found at the edges of plate boundaries where the part of the Earth's crust is sinking down into the mantle. Because of this, these boundaries are also destructive plate boundaries.
- Earthquakes can be used to map these boundaries and provide evidence for the type of plate movement there.

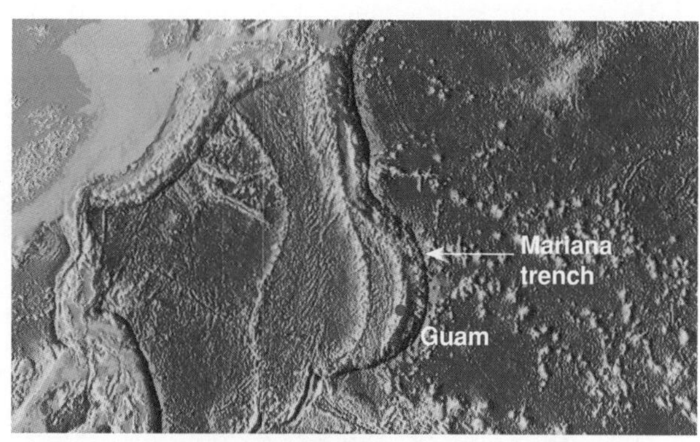

1. The data below shows earthquake depths recorded at the Tonga Trench in the western Pacific Ocean.
   (a) Plot a scatter graph of the data on the grid provided:

Tonga trench	
Longitude (°W)	Depth (km)
176.2	270
175.8	115
175.7	260
175.4	250
176.0	160
173.9	60
174.9	50
179.2	650
173.8	50
177.0	350
178.8	580
177.4	420
178.0	520
177.7	560
177.7	465
179.2	670
175.1	40
176.0	220

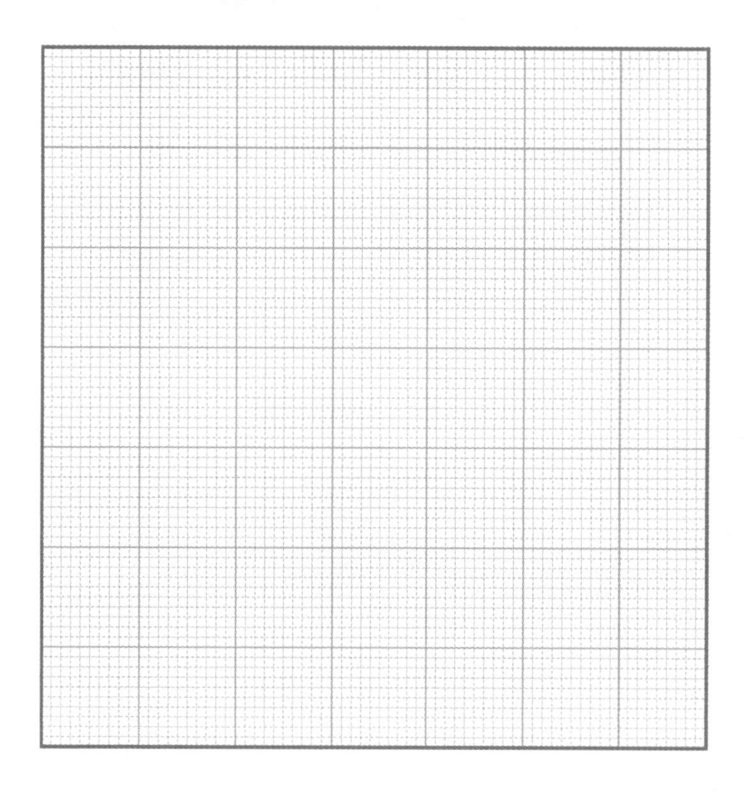

   (b) Add a line of best fit through the data points:

   (c) Draw a diagram below to show how the tectonic plates are moving at the Tonga Trench. Include relevant labels:

ISBN: 978-1-98-856632-0

Plate movement

- The Hawaiian islands are well known for their volcanic activity. A fissure of the Kilauea volcano on Hawai'i (Big Island) erupted on May 3, 2018. Huge flows of lava swept towards the coast, destroying many homes along the way. Kilauea has been in an almost continuous state of eruption since 1983.
- Volcanic activity becomes less on other islands the further away you travel from Big Island.
- Images of the islands taken by satellite show a chain of islands and seamounts that are the remains of ancient volcanoes. The oldest are in the north-west, the youngest in the south-east. Only the islands at the south-east end of the chain are still volcanically active.

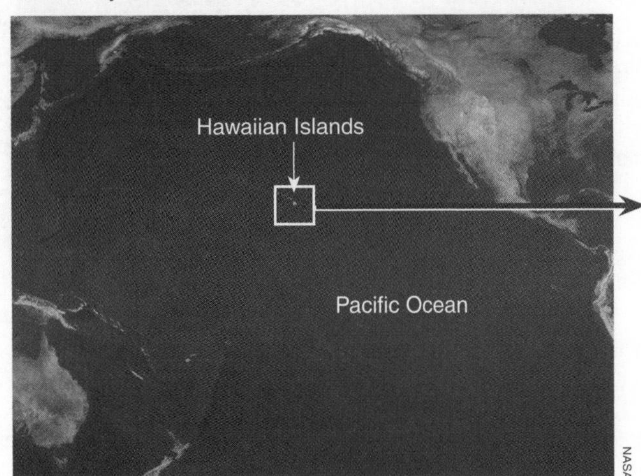

2. (a) Use the information below to produce a graph of the **age of the volcanoes** in the Hawaiian island chain compared to their **distance from the Kilauea volcano** on Big island.

Name	Distance from Kilauea (km)	Age (millions of years)
Kilauea	0	0
Mauna Kea	54	0.375
Kohala	100	0.43
East Maui	182	0.75
West Maui	220	1.32
East Molokai	256	1.76
West Molokai	280	1.9
Koolau	339	2.6
Waianae	374	3.7
Kauai	519	5.1
Nihoa	780	7.2
Necker	1058	10.3

(b) Use the data to calculate the rate of the movement of the Hawaiian island chain:

(c) You have seen that the plates of the Earth's crust move about. The Hawaiian islands are in the middle of the Pacific, away from any plate boundaries. How might the volcanic activity seen on them be explained?

3. Recall what you know about the Earth's interior. How might this explain the information above and on the previous page?

ISBN: 978-1-98-856632-0

The tectonic plates

- The map below shows the boundaries of the Earth's tectonic plates and the direction the plates are moving. Plate tectonics is a relatively recent scientific theory. In 1912, Alfred Wegener described what he called continental drift and cited evidence such as the matching of the coast lines of South America and Africa. It wasn't until the 1960s that plate tectonics was accepted after sonar and magnetic surveys of the seafloor revealed plate boundaries and areas of sea floor spreading. There is still debate over exactly where some of the boundaries are or whether a plate exists or is simply a fault on a larger plate.

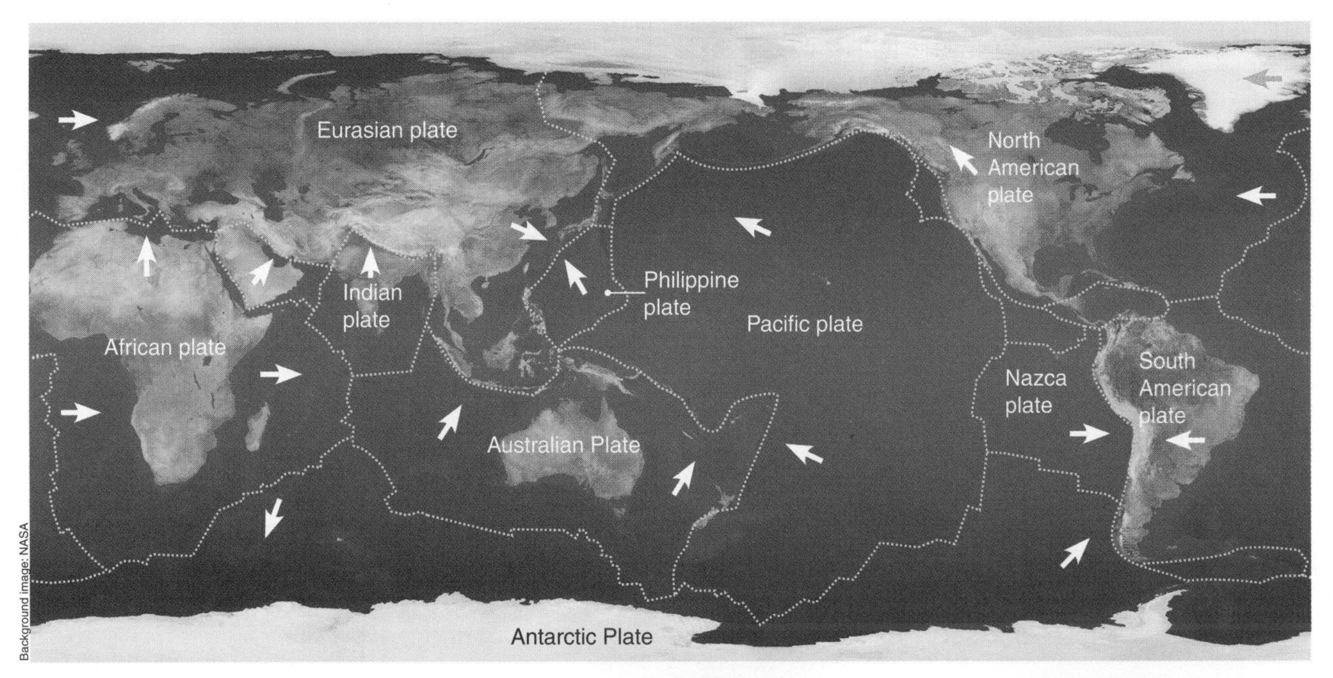

- The evidence for past plate movements comes from several sources:
  - mapping of plate boundaries,
  - the discovery of sea floor spreading,
  - measurement of the direction and rate of plate movement,
  - geological evidence such as the distribution of ancient mountain chains, unusual deposits, and fossils.
- The size of the plates is constantly changing, with some expanding and some getting smaller. The extent of the tectonic plates is shown in the diagram above and right. The Pacific plate is by far the largest, measuring 103 million km^2.

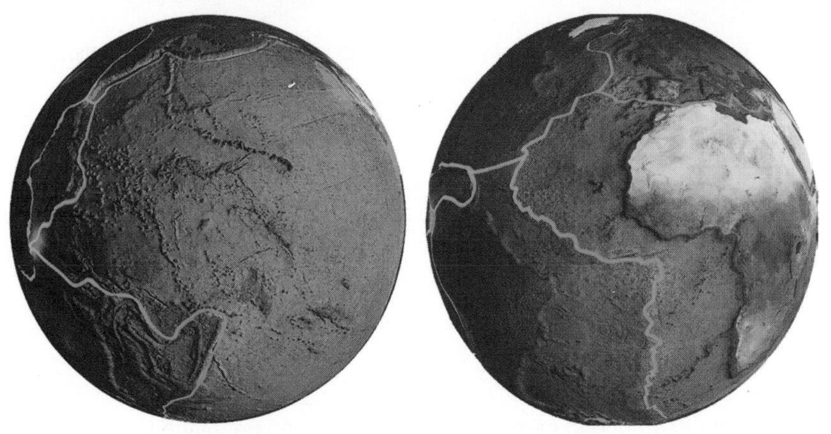

4. The diagram right shows the Pacific plate and the Nazca plate. The white dotted line shows the location of the plate boundaries. The red dotted line shows the location of subduction zones along those boundaries.

   Compare this diagram with the earlier diagrams of volcanoes and earthquakes. What do you notice?

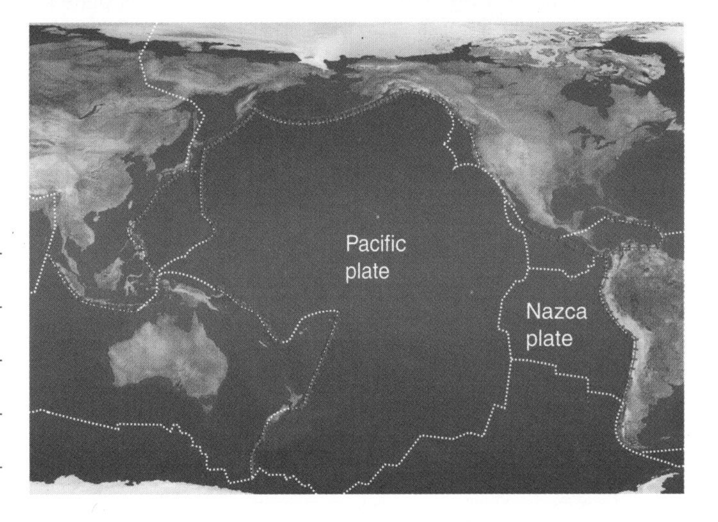

5. On the globes above, label the plates (or parts of plates) shown:

ISBN: 978-1-98-856632-0

The mechanism of plate movement

- The relatively cool **lithosphere** overlies the hotter, plastic and more fluid **asthenosphere**. Heat from the mantle drives two kinds of asthenospheric movement: **convection** and **mantle plumes**. Plate motion is partly driven by the weight of cold, dense plates sinking into the mantle at trenches (subduction zones). This heavier, cooler material sinking under the influence of gravity displaces heated material, which rises as mantle plumes.
- The movements of the tectonic plates puts the brittle rock of the crust under strain, creating **faults** where rocks fracture and slip past each other. Earthquakes are caused by energy release during rapid slippage along faults. Consequently, the Earth's major earthquake (and volcanic) zones occur along plate boundaries.

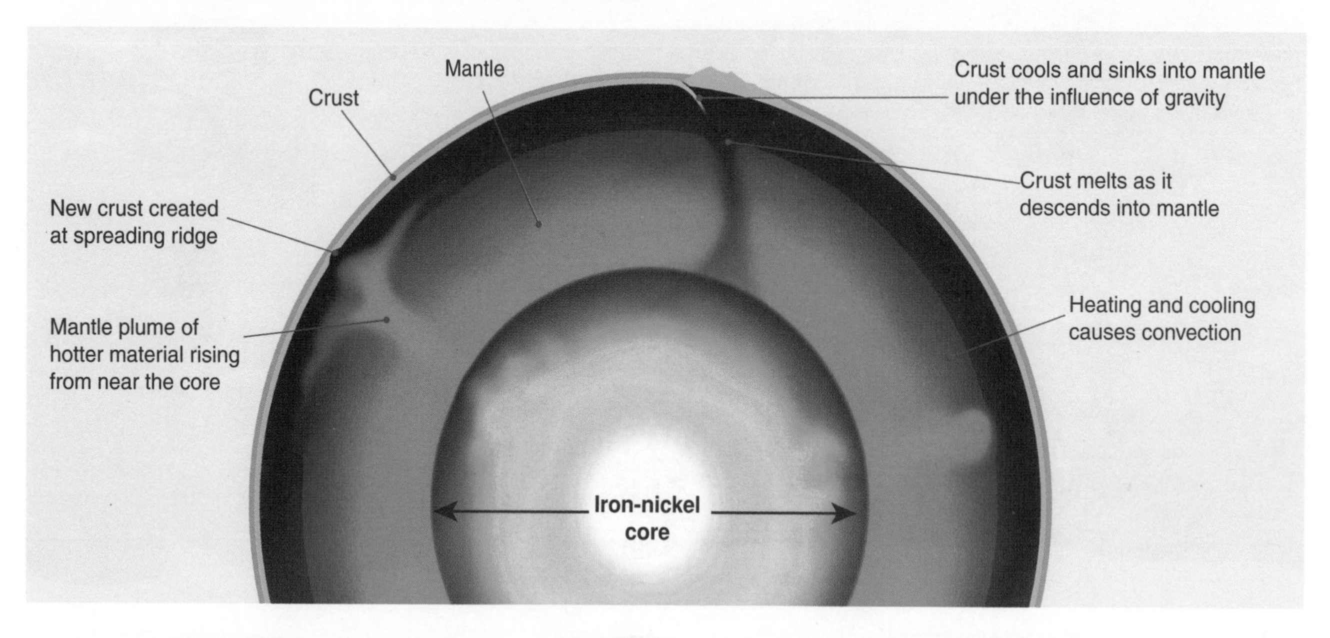

6. On the diagram above draw in arrows to show the convection currents in the mantle:

7. Why do you think volcanoes form where they do? ______________________________

8. Satellite tracking and measurements of the movement of the plates and mantle show some plates are moving faster than the underlying mantle. For example, the Nazca plate is moving towards South America at about 10 cm a year, while the mantle underneath is only moving at about 5 cm a year. Examine the diagrams on this and the previous page and suggest an explanation for this movement:

9. Why are earthquakes more common along plate boundaries than elsewhere in the world? ______________________________

ISBN: 978-1-98-856632-0

62 Soil and Soil Dynamics

Key Question: How do soils form and what influences their development?

Soils are a complex mixture of unconsolidated weathered rock and organic (carbon-based) material. Soils are essential to terrestrial life. Plants require soil, and the microbial populations that recycle organic wastes live in the soil and contribute to its fertility. Soils are named and classified on the basis of the physical and chemical properties of their horizons (layers). Soils have three basic horizons (A,B,C). The A horizon is the topsoil, which is rich in organic matter. If there is also a layer of litter (undecomposed or partly decomposed organic matter) this is called the O horizon, but it is often absent. The B horizon is a subsoil containing clay and soluble minerals. The C horizon is made up of weathered parent material and rock fragments. Soils and their horizons differ widely. They are grouped according to their characteristics, which are determined by the underlying parent rock, the age of the soil, and the conditions under which the soil developed. A few soils weather directly from the underlying rocks and these residual soils have the same general chemistry as the original rocks. More commonly, soils form in materials that have been deposited from elsewhere.

Development of soil horizons

The parent rock is broken down by weathering to form a **regolith** which overlies the solid bedrock. The soil that forms is part of the regolith.

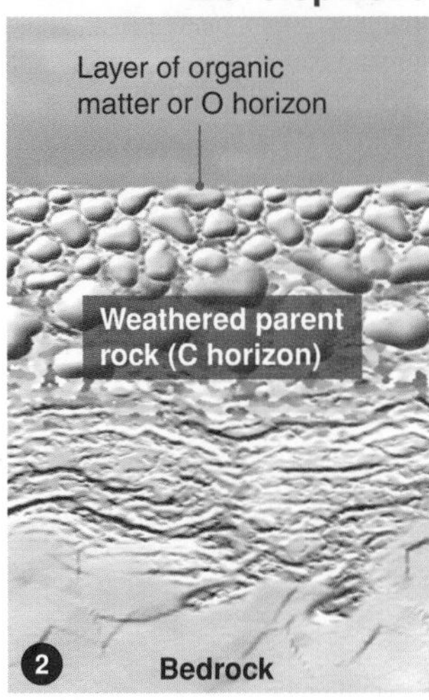

Plants establish and organic material builds up on the surface. The organic material aids the disintegration of the parent material.

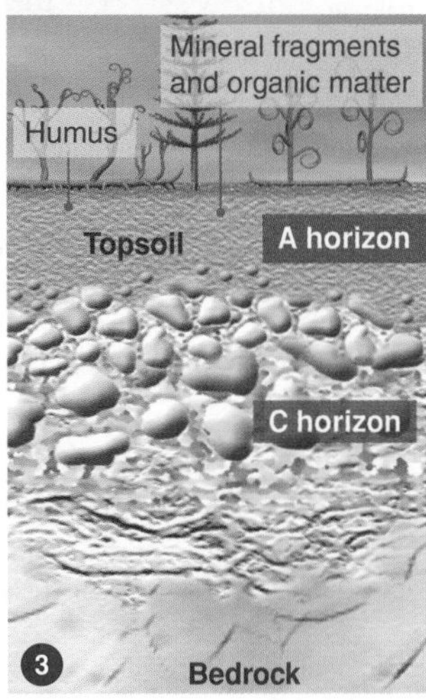

As the mineral and organic content mix, horizons begin to form, with humus-rich layers at the surface and mineral-rich layers at the base.

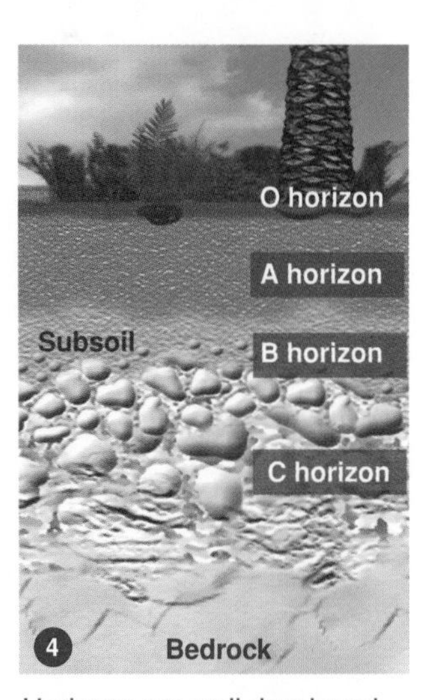

Horizons are well developed in mature soils. The final characteristics of the soil are determined by the regional conditions and the rock type.

Soil horizons in different climates

Soils are formed by the breakdown of rock and the mixing of inorganic and organic material. The soil profile is a series of horizontal layers that differ in composition and physical properties. Each recognizable layer is called a horizon. The development of these horizons is influenced by the environment and so soil profiles can be very different depending on the conditions during development.

ARID REGIONS

Dry, reddish A horizon

Desert soils are alkaline mineral soils with variable amounts of clay, low levels of organic matter, and poorly developed vertical profiles.

HUMID TROPICS

Tropical soils are acidic because of leaching and chemical weathering. Aluminum and iron oxides accumulate in the deep B horizon.

MID-LATITUDES

Grassland soils are mature, alkaline, deep, and well drained. They are typically nutrient-rich and productive with a high organic content.

POLAR REGIONS

Polar soils are formed under very low temperatures. This slows the decomposition of organic matter and maintains the permafrost layer in these frozen soils.

TEMPERATE

Weathered forest soils are well developed soils with a deep organic layer and accumulated clay at lower levels.

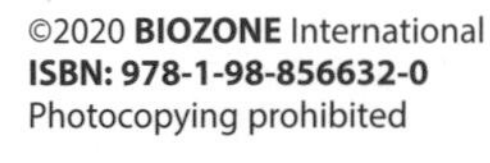

ISBN: 978-1-98-856632-0

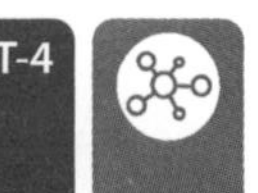

Influences on soil development

The composition of the parent material is important in determining the properties of a soil. Parent materials include volcanic deposits, and sediments deposited by wind, water, or glaciers.

The occurrence of freeze-thaw and wet-dry cycles, as well as average temperature and moisture levels are important in soil development. Climate also affects vegetation, which in turn influences soil development.

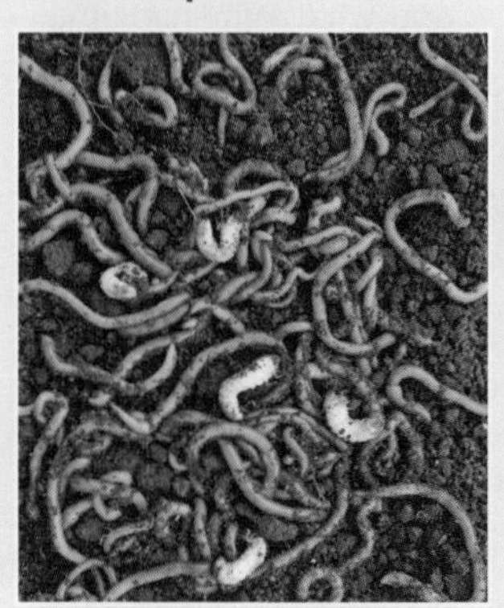

Living organisms help to create a soil both through their activities and by adding to the soil's organic matter when they die. Moist soils with a high organic content tend to be higher in biological activity.

The topography (hilliness) of the land influences soil development by affecting soil moisture and tendency towards erosion. Soils in steep regions are more prone to the erosion of both topsoil and subsoil.

1. What determines the particular characteristics of a soil? ______________________________

____

____

2. Describe the role of soil organisms in soil structure and development: ______________________________

____

____

3. Identify which feature of a soil would most influence its:

   (a) Fertility: ______________________ (b) Water-holding capacity: ______________________

4. Explain how the characteristics described below arise in each of the following soil types:

   (a) Accumulation of organic matter in the frozen soils of the Arctic: ______________________________

   ____

   ____

   (b) Shallow A horizon and poorly developed vertical profile of a desert soil: ______________________________

   ____

   ____

5. In the two soil profiles below identify the following: *A horizon, B horizon. organic matter:*

(a)

(b)

ISBN: 978-1-98-856632-0

63 Soil Erosion and Water Quality

Key Question: How does soil erosion affect water quality?

Soils are important not only for agriculture, where they provide nutrients and a growing medium for plants, but they are also important for filtering water. Water falling on the ground penetrates through the soil and subsoil, and any cracks or faults in the bedrock. Eventually it makes its way to waterways, such as a rivers or lakes. This may take many years depending on the path taken (in some cases hundreds or even thousands of years). This movement of water filters dissolved sediments and bacteria, producing clean water.

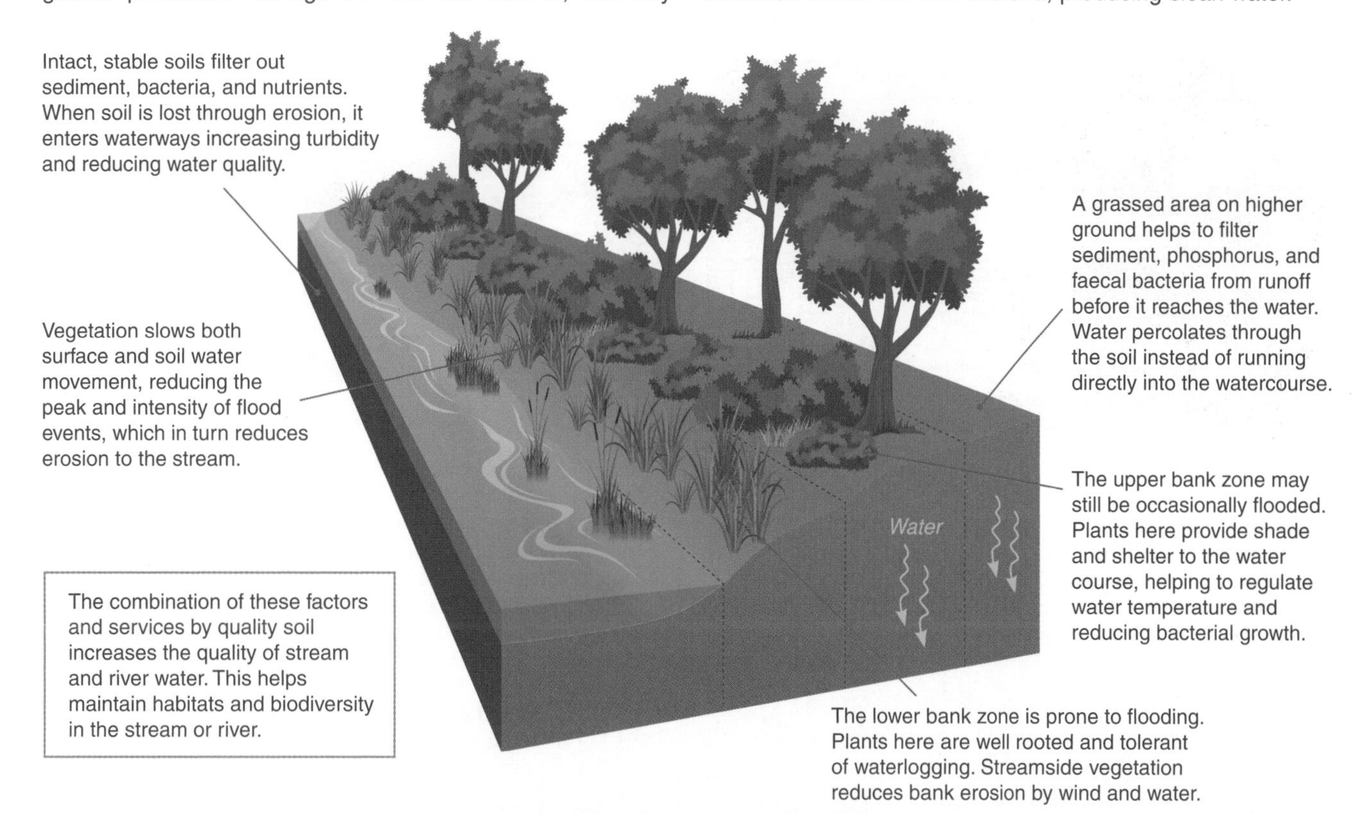

Erosion occurs when ground cover has be removed. When this happens, water has no chance to soak into the ground. Instead it washes straight into waterways along with sediments and any surface pollutants, fouling the water there.

Water filtering through the ground can be very pure (free of bacteria), making it safe to drink. It is also particularly optically clear. High water clarity allows light to reach aquatic plants at depth, providing a variety of habitats.

Plants along the edge of a river hold soil in place, stopping erosion. Plant roots slow water movement and take up nutrients from the soil, stopping them from reaching the stream and causing accelerated plant growth (eutrophication).

1. How does soil erosion affect water quality? ______________________________

____

____

____

2. How does protecting soils from erosion increase water quality? ______________________________

____

____

____

____

ISBN: 978-1-98-856632-0

64 Moisture Content and Soil Erosion

Key Question: How does the water content of the soil affect its rate of erosion?

The cohesive and adhesive properties of water help bind soil particles together. This binding can influence the rate of erosion in soils. Dry soils are easily blown away by the wind. In deserts, this effect can be seen in the movement of sand dunes. The dune slowly creeps in the direction of the wind flow as dry sand is blown up a dune and tumbles over the front. When water is at low to medium concentrations, its cohesive and adhesive properties bind soil particles together into clumps, increasing soil stability and making it harder for the wind to move the soil particles away.

Cropping, plowing, and planting carried out in the spring/summer months when soil moisture is low (but growing conditions are favorable) can risk the loss of top soil. Valuable top soil can be lost if the land is struck by high winds at this time. Soil moisture may be reduced due to drought, poor irrigation management, or a lack of vegetation cover. The lack of moisture in soil also contributes to dust storms.

USDA

Testing aspects of soil erosion is an important part of developing more effective farming techniques. The portable wind tunnel above is used to determine the susceptibility of a farmer's soil to erosion by the wind. The device can be moved to different parts of the farm to test the soil *in-situ*, providing specific results for each part of the farm which can be addressed with specific irrigation and cropping solutions.

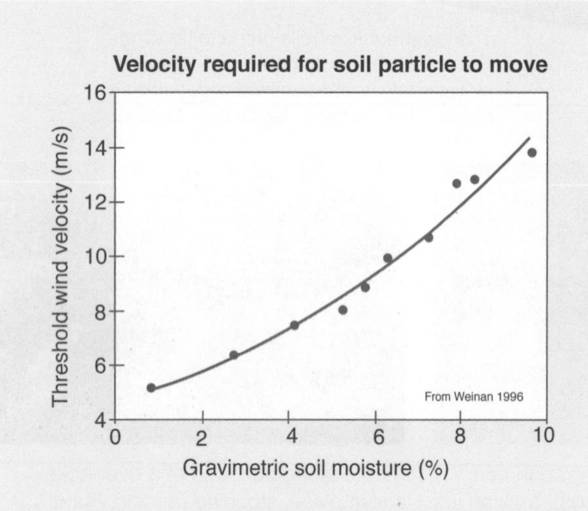

The graphs above and right show the effect of wind velocity on soil movement.

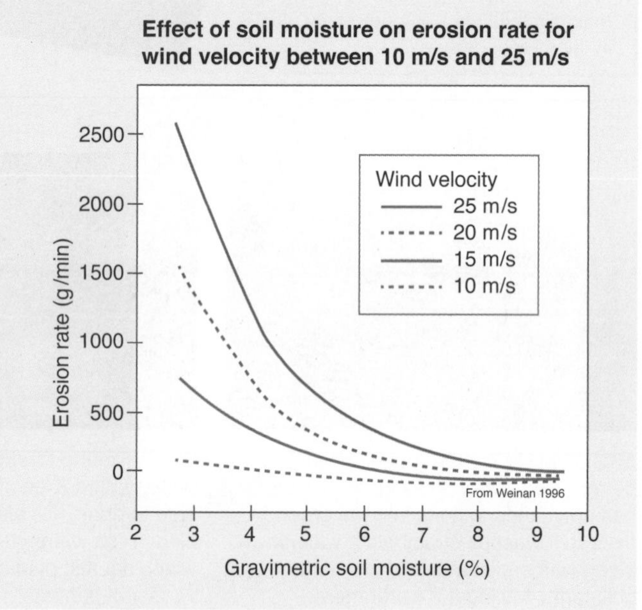

1. (a) What is the wind velocity needed to move soil with a moisture of 3%? ______________________

   (b) What is the wind velocity needed to move soil with a moisture of 8%? ______________________

2. How many times more erosion occurs in a soil with 3% moisture than a soil with 7% moisture in a 15 m/s wind?

   ____

3. At what soil moisture does wind speed make little difference to erosion rate? ______________________

4. Why is testing erosion caused by the wind *in-situ* more useful for farmers than testing wind erosion in a lab?

   ____

   ____

   ____

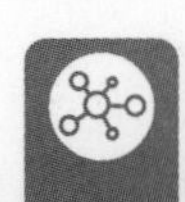

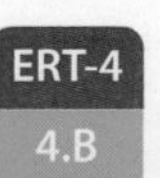

ERT-4

4.B

ISBN: 978-1-98-856632-0

65 Soil Textures

Key Question: How do we find and define soil texture?

Soil texture depends on the amount of sand, silt, and clay present. A loam contains a 40/40/20 mix of sand, silt, and clay and is considered the ideal soil for cultivating crops. Soils with too much clay hold water, become heavy, and are difficult to work, whereas soils with too much sand allow water to drain away too quickly and do not bind together well. A loam contains enough clay to bind the water and hold it in place, but also enough sand to create spaces between the particles, allowing air to penetrate and water to drain. Because of these features a loam is able to retain nutrients and humus better than other soil types.

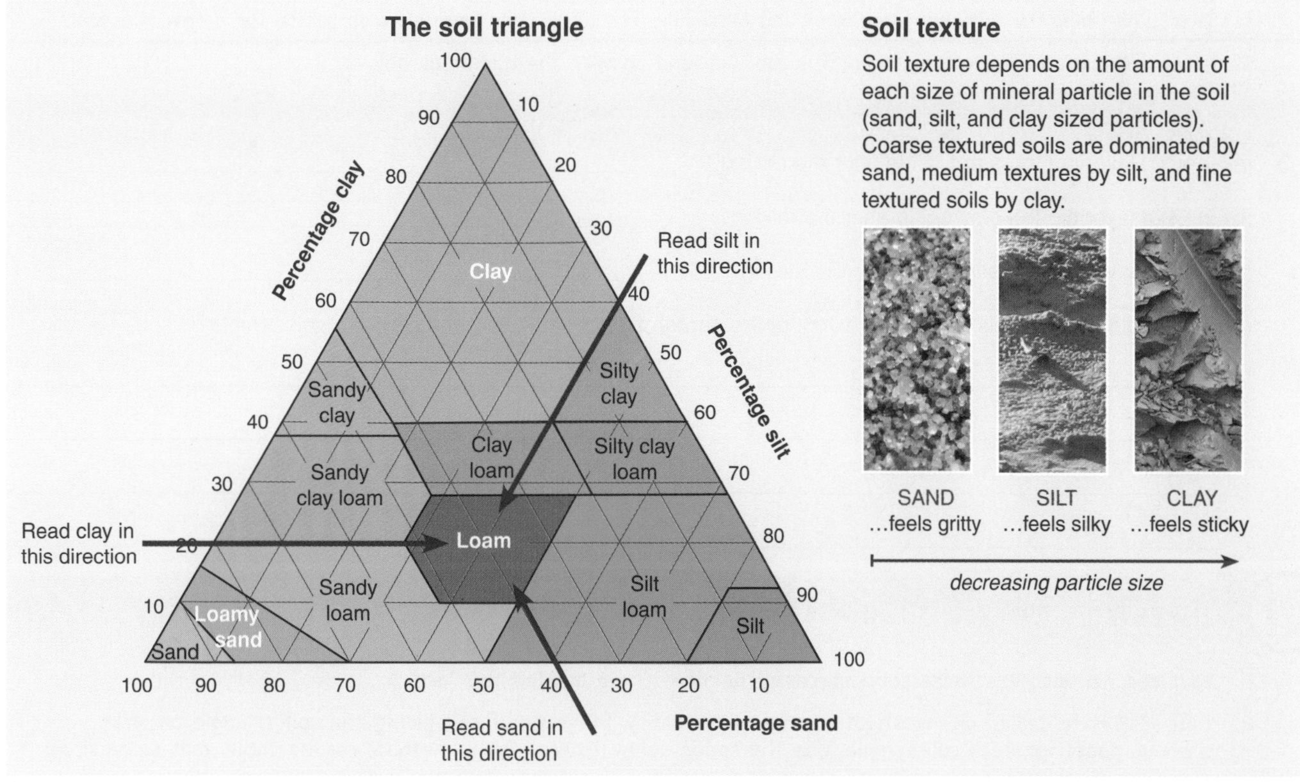

- A loam consists of around 20% clay, 40% sand, and 40% silt. Around this point, various other loams exist which are named after their primary components. For example a sandy loam consists of around 65% sand, 35% silt, and 10% clay.

	Clay	Silt	Sand	Loam
Nutrient holding capacity	++	+	0	+
Water infiltration capacity	0	+	++	+
Water holding capacity	++	+	0	+
Aeration	0	+	++	+
Workability	0	+	++	+

0 = low + =medium ++= high

Loams are easily worked...

...but silts and clays can be very muddy.

- The capacity of soil to be worked and produce viable crops depends on the mixture of particles within it. Silt provides a moderate capacity in all areas because of its intermediate particle size. By itself though, it does not provide good soil because it too easily turns to mud when wet and is blown away by winds when dry. Loam consists of a variety of particle sizes and so remains more consistent in texture when both wet and dry.

1. Explain the term loam and how it applies to soil: ______________________

____

____

____

____

2. Explain why loamy soils are more easily worked and produce better crops than other soil types:

____

____

____

ISBN: 978-1-98-856632-0

INVESTIGATION 4.1: Identifying soil type part 1

See appendix for equipment list.

1. Your teacher has a supply of sand, silt, and clay in separate containers. Obtain three measuring cylinders and place a 20 mL sample of either sand, silt, or clay in each one.
2. Study each sample. Note the texture of each type and the particle size.
3. Now place all three samples into one measuring cylinder. Add enough water to cover them completely.
4. Thoroughly mix the samples together using a stirring rod or spatula and leave to settle for a few minutes.
5. After settling study the layering of the mixture and answer the questions below:

3. (a) In what layer did the **sand** settle after the mixing? ______________________

   (b) In what layer did the **clay** settle after the mixing? ______________________

   (c) In what layer did the **silt** settle after the mixing? ______________________

   (d) How could you use this layering to work out the percentage of sand, silt, and clay in a soil sample?

   ____

   ____

   ____

   ____

INVESTIGATION 4.2: Identifying soil type part 2

See appendix for equipment list.

1. Your teacher also has three soil samples of unknown type labeled 1, 2, and 3.
2. Your task is to design an investigation that will identify the type of soil (using the soil triangle on the previous page) for each soil sample. Use the space below to write your method, results table, and conclusions:

ISBN: 978-1-98-856632-0

66 Earth's Atmosphere

Key Question: What is the structure and composition of the Earth's atmosphere?

The Earth's atmosphere is a layer of gases surrounding the globe and retained by gravity. It contains roughly 78% nitrogen, 20.95% oxygen, 0.93% argon, 0.038% carbon dioxide, trace amounts of other gases, and a variable amount (average around 1%) of water vapor. This mixture of gases, known as air, protects life on Earth by absorbing ultraviolet radiation and reducing temperature extremes between day and night. The atmosphere consists of layers around the Earth, each one defined by the way temperature changes within its limits. The outermost troposphere thins slowly, fading into space with no boundary. The air of the atmosphere moves in response to heating from the sun. Globally, the atmospheric circulation transports warmth from equatorial areas to high latitudes and returning cooler air to the tropics.

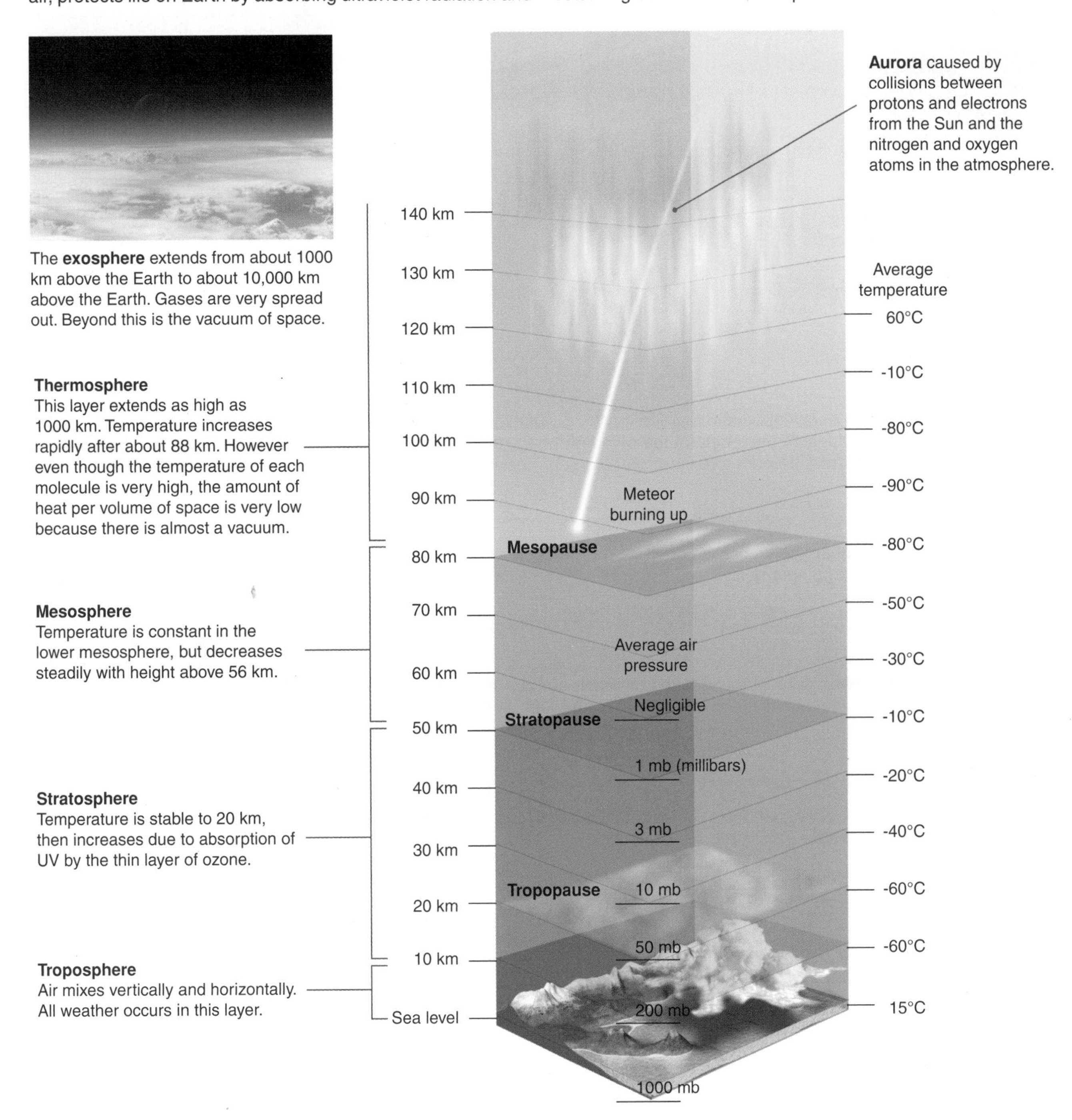

1. Use the model of the atmosphere above to describe the characteristics of the atmosphere in relation to altitude:

At lowest altitude weather occurs & has highest air pressure. Air thins with increasing altitude. Temperature rises again in thermosphere.

ISBN: 978-1-98-856632-0

67 Global Wind Patterns

Key Question: What causes Earth's wind patterns?
Global wind patterns arise from the interactions of two main causes: the differential heating of the atmosphere by the Sun and the rotation of the Earth itself.

Heating the atmosphere

- The Earth and therefore the atmosphere is curved as in the diagram below:

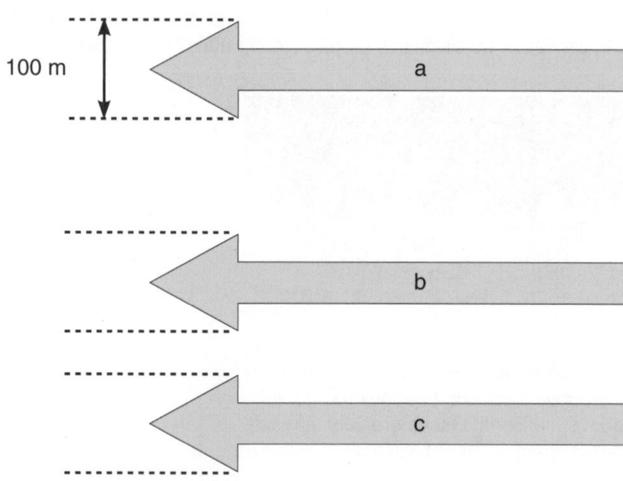

1. The distance between each dotted line represents 100 m. Continue the dotted lines above until they reach the curved surface of the Earth. Measure the length of the curve of the Earth contained within each of the dotted lines. Use the scale to convert your measurement to meters. Record your answer below:

   (a) ______________ (b) ______________ (c) ______________

2. Divide 100 by the number you recorded above. This represents the proportion by which the 100 m of sunlight has been spread out. Record the number below:

   (a) ______________ (b) ______________ (c) ______________

3. Each beam of sunlight (a, b, or c above) delivers 1300 joules of energy per second (i.e. 1300 watts) over a 1 m surface of the upper atmosphere, perpendicular to the direction of the beam (i.e. the beam hits a flat surface). Given that the sunlight spreads out when it hits the Earth, use your answers from 2 above to calculate the amount of energy that is actually delivered per 100 m of surface in each of sunlight beams a, b, and c.

   (a) ______________ (b) ______________ (c) ______________

4. From your calculations above, what can be said about the relationship of the amount of heat being delivered to the surface of the Earth and the curvature of the Earth:

5. Recall the effect of heating on the circulation of the Earth's mantle from activity 61 '*Plate Tectonics*'. How does the difference in energy being received from the Sun at different points on the planet affect how the atmosphere moves above the Earth? Draw a diagram to show this movement:

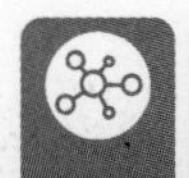

ISBN: 978-1-98-856632-0

Earth's rotation and the atmosphere (the Coriolis effect)

- As the air in the atmosphere moves from the tropics to the poles and back, the Earth rotates underneath. This movement of the air is independent of the Earth's rotation and this causes some interesting effects:

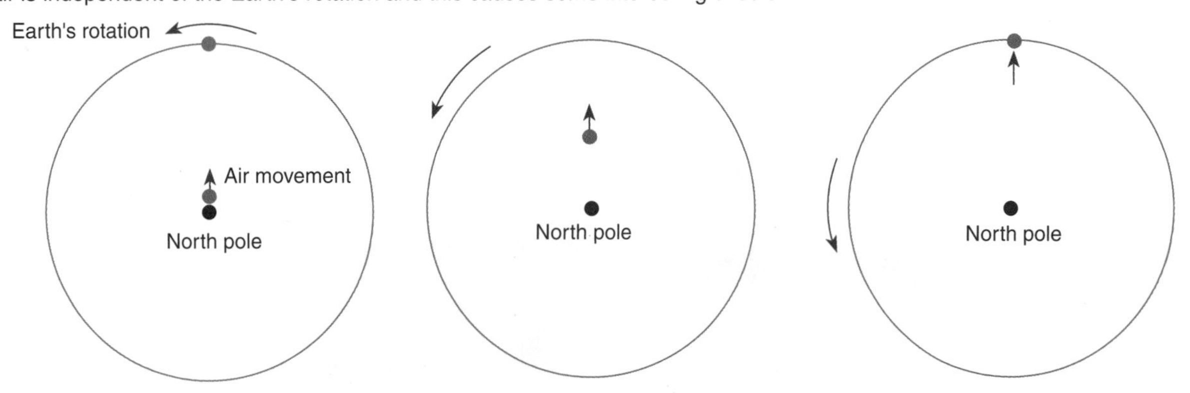

6. The blue dot in the diagrams above is an air particle. The red dot is a fixed point of the Earth's surface. In the three diagrams the Earth rotates a total of 90°counterclockwise. Draw where the red dot would be after the rotation of:

   (a) 45°:

   (b) 90°:

   (c) What would the blue dot appear to do to a person sitting at the North pole (and rotating with the Earth, i.e. looking at the red dot)? Describe it below and draw a diagram (right):

   (d) Now imagine a person was sitting at the South pole in the scenario above. Describe (below) and draw a diagram (right) to show what a person would see if the blue dot moved from the South pole to the equator:

   (e) Now complete the diagram to show the movement of the air particle as seen by someone in space looking at a fixed point on the Earth's equator (i.e. in a synchronized orbit):

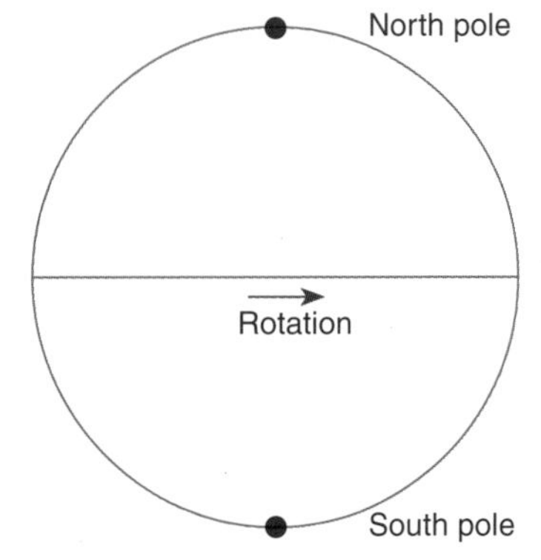

7. Combine your observations to explain the movement of air as it moves over the Earth's surface:

ISBN: 978-1-98-856632-0

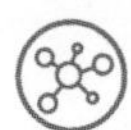

The tricellular model of atmospheric circulation

- High temperatures over the equator and low temperatures over the poles, combined with the rotation of the Earth, produce a series of cells in the atmosphere. This model of atmospheric circulation, with three cells in each hemisphere, is known as the **tricellular model**.

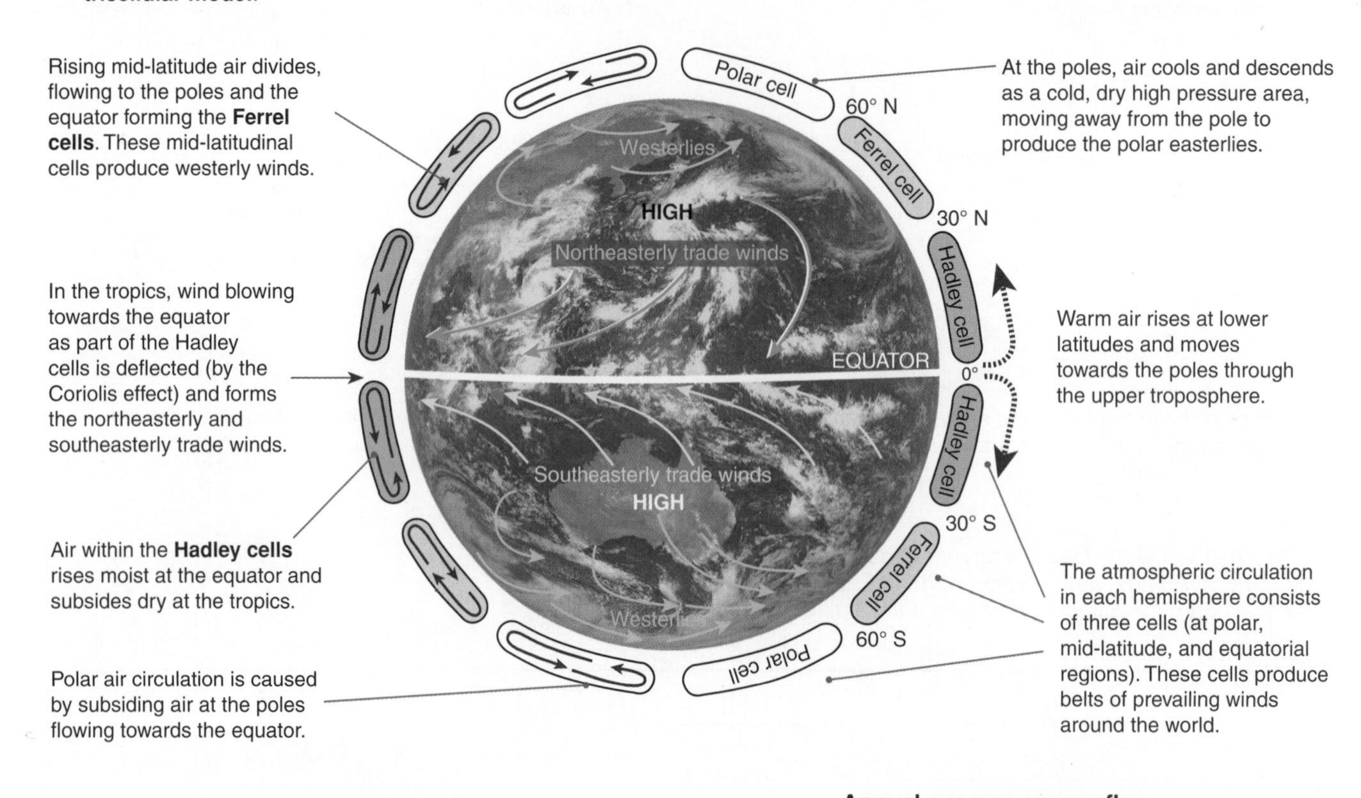

- The energy gained from solar radiation becomes progressively less from the equator to the poles. Heat gained at the tropics is transferred to cooler regions by atmospheric circulation, producing a more even spread of temperatures over the globe than would otherwise occur if there was no atmosphere. In a similar way, heat gained by the oceans also transfers heat about the globe. The ice caps of the poles reflect so much of the sunlight they receive that they produce a permanently cold climate.
- If there was no heat flow, the poles would be about 25°C cooler and the equator about 14°C warmer.

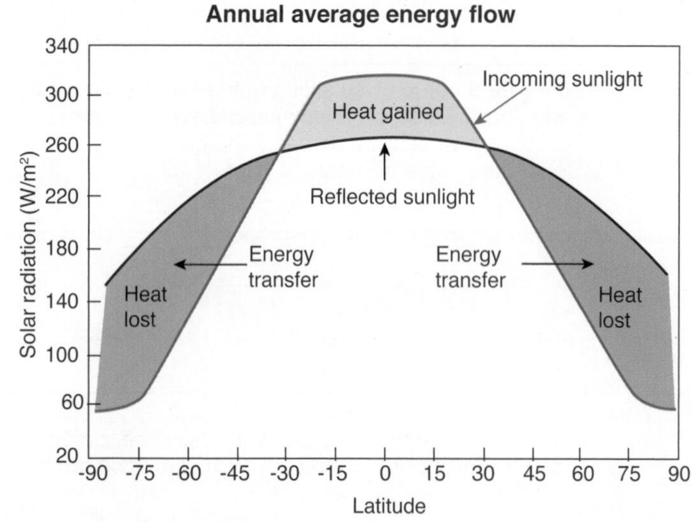

8. Describe how the Earth's atmosphere helps maintain a stable global environment: ______________________

9. How does the tricellular model explain why the tropics are hot and wet and the deserts to either side of the tropics are hot and dry:

ISBN: 978-1-98-856632-0

68 Watersheds

Key Question: What features characterize a watershed?

A watershed (or drainage basin) is an area of land that drains into a common outlet such as a stream or river mouth. It is bounded above by a ridge or drainage divide and below by the level of the outlet. A watershed can be as small as a trickle of water or as large as an entire river basin. Large watersheds will contain many smaller watersheds as smaller rivers (tributaries) connect to form bigger rivers. A hierarchy is applied to the contributing rivers within any watershed, starting with the largest possible watershed (e.g. a continental area) and dividing and labeling each basin as a river gets further from the sea.

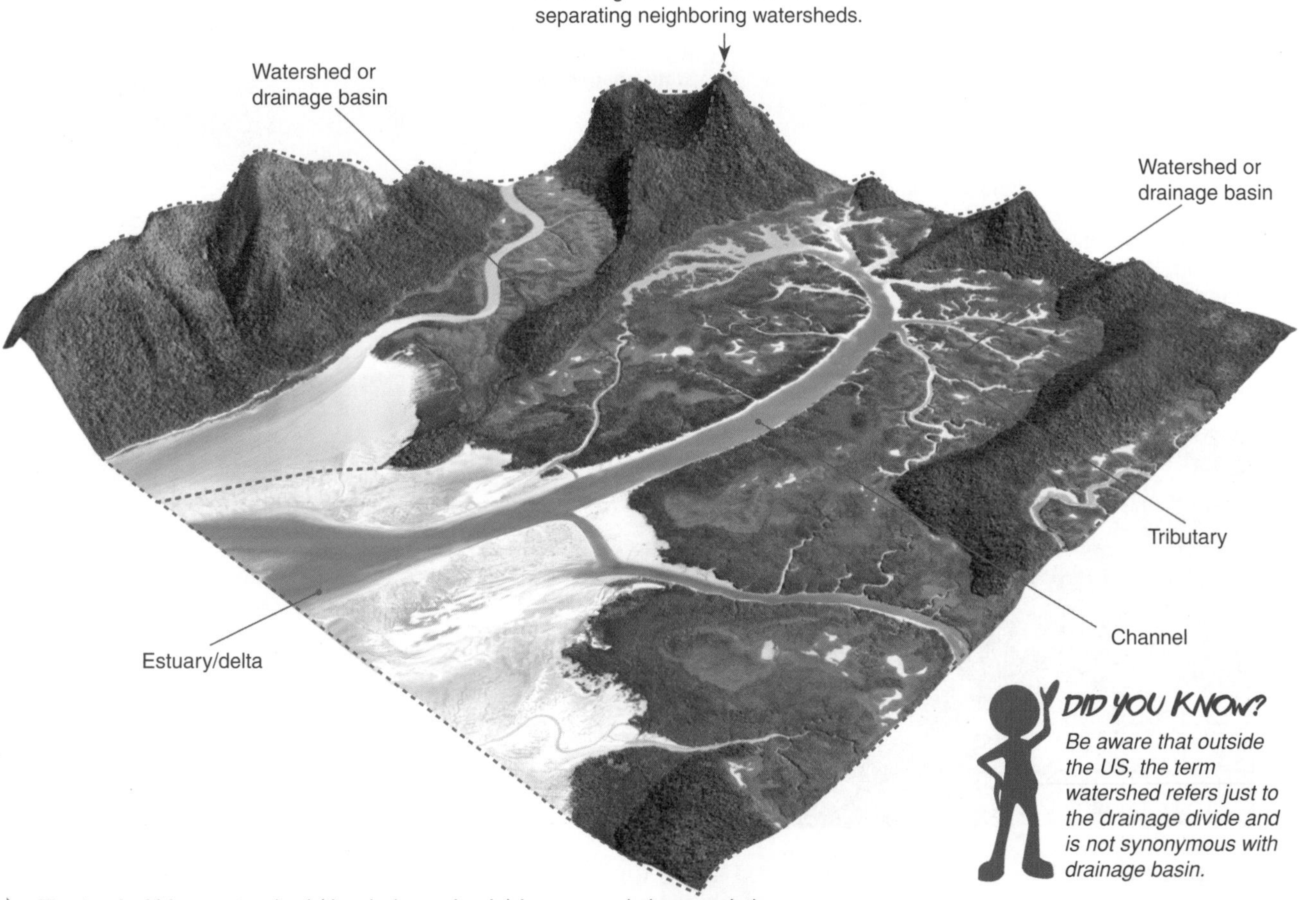

DID YOU KNOW?

Be aware that outside the US, the term watershed refers just to the drainage divide and is not synonymous with drainage basin.

- The land within a watershed (the drainage basin) has several characteristics:
  - **Morphology**: This depends on the topography (shape) of the land and the extent of the river system within it.
  - **Soil factors**: Soils are important in the moisture retention levels of the drainage basin. Porous soil lose water more quickly. Fine soils may erode and add to the particle load of the rivers.
  - **Geologic structure**: The characteristics of the underlying rock are important in the movement of ground water and the shaping of the river system (e.g. placement of river channels and slope of terrain).
  - **Vegetation**: The extent and type of vegetation affects the rate at which water and soil particles are added to the river system. Dense vegetation holds and removes water (via uptake by plants) and holds soil together.
  - **Climate**: The volume of rain, and the temperature and humidity are all important factors in the development and shaping of the drainage system and the water that it carries.

1. Explain how the underlying geology of the land may affect the morphology of the drainage basin:

____

____

____

____

2. Explain how the climate would affect the way a drainage basin develops: _______________________

____

____

____

ISBN: 978-1-98-856632-0

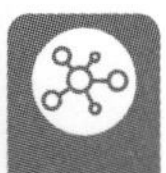

Continental drainage divides

- Watersheds can be seen at any scale. The North American continent can be divided into seven main watersheds based on which ocean, sea, or bay the water eventually flows to. Each of these can be divided again for each of the major river systems. In the US, watersheds are divided into 6 levels. There are 21 hydrologic regions (level 1), 221 subregions (level 2), and 22,000 watersheds (level 5).
- **Triple Divide Peak** is a special hydrological point. It is the hydrological high point of the North American continent and sits on the border between three major continental drainage basins. It is the only point in North America where water drains to three different oceans.
- The **Great Basin** is a unique basin in North America. Instead of water flowing to a sea or ocean, water remains within the basin, flowing to a central low point. This type of drainage basin is called a **endorheic** drainage basin.

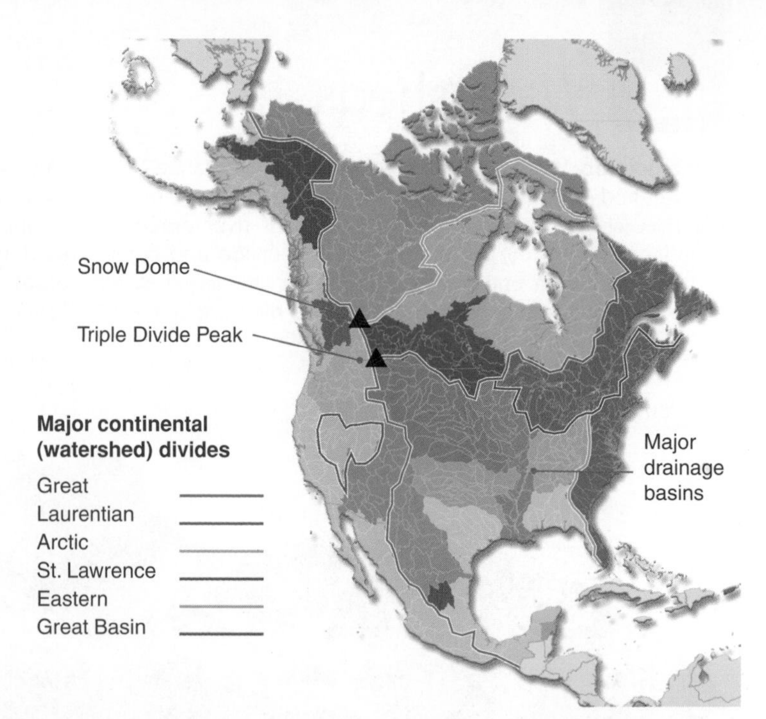

3. How do the watersheds pictured below differ? Describe the characteristics of each watershed and explain how this will affect the way water runs off the land.

(a)

(b)

(c)

ISBN: 978-1-98-856632-0

69 Energy From the Sun

Key Question: How is the energy the Earth receives from the Sun modified by various features of the Earth itself?

The amount of solar radiation reaching Earth from the Sun is about 174 petawatts, (174 x 10^{15} joules per second). At the equator, this is 1.361 kilowatts per square meter (kW/m^2) at the upper atmosphere and about 700 W/ m^2 at the surface. Over the entire surface of the Earth, the figure is about 342 W/m^2. Not all of the incoming solar radiation (insolation) reaches the Earth's surface. A large amount of it is reflected off clouds, absorbed by the atmosphere, or reflected off the Earth's surface. The energy from the Sun is also not distributed evenly about the globe. Because the Earth is spherical, the poles receive less energy per square kilometer than the equator. Earth's angle of rotation relative to the Sun further influences the uneven distribution of the energy received at the Earth's surface.

1. Complete the diagram below of incoming and radiated energy. Write your answers in the spaces below.

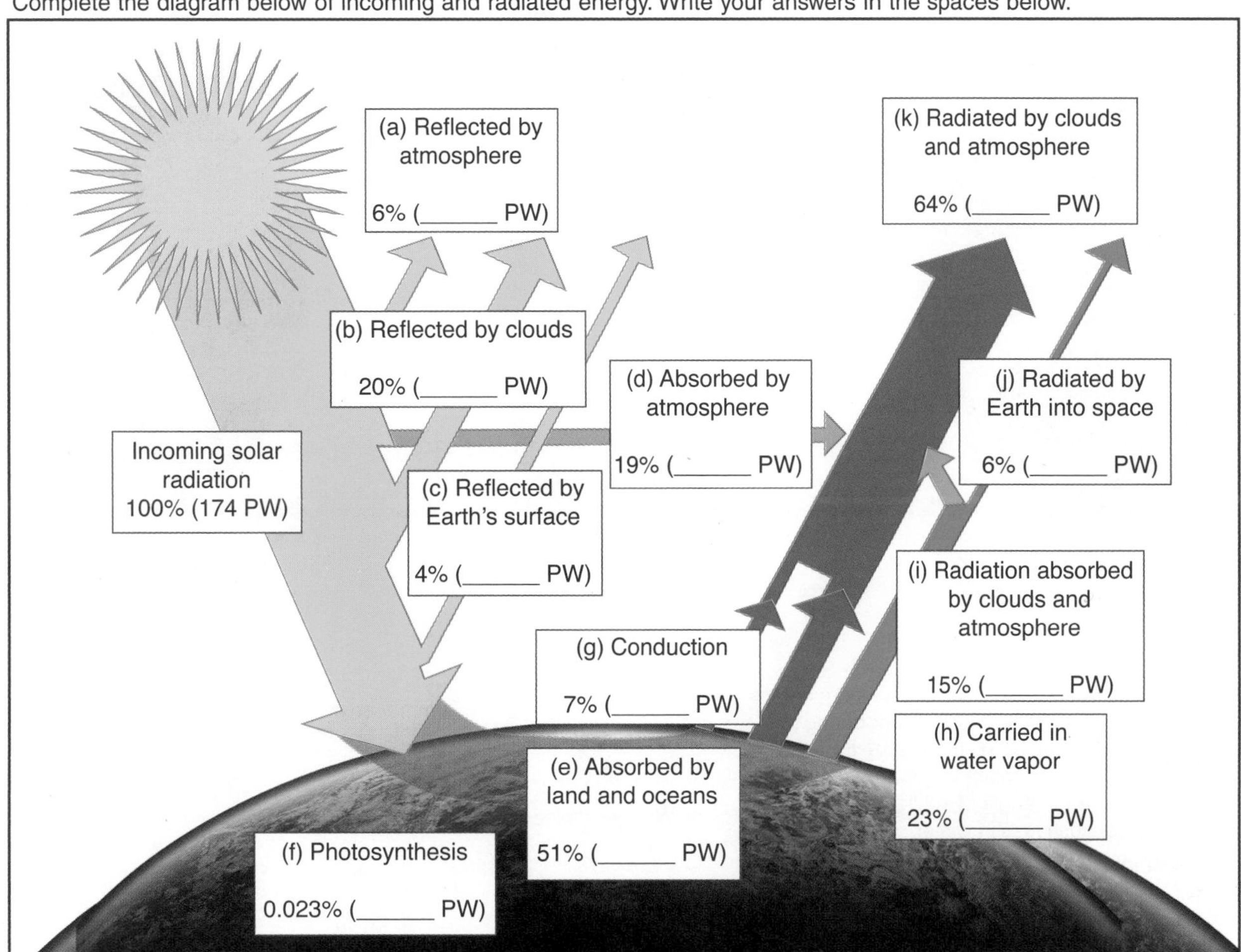

2. Use the diagram to explain how the Earth's surface temperature remains stable: ______________________

3. The amount of solar energy received at any point on the Earth can be calculated using the equation:

$$A' = A \times \text{cosine } x$$

Where **A** = the amount of solar radiation at the equator, **A'** = the amount of solar radiation at latitude x.
x = the latitude of the point on the Earth.

For each of the following lines of latitude, calculate the amount of solar energy received, assuming 700 W/m^2 of energy is received at the equator and no tilt to the Earth (i.e. at the spring and fall equinoxes). The first one is completed for you:

(a) Tropic of Cancer (23.4° North): $A' = 700 \times \cos 23.4 = 700 \times 0.917 = 641.9$ W/m^2

(b) 45° North: ______________________

(c) Arctic circle (66° North): ______________________

(d) North pole (90° North): ______________________

ISBN: 978-1-98-856632-0

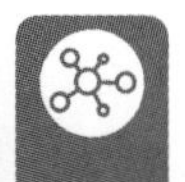

70 Earth's Seasons

Key Question: How does the Earth's tilt change the angle of the Sun in the sky and how is this related to the seasons? The Earth is tilted at 23.4° with respect to its axis of orbit around the Sun. The angle remains the same as it travels around the Sun. This results in the North pole pointed towards the Sun during the months of June, July, and August, (the northern summer) and away from the Sun six months later during December, January, and February (the northern winter). The opposite happens in the Southern Hemisphere (below). An easily observable effect of this is the change in the angle of the Sun at noon during the summer (more overhead) and winter (lower to the horizon). The change in temperature during the seasons is a direct result of this change in the angle of sunlight striking the Earth.

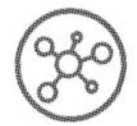

Seasons and the Sun

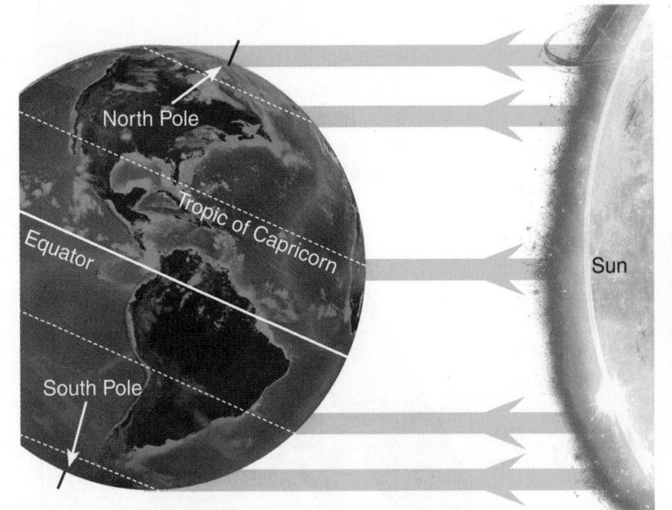

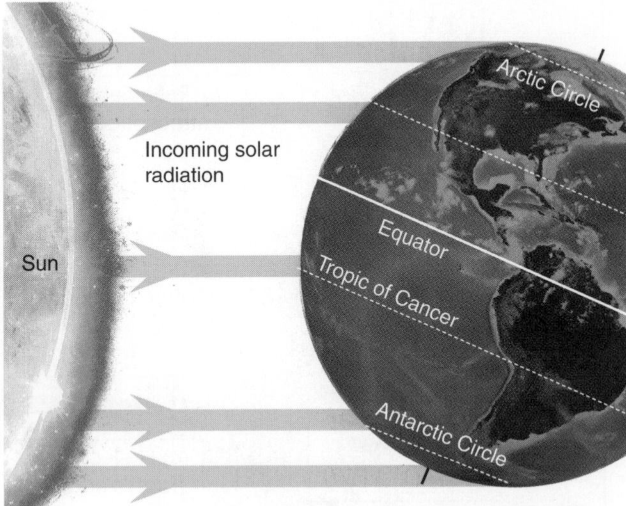

Northern Hemisphere: Summer
Southern Hemisphere: Winter

Northern Hemisphere: Winter
Southern Hemisphere: Summer

- The energy received from the Sun is more or less constant, so why is it so much colder during the winter? The answer is that the energy from the Sun is spread over a much larger area during the winter because the angle of sunlight hitting the ground is so much less in winter.
- For example, a shadow at noon in the summer is short. The shadow represents the area of ground that the sunlight would have hit. In winter, the shadow is much longer and therefore the area of ground the sunlight would have hit is greater. Thus the energy per square meter is less, resulting in a lower overall temperature.

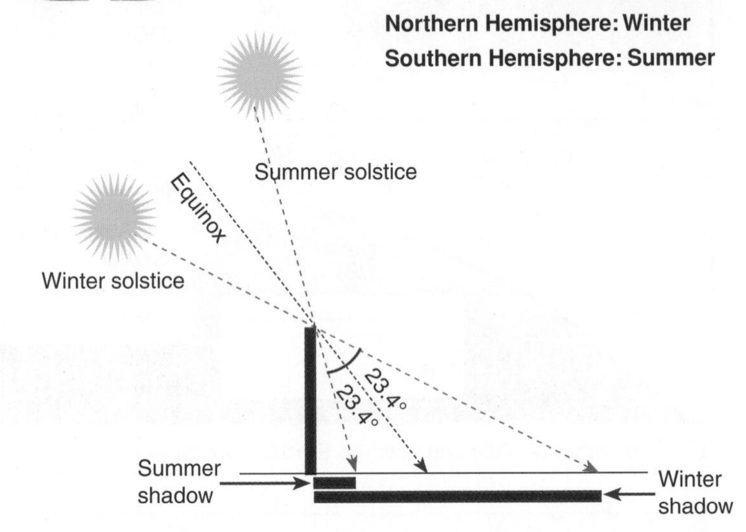

1. What causes the change in seasons on Earth? ______

2. What effect does the change of seasons have on the angle of the Sun above the horizon at noon?

3. The angle of Earth's tilt changes from about 22° to 24° over tens of thousands of years. How would these changes affect the extremes of summer and winter temperatures over time?

ISBN: 978-1-98-856632-0

INVESTIGATION: 4.3 Measuring Energy

See appendix for equipment list.

1. Using a stand and protractor to measure angle, set up a flashlight pointing straight down (90° angle) at a piece of grid paper from a distance of 30 cm (a darkened room works best) as shown in the diagram below:

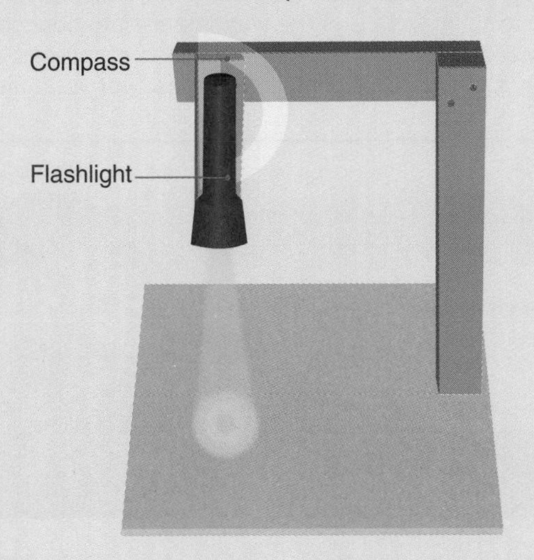

2. Draw around the illuminated part of the grid paper and then use the grid paper to help find the area illuminated.
3. Area illuminated (90°): ______
4. Tilt the clamp stand to a 66° angle, measuring 30 cm from the center of the flashlight front along the angle to the center of the illuminated area on the grid paper. Again, draw around and calculate the area of grid paper illuminated.

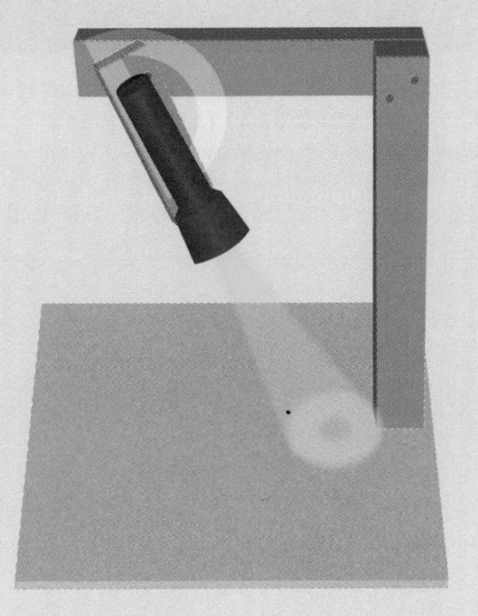

5. Area illuminated (66°): ______
6. Repeat this procedure for 45° and 33°.

   Area illuminated (45°): ______ Area illuminated (33°): ______

4. (a) How does the area of graph paper illuminated change with the angle of the flashlight? ______

   (b) For each angle of the flashlight, calculate the amount of light energy (watts) received per cm^2 on the grid paper. You could use a light meter to measure the light output of the flashlight if you don't know it or (assuming its output is constant) start with a general light output of 3 W. (Hint if the light bulb is a 3 W bulb, each square cm of paper is receiving how many watts?). Write your answers next to your outlines on the graph paper.

   (c) Attach all your graph paper records to this page.

ISBN: 978-1-98-856632-0

71 Geography and Climate

Key Question: How does geography affect climate and weather?

Mountains affect climate by deflecting air currents to higher levels of the atmosphere. The air cools as it rises, and the moisture in it condenses to fall as rain, producing a wet, cool climate. Having lost its moisture, the air passes over the mountain and descends as dry air. As it descends, it warms and can hold more moisture, producing a warm, dry climate. This effect is called a rain shadow and it occurs anywhere there are tall mountain ranges that block air flow. Mountain building via plate tectonics (orogeny) occurs in many parts of the world near plate boundaries. It is a long term process, and can last tens of millions of years, producing long term climatic changes over large areas of land.

The rain shadow

Rain shadows can cause some extreme effects. In Chile, the Andes block moist winds from the Amazon basin, producing the Atacama desert, the driest non-polar desert on Earth. The Atacama is estimated to be at least 3 million years old.

The Southern Alps in New Zealand produce one of the most extreme rain shadows in the world. On the western slopes, rainfall can reach 8900 mm a year. On the eastern slopes, annual rainfall drops to just 380 mm in some areas.

Death Valley in California is in the rain shadow of the Sierra Nevada mountains. The valley has recorded the hottest temperatures on Earth (56.7°C). Death Valley formed after the last glacial period and receives only 60 mm of rain a year.

Ocean currents

Ocean currents also have a large effect on the climate and weather of coastal land. The cold Humboldt current sweeps northwards along the coast of South America. Above it the air cools and picks up less moisture by evaporation. This adds to the rain shadow effect in the Atacama desert, further intensifying the desert environment. Off the coast of Nova Scotia, the cold Labrador current meets the warm Gulf stream. This causes warm moist air above the Gulf stream to suddenly cool as it moves over the Labrador current. This causes the thick fogs the region is well known for.

1. Use examples to explain how the geological characteristics of an environment can affect the climate and weather of that environment:

____

____

____

____

____

____

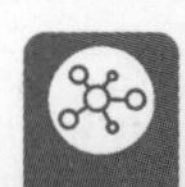
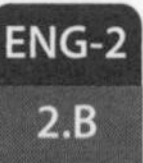

ISBN: 978-1-98-856632-0

72 El Niño and La Niña

Key Question: How do the climate patterns of El Niño and La Niña occur and what is their effect on the environment?

Interactions between atmospheric and oceanic circulation are at the core of most global climate patterns. The El Niño-Southern Oscillation cycle (ENSO) is the most prominent of these global oscillations and can have significant effects on the Pacific region, causing weather patterns involving increased rain in specific places but not in others. It is one of the many causes of drought. The oscillation comes in two main phases. El Niño ("the boy") is the warm phase and La Niña ("the girl") is the cool phase. La Niña events usually follow El Niño events, which occur every two to seven years.

Normal climatic conditions

- In normal conditions (below), the rotation of the Earth produces winds that blow east to west (the trade winds) across the Pacific from South America towards South-east Asia. These winds drive the warm South Equatorial Current towards the Australian and South-east Asian coast. Off the coast of South America, upwelling of cold water replaces the surface waters as they move.

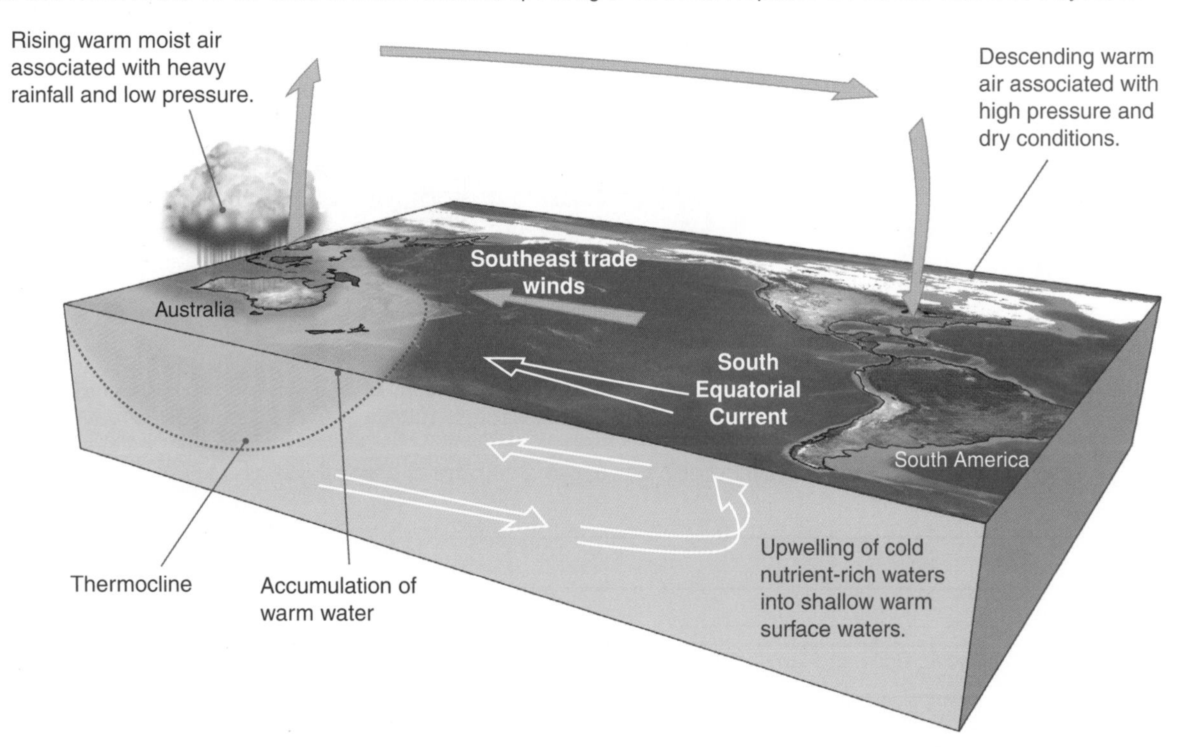

El Niño effect

- In an El Niño event (below), the pressure systems over Australia and South America are weakened or reversed, beginning with a rise in air pressure over the Indian Ocean, Indonesia, and Australia. Warm waters move eastwards across the Pacific and block the cold upwelling along the west coast of the Americas. In North America, this results in an intensification and southward shift in the jet stream (high altitude winds) producing heavier rains in southern USA and drier weather in the north.

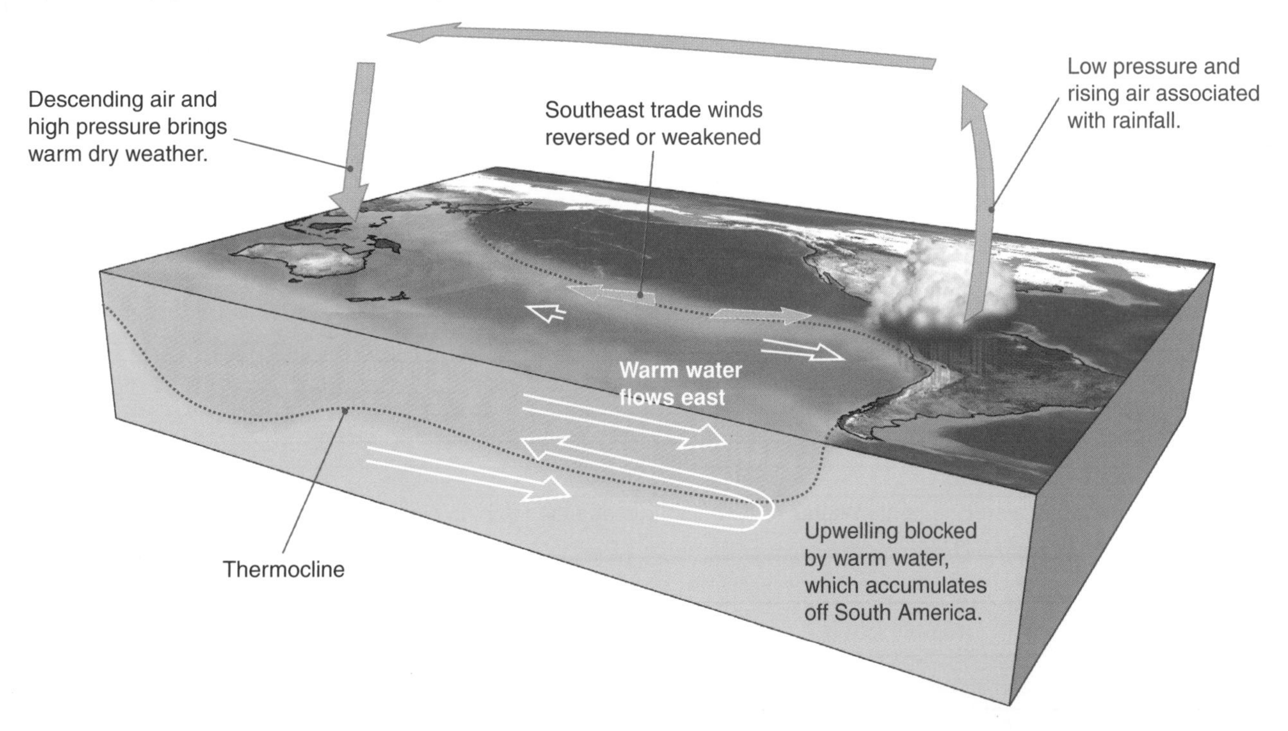

ISBN: 978-1-98-856632-0

159 → 67 ← 33 ←

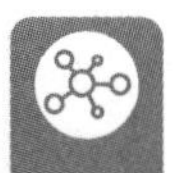

La Niña effect

- La Niña is a more intense system than is seen in normal conditions. It is characterized by lower than normal air pressure over the western Pacific, strong southeast trade winds and a build up of cooler than normal water in the tropical Pacific. The ocean currents and unusually strong trade winds moving east bring the cold water to the surface. This causes a drop in sea-surface temperatures by as much as 4°C. In North America this results in the jet stream moving north, producing heavy rain in the north and drier weather in the south.

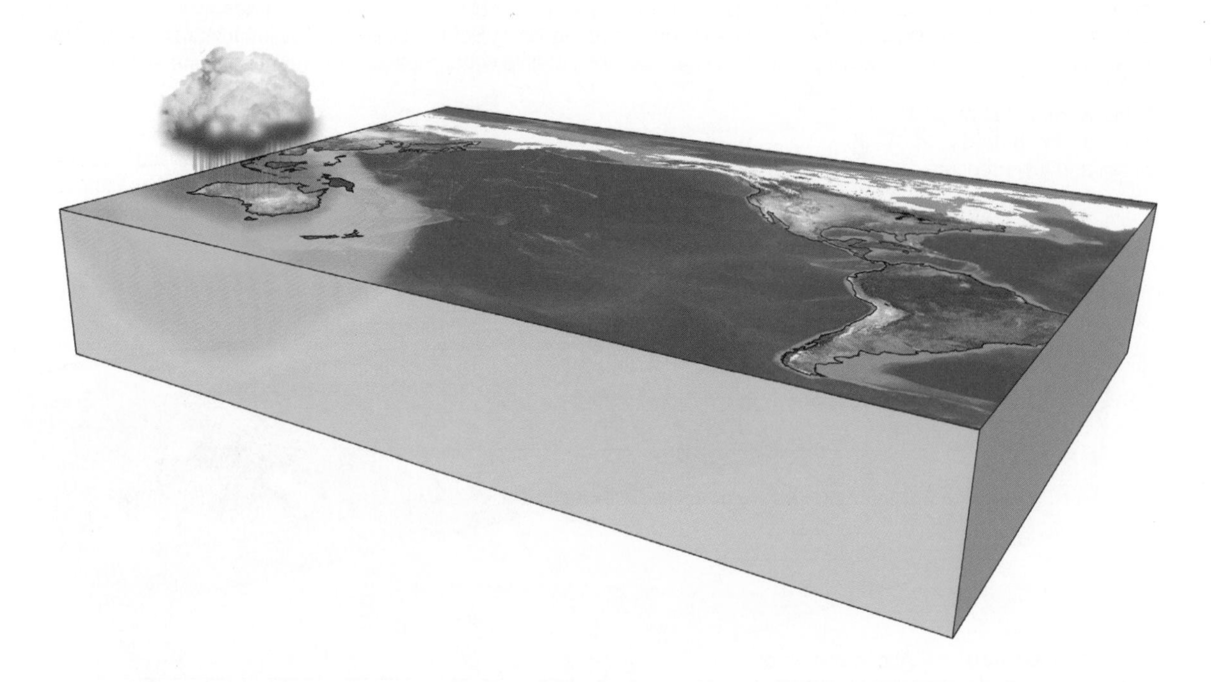

1. On the blank map above, draw and label in the La Niña effect as in the diagrams on the previous page:

2. Describe the events that cause El Niño conditions and its effects on ocean circulation and climate:

____

____

____

3. What would you expect the effect of an El Niño year to be on:

   (a) The climate of the western coast of South America? Explain: _______________________

   ____

   ____

   ____

   (b) The climate of Indonesia and Australia? Explain: _______________________

   ____

   ____

   ____

4. Evidence shows sea surface temperatures to be rising in response to rising global air temperatures. How might this affect El Niño and La Niña conditions?

____

____

____

ISBN: 978-1-98-856632-0

73 Personal Progress Check

Answer the multiple choice questions that follow by circling the correct answer. Don't forget to read the question carefully!

1. Name the layer of the Earth labeled **B** right:
   (a) Crust
   (b) Inner core
   (c) Upper mantle
   (d) Outer core

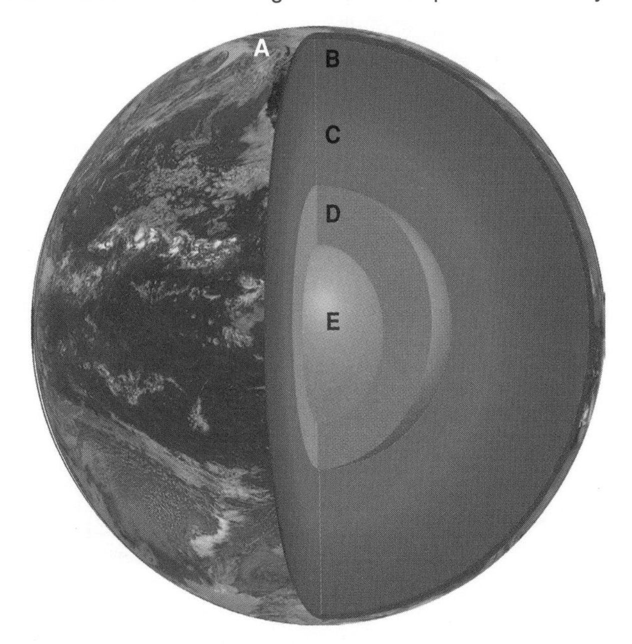

2. The state of the layers of the Earth A-E right are:
   (a) Solid, solid, liquid, solid, solid
   (b) Solid, liquid, liquid, solid, solid
   (c) Solid, solid, solid, liquid, solid
   (d) Solid, solid, liquid, solid, liquid

3. Movement of layer B is responsible for:
   (a) Earthquakes
   (b) Volcanic eruptions
   (c) Movement of the tectonic plates
   (d) All of the above

The graph right shows the depth of earthquakes at a plate boundary off the coast of Chile:

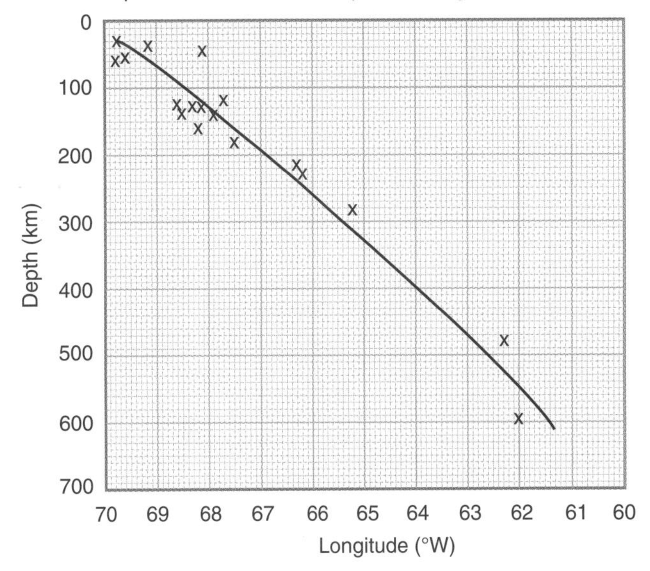

4. This plate boundary
   (a) Is a transform boundary
   (b) Forms a subduction zone
   (c) Is a divergent boundary
   (d) Forms a rift valley

5. Which of the following statements is true?
   (a) The data shows earthquakes only occur off the coast of Chile
   (b) The data shows two tectonic plates are moving apart
   (c) The data shows one tectonic plate is moving under another tectonic plate
   (d) Earthquakes get deeper from east to west

6. The image right shows the major rock types in the South Island of New Zealand. The Alpine Fault is marked on the diagram. The rock types labeled X match. The process responsible for their current position is:
   (a) Movement of the Australian plate along the Alpine Fault to the northeast and the Pacific plate to the southwest
   (b) Movement of the Australian plate along the Alpine Fault to the southwest and the Pacific plate to the northeast
   (c) Movement of the Australian plate under the Pacific plate causing folding of the land along the Alpine Fault
   (d) Rotation of the Pacific plate counterclockwise causing the land to stretch along the Alpine Fault

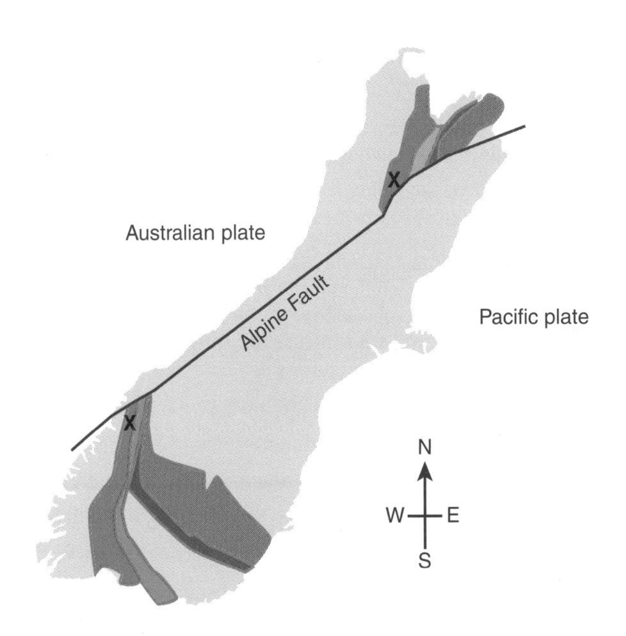

7. The movement of the Alpine Fault is caused by:
   (a) A subduction zone
   (b) A transform fault
   (c) A divergent plate boundary
   (d) A convergent plate boundary

ISBN: 978-1-98-856632-0

8. The A soil horizon:
   (a) Is located below the O horizon
   (b) Is rich in organic matter
   (c) Can vary in thickness
   (d) All of the above

9. Using the soil triangle right, the soil sample shown is:
   (a) A sandy clay
   (b) A silt loam
   (c) A loam
   (d) A sandy clay loam

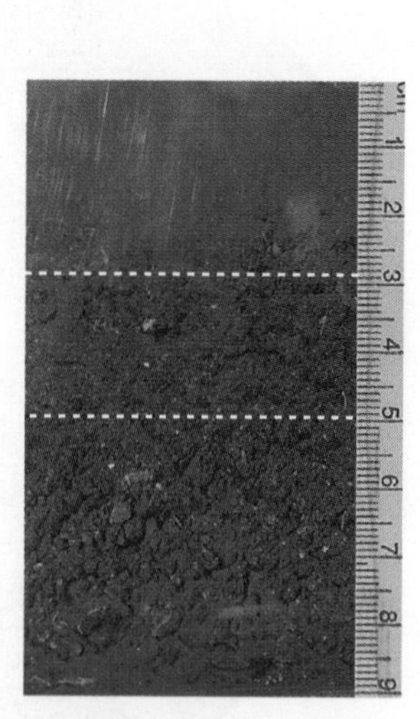

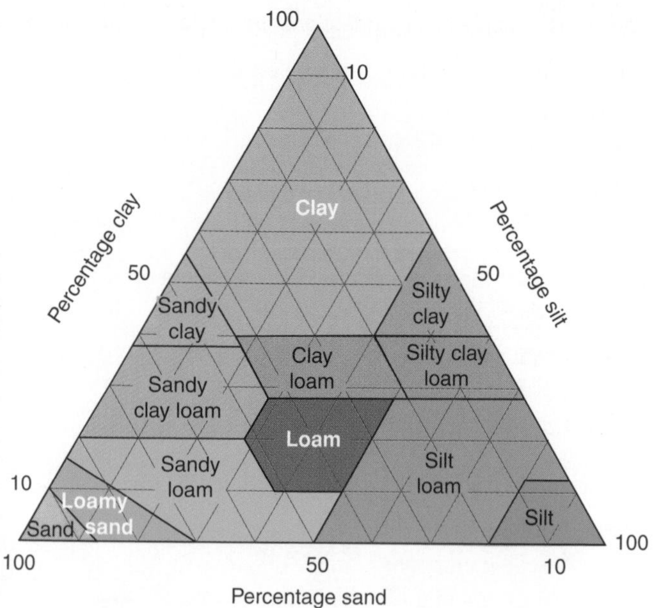

10. Using the soil triangle right, a soil that is 10% clay, 60% sand, and 90% silt is:
   (a) A sandy clay
   (b) A sandy loam
   (c) A loam
   (d) A silty clay loam

11. A rain shadow is caused by:
   (a) Moist air being deflected upwards by a high mountain range.
   (b) Clouds dropping rain on the windward side of a mountain range.
   (c) Dry air descending from a mountain range to a plain below.
   (d) All of the above.

12. The tricellular model of atmospheric circulation describes how air moves about the globe. In this model:
   (a) Air rises at the equator due to heating by the Sun.
   (b) Dry air descends at 30° North and South producing deserts.
   (c) Cold air flowing from the poles produces easterly winds.
   (d) All of the above.

13. The diagram right shows a river system within a watershed. Two storms rain on the river system, storm A and storm B, as shown. Both storms produce the same volume of rain in the same amount of time. The water moving through point X:
   (a) Is greater during storm A
   (b) Is greater during storm B
   (c) Is the same during both storms
   (d) Rises more at point Y that at point X

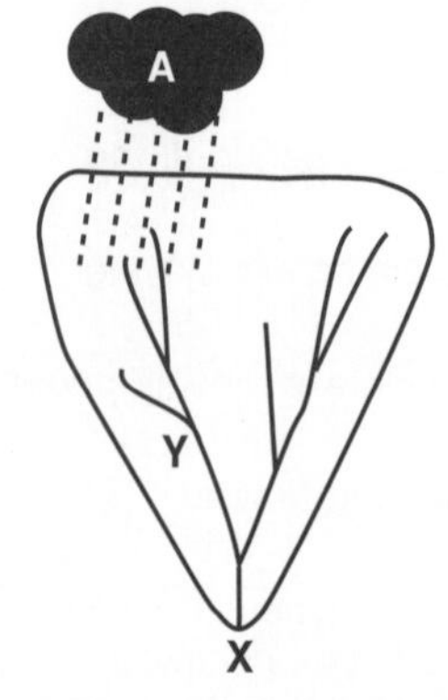

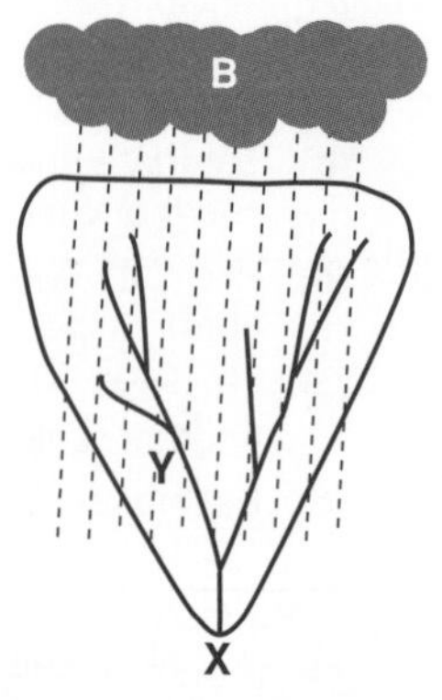

14. During a La Niña event, extra strong trade winds blow from west to east across the Pacific Ocean. Which of the following best describes the effect of this:
   (a) Cold water will well up in the eastern Pacific. The jet stream over North America will move south producing more rain in the north and drought in the south
   (b) Cold water will well up in the eastern Pacific. The jet stream over North America will move south producing drought in the north and more rain in the south
   (c) Cold water will well up in the eastern Pacific. The jet stream over North America will move north producing more rain in the north and drought in the south
   (d) Cold water will well up in the eastern Pacific. The jet stream over North America will move north producing drought in the north and more rain in the south

15. The Earth is tilted at 23.4° relative to the Sun. Which of the following statements is true?
   (a) When it is summer in the Northern Hemisphere the North Pole points away from the Sun.
   (b) The tilt of the Earth is responsible for the change in the amount of sunshine hours through out the year.
   (c) The Northern Hemisphere is warmer in summer because the Earth's tilt brings it closer to the Sun
   (d) The tilt of the Earth has no effect on the seasons in the tropics.

ISBN: 978-1-98-856632-0

16. The loss of topsoil from farmland is a primary concern for farmers, especially in horticultural industries. Topsoil can be lost by being washed away by runoff after rain, or being blown away by the wind. The moisture content of soil plays an important role in the amount of soil lost if it is windy after plowing.

(a) Design an experiment to show the effect of soil moisture on soil lost by the wind.

i. State the hypothesis for your experiment
ii. Describe the method you would use to test your hypothesis
iii. Identify the dependent and independent variables

(b) Describe the experimental results that would support your hypothesis in (a) i.

(c) One strategy to deal with loss of topsoil is to leave the soil unplowed and instead undersow seed (planting directly into the soil underneath the remains of the previously harvested crop).

i. Describe how this strategy would reduce soil loss
ii. Outline how this strategy to reduce soil loss could be tested with respect to wind speed.

You may draw diagrams of your design and use and attach extra paper if needed.

ISBN: 978-1-98-856632-0

5. Land and Water Use

Developing understanding

Content: This unit explores the human activities that disrupt ecosystems and what methods are used to reduce those impacts. Human use of natural resources is addressed with reference to forestry, mining, agriculture, and fisheries. The impact of resource use and urbanization on supplies of fresh water is an important consideration and one that will drive decision-making in the drive for a sustainable future.

Skills: In this unit, you can practice identifying environmental problems and thinking critically about them when evaluating possible solutions. Being able to describe and propose viable solutions for environmental problems is critical for this unit. As in other units, the role of legislation in implementing workable environmental solutions must be understood.

5.1 The tragedy of the commons .... activity 74

☐ 1. Explain the concept of the tragedy of the commons and its implications for resource use and availability.

5.2 Clearcutting .... activity 75

☐ 2. Describe the effects of clearcutting of forests, including economic benefits and environmental consequences.

5.3 The Green Revolution .... activity 76

☐ 3. Describe the agricultural innovations of the Green Revolution, including their benefits and more negative consequences.

5.4 Impacts of agricultural practices......... activity 77

☐ 4. Describe agricultural practices that cause environmental harm, including tilling, slash and burn and fertilizer misuse.

5.5 Irrigation methods .... activity 78

☐ 5. Describe different methods of irrigation and compare and contrast these for their efficiency of water use, cost, and environmental consequences (including soil erosion, salinization, and depletion of aquifers).

5.6 Pest control methods .... activities 79 - 80

☐ 6. Describe the benefits and disadvantages of different methods of pest control, including the increasing incidence of pesticide resistance and the difficulties with using genetic engineering as a solution to pesticide use.

5.7 Meat production methods .... activities 81 - 82

☐ 7. Identify different methods of meat production, including free-range grazing and concentrated animal feeding operations. Describe the benefits and drawbacks of each of these methods with respect to cost, land use, efficiencies, and environmental impacts.

☐ 8. Evaluate the environmental impacts of meat production compared to the production of other food types.

5.8 Impacts of overfishing........................ activity 83

☐ 9. Describe the causes of overfishing and the problems that are associated with it, including loss of food resources and livelihoods, and reduction in biodiversity.

5.9 Impacts of mining............................. activity 84

☐ 10. Describe the extraction of natural mineral resources through mining. Describe the ecological and economic impacts of different mining techniques. At what point does mineral resource extraction become too costly?

5.10 Impacts of urbanization .... activity 85

☐ 11. Explain what is meant by urbanization and describe its effects on the environment (positive and negative). Include reference to effects on the hydrologic and carbon cycles, on land use, and on natural hazards such as flooding.

5.11 Ecological footprints .... activity 86

☐ 12. Describe the concept of the ecological footprint and explain how it is calculated. What does the ecological footprint of the current global human population tell us about human resource use and waste production?

5.12 Introduction to sustainability .... activity 87

☐ 13. Explain the concept of sustainability and describe the environmental indicators that define sustainable practices Explain how the concept of sustainable yield is applied to resource use and describe problems with its implementation.

5.13 Methods to reduce urban runoff .... activity 88

☐ 14. Describe methods for mitigating problems related to urban runoff and increase infiltration. Include reference to construction options and choices of paving materials, use of public transport, and limitations of urban sprawl.

5.14 Integrated pest management .... activity 89

☐ 15. Describe the principles and methods involved in integrated pest management. Describe its environmental and economic benefits and drawbacks, and discuss its role in sustainable agriculture.

5.15 Sustainable agriculture .... activities 90 - 91

☐ 16. Describe the methods by which agriculture and food production can be made more sustainable. Describe the scope of sustainability practices, including preservation and promotion of soil health and fertility, efficiency of water use, and reduction of soil losses.

5.16 Aquaculture .... activity 92

☐ 17. Describe the benefits and drawbacks of aquaculture. Explain the reasons for the rapid expansion in aquaculture and the economic and ecological consequences of this expansion.

5.17 Sustainable forestry .... activity 93

☐ 18. Describe methods for mitigating the impact of humans on forests. These include sustainable forestry practices (including reforestation), sustainable choices in wood used for construction, methods to protect forests from pests and diseases, and the use of prescribed burns to control the incidence and severity of fires and promote regeneration.

74 The Tragedy of the Commons

Key Question: What is the effect of exploiting a shared resource when individuals act according to their own interests? The Tragedy of the Commons is a paper originally written by Garrett Hardin in 1968 explaining how commonly held resources are depleted over time. A commons is shared resource. Often today commons are thought of as parks and reserves, but common land can include areas for grazing. Common areas can also include areas for fishing, such as ponds, rivers, and the sea and oceans. With many people using the same resource and acting independently there is a risk of over exploitation, especially if each person using the resource is unaware of other people's use of the resource.

Exploiting the commons

- In the United States, permits are required to graze public land. Grazing on public land is regulated by the Bureau of Land Management and the United States Forest Service. This is in response to a series of "range wars" in the mid to late 19th century during which there was open conflict between ranchers over perceived grazing rights. Before the introduction of the Taylor Grazing Act in 1934, which formally regulated grazing rights, range lands in the West were exploited as a common resource. The activity below investigates the effect of grazing cattle for personal gain on common grazing land.

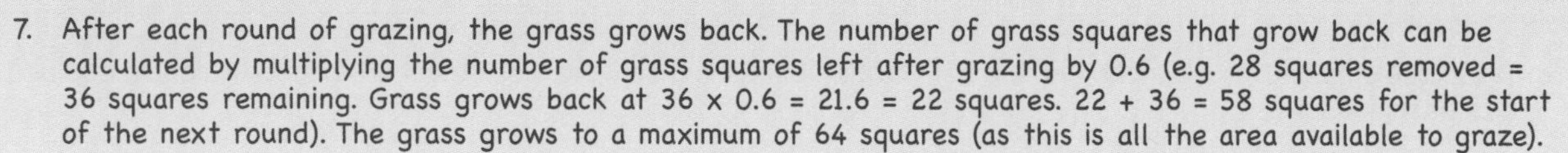

INVESTIGATION: 5.1 The Tragedy of the Commons See appendix for equipment list.

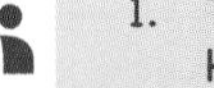

1. This activity works best with a group of 4 and 1-2 bags of wrapped candy (e.g. Hershey's Kisses or Jolly Ranchers). Read the instructions carefully before you start.
2. Using an A4 or US letter sheet of paper rule an 8 x 8 grid of squares. Each square should be 3 cm by 3 cm. Cut this grid up using scissors to make 64 squares.
3. Each player should cut out the "cattle" on the following page and all of the numbers 1-3. These should be put in 4 piles (cattle and numbers 1, 2, 3). One person should be in charge of distributing the cattle and the numbers (the Banker).
4. Layout the 64 squares in a 8 x 8 grid. This represents the common grazing land for the cattle.
5. The object of the game is to accumulate as much candy as possible. The game will last ten rounds or until the candy is gone or until there is not enough grass to graze all the cattle, whichever comes first.
6. Give each person 1 cow and 2 pieces of wrapped candy to start the first round. Each cow grazes 2 squares of grass per round. During each round, each person removes the appropriate number of grass squares from the common grazing land (2 squares per cow owned).
7. After each round of grazing, the grass grows back. The number of grass squares that grow back can be calculated by multiplying the number of grass squares left after grazing by 0.6 (e.g. 28 squares removed = 36 squares remaining. Grass grows back at 36 x 0.6 = 21.6 = 22 squares. 22 + 36 = 58 squares for the start of the next round). The grass grows to a maximum of 64 squares (as this is all the area available to graze).
8. At the start of each round calculate the number of grazing squares in the common (as in step 7) and reset the common accordingly. This is now the number of squares available to graze for the next round.
9. After the first round, extra cattle may be bought from the cattle pile at the cost of 1 piece of candy each. Candy is paid to the Bank. The Bank distributes cattle to those who have bought them.
10. Cattle that have been through 1 round now have the number 1 placed beside them from the number pile (distributed by the Banker). After each round the numbers are changed to show the number of rounds the cattle have survived.
11. When a cow has been through 3 full rounds it can be sold to the Bank for 3 pieces of candy (it has grown, is larger, and therefore worth more). In other words, the first lot of cattle can be sold at the end of the 3rd round and before the 4th round begins.
12. When the grass growth has been calculated and the common reset, and all the cattle have been bought and sold, or had their "round-survived" numbers changed, you are ready to begin the next round.
13. The profit in candy can be used to buy more cattle to graze on the common. By buying, grazing, and selling cattle you could amass a considerable fortune in candy by the end of the game.
14. Once the game is over you may eat the candy.
15. The game can be modified to make it more complex (or simpler) to raise cattle. The rate of grass growth could be changed to represent the change in seasons (faster in spring, slower in winter). Cattle can be made worth more or less. Players can work together to maximize their candy profit rather than individually.

ISBN: 978-1-98-856632-0

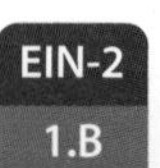

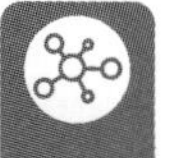

1. (a) How many rounds did your game last? ______

   (b) Was there an absolute winner, or did all farmers/players profit? ______

   (c) Was there much candy left in the Bank? ______

   (d) What was the maximum number of cattle on the common? ______

   (e) How did the numbers of cattle on the common change over the course of the game? ______

   (f) Did you notice if players were working individually or collectively? ______

   (g) What was the carrying capacity of the commons (how many cattle could it support)? ______

   (h) Was there a tragedy in your commons? ______

   (i) If you ran out of grass before the end of ten rounds, how might the game have been replayed to gain the maximum pieces of candy per person, i.e. how could the game be played to be more sustainable?

Why a tragedy?

- A common resource is one which is both **nonexcludable** and **rival**. This means it is a resource that people cannot be stopped from using (by some inalienable right of use or by no current regulation) but the more people that use the resource, the less there is of that resource for anyone else i.e. the resource becomes depleted. These two combined characteristics often result in the over-exploitation of a resource as people try harder to use what resource there is remaining before someone else does. Virtually all fisheries in international waters are examples of this, and most fisheries in exclusive economic zones are as well. Fisheries such as South American anchovies, Pacific bluefin tuna, and North Sea cod have all suffered catastrophic tragedy of the commons scenarios since the 1970s.

2. The important question is why does the tragedy of the commons occur in common resources but not in privately owned resources? Consider the difference between a common fisheries with no regulatory constraints over harvest and a beef farmer who owns a herd of breeding cattle that can be sold for a profit.

   (a) What would happen to the income of the beef farmer if they sold all of their stock at once?

   (b) What would happen to the income of the beef farmer if they sold only the stock that had reached saleable age and size each season?

   (c) Which is the better long term strategy for the farmer? ______

   (d) Now consider a fisher fishing a common fishery in rivalry with other fishers. What happens if the fisher does not go fishing for a day?

   (e) Why does this provide no incentive to not fish for a day? ______

   (f) Why does this in fact provide an incentive to fish as much as possible? ______

   (g) Explain how the tragedy of the commons occurs: ______

ISBN: 978-1-98-856632-0

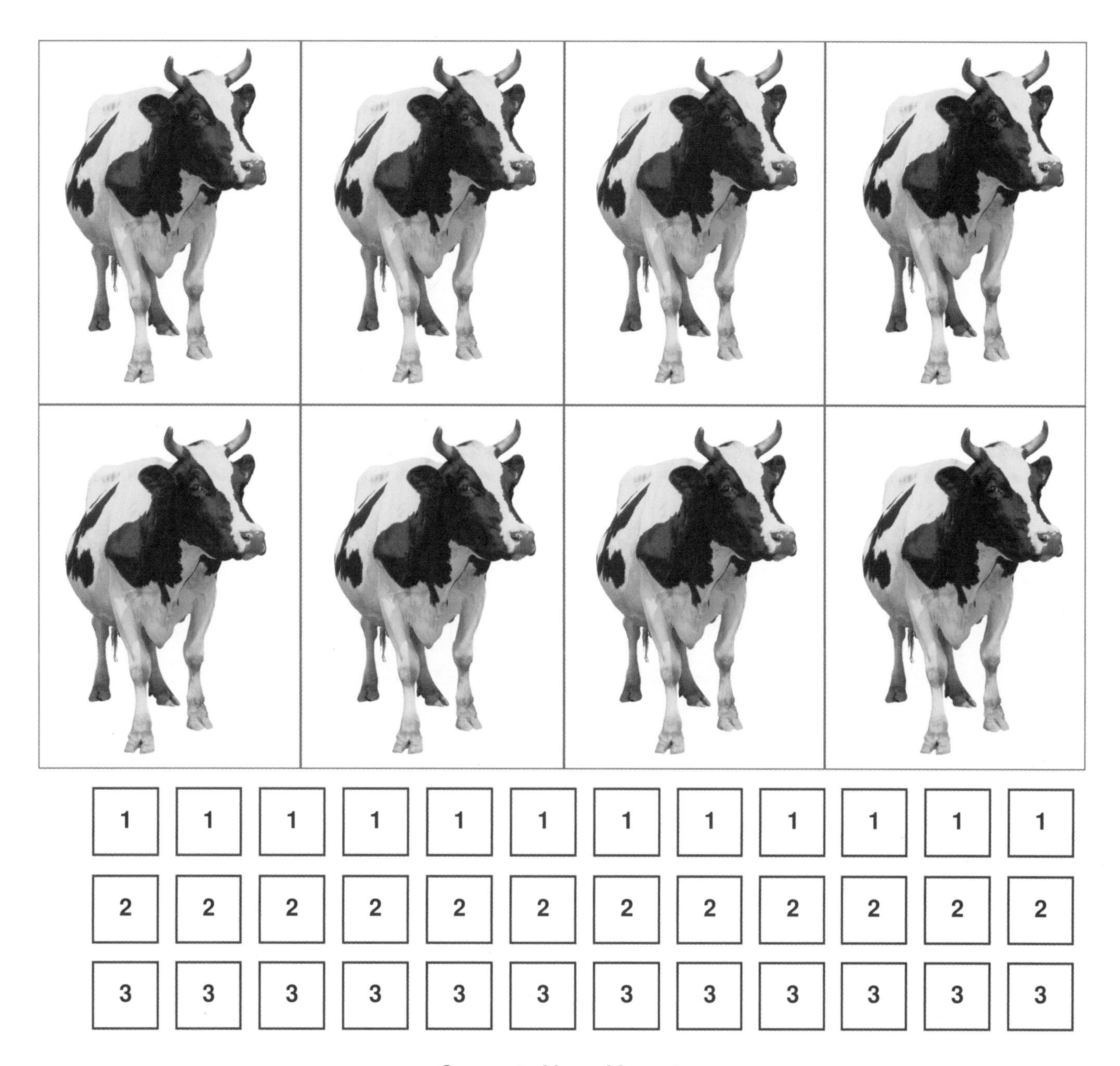

Suggested board layout

Player 3

2 2

Cow being grazed

2

Player 4

2

1

1

Player 1

2

1

Rounds this cow has been through

1 2 3

Player 2

Total cattle being grazed: 10

Squares grazed: 20

ISBN: 978-1-98-856632-0

THIS PAGE HAS BEEN DELIBERATELY LEFT BLANK

ISBN: 978-1-98-856632-0

75 Clearcutting

Key Question: What is clearcutting, what are its advantages and disadvantages, and what effects does it have?

Clearcutting is a forestry method in which all the trees in a specified area are felled and removed. This method of logging is very common and is by far the easiest and cheapest method of obtaining lumber. However, unless practiced carefully it is also extraordinarily destructive. Clearcutting is carried out in different ways in different parts of the world, usually based on factors such as common or public ownership of forest, historical land use, and government regulations.

Why clearcut?

The reasons for clearcutting vary from country to country. Many of these reasons are based on economic factors including the skill of the foresters and the equipment required. However some factors may be social and in some cases even political.

State forest Oregon, US

Logging operation, Indonesia

Gum plantation Australia

Regulated forestry on public land

- Permits for logging.
- Specific rules about how and where trees can be cut and replanted.
- Rules on effect of logging on natural resources.
- Income depends on ability to continue holding logging permits.
- Income depends on reduction of costs.

Public forest but unregulated

- No rules on logging or rules are not enforced by authorities.
- Cleared land can be used for farming.
- Other loggers will take trees if you don't.
- Logging creates jobs for low income communities.

Private plantations

- Rules for effect on environment.
- Income depends on continued presence of forest.
- Income depends on quality of trees.
- Income depends on speed of tree growth.
- Income depends on reduction of costs.

Advantages of clearcutting

▶ The advantages of clearcutting vary. Some of these are economic, some are environmental. It costs less to enter the forest once, log the trees, and leave. This may reduce the impact of repeated entry to the forested area. In some cases, clearcutting may mimic natural events such as land slides, wind damage, and forest fires. Clearcutting is also simpler. It does not require specialized equipment or planning to remove specific trees. This can reduce costs.

Disadvantages of clearcutting

▶ There are some serious environmental disadvantages of clearcutting. Initial biodiversity is reduced along with ecosystem services and processes. Forest surrounding the cleared area is more susceptible to wind damage and weed invasion. Large openings can expose the forest floor to erosion. However if branches and debris are left, the ground is more protected from wind and rain, and buffer strips left on waterways help to reduce the impact of floods.

Heikki Valve cc 3.0

1. Forestry companies working on regulated public land and those working on private plantations have incentives to keep their operations sustainable. Identify these incentives and compare and contrast them for the two types of operations:

2. Unregulated forests or forests in areas where regulations cannot be enforced are vulnerable to tragedy of the commons scenarios. Explain why. If you can, provide examples of where this kind of forestry might be happening:

ISBN: 978-1-98-856632-0

Clearcutting and the environment

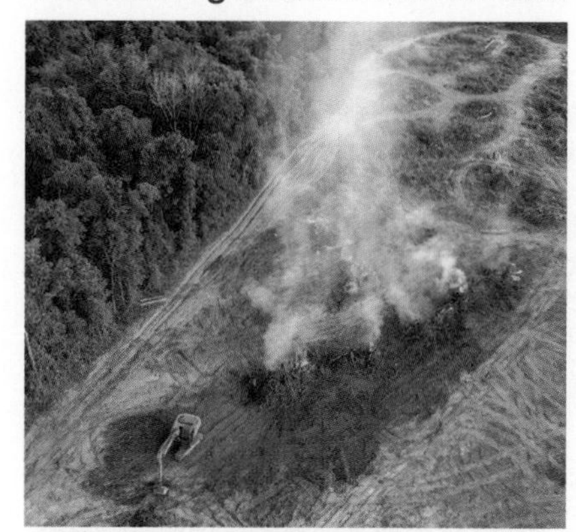

Clearcutting forests to make way for farms or plantations of other tree types (e.g. oil palms) can produce large amounts of carbon dioxide through the burning of undergrowth and scrub to clear the land after the logs have been removed. This contributes to the rise in carbon dioxide in the atmosphere and so to climate change. Clearcutting in this way is not sustainable and causes huge environmental damage from erosion and loss of habitat. However if the area is replanted for forestry, biodiversity and habitat may recover over time, although in a reduced state.

Clearcutting forests in a managed way can minimize environmental effects. Logging provides building material, i.e. lumber. The carbon in lumber is usually locked up for long periods of time especially if used for furniture or framing for houses. Use of lumber in this way acts as a carbon sink. Trees are replanted and remove more carbon from the atmosphere as they grow and so the process continues. Although this sink is small, it helps managed forestry to be relatively carbon neutral or at least produce minimal emissions.

Many plantation forests are managed sustainably. Mature blocks of trees are clearcut and replanted. Plantations are big enough that blocks of trees can be rotated through planting, growth, and felling in an economically sustainable way. It may be twenty years between clearcutting the same block of trees. However most plantation forests are on land that was once old growth forest. This may have been felled during colonization of an area or at the beginning of the industry. In this case, the biodiversity of the old growth forest may never return.

3. What is clearcutting? ____________________

4. Describe how this can be economically advantageous: ____________________

5. Describe the disadvantages of clearcutting: ____________________

6. How can clearcutting practices mitigate (reduce) the effect they have on the environment?

7. Consider the following scenario: You are a subsistence farmer in a third-world country (low economic development and generally poorly regulated government). Your small piece of land is next to a larger forest. Government laws prohibit logging or deliberate clearing of the forest but law enforcement in your area is often underfunded and ineffective. Illegal loggers have been operating nearby, and some neighboring farmers have recently cleared land to increase their cropland. International conservation groups insist that the forest should be saved and are lobbying the government to stop small land owners clearing land. You have never seen any conservationist in your area. You agree that the forest should be left standing and is an important natural resource but you can only just grow enough for your family on your small piece of land. Having a little more would do a lot to improve your income and quality of life. Some of the timber from the forest would come in useful for fences or buildings. You are worried the loggers and other farmers may claim the area and remove this resource or ruin the soil so it can't grow anything.

Discuss in groups: what would you do? Should you follow the regulations and the advice of the conservation groups and leave the forest standing, or should you get in before the loggers and clear and claim some more land in case the government listens to the conservation groups and regulates the activities of small farmers? On a separate piece of paper, summarize your discussion and add a reasoned argument for your view point. Attach the paper to this page.

ISBN: 978-1-98-856632-0

76 The Green Revolution

Key Question: What was the Green Revolution and how has it affected global food production?

There have been three agricultural revolutions in the history of human agriculture. The first occurred during the transition of human societies from hunting and gathering to farming (between about 10,000 BC and 2000 BC). This is also called the Neolithic Revolution. The second, called the British Agricultural Revolution, began around the mid 1600s and saw a massive increase in agricultural production due to new cropping techniques (including crop rotation), improved irrigation and cultivation, and an increase in farm labor. The third revolution (the **Green Revolution**) occurring between the 1940s and the late 1960s was the result of adopting new technologies to increase crop yields, including selective crop breeding, increased mechanization, and use of agrochemicals and irrigation. This suite of practices vastly increased global yields of staple food crops (e.g. wheat, rice, maize) on which populations depended for food. The center of this revolution was Mexico with support from the United States. Many believe we are now on the brink of a fourth agricultural revolution, aided by new digital technologies capable of improving farming efficiencies and outcomes.

What was involved in the Green Revolution?

Billy Hathorn CC 3.0

Political will and NGOs

Post WWII the Mexican government moved to improve Mexican agriculture by increasing technological input. This was supported by the US Department of Agriculture (USDA) and the Rockefeller Foundation. The goal was not only to help in the development of a neighboring country but also to provide a test case for new agricultural practices, and stem any move there toward Communism. The US agronomist Norman Bourlaug was a key figure in these new crop developments.

USDA

Cross breeding and hybridization

By using cross breeding and hybridization, Bourlaug's team developed a semi-dwarf wheat that was resistant to rust and carried a larger seed head. Mexico's wheat output went from half a million tonnes in 1940 to 5.5 million tonnes by 1985. Bourlaug's team also carried out this process with wheat in India and Pakistan, and with rice in Asia. The techniques and plant varieties developed by Bourlaug's team were quickly adopted around the world.

Intensive agriculture

Optimizing plant growth is key to improving crop output. Economies of scale also play a role. This leads to increased mechanization, and the introduction of ever bigger tractors, irrigators, and harvesters. The introduction of tractors allows the soil to be optimally prepared by plowing and rotary hoeing, more seed to be planted at any one time, and the crop kept clear of weeds by mechanical hoes. Mechanization also allows more efficient and large scale application of fertilizers and pesticides.

Problems with intensification and Green Revolution practices

- Failure to use pesticides carefully or correctly has led to resistance in some pest species. Overuse of fertilizers leads to eutrophication of waterways.
- As with any technology, seed development is open to commercialization. Seed production companies hold the rights to many important seeds, fertilizers, and pesticides. This has led to moral conflicts. Should those who invested in the development have control of seed supplies? What if a small operation cannot remain viable because it can't afford seed?
- The increase in mechanization during the Green Revolution has been accompanied by rise in fossil fuel use in the agricultural sector globally. Increased irrigation can lead to salinization of the soil in dryland areas as evaporation and irrigation losses concentrate salts near the surface.
- The Green Revolution has had conflicting outcomes. Intensification allows the production of more food, but uses more fossil fuel. More food supports increased population growth, and larger populations demand more food and so on. It may end only when we reach the carrying capacity of the planet. But how does carrying capacity change as technology advances?

1. What were the important factors in the beginning of the Green Revolution?

ISBN: 978-1-98-856632-0

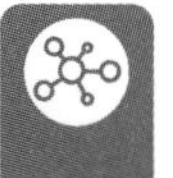

The gene revolution

IRRI CC 2.0

- The second stage of the Green Revolution is sometimes called the **gene revolution**. It is based on developments in **selective breeding** and, later on, **genetic engineering**. Although cross breeding and hybridization has grown rapidly in scope and importance since it began in 1967, extensive research has been carried out on genetically modified seeds since the 1980s. Genetic modification (GM) has been used to create plants with higher yields and specific tolerances (e.g. pest resistance, herbicide tolerance, or drought tolerance). GM seed is also used to improve the nutritional quality of crops e.g. by increasing protein or vitamin levels.
- An example of this is golden rice (right). Golden rice is genetically engineered to contain higher than normal levels of beta-carotene, which is converted in the body to vitamin A. This may allow better nutrient delivery to people in developing countries where rice is the staple food. Other areas of research include improving yields and improving the resistance of rice to insects, bacteria, and herbicides.

2. The data below shows the crop yields for corn and wheat in the United States. Plot the corn yield on the left axis and the wheat yield on the right axis. Include a key:

Year	Corn production for grain (t/ha)	Wheat production (t/ha)
1910	1.88	0.94
1920	2.02	0.94
1930	1.41	0.94
1935	1.61	0.81
1940	1.95	1.01
1945	2.22	1.14
1950	2.49	1.14
1955	2.82	1.35
1960	3.70	1.75
1965	4.98	1.82
1970	4.84	2.08
1975	5.78	2.08
1980	6.12	2.56
1985	7.94	2.56
1990	7.94	2.69
1995	7.67	2.42
2000	9.21	2.82
2005	9.95	2.82
2010	10.29	3.09
2015	11.3	2.96
2017	11.9	3.09

Data source USDA

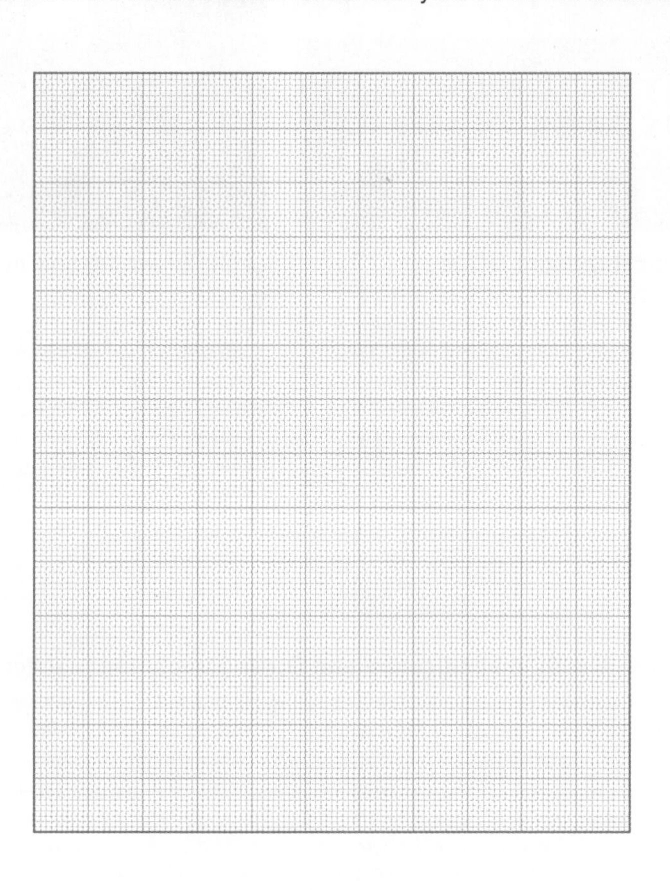

3. Explain how the technologies of the Green Revolution were used to improve crop yields: ______

4. How has the Green Revolution led to some conflicting outcomes for the population of the Earth? ______

5. Some authorities argue the Green Revolution failed in many countries including Mexico, normally touted as the birthplace and one of the best examples of the Green Revolution. Use the internet to search for one of these arguments (**BIOZONE's Resource Hub** has some useful sites). For your example, describe the author's perspective and any assumptions they made. Are they presenting a reasoned, unbiased argument? Write your argument and conclusion on a separate piece of paper and attach it to this page.

ISBN: 978-1-98-856632-0

77 The Impact of Farming

Key Question: How do some agricultural practices cause environmental damage?

Agricultural practices vary widely between countries and between regions within countries. While all agriculture will affect the environment in some way, some practices can cause significantly more environmental damage than others. In many industrialized nations these practices have been replaced, either because they are no longer appropriate environmentally, socially, or economically, or because more efficient, sustainable techniques have been implemented. Changing to less damaging techniques is not always easy. In industrialized countries it can mean the difference between being an importer rather than an exporter of food. In many developing countries, changing farming practices without suitable education and upgrades to technology (which many countries can't afford) could mean widespread famine.

Crop growing after slash and burn , Madagascar

Frank Vassen CC 3.0

Slash and burn

Slash and burn is a farming method in which forested or scrub-covered land is cut down and burnt. The ashes remaining act as fertilizer for the crop. This method is ancient and, not surprisingly, very damaging to the environment. Many industrialized nations used it during periods of colonization to clear land for pasture. However, if the land is to continue to be productive it has to be properly managed, as many industrialized farms are today. Slash and burn is still used in many developing nations, often by small farmers. In Brazil, it is estimated 0.5 million hectares of forest a year is lost as a result of slash and burn.

Tillage

Tillage is an important agricultural practice as it prepares a flat even surface for planting. This is especially the case for vegetable crops. Done carefully and on suitable ground it can have a relatively low impact on the environment. Tillage is usually done in two stages. The first stage plows the field into furrows, lifting the surface and turning it over. The second stage breaks up the furrows and prepares an even surface. Tillage exposes the topsoil to the wind and rain so it can result in a loss of topsoil through erosion. Tillage at the wrong time of season can result in heavy soil losses.

Fertilizers

The use of synthetic fertilizers (e.g. urea) has increased crop yields many times over. However overuse can have long lasting detrimental effects on the environment. This is often in the form of eutrophication of waterways. Fertilizers leach nutrients into nearby rivers and lakes and can cause a rapid growth in algae, often resulting in waterways becoming clogged with algal growth. Algal decomposition depletes oxygen levels in the water and can result in large die-offs of aquatic organisms.

Pesticides, herbicides, and fungicides

Chemical sprays are used extensively to control crop pests and diseases in industrialized agriculture. Indiscriminate use of these leads to increased resistance to commonly used chemicals, contamination of land and water, and often loss of beneficial non-target species. Some species, such as the Colorado potato beetle are now resistant to many different pesticides. The genetic engineering of some crops to be herbicide resistant (e.g. round-up ready crops) has contributed to overuse of chemical sprays.

1. Describe the effects intensive farming can have on the environment: ____________________

____

____

____

____

ISBN: 978-1-98-856632-0

78 Irrigation

Key Question: What methods of irrigation are used to water crops, and which are the most efficient?

Crops require water. Humans have designed a range of techniques to deliver water to crops. Some are very simple, others require a high degree of technology. Some methods are very wasteful, others are highly efficient. The method of irrigation depends on how the water is being sourced, where it is being used, and the technology available to deliver the water. Irrigation of crops is so important that 70% of the world's freshwater withdrawals are used for that one purpose.

Methods of irrigation

Flood irrigation

Water is applied rapidly to the entire surface and left to infiltrate the soil. This system only works on relatively flat or enclosed land. A large percentage of water is lost via evaporation and unless carried out carefully there is a risk of water-logging the soil, which can reduce plant growth.

Spray irrigation

Spray irrigators use a nozzle to spray water over a large area. They can be adjusted to spray in specific directions and target specific areas. Very high water pressure is needed for these to operate and so they require pumps, often run from a tractor or a farm wide system. Depending on conditions, as much as a quarter of the water might evaporate or be otherwise lost.

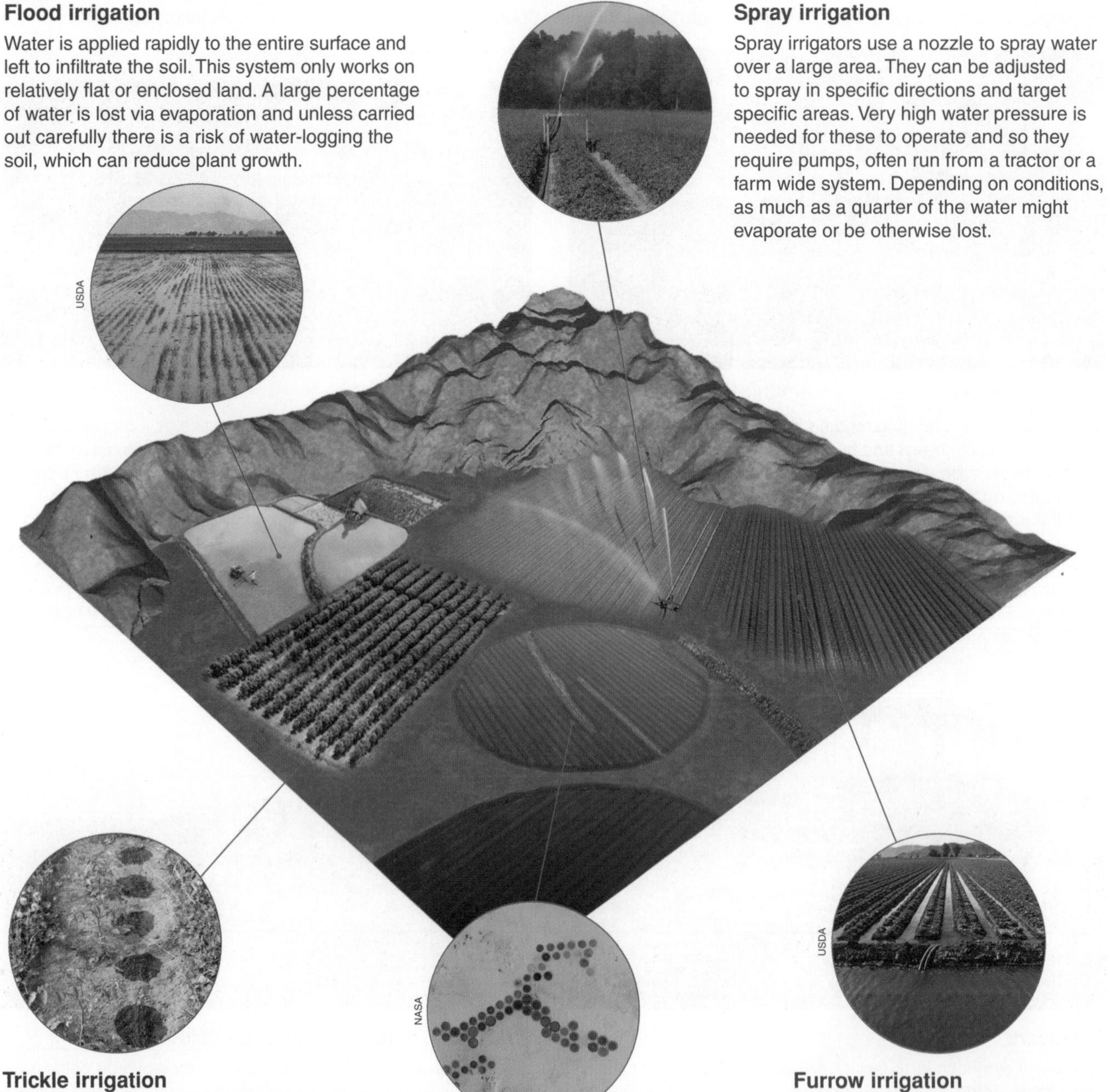

Trickle irrigation

Trickle or drip irrigation uses water running through thin piping that runs either along the ground near the crop or is attached to permanent trees. The water trickles into the ground next to the plant. Very little water is lost as a result and water is targeted directly to individual plants. In some cases, the pipes can be put underground, stopping any evaporation. However the system must be removed from the ground before harvesting or plowing and so must be reset every season.

Pivot irrigation

Pivot irrigation is a method of spray irrigation. The irrigator is fixed at one end and moves in a circle spraying water directly below the irrigator. These irrigators can be huge, up to 500 m long, watering 78 hectares of land and easily visible with satellites. These massive irrigators have successfully brought agriculture to barren deserts. Increases in the efficiency of these irrigators have been offset by farmers growing crops that require more water.

Furrow irrigation

This involves cutting furrows or ditches in the field and letting water run through them from a main water supply. In some cases this system doesn't require pumps and so is very simple and inexpensive. However it is inefficient with up to a third of the water failing to be used by the plants. Most is lost by evaporation.

ISBN: 978-1-98-856632-0

NASA
Crops watered from the Ogallala Aquifer, Kansas

Irrigation has allowed the cultivation of food crops in places that were never viable before, but the production comes at a cost. The water irrigating many barren lands is pumped up from deep aquifers at a faster rate than it is replenished. As a result, these aquifers are slowly being depleted. The Ogallala Aquifer beneath the Great Plains in the United States provides water for irrigation in eight states. However the extraction rate for irrigation is many times greater than the recharge rate. Estimates vary but the aquifer could be effectively empty within a few decades.

Salt damage to soil

Another effect of irrigation is salinization. This is the increase in salts in the topsoil which can severely reduce crop production. All water contains some amount of soluble salts (even rainwater). As irrigation water evaporates, these salts are left behind in the top soil. Over time the salt concentration increases, making the land less productive. A higher rate of irrigation can cause the salts to leach and so be removed. However, poor drainage can greatly increase salt concentration in the soil as can the use of groundwater already high in salt.

USGS
Colorado River

Many rivers and streams have been diverted or dammed to improve irrigation. The Colorado River no longer reaches the sea due to dams and diversions for irrigation and other water use. This reduces water in the river delta and has caused the loss of wetland habitats. The Colorado River delta is now only about 5% of its size before the Hoover and Glen Canyon dams were built, supplying water for agricultural, industrial, and domestic use. Similarly, the Rio Grande, which runs the length of New Mexico, often runs dry as a result of over-irrigation during dry periods.

1. Describe the methods of irrigation below and their advantages and disadvantages in terms of water delivery:

   (a) Trickle irrigation: ______

   (b) Spray irrigation: ______

   (c) Flood irrigation: ______

   (d) Furrow irrigation: ______

2. The diversion and storage of water in dams and its use by pumps was part of the solution to feeding the people of world. As with many solutions, there are always unseen consequences.

   (a) Describe some of these unseen consequences in relation to irrigation: ______

   (b) In groups, discuss the benefits and undesirable consequences of irrigating arid lands. Decide if the benefits outweigh the consequences and what might be done to mitigate the detrimental effects. Summarize your points below:

ISBN: 978-1-98-856632-0

79 Pest Control Methods

Key Question: What are the advantages and disadvantages of different methods of pest control?

Control of pests in agriculture is very important because single-species crops (monocultures) are very vulnerable to pest infestations. They provide an enormous amount of food for pest species and, without control, these pests can feed and reproduce rapidly, quickly ruining a crop. Although biological and cultural methods of pest control are widely used, chemical pest control is often the preferred and simplest option, especially if an infestation has occurred. This applies not only to insect pests in commercial agriculture, but also in urban areas, e.g. cockroaches. Pesticides are also used to control rodents, weeds, and fungi in both agricultural and urban areas.

- A pesticide is any chemical that kills or discourages pests (unwanted or damaging organisms). Pests generally include insect pests on crops or animals, damaging fungi and microbes, and vermin such as rats and mice. Various specific chemicals have been developed to control these pests and are named after their specific use, e.g. herbicide, fungicide, insecticide, or rodenticide.
- Chemical controls must be used carefully to avoid pests becoming resistant or bait shy. Also care must be taken to avoid build up of residues in the environment, and many sprays now degrade quickly. However this means they must be regularly applied.

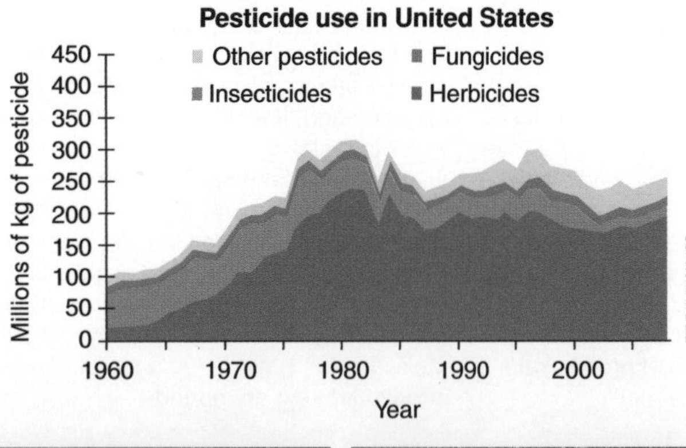

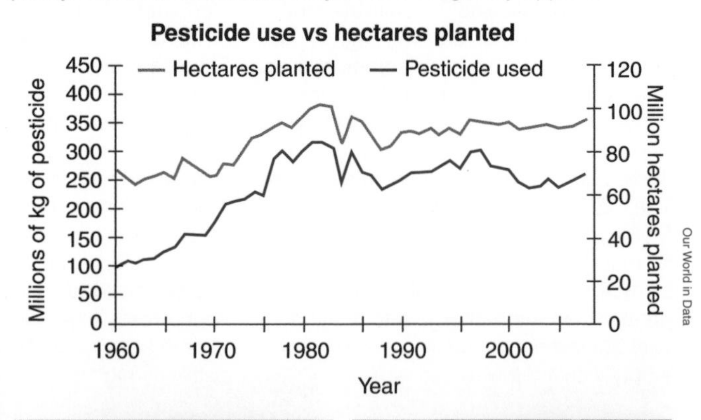

Fungicides prevent damage by rusts, molds, and mildews. Like all pesticides applied to plants, they may be contact or systemic. Contact sprays kill where they touch. Systemic sprays are circulated in the plant and kill at any point.

Mnolf CC 3.0

Glyphosate is the most common broad spectrum herbicide in use. It inhibits a metabolic pathway present in plants but not mammals, making it relatively safe to use. It only works on growing plants and so does not affect seeds.

K Pryor

The most common rodenticide is Brodifacoum, which is a highly lethal anticoagulant. It has a long life, even after the death of the rodent and so secondary poisoning can be problematic if the rat is eaten by other mammals or birds.

Insecticides range from those used in agriculture to fly sprays used inside buildings. Insecticides work in various ways, such as over-stimulating the nervous system. Pyrethroids are natural insecticides commonly used in homes.

- An important piece of legislation concerning pesticides and food was the **Delaney Clause** of the Federal Food, Drug, and Cosmetic Act. This clause prohibits the use of any food additive found to cause cancer. It applied to pesticides in processed foods where the pesticide residue becomes more concentrated during processing. The clause was very restrictive because it set a zero level of risk. No amount was permitted, even when well below the level that would cause any heath issues. As testing became more sensitive, pesticides were found more often, and the clause became more difficult to administer. It was replaced in 1996 with the Food Quality Protection Act which placed specific standards and limits on pesticide residues.

1. (a) What was the trend in pesticide use between 1960 and 1980? ____________________

   (b) What was the trend in pesticide use between 1980 and the present? ____________________

   (c) What has driven these trends? ____________________

   ____

   (d) Which type of pesticide has seen the greatest increase in use over time? ____________________

   (e) Why might this be? ____________________

   ____

2. Why does glyphosate target plants specifically? ____________________

   ____

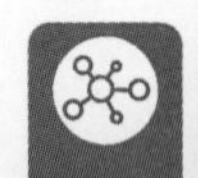
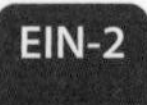
EIN-2

ISBN: 978-1-98-856632-0

Genetic engineering

- Genetic engineering (GE) is the introduction into or removal of genes from an organism. Numerous GE crops have been developed, for example Bt corn.
- Bt corn is a corn variety genetically engineered to contain a gene from the soil bacterium *Bacillus thuringiensis*. The gene allows the corn to produce a toxin, which acts as a pesticide against butterfly and moth larvae but does not affect other insects such as beetles or bees (or indeed any other animal). The target insect pest for Bt corn is the larval stage of the European corn borer, which causes hundreds of millions of dollars worth of damage to crops annually. The Bt endotoxin had been used since the 1960s as a microbial insecticide and is considered safe because of its selectivity.
- Some GE crops are engineered for enhanced crop production or resistance to drought. In 1996, "Roundup Ready" corn become available, engineered to withstand glyphosate herbicide. Corn crops could be sprayed with herbicide and while the weeds would die the corn would keep on growing, allowing less targeted spraying applications.
- One of the problems with crops engineered to be pest resistant is that over time the pests also become resistant in the same way that they become resistant to conventional pesticides. This means that the plant must be continually engineered or cross-bred to produce different strains.
- Similarly, where glyphosate has been incorrectly applied, weed species are also becoming resistant.
- Plant breeders must be careful to preserve the genetic diversity of crops. A lack of genetic diversity makes a crop more vulnerable to a disease or pest outbreak. In a genetically diverse crop, some individuals will be naturally more resistant.

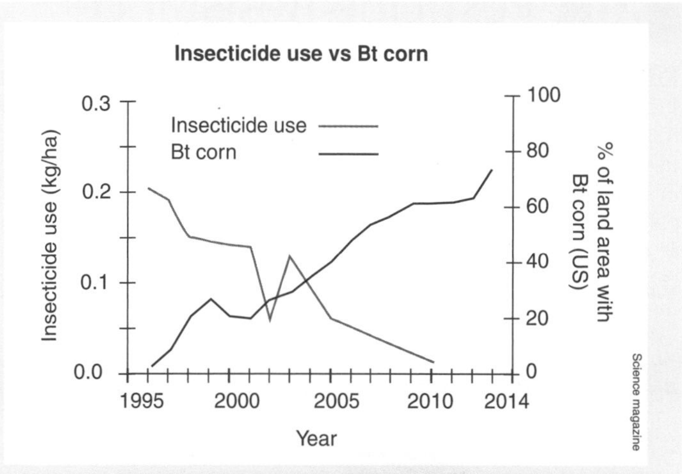

The corn borer burrows into corn stems, causing the plants to collapse

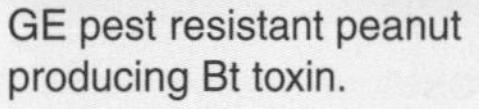

GE pest resistant peanut producing Bt toxin.

Non resistant peanut damaged by the lesser cornstalk borer.

3. What are some advantages and disadvantages of pesticides? ____________________

4. (a) What is the trend in the use of Bt corn over time? ____________________

   (b) What effect has this had on the use of insecticides on corn crops? ____________________

5. Suggest some advantages and disadvantages of genetic engineering for pest resistance in crop plants:

6. Why is genetic diversity important in crop plants. ____________________

ISBN: 978-1-98-856632-0

80 Pesticide Resistance

Key Question: How does pesticide resistance occur?

Insecticides are pesticides used to control insects considered harmful to humans, their livelihood, or environment. Insecticide use has increased since the advent of synthetic insecticides in the 1940s. Their widespread but often inefficient use of can lead to resistance to the insecticide in the target species. Mutations may also produce traits that further assist with resistance. Ineffectual application may include application at the wrong time, e.g. before the majority of the population has established or close to rain, and applying contact sprays that may be avoided by hiding under leaves. To combat increasing resistance, higher doses of more potent pesticides are sometimes used. This drives the selection process, so that increasingly higher dose rates are required to combat rising resistance (the **pesticide treadmill**). This cycle of increasing resistance in response to increased doses is made worse by the development of multiple resistance in some insect pest species such as the Colorado potato beetle (below).

Pesticide resistance in the Colorado potato beetle

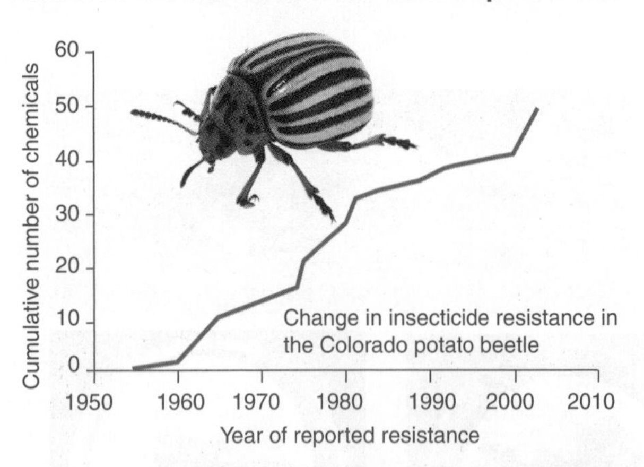

The Colorado potato beetle (*Leptinotarsa decemlineata*) is a major potato pest that was originally found living on buffalo-bur (*Solanum rostratum*) in the Rocky mountains. It has an extraordinary ability to develop resistance to synthetic pesticides. Since the 1940s, when these pesticides were first developed, it has become resistant to more than 50 different types.

Mechanisms of resistance in insect pests

Insecticide resistance in insects can arise through a combination of mechanisms.

- Increased sensitivity to an insecticide will cause the pest to avoid a treated area.
- Certain genes result in stronger physical barriers, decreasing the rate at which the chemical penetrates the insect's cuticle.
- Detoxification by enzymes within the insect's body can render the insecticide harmless.
- Structural changes to the target enzymes make the insecticide ineffective.
- No single mechanism provides total immunity, but together they transform the effect from potentially lethal to insignificant.

The evolution of resistance

The application of an insecticide can act as a potent selection pressure for resistance in pest insects. Insects with a low natural resistance die from an insecticide application, but those with a higher natural resistance may survive if the insecticide is not effectively applied. These will act as founders for a new generation which will, on average, have a higher resistance to the insecticide.

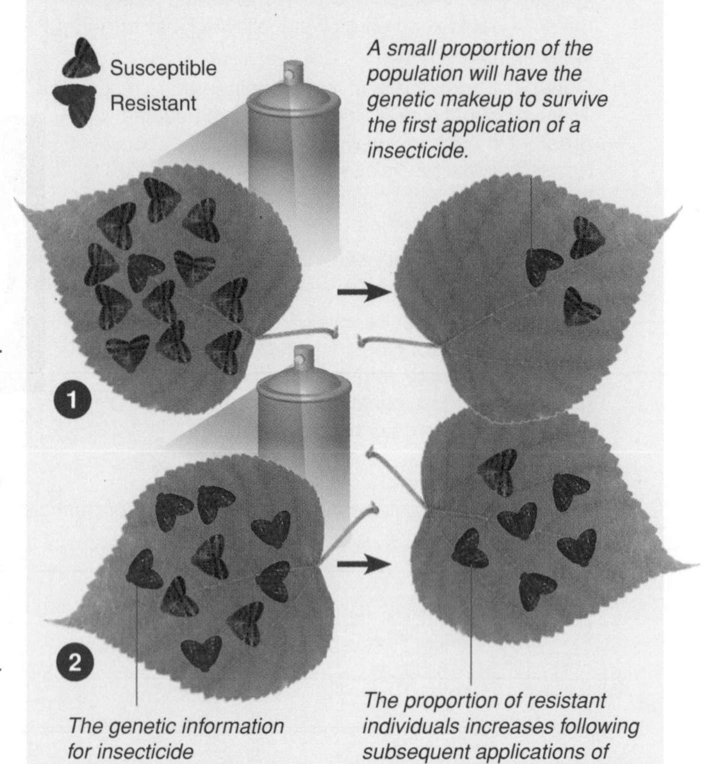

1. Explain how repeated insecticide applications acts as a selective agent for evolutionary change in insect populations:

2. Some insects have become resistant to various type of pesticides. Suggest a way that this resistance and future development of resistance might be reduced. Explain your claim.

ISBN: 978-1-98-856632-0

81 Meat Production Methods

Key Question: What are some common meat production methods and what are their advantages and disadvantages? The method of meat production depends greatly on the type of livestock being raised and often on the country and local environment it is raised in. Global meat production, which includes beef, pigs, poultry, and sheep, has been steadily increasing since the 1950s. Part of this is because of the increasing wealth of the middle classes in developed and now increasingly in developing countries. This increase in wealth allows more expenditure on luxury items, including meat, which for the longest part of human history has been a luxury item. Meat production requires a large amount of land for grazing and supplemental feed and, due to the laws of trophic efficiency, will always be less efficient than growing crops for food. However different methods of raising livestock can increase or decrease this efficiency.

CAFOs

- Concentrated animal feeding operations (CAFOs) are used in areas where grazing land is limited or not available throughout the year, or as a way of quickly raising animals to slaughter weight. As defined by the USDA, a CAFO is specifically an operation where over 1000 animal units are raised in a confined space (e.g. a barn or stall) for over 45 days of the year. An animal unit is about 500 kg of live weight, so equates to 1000 cattle. Confinement of animals varies depending on the type of animal and the particular method being used, as well as local legislation.
- A CAFO is typically made up of one or more large covered barns. Because of the waste produced by the animals inside, the barns are usually located near to a large wastewater lagoon where effluent is stored. Large CAFOs may be made up of dozens of large barns. There is no upper limit to the number of barns or animals within a CAFO. For example, some of the largest swine (pig) CAFOS house more than 79,000 animals.
- There are many benefits of CAFOs, including faster growing rates, being able to raise animals in all climate conditions, and providing low cost meat to consumers. However, there are also numerous disadvantages. Having the animals so close together means disease can spread quickly. Animals are regularly given antibiotics to guard against this, whether they are sick or not. Waste management is an important issue. Failure to store, treat, and dispose of waste correctly can cause major environmental problems, including air and water pollution. There are also many animal health issues, often to do with the rate of animal growth and confinement of and proximity to other animals.

Free range

- Free range grazing requires large amounts of land. Typically one cattle beast needs slightly less than a hectare of grass to graze over a year. This varies depending on the breed of cattle and the growing conditions. Thus farms and ranches with hundreds of cattle require hundreds of hectares. This can be reduced by providing supplemental winter feed (e.g. silage or corn) that was grown in the spring and summer during better growing conditions.
- There are several advantages to raising free range animals. Essentially, these are the result of removing the disadvantages of CAFOs. Animals do not require regular antibiotics because they are less confined, and waste management problems are reduced because the animal waste acts as fertilizer on the pasture. Animals tend to grow more slowly and have room to move easily so there are fewer animal health issues.
- Free range livestock take longer to grow, so costs are higher, and each animal requires more food and water over its lifetime to reach slaughter weight.
- Because energy is lost in the conversion of forage to animal protein, raising animals is always less efficient that growing crops. However, efficiency can be increased through careful management and taking advantage of environmental conditions. For example, studies have shown it is four times more energy efficient to raise and process lamb in New Zealand and ship it 18,000 km to the UK, than to raise and process the lamb in the UK itself. This is partly because New Zealand has a generally mild climate suited to year round production, as opposed to England's cooler climate. This mean production costs are lower and yields are higher.

1. Describe the advantages and disadvantages of CAFOs: ______________________________

____

____

____

2. Describe the advantages and disadvantages of free-range grazing: ______________________________

____

____

____

ISBN: 978-1-98-856632-0

Global meat production

Since 1961, world annual meat production has increased almost five fold. The graphs below compare aspects of food production. Upper panel. Left: Changes in meat production since 1961. Right: Meat consumption vs GDP (a measure of wealth). Lower panel. Left: Land used to produce various foods. Right: Greenhouse gas emissions per kg of food for different food types).

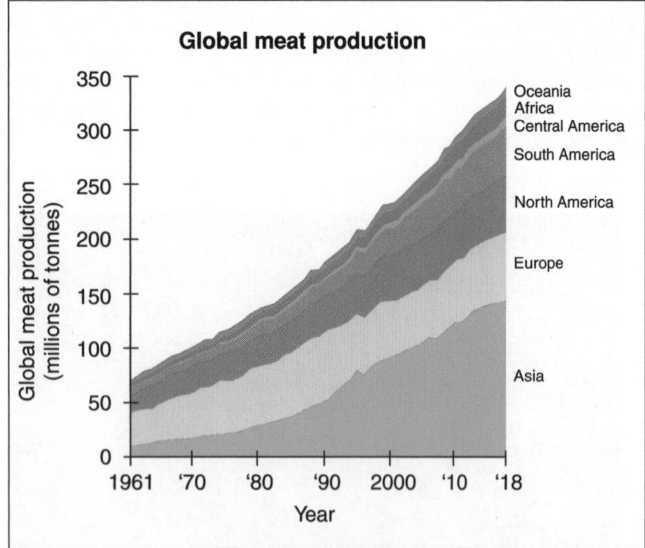

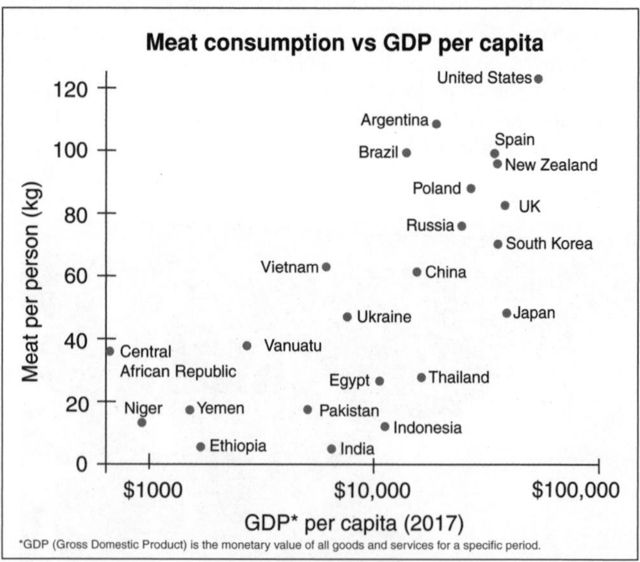

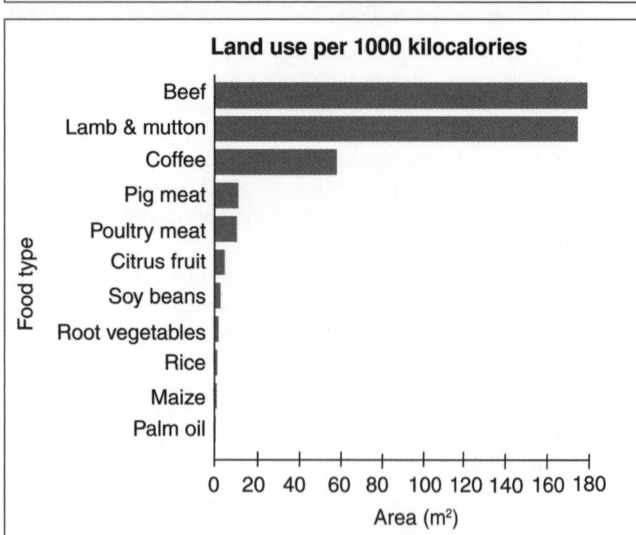

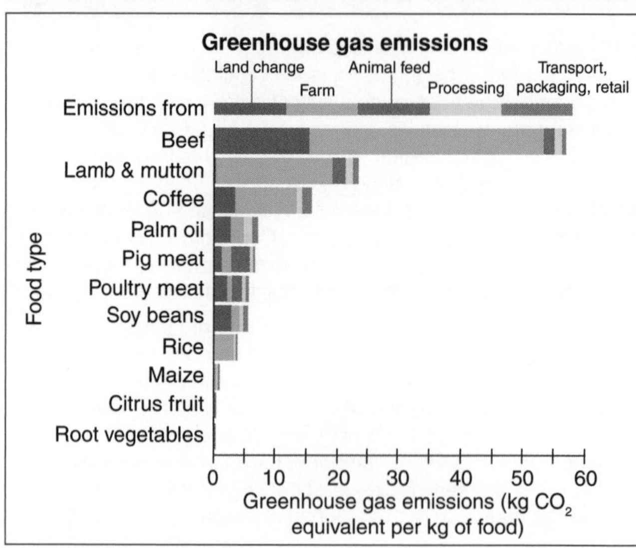

All data: World in data

3. Using the graphs above answer the following:

(a) Which part of the globe has increased its production of meat the most since 1961? ______________________

(b) By approximately how many times has meat production increased in North America since 1961? ______________________

(c) What is the relationship between a country's GDP and the amount of meat eaten per capita? ______________________

____

(d) What does this actually mean? ______________________

(e) Which food produces the most greenhouse gases in its production? ______________________

(f) What are the two largest factors contributing to greenhouse gas emissions in the production of this food?

____

(g) Which meat is the least efficient to produce in terms of calories per square meter? ______________________

(h) What does this data tell us overall about meat production? ______________________

____

____

____

ISBN: 978-1-98-856632-0

The environmental impact of beef production

Beef production in the United States is an important part of the economy, both in the production and export of beef, and in the associated industries. About 20% of the global beef supply is produced in the United States, worth around US$8 billion in exports per year. However beef production and agriculture in general produces a significant proportion of the country's greenhouse gas emissions and also contributes to other environmental issues (below).

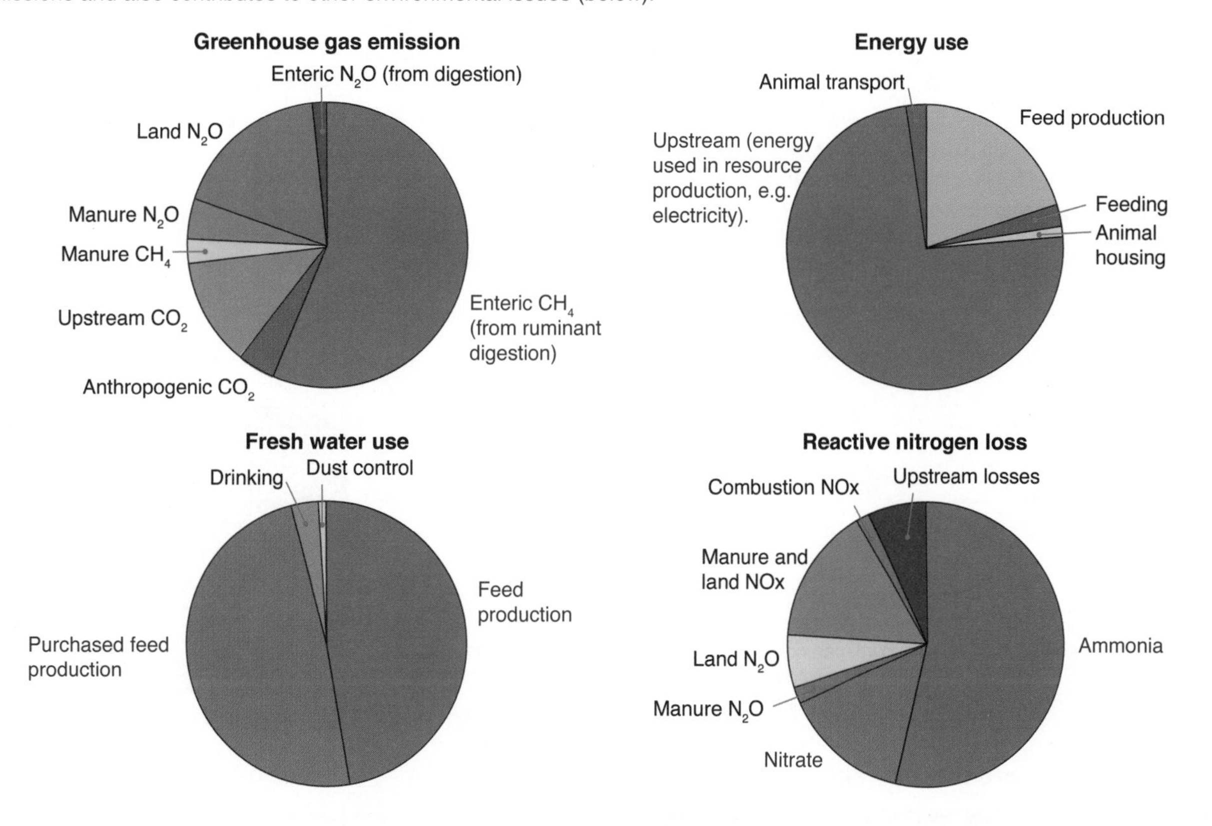

Emissions from beef farming:

Greenhouse gases 213,292 Gg CO_2-eq **Fossil energy** 474,584 TJ **Fresh water** 19,191 GL **Reactive N** 1476 Gg

4. With respect to beef production:

(a) What gas is the largest contributor to greenhouse gas emissions? ______________________

(b) What contributes most to the energy used? ______________________

(c) What does this include? ______________________

____

____

(d) What are the major uses of water in beef production? ______________________

____

(e) N_2O makes up approximately what % of greenhouse gas emissions? ______________________

(f) What gas contributes most to reactive nitrate losses? ______________________

5. Lower meat consumption would lead to a reduction in CO_2, methane, and N_2O emissions, conserve water, and reduce use of antibiotics. This may have a positive effect on the environment but is it reasonable to expect farmers to reduce production, ask consumers to eat less meat, and expect grain farmers to grow and sell less feed? As a class or in groups debate this topic as two sides, those arguing for a reduction in beef production, and those arguing for the status quo. Outline the arguments of each side as notes below. Use more paper for a more in depth analysis if you wish:

____

____

____

____

____

ISBN: 978-1-98-856632-0

82 Managing Rangelands

Key Question: How can managing rangelands help maintain or improve productivity while grazing.

Rangelands are large, relatively undeveloped areas populated by grasses, grass-like plants, and scrub. They are usually semi-arid to arid areas and include grasslands, tundra, scrublands, coastal scrub, alpine areas, and savanna.

Globally, rangelands cover around 50% of the Earth's land surface. The US has about 3.1 million km^2 of rangeland. Rangelands are often used to graze livestock such as sheep and cattle but, because they occur in low-rainfall areas, they do not regenerate rapidly. Careful management is required to prevent damage and soil loss as a result of overgrazing.

- Grasses (below right) grow continuously from a meristem close to the ground, so the leaf can be cropped without causing growth to stop. This allows a field to be grazed in a near-continuous fashion. Grazing by animals stimulates grass to grow and removes dead material. Grasslands cropped at their optimum capacity can be much more productive than if left uncropped (below left).
- Overgrazing occurs when too many animals are grazed for too long on a section of pasture and the grass does not have enough time between cropping to regrow. Overgrazing may destroy the meristem, in which case plant regeneration stops. Exposed soils may become colonized by invasive species (bottom right) or eroded by wind and rain.

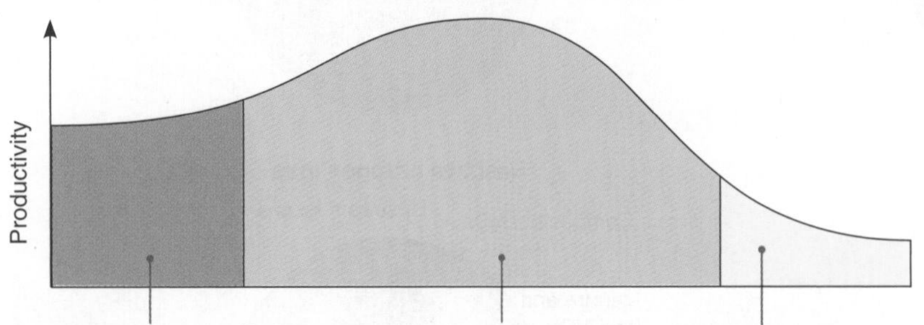

Undergrazing
Net productivity is reduced because standing dead material leaves little room for new growth to come through.

Optimum grazing
Old material is removed so new growth can come through, but enough growing material is left to allow recovery.

Overgrazing
Too much material is removed and new growth cannot become established. Plants die and erosion occurs.

Tallgrass prairie (Konza prairie, Kansas).

Effect of grazing on productivity and plant species composition

Total net primary production and efficiency of grazed and ungrazed grasslands

		Net production (kcal/m)	Efficiency (%)
Grazed	Desert	1081	0.13
	Shortgrass plains	3761	0.80
	Mixed grasslands	2254	0.51
	Prairie	3749	0.77
Ungrazed	Desert	1177	0.16
	Shortgrass plains	2721	0.57
	Mixed grasslands	2052	0.47
	Prairie	2220	0.44

From Ecology and Field Biology, R. Smith

Intensive grazing causes changes in the species composition. Species that perform better under grazing will increase their range, while others will reduce their range. Grazing also opens gaps in plant distribution, which allows invasive species to establish or increase in range.

Ungrazed

Moderate grazing

Overgrazed

Species reaction to grazing

Decreasers Increasers Invaders

1. Describe the effect of grazing on the diversity of rangeland plants:

2. Discuss the relationship between a rangeland's productivity and the number of animals grazed on the land:

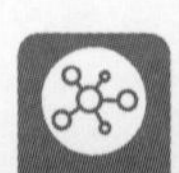

EIN-2

ISBN: 978-1-98-856632-0

Rotating grazing

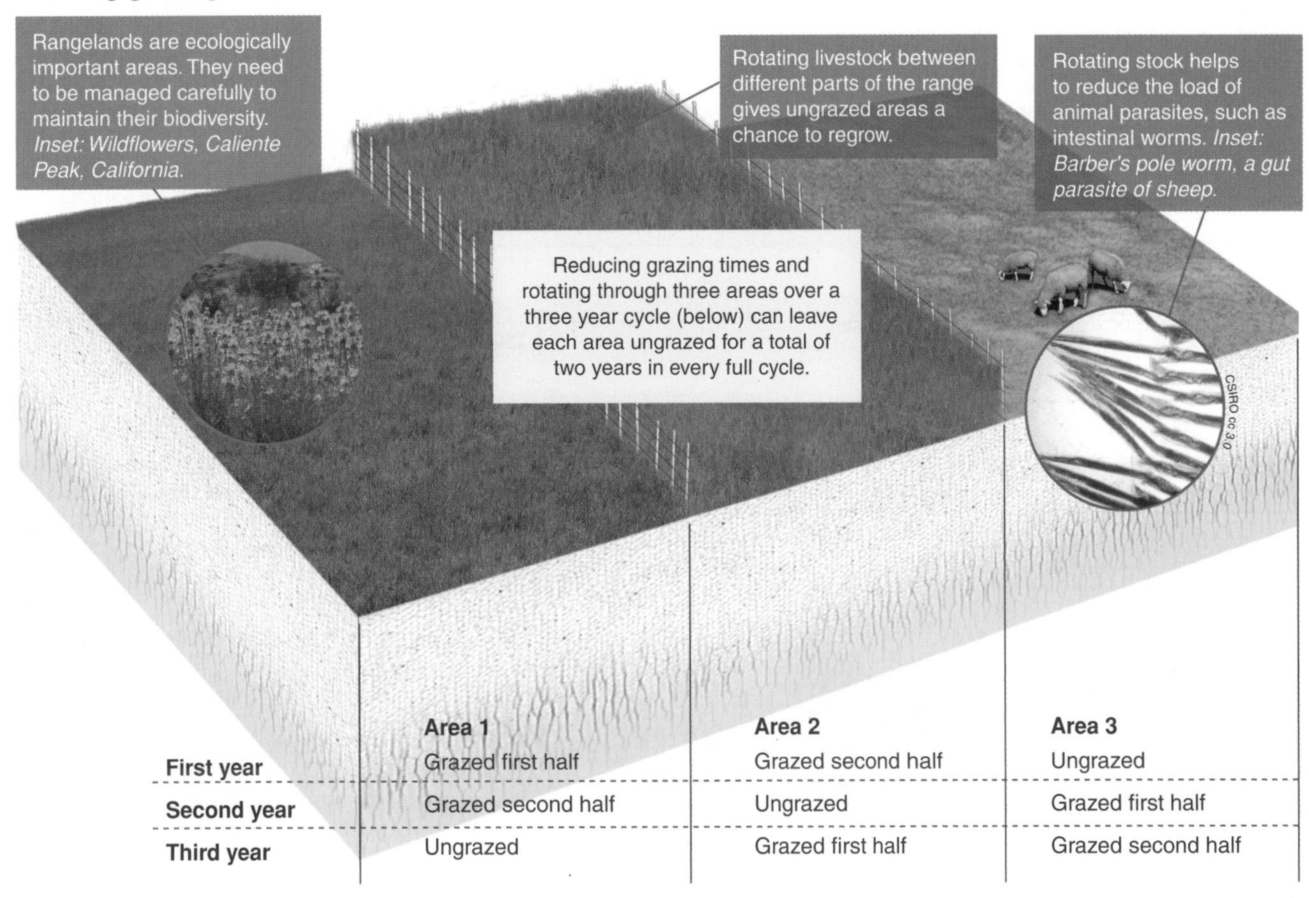

	Area 1	Area 2	Area 3
First year	Grazed first half	Grazed second half	Ungrazed
Second year	Grazed second half	Ungrazed	Grazed first half
Third year	Ungrazed	Grazed first half	Grazed second half

The land along either side of a waterway is called the **riparian zone**. It provides important habitat for many species, helps to reduce flooding and silting, and reduces soil erosion from the banks of the waterway. Situating livestock watering areas away from rivers and streams decreases damage to riparian zones. If left undisturbed, the streamside vegetation returns to a natural state within a relatively short period (above).

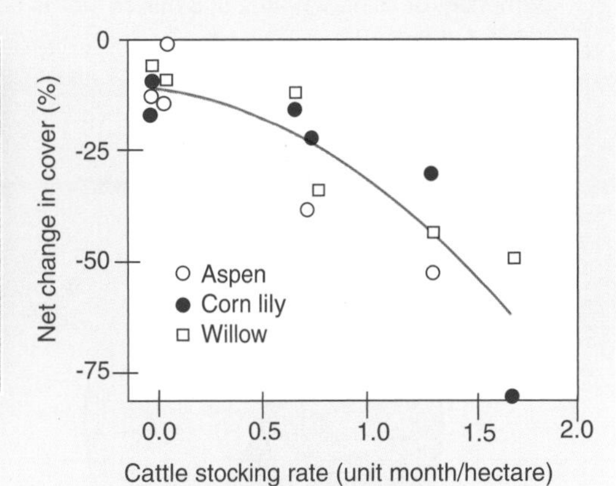

High stock levels can significantly deplete the amount of plant cover in an area, leaving little shelter for other animals (above).

3. Describe the effects of livestock rotation on pasture and rangeland biodiversity: ______

4. Explain why overstocking could eventually lead to ecosystem collapse: ______

ISBN: 978-1-98-856632-0

83 Impact of Overfishing

Key Question: What has been the effect of overfishing on commercial fish populations.

Fishing is an ancient human tradition, and is economically, socially, and culturally important. Today, it is a worldwide resource extraction industry. Several decades of overfishing in all of the world's oceans has pushed commercially important species (such as cod) into steep decline. The United Nation's Food and Agriculture Organization (FAO) reports that, of the commercially targeted marine fish stocks in 2017, ~34% are overfished, ~60% are maximally sustainably fished, and ~6% underfished. This is somewhat improved on the 1989 figures partly because of better fisheries management. In general though, the maximum sustainable yield (MSY) is too often exceeded, often using wasteful and destructive methods.

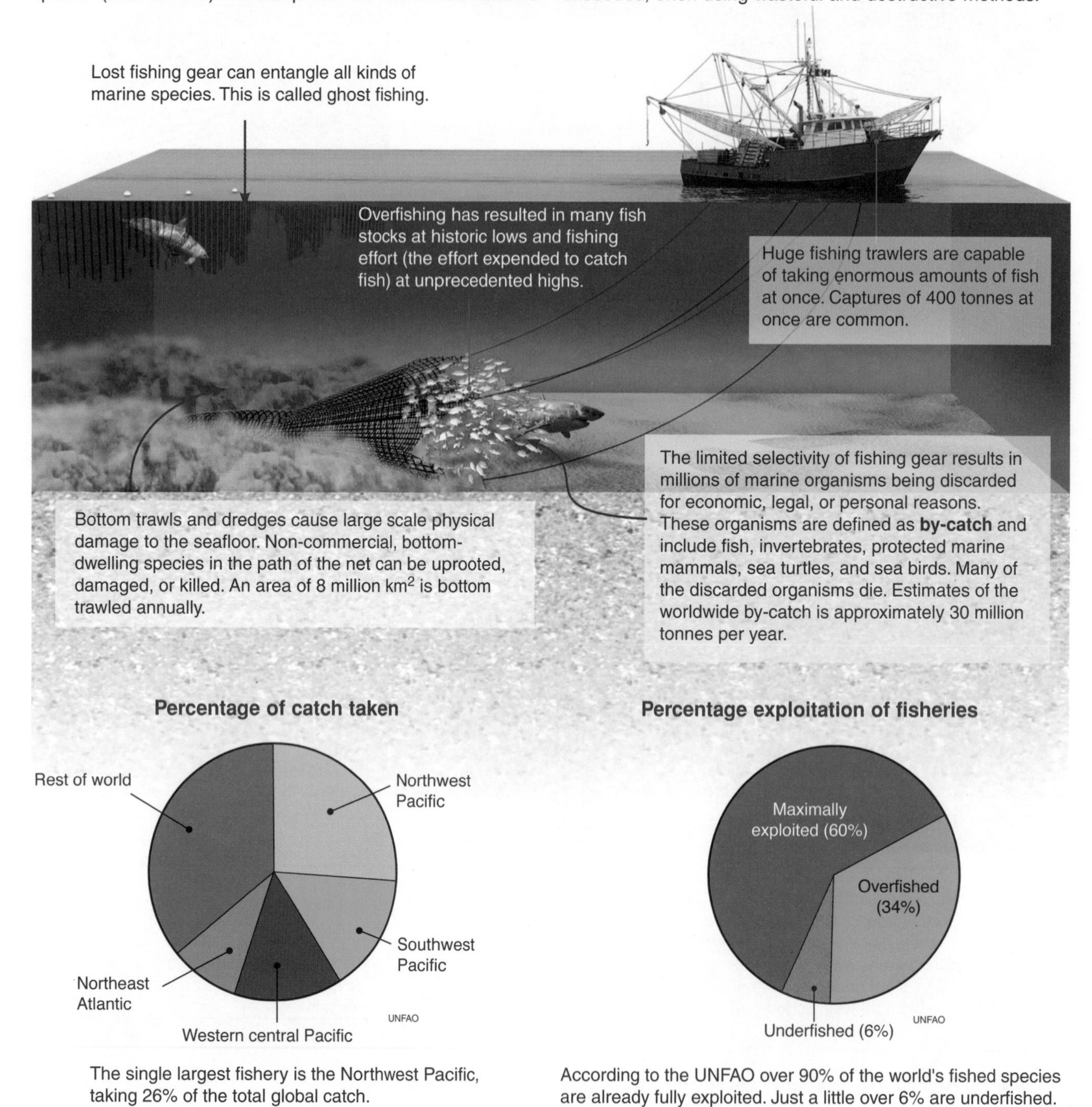

The single largest fishery is the Northwest Pacific, taking 26% of the total global catch.

According to the UNFAO over 90% of the world's fished species are already fully exploited. Just a little over 6% are underfished.

1. Describe some effects of overfishing: ______________________

____

____

____

2. What is meant by the by-catch and why is it important: ______________________

____

ISBN: 978-1-98-856632-0

Human impacts on fisheries

NOAA

Fishing techniques have become so sophisticated and efforts are on such a large scale that thousands of tonnes of fish can be caught by one vessel on one fishing cruise. Fishing vessels can reach over 100 m long. In the photo above, 360 tonnes of Chilean jack mackerel are caught in one gigantic net.

NOAA

Tuna is a popular fish type, commonly found canned in supermarkets and as part of sushi. However virtually all tuna species are either threatened or vulnerable. Demand for the fish appears insatiable with a record price of $1.7 million being paid in 2013 for a 221 kg bluefin tuna.

Derek Quinn

Illegal fishing was a major problem in the 1990s. Thousands of tonnes of catches were being unreported. International efforts have reduced this by an estimated 95%, helping the recovery of some fish stocks. Naval patrol vessels (e.g. HMNZS *Wellington* above) have helped in targeting illegal fishing vessels.

Fisheries monitoring usually focuses on large scale fisheries, such as trawlers. The effect of small scale fisheries is often overlooked. New studies show small scale fishing operations could account for up to 30% of the global catch, at around 22 million tonnes.

In the United States, fishing and fishing related industries contribute more than $260 billion to the national GDP. Over-fishing would threaten this substantial part of the economy. In 1992 Canada closed the Atlantic cod fishery due to overfishing, at a loss of 20,000 jobs and $700 million a year.

Nicholls H

An example of the effect a fishery can have on fish stocks is the Galápagos Island sea cumber population (sea cucumbers are a type of invertebrate related to starfish). The commercial fishery began in 1993 and by 2004 the sea cucumber population had fallen by 98%.

3. Explain why setting a maximum sustainable yield for a fish species is not a complete solution to overfishing:

4. Why is returning by-catch to the sea not always as useful as it might appear?

5. Identify three ways in which fish stocks are over-exploited:

ISBN: 978-1-98-856632-0

84 Impacts of Mining

Key Question: What are the main mining practices and how does mining affect the environment?

Mining minerals has been part of human culture for thousands of years, with the oldest mines known dated to about 43,000 years old. Minerals are the raw materials for the multitude of human uses and technologies. However these mineral resources are non-renewable. As they become harder to find or more in demand, mining operations turn from extracting the more easily found or higher grade deposits to harder to extract or lower grade deposits. In either case, it costs more in both energy and equipment. Either more ore has to be extracted or more time and effort must be taken to find it. The result of changes in mineral availability is often that the mining operation results in more waste and air and water pollution.

Surface mining

Ore from the mine is crushed and mixed with water to form a slurry. This is processed to remove useful minerals. In coal mines, coal can be sent directly to power plants, or crushed to a finer size.

Waste rock produced after the ore as been removed (**tailings**) may be stored in large piles. This must be carefully managed as tailings can leach toxic chemicals into the environment.

Ore is mined from the working level. This may be tens of meters below the ground. The shape of the mine depends on the size of the ore deposits and the slope needed for truck access.

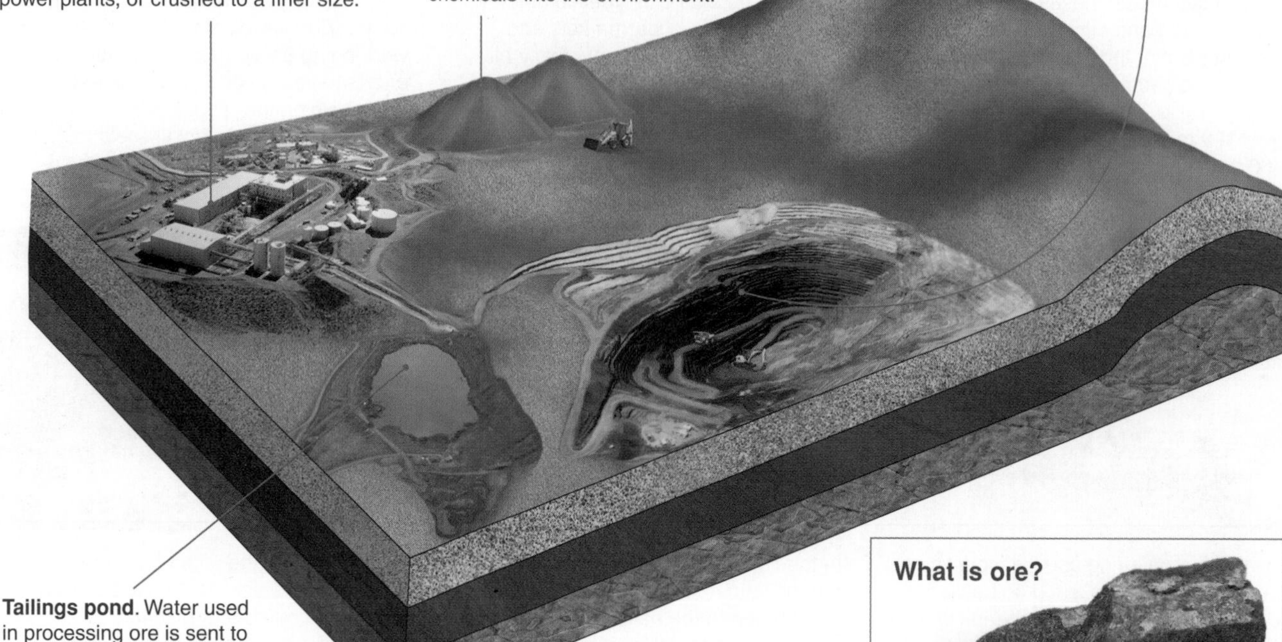

Tailings pond. Water used in processing ore is sent to a tailings pond where fine particles settle before the water is sent for treatment.

What is ore?

Uranium ore

Ore is a natural rock or sediment containing useful minerals. High grade ores have a higher percentage of useful minerals than low grade ores. The cost and method of mining them depends on the grade of the ore, its location, and how easily it can be extracted.

- Surface mining includes strip mining, open-pit mining, and mountain top removal. In each case, overlying material (such as soil and subsoil), called **overburden**, is removed to expose the mineral containing layer.
- Surface mining usually occurs on a large scale (often tens or hundreds of hectares) where the removal of the overburden is relatively easy, such as a flat plain or open and accessible mountain tops with deposits close to the surface.
- Preparing the site involves removing the site's vegetation. The overburden, which consists of hundreds of thousands of cubic meters of soil and rock must be stored, often creating huge mounds of unstable rock that can leach minerals into waterways.

Strip mining occurs on relatively flat land where the ore is near the surface. Overburden is removed. The target mineral is removed in one long strip and the overburden replaced before moving to the next strip. Some of the biggest machines ever built are used in this type of mining.

Matt Wasson cc 2.0

Mountaintop removal mining is performed at the top of the mountain or ridge line. Overburden may be removed and used to fill neighboring valleys. All surface mining is highly destructive. Many mines are remediated (and many are not) but even so the land is irreversibly changed.

As reserves of minerals become depleted, ore that was once not economical to mine becomes more so. This is also true as technology improves and becomes more efficient. Ancient deposits once contained 25% copper, whereas today even the best ores contain only 0.5% copper.

ISBN: 978-1-98-856632-0

Subsurface mining

- Subsurface mining is used when mineral deposits are too deep for removing the surface layers to be feasible or economic. The world's six deepest mines extend more the 3 km into the ground. The deepest is the Mponeng gold mine, which descends 4 km underground (equivalent to 10 Empire State Buildings end on end). The trip from top to bottom takes nearly 90 minutes.
- Subsurface mining causes far less land disturbance than surface mining. However, it is far more dangerous and requires specialized equipment. Risks include roof collapse, build up of explosive or toxic gases, and lung diseases from inhaling fine dust. Although less land is disturbed by digging, land subsidence can leave ripples or holes in the land above.
- Subsurface mining is usually used only when surface deposits have become rare and it is too risky and costly to mine them.
- Two methods dominate in subsurface mining. Room and pillar mining remove large areas of ore or coal, leaving rock pillars that help support the roof of the mine (below center). In long wall mining, machines move along the ore face (below right).

Subsurface mines are prone to collapse with subsidence of the land above. Subsidence may happen if the rock overlying the mine fails and collapses into the mine underneath. Sometimes the pillars left behind to hold up the mine roof fail or cannot hold the mass of rock above them and collapse.

Underground mining requires specialized low profile machines for ease of manoeuvring. The deeper a mine is, the more difficult it is to operate and thus the more valuable the ore must be to be worth removing. The Mponeng gold mine produces more than 6 tonnes of gold a year but requires enormous technical effort and expense to operate.

Subsurface mining can be divided into soft rock and hard rock. Soft rock mining extracts coal and sedimentary rocks from layered deposits. Hard rock mining extracts minerals such as gemstones and metals. The techniques used are different due to the different rocks involved. In the image above, rock phosphate is mined using long wall mining.

1. (a) When is surface mining used? ______________________________

   (b) Give a general description of how surface mining is carried out and its advantages and disadvantages:

   ____

2. (a) When is subsurface mining used? ______________________________

   (b) Give a general description of how subsurface mining is carried out and its advantages and disadvantages:

   ____

3. (a) Why is it getting harder to find high grade ores? ______________________________

   (b) Why is it sometimes still economic to mine a low grade ore? ______________________________

ISBN: 978-1-98-856632-0

Environmental effects of mining

- All mining operations affect the environment, most in multiple and negative ways. Regulations on mining have become tighter over time but even old decommissioned mines can still have long lasting effects on the environment around them.

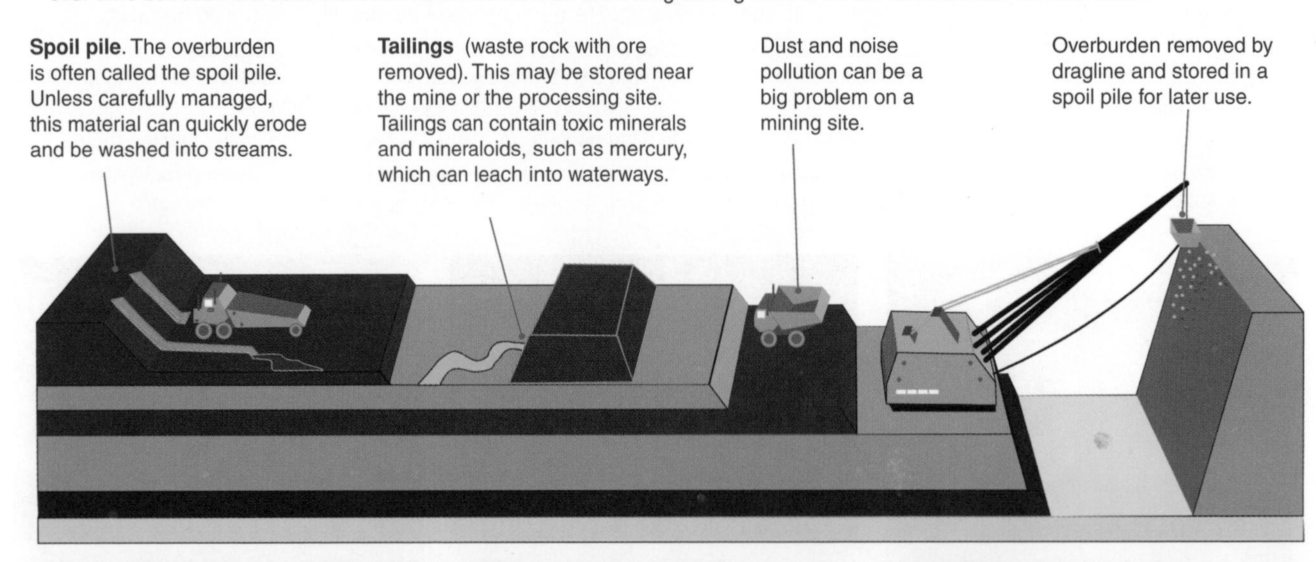

NASA

Water introduced into a mine (e.g. from groundwater), or into overburden or tailings (e.g. from heavy rain) can dissolve the minerals in the rocks. These may be acidic. Water may then drain into streams and rivers, polluting them and causing considerable damage to aquatic life.

Lorrie Graham/AusAID CC 2.0

Habitat destruction is an almost inevitable outcome of mining, especially surface mining. The very nature of having to remove overburden means the natural community there will be destroyed. Efforts are sometimes made to relocate wildlife, but these are not always successful.

Mining, especially subsurface mining, can have detrimental effects on human health, especially in countries where regulations are absent, not enforced, or not followed. Mining can contaminate streams and aquifers supplying drinking water, and dust inhalation can cause lung disease.

4. What is the difference between overburden and tailings? ____________________

____

____

5. Why must tailings be carefully stored and disposed of? ____________________

____

____

____

6. Describe some of the detrimental environmental effects of both surface and subsurface mining: ____________________

____

____

____

____

____

____

____

ISBN: 978-1-98-856632-0

7. A mining company explores two potential surface mining areas using a drill to provide core samples. The costs and mineral content of each site are shown below:

	Area 1 (surface area approximately 20 km^2)	Area 2 (surface area approximately 10 km^2)
% gold (value per kilogram = $43,000)	0.0006%	0.0005%
% silver (value per kilogram = $650)	0.01%	0.07%
% copper (value per kilogram = $4.70)	0.9%	0.0%
% lead (value per kilogram = $1.80)	0.0%	3.0%
% zinc (value per kilogram = $2.15)	5.0%	2.5%
Average depth of ores (m)	100 m	50 m
Access to mine site	Moderate	Difficult
Start up cost	$40 million	$50 million
Extraction rate (total rock + ore per day)	5200 tonnes	4700 tonnes
Cost of running mine facility	$100 per tonne	$115 per tonne
Cost of restoring the environment per km^2	$1,200,000	$3,100,000
Approximate mine lifetime	15 years	10 years

As well as these findings, the potential mine sites are located within forested areas. In order for the mine to operate, the forest would have to be removed and roads and other infrastructure put in place. Both sites are away from areas commonly used by the public, but have particularly diverse habitats. The state government determines the income and job opportunities from either mine would exceed the income from the forest in terms of tourism or logging.

Use the data to decide which of these areas is the most suitable for mining, giving any reasons and calculations to support your decision. Identify any environmental problems and suggest how these could be solved or mitigated:

ISBN: 978-1-98-856632-0

85 Urbanization

Key Question: What is urbanization and what are its positive and negative effects on the environment?

Urbanization describes the movement of people out of rural areas into cities. In the United States, an urban area is an area with more than 386 people per square km (1000 people per square mile). For most of human history, more people have lived in rural areas than in cities. Rural areas provided land to grow crops, raise livestock, or hunt game to supply food and income. Only those who could afford to have other people do this, via trade or wealth, could live in any kind of urban environment. The Industrial Revolution changed this. The increasing mechanization of farming meant fewer people were needed to work on farms to grow food. At the same time, the mechanization and expansion of industry in urban areas required more workers in factories. As a result, cities grew as people moved in from rural areas. In 2007 (by UN estimate) the world passed the milestone of more people living in cities and urban areas than in rural areas. Today, approximately 4.1 billion people live in urban areas and 3.4 billion are designated rural. Urbanization has occurred more quickly in industrialized nations. In the US, the 50% urban population milestone was passed around 1940 and approximately 84% of the US population now lives in urban areas. In contrast, more than 50% of sub-Saharan Africa is still rural.

The benefits of cities

- Cities (urban areas) have one major benefit over rural areas and that is economies of scale. This benefit encompasses all other benefits. Concentrating people in one place makes it simpler to provide services to the population. These may be economic, such as factories and shops, or recreational such as swimming pools and museums. If populations are dispersed, it is more costly to operate and maintain these facilities and more difficult for people to access them. In a city, the cost per person is very low.
- Cities provide benefits such as more jobs, better utilities, faster access to medical facilities, and more options for education. Cities also provide some environmental benefits in terms of footprint. Concentrating development in one place allows wild places to be preserved. For example, ~3% of land area in the USA is defined as urban, yet it contains over 80% of the population.

Cities allow arts and culture to flourish as different cultures come together and wealth and talent are concentrated enough to support them.

Cities are often centers of science and education. Having large numbers of people sharing ideas and skills builds knowledge and encourages innovation.

Having a large number of workers nearby means large construction projects can be undertaken. Even small business is simpler with a large customer base.

Environmental effects of urbanization

Concentrating people in cities inevitably has consequences (i.e. unwanted effects). The problems of what to do with waste or where to get water are magnified by the daily requirements of large numbers of people. Extensive infrastructure is needed to deal with these problems.

Stormwater surges and flooding

- Cities are known as concrete jungles for good reason. Aside from the buildings, much of the ground is covered with concrete or asphalt, e.g. roads, sidewalks, and carparks. This aids safety and ease of movement, but these surfaces are also impervious to water. Water from rainfall cannot soak naturally into the ground and moves directly, without treatment, into stormwater drains and then into streams and rivers. This has a number of consequences:
  - Urban runoff includes pollutants that have accumulated on hard surfaces, including sediment, bacteria, metals, plastics, and residues from vehicle exhausts.
  - As runoff increases, the amount of water that soaks into the soil (groundwater recharge) reduces, so urban development can result in a low water table.
- Any blockages to water into stormwater drainage can very quickly lead to surface flooding. The flow rate of rivers that flow through cities can rise and fall very quickly due to the sudden stormwater inflows after rain (right). Natural drainage systems show a much more moderate response to rainfall.

A culvert discharging stormwater after heavy rain (Illinois).

Stream flooding before and after urbanization

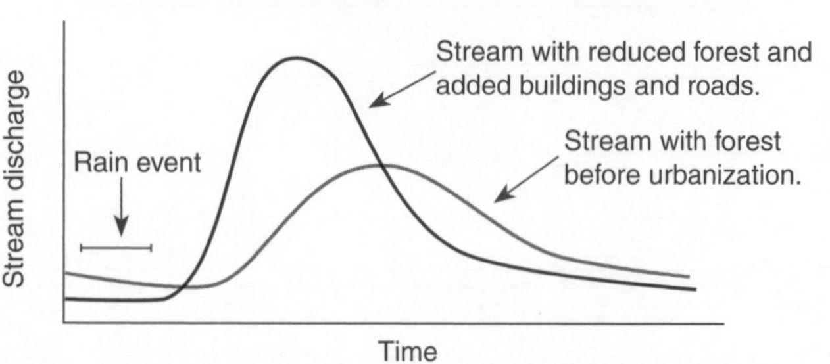

ISBN: 978-1-98-856632-0

Resource depletion and salt water intrusion

- Supply of fresh water for domestic and industrial use is a major challenge to cities with rapidly growing population. Some urban centers are naturally better supplied with fresh water than others. New York City for example has well protected watersheds and has restricted development surrounding them. In other coastal cities, which depend at least in part on groundwater supplies of fresh water, intrusion of saltwater into coastal aquifers is a significant problem and threatens reliable supplies of fresh water.
- Multiple factors, including increases in the number of large storm surges and rising sea levels, contribute to coastal erosion and saltwater intrusion into groundwater aquifers and estuaries. The construction of levees to control flooding and navigation canals, as in New Orleans, also contribute to saline intrusion.
- The increased water demand of urbanization can result in groundwater aquifers becoming depleted and this alone increases the tendency for saline water to enter freshwater aquifers, even before climate change factors, such as rising sea levels, are considered. Near the coast, saline water and fresh water are hydraulically connected. Water flowing into a freshwater aquifer normally produces enough pressure to overcome the inflow of the denser saltwater. However overuse of the freshwater aquifer can lower this pressure and so allow the denser saltwater to push into the aquifer. Over time this can lead to the salt contamination of the remaining fresh water.

Catfish Point Control Structure, Louisiana, is a salt water intrusion barrier to prevent Gulf of Mexico waters from intruding into freshwater systems.

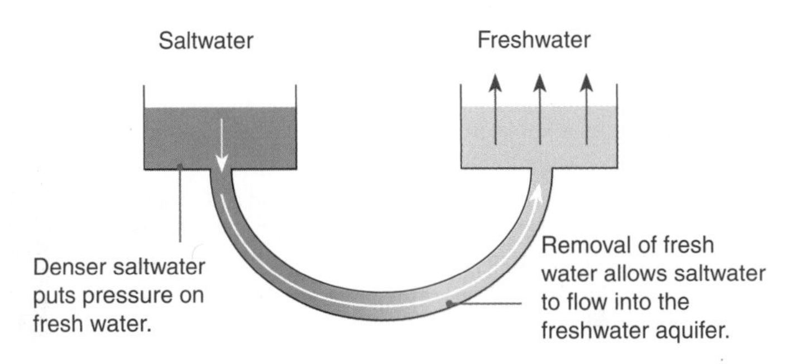

1. What are some of the reasons people move into urban areas? ______________________________

2. Explain the socioeconomic and environmental benefits of urbanization: ______________________________

3. How does urbanization affect the hydrology of the watershed, including flooding and groundwater recharge?

4. Discuss the contribution of urbanization to the problem of saltwater intrusion into groundwater aquifers: ______________________________

ISBN: 978-1-98-856632-0

Urban sprawl

- Urban sprawl (right) occurs when the city's population begins to move out of the city proper and into surrounding areas. These people remain close enough to benefit from the city's facilities but generally have larger properties and individual houses. These areas are termed suburban and the areas occupied are called suburbs. Suburbs can take up vastly more space than urban areas due to the population living in individual single family properties, rather than in dense apartment buildings. This movement away from the city directly affects the surrounding environment as land is taken up for housing developments.
- Having thousands or millions of people in one place presents challenges for waste disposal, both solid rubbish and sewage. New York city produces more than 14 million tonnes of rubbish a year. Although most Western cities have effective waste systems involving a complex system of transport and disposal, many cities in developing countries do not. Large amounts of rubbish and sewage are still dumped directly into rivers and the sea. Rivers such as the Ganges (India) and the Citarum (Indonesia) act as open waste dumps and are the most polluted in the world. Rubbish that is not dumped may be incinerated. While this produces useful energy, it also produces a large amount of air pollution (including greenhouse gases) if not filtered carefully.
- Cities are transport hubs. People commute to and from them everyday, often many kilometers. Most of this transport relies on fossil fuels, mostly as diesel and gasoline in cars, trucks, and buses. Burning fossil fuels produces CO_2 which contributes to global warming. However it also produces various other polluting gases, such as NO_2 and CO, which contribute to smog (right).

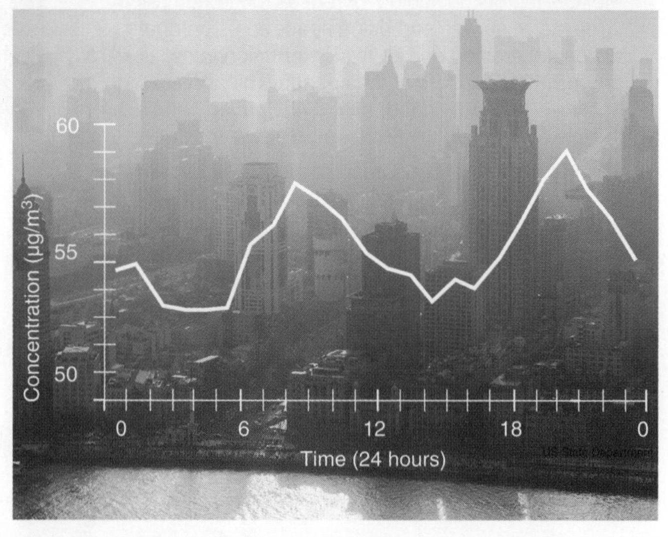

Graph: Average daily variation in fine particulate matter ($PM_{2.5}$) in Shanghai, December 2011–July 2014 $PM_{2.5}$ poses a health risk.
Background image: Smog, Shanghai cityscape.

5. (a) How does air pollution change during the day in Shanghai? ______

(b) How would you explain this pattern? ______

6. Describe the (often unintended) consequences of urbanization on the environment: ______

ISBN: 978-1-98-856632-0

86 Ecological Footprint

Key Question: How can we use the concept of an ecological footprint to compare human resource demands with the Earth's capacity to regenerate those resources?

An ecological footprint is often expressed as the number of Earths required to sustain the human population or the amount of space (in hectares) needed to sustain one individual. The calculation of the footprint is based on the amount of land required to provide the amount of food and energy for a human and the amount of land required to absorb the carbon dioxide and other waste emissions produced. Currently the global ecological footprint is about 1.75 Earths, with each human requiring about 2.7 global hectares (globally standardized hectares with a world average productivity).

Components of an ecological footprint

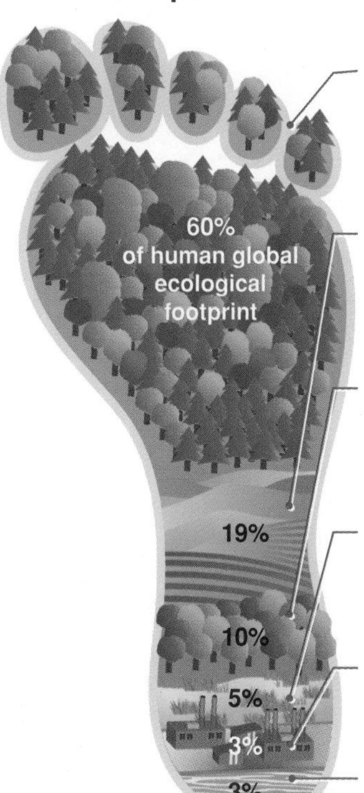

Carbon footprint land is the land required to absorb the carbon dioxide waste produced by human activities and natural events (such as volcanic eruptions).

Cropland consists of all the lands required to produce crop products including livestock feed, oil crops and rubber.

Forest land is a measurement of the annual harvest of fuelwood and timber compared to the rate of forest replenishment.

Grazing land includes land used to support livestock in addition to livestock feed from cropland.

Built-up land includes all the land required for human settlement, transport, industry, and energy.

Fishing grounds are calculated based on the annual primary production required to sustain harvested species.

The calculations required to produce an ecological footprint can be simplified into two equations.

- The first calculates the land required to produce the food and materials used by a person.
- The second calculates the amount of land required to absorb carbon dioxide waste.

The sum of the two equations gives a general measure of the ecological foot print per person.

Equation 1

$$\textit{per capita} \text{ land requirement for food production (ha)} = \frac{\textit{per capita} \text{ food consumption (kg/yr)}}{\text{mean food production per hectare (kg/ha/yr)}}$$

Equation 2

$$\textit{per capita} \text{ land requirement for absorbing } CO_2 \text{ (ha)} = \frac{\textit{per capita } CO_2 \text{ production (kg C/yr)}}{\text{net carbon fixation per hectare (kg C/ha/yr)}}$$

Multiplying the answer by the global human population gives a **global ecological footprint**.

Ecological footprints and human development

The human development index (HDI) is an index based on national income, education, and life expectancy. The higher the index (from 0-1), the better a country's living conditions and development. Countries with high HDIs tend to have high ecological footprints.

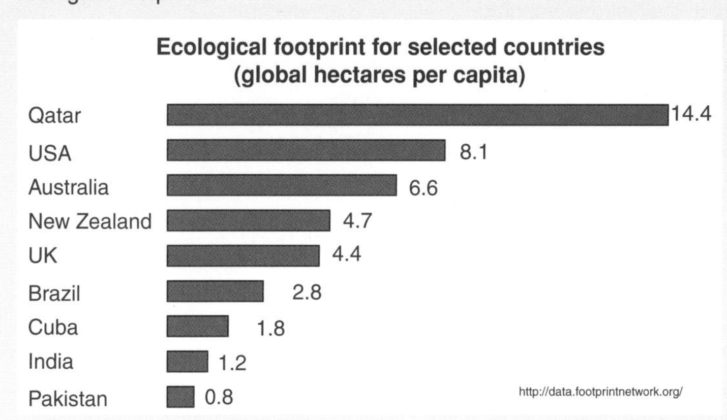

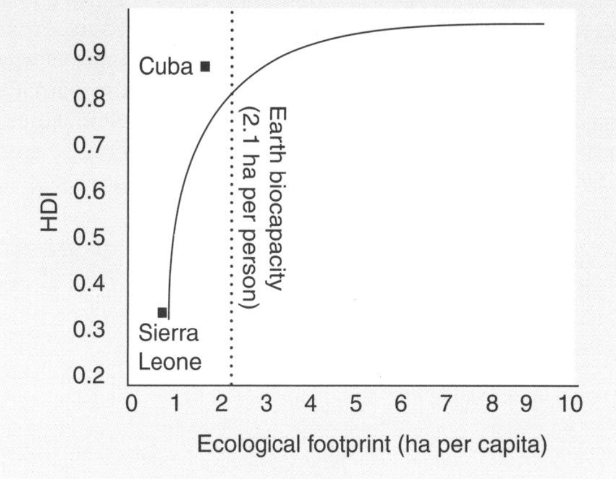

1. Why might developed countries have much larger ecological footprints than undeveloped countries?

____

____

____

2. Calculate the area (in hectares) required to support the world population (7.5 billion) based on the ecological footprint of the countries below. Compare this to the size of the planet (13.4 billion productive hectares).

(a) USA: ____________________ (b) UK: ____________________

ISBN: 978-1-98-856632-0

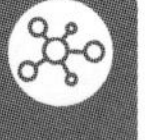

87 Introduction to Sustainability

Key Question: What is sustainability and how do we ensure we use resources sustainably?

In general, sustainability means the ability to use resources without using them up faster than they are renewed. The unfortunate outcome of this statement is that the vast majority of the resources used by humans are either non-renewable (such as coal) or are being used faster than they are being renewed, i.e. unsustainably. The human world, as it currently stands, depends on non-renewable resources, such as coal. This is because the energy required to run the human world is currently nearly 550×10^{18} J per year. Only fossil fuels are currently able to provide this kind of energy. However, aside from the pollution they cause, because they are non-renewable, they will eventually run out. For human society to become sustainable it will need to substantially reduce its energy use and build new more sustainable energy sources.

Indicators for sustainability

Richard Ling cc2.5

Biodiversity plays an important part in sustainability. A diverse ecosystem is able to more efficiently provide the ecosystem services that humans require, such as fresh water and clean air. A decrease in biodiversity likely indicates one or more unsustainable practices.

The human need for food production is massive. Key indicators of sustainable food production include the energy required to produce the food, the amount of food produced, particularly the amount produced per capita. If this falls, it indicates that the growth of the population is outpacing our ability to feed it.

A rapid increase in average global surface temperature is a good indication of unsustainable practices. Global surface temperatures are linked to many environmental factors that are generally in equilibrium. A sustained increase in global temperature indicates that external factors are affecting this equilibrium.

Wknight94 CC 3.0

Global temperature is linked to atmospheric CO_2 concentrations (and other gases such as methane). Environmental processes are generally in equilibrium, so increases in atmospheric CO_2 indicate that carbon is being returned to the atmosphere faster than it is being stored in the biosphere. This imbalance is not sustainable.

The human population has increased exponentially in the last one hundred years. Population studies of other organisms show that such increases are normally followed by rapid declines. Studying how the human population is changing can help us understand if the growth is sustainable or not.

Resource depletion is inevitable when mining a mineral on a finite world. There is only so much gold, or coal, or oil. Many resources can be replenished (e.g. water), but using them at a faster rate than they are replenished is not sustainable. This includes many groundwater aquifers, forests, and animal resources such as fish.

1. Why will human society need to reduce its energy use or build new sustainable energy sources? ___________

____

____

____

2. Why would a decrease in biodiversity indicate an unsustainable practice occurring? ___________

____

____

____

3. Why might studying human population growth help us understand if the growth is sustainable? ___________

____

____

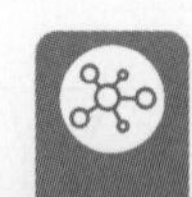
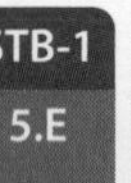

ISBN: 978-1-98-856632-0

Sustainable yield

- The sustainable harvesting of any resource requires that its rate of harvest is no more than its replacement rate. If the harvest rate is higher than the replacement rate then the resource will reduce at ever increasing percentages (assuming a constant harvest rate) and eventually be lost. This applies to many renewable resources.
- The **sustainable yield** (SY) is the amount of resource that can be removed (the harvest) without reducing the available supply year to year. Sustainable yields are often described with reference to forestry or fisheries, but they are applied without considering environmental variations (or real changes in the stock). It assumes that the environmental conditions are stable and do not contribute to fluctuations in the resource.

SY = total biomass at time t + 1 – total biomass at time, t

- The equation above is often simplified as the annual gain in biomass or energy through growth and recruitment.
- A yield curve is derived from the logistic curve of population growth. The theoretical maximum sustainable yield (N_{MSY}) occurs when a population is at half the carrying capacity (½K). At this point, the population growth rate will also be at its maximum.
- Fisheries managers must determine to what level they can reduce the stock biomass to maximize yield and remain sustainable.

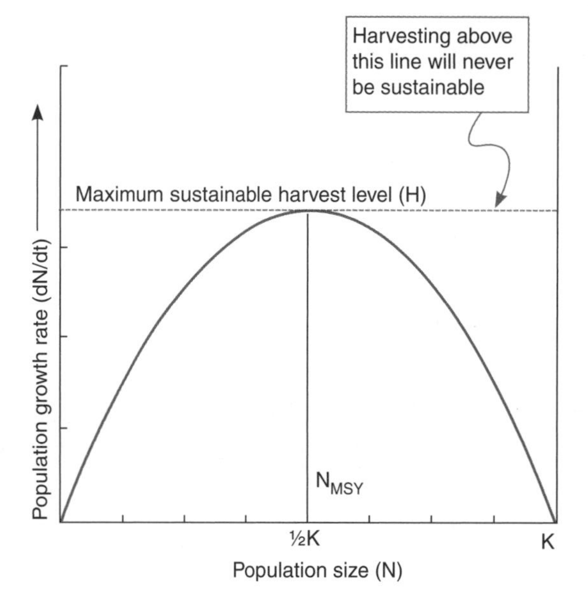

Under ideal conditions, harvesting at the rate indicated by the red dashed line (H) should be able to continue indefinitely. However, the growth rate of populations are rarely the same year to year (it fluctuates).

4. (a) A town has a population of 70,230 in the year 2020. Over the next five years, 6556 people move into the town for work, but 4096 move to other parts of the country. A baby boom sees the birth of 5225 babies but there are also 4978 deaths. What is the population of the town in 2025?

   ____

   (b) What is the percentage growth over the 5 years? ____________________________

   (c) The town uses water from a reservoir that holds 200 million L and is replenished at a rate of 60 million L a day. In 2020, the town used 46 million L per day. Calculate the average water use per person per day.

   ____

   (d) How much water would be used per day in 2025 if each person used the same amount of water as in 2020?

   ____

   (e) Assuming the town underwent the same rate of growth every 5 years into the future, when would the reservoir begin to fill more slowly than it was being used (i.e. the tipping point at which the water supply becomes unsustainable?

   ____

   (f) At the end of 2035, the town introduces measures to extend the life of the water supply by asking people to cut their water use by 10%. Under these new measures, when will the water supply become unsustainable?

   ____

5. (a) What is a sustainable yield? ____________________________

   ____

   (b) In the production curve above, explain why harvesting above the red dashed line is not sustainable: ______________

   ____

   (c) A fishery has a population of 5 million fish. Studies show that this number fluctuates slightly over time. At ½K the growth rate is estimated at 2% of the population annually.

      i. How many fish can be removed from the population before ½K is reached? ______________

      ii. What is the sustainable yield of this population at ½K? ______________

      iii. Why would this number be dangerous for the population to be fished at ½K? ______________

      ____

      ____

ISBN: 978-1-98-856632-0

88 Methods to Reduce Urban Runoff

Key Question: What methods could be used to reduce runoff or mitigate the effects of runoff?

Localized flooding can be a real problem in cities where hard surfaces cover almost every part of the ground. Complex and costly drainage systems must be installed and maintained to remove stormwater, but if these become blocked, flooding can quickly occur. Changing ground coverings can change the rate of flooding and runoff and reduce the need for complex drainage systems. Some systems can help absorb and so reduce pollutants such as oil from stormwater runoff.

INVESTIGATION 5.2: Testing water runoff

See appendix for equipment list.

1. Different kinds of pavement and ground cover have different rates of water infiltration and water holding capacity and so different rates of water runoff. In this investigation you will measure those rates.
2. Set up the following:

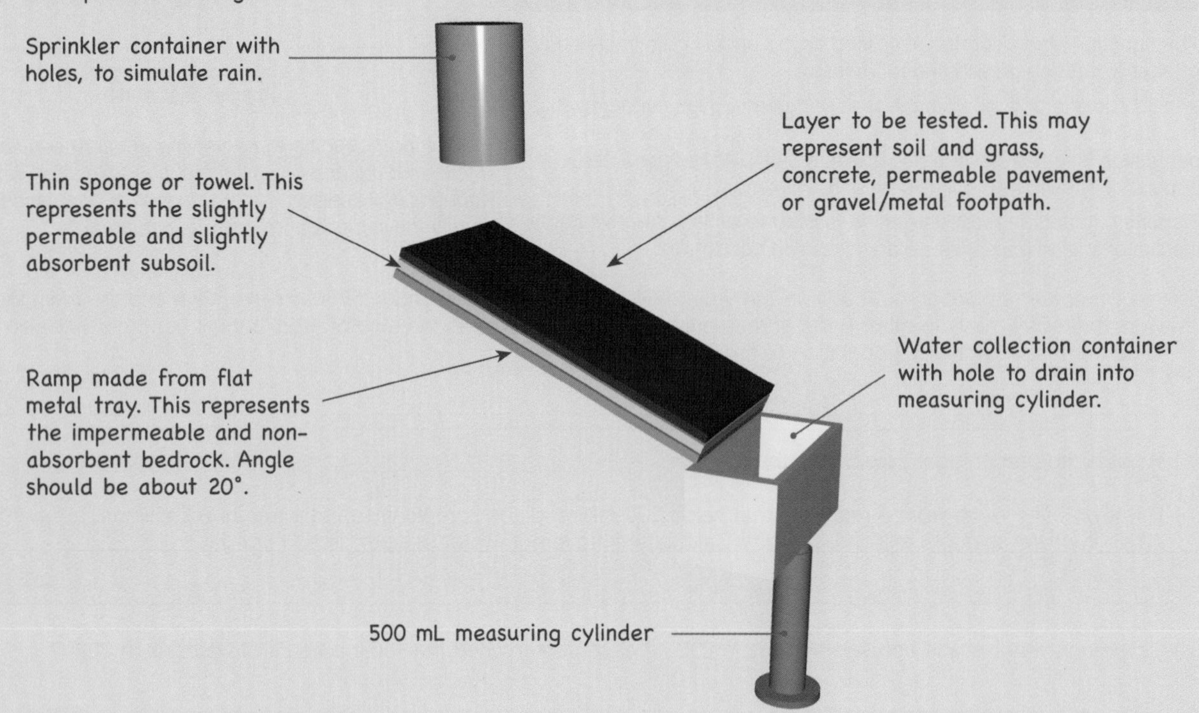

3. The layers to be tested will be concrete, permeable pavement, gravel/metal footpath, and soil. To make it easier, these will be represented as more easily obtainable materials as follows:
   Concrete = one large floor tile,
   Permeable pavement = multiple small tiles placed side by side to cover the entire ramp.
   Gravel/metal footpath = layer of gravel and sand
   Soil and grass = large thin sponge or smaller sponges laid side by side.
4. To test the rate of water runoff for the first material, first wet the subsoil sponge, then wring it out as much as possible. Place the tile on top of the sponge on the ramp as shown above.
5. Measure 500 mL of water. Rather than just pouring the water straight onto the tile, you need to simulate rainfall. This can be done using a sprinkler container (e.g. a container with holes in the bottom, such as a metal can). This will also help to regulate the rate at which the water hits the surface being tested.
6. When you have set up the equipment start a stopwatch and pour all the water into the rain container. Direct the water onto the top of the ramp so it runs down into the collection container and into the measuring cylinder.
7. In a notebook or your logbook, record the time it takes for the water to fill the measuring cylinder to 100 mL, 200 mL, 300 mL, 400 mL, and 500, mL. Record the total amount of water collected. In some cases it may not be all the original 500 mL, so you might not record a time for 500 mL, or even 400 mL.
8. Wring out the flat subsoil sponge as much as possible and repeat the process above twice more. Record the times and final water volume collected each time. Average the time it took to reach each volume (100 mL to 500 mL). Calculate a mean of the final water volume collected.
9. Repeat steps 4-7 for the small tiles, to represent permeable pavement.
10. Repeat steps 4-7 for the gravel and sand, to represent a gravel/metal footpath.
11. Repeat steps 4-7 for the sponge, to represent soil.

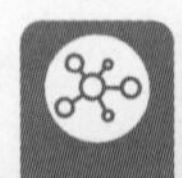

ISBN: 978-1-98-856632-0

1. Graph your results for filling rates for 100 mL to 500 mL for each of the four different ground coverings. Use a key to distinguish each type of covering:

Key:

2. List the average volume of water collected for each covering type:

(a) Concrete (tile): ______

(b) Permeable pavement (small tiles): ______

(c) Gravel/metal footpath (gravel and sand): ______

(d) Soil and grass (sponge): ______

3. (a) Which surface produced the **greatest** water runoff? ______

(b) How would this affect the way water enters gutters, stormwater drains, and rivers? ______

(c) What would this do to the flow rate of receiving rivers during a rain event? How would this affect the organisms in the river? How would groundwater recharge be affected?

ISBN: 978-1-98-856632-0

4. (a) Which surface produced the **least** water runoff? ___

(b) How would this affect the way water enter gutters, stormwater drains and rivers? ___

(c) What would this do to the flow rate of receiving rivers during a rain event? How would this affect the organisms in the river? How would groundwater recharge be affected?

5. Are there any ways your findings could be put to use in a city? ___

Reducing water runoff

▸ Reducing the need to remove water runoff from hard city surfaces can be achieved using a variety of methods.

Public transport can reduce water runoff in two ways. Use of public transport requires fewer roads and so fewer hard surfaces. The rail system of trains usually has bedding and grass strips which are permeable and allow water to infiltrate.

Sidewalks that are built using pavers rather than poured concrete create gaps through which water can escape. Planting trees also give spaces for water to infiltrate. The trees help by absorbing any excess water that enters the ground.

Building up rather than out (creating urban sprawl) can allow more area for green space and increase the surface area for water infiltration and groundwater recharge. This greatly reduces runoff and the need for complex stormwater systems.

6. Why would reducing stormwater runoff be of benefit to a city? ___

7. Look at the picture of the pavement above center carefully. Explain why this method of reducing water runoff has its own set of problems:

8. Creating green spaces has both advantages an disadvantages. Divide the class into two groups. One group will discuss and summarize the benefits of green spaces. The other group will discuss and summarize the potential disadvantages of green spaces. You can draw on what you have learned so far and do your own research if you wish.

Summarize your discussion in point form and have one member of your group present the group's summary to the class. Keep a summary of the arguments from both sides and attach it to this page (organize the summary as a table if you wish). Do you think the advantages of green spaces outweigh the disadvantages?

ISBN: 978-1-98-856632-0

89 Integrated Pest Management

Key Question: How do integrated pest management (IPM) schemes reduce pest damage to crops?

Integrated pest management is an approach to pest control that uses a combination of chemical, biological, and mechanical controls. The aim of most IPM programs is to reduce crop damage by pests to economically tolerable levels rather than total pest eradication. Well managed IPM programs can have outstanding success and provide economically and ecologically sound alternatives to conventional pest management methods. IPM can be slower to take effect than conventional controls and expert knowledge of crop and pest ecology is required to obtain the best results. Well designed IPM programs can reduce costs and pesticide use by 50-90%, reduce fertilizer use, and slow the development of pesticide resistance. IPM emphasizes the use of ecologically sensitive pesticides which tend to be specific to the target pest and harmless to non-target species. They are less likely to cause resistance, and are non-persistent and cost effective.

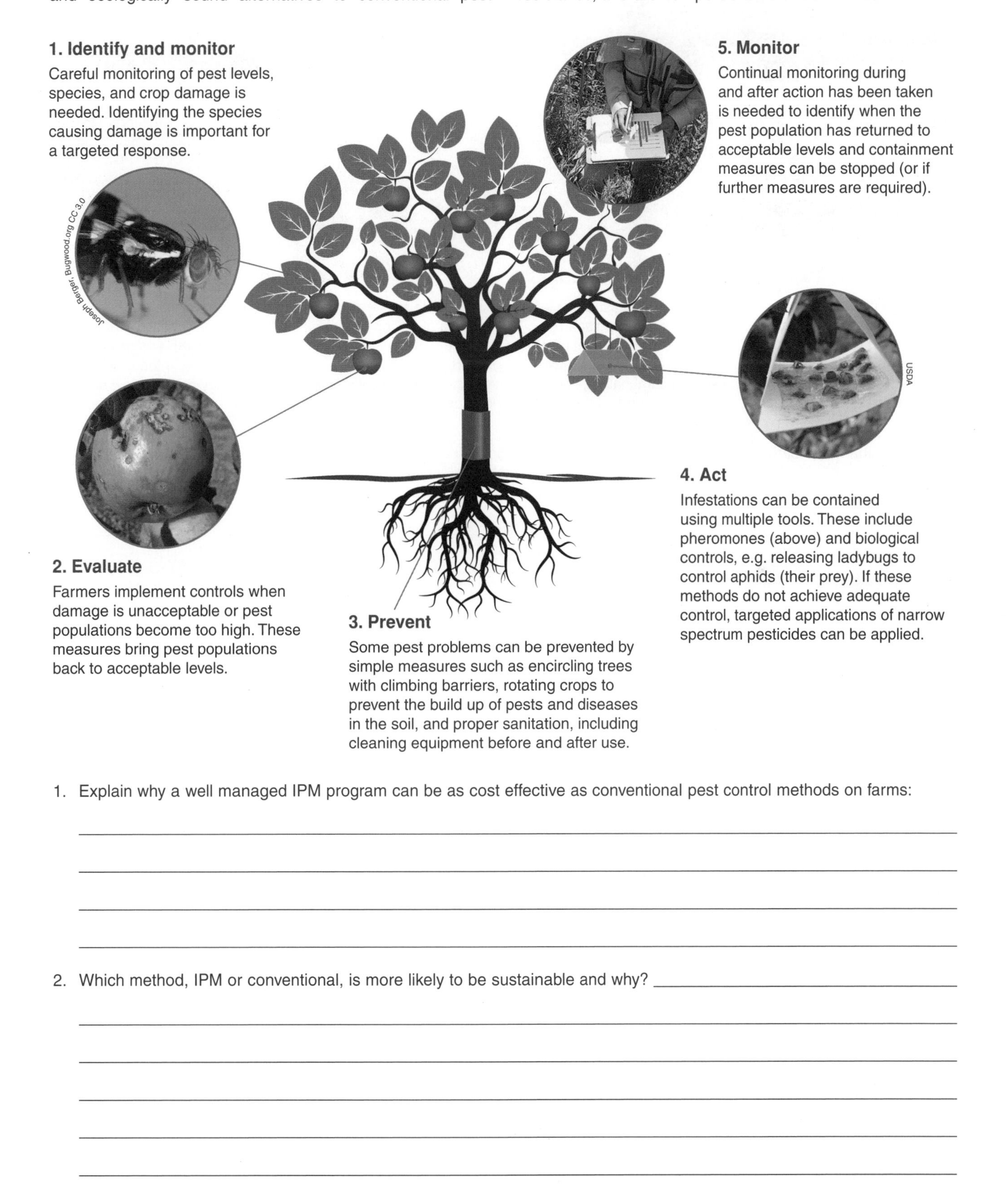

1. Explain why a well managed IPM program can be as cost effective as conventional pest control methods on farms:

____

____

____

____

2. Which method, IPM or conventional, is more likely to be sustainable and why? ______________________

____

____

____

____

____

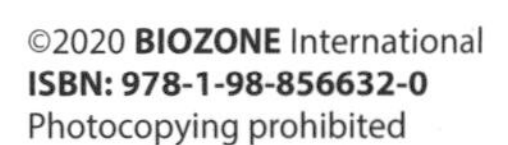

ISBN: 978-1-98-856632-0

IPM for control of gypsy moth *(Lymantria dispar dispar)*

Gypsy moth defoliation of hardwood trees, Pennsylvania 2007

- The gypsy moth is a Eurasian moth that was introduced to Massachusetts, USA in 1869 with the intention of using it in the silkworm industry. It quickly became a pest, spreading both south and west. Its larvae cause widespread defoliation (left) of over 300 species of trees and shrubs, including oaks, apples, alders, and birches. Defoliation losses have cost millions in damages and have had a profound effect on forest ecology.
- Initially, outbreaks were controlled using chemical pesticides but 100 years of research has replaced this with a comprehensive IPM program involving rigorous monitoring and containment of outbreaks, pheromone trapping, male sterilization, biopesticides, and biocontrols. Eradication is not possible, so slowing the spread is the primary goal.

Gypsy moth larva. As well as defoliating trees, the larvae produce a rash when touched.

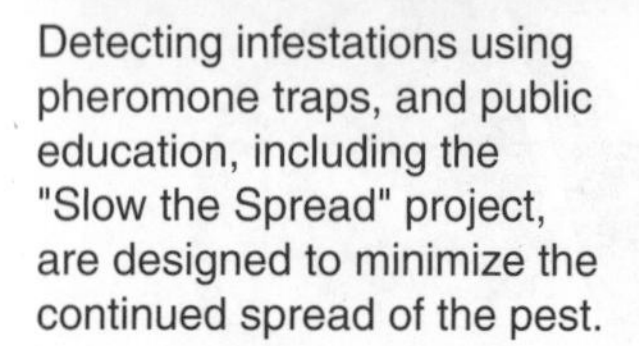

Detecting infestations using pheromone traps, and public education, including the "Slow the Spread" project, are designed to minimize the continued spread of the pest.

Larva killed by a virus

Biopesticides based on viruses (Gypchek®) or bacteria (Btk toxin) are an important part of the IPM toolkit. These make use of natural pathogenic microbes to control the larvae.

Male moth

The release of sterile males and use of sex pheromones to disrupt mating are two important strategies for reducing reproductive success in gypsy moth populations.

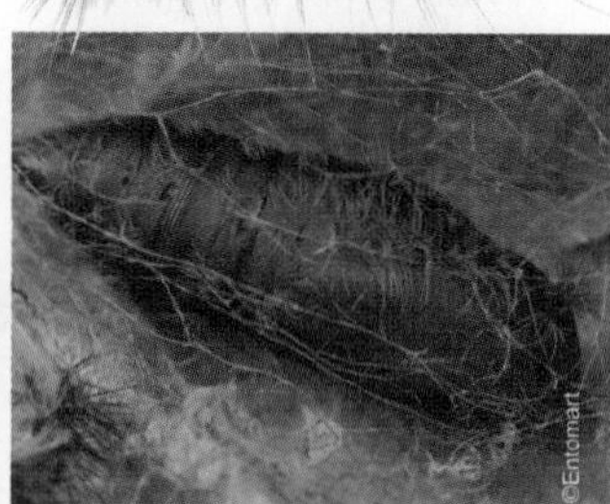

Insect growth regulators (IGR) mimic hormones and prevent normal growth and development of the larvae. If the larvae cannot molt, they cannot grow and enter the pupal stage (above).

3. Identify the main features of an IPM program, stating the importance of each to an effective pest management solution:

(a) ______________________________

(b) ______________________________

(c) ______________________________

(d) ______________________________

4. (a) Explain the general principle underlying the biological control of pests: ______________________________

(b) Explain what precautions should be taken when implementing a biocontrol program: ______________________________

ISBN: 978-1-98-856632-0

90 Sustainable Agriculture

Key Question: How can changes to agricultural practices help to provide a more sustainable way of farming?

Sustainable agriculture refers to farming practices that maximize the net benefit to society by meeting current and future food and material demands while maintaining ecosystem health and services. Two key issues in sustainable agriculture are biophysical and socio-economic. Biophysical issues center on soil health and the biological processes essential to crop productivity. Socio-economic issues center on the long-term ability of farmers to manage resources, such as labor, and obtain inputs, such as seed. Sustainable agricultural practices aim to maintain yields and improve environmental health. Crops are often grown as polycultures (more than one crop type per area), which reduces pest damage by providing a trap crop or pest confuser (e.g. planting onions in a carrot crop masks the carrots' odor and reduces damage by carrot sawfly). However yields obtained using sustainable practices can be up to 25% lower than those obtained using intensive practices. Food needs are projected to be 50% greater by 2050 than today, so this is a major disadvantage that must be overcome, either in the management of the agriculture or by society as a whole.

Some features of sustainable agriculture

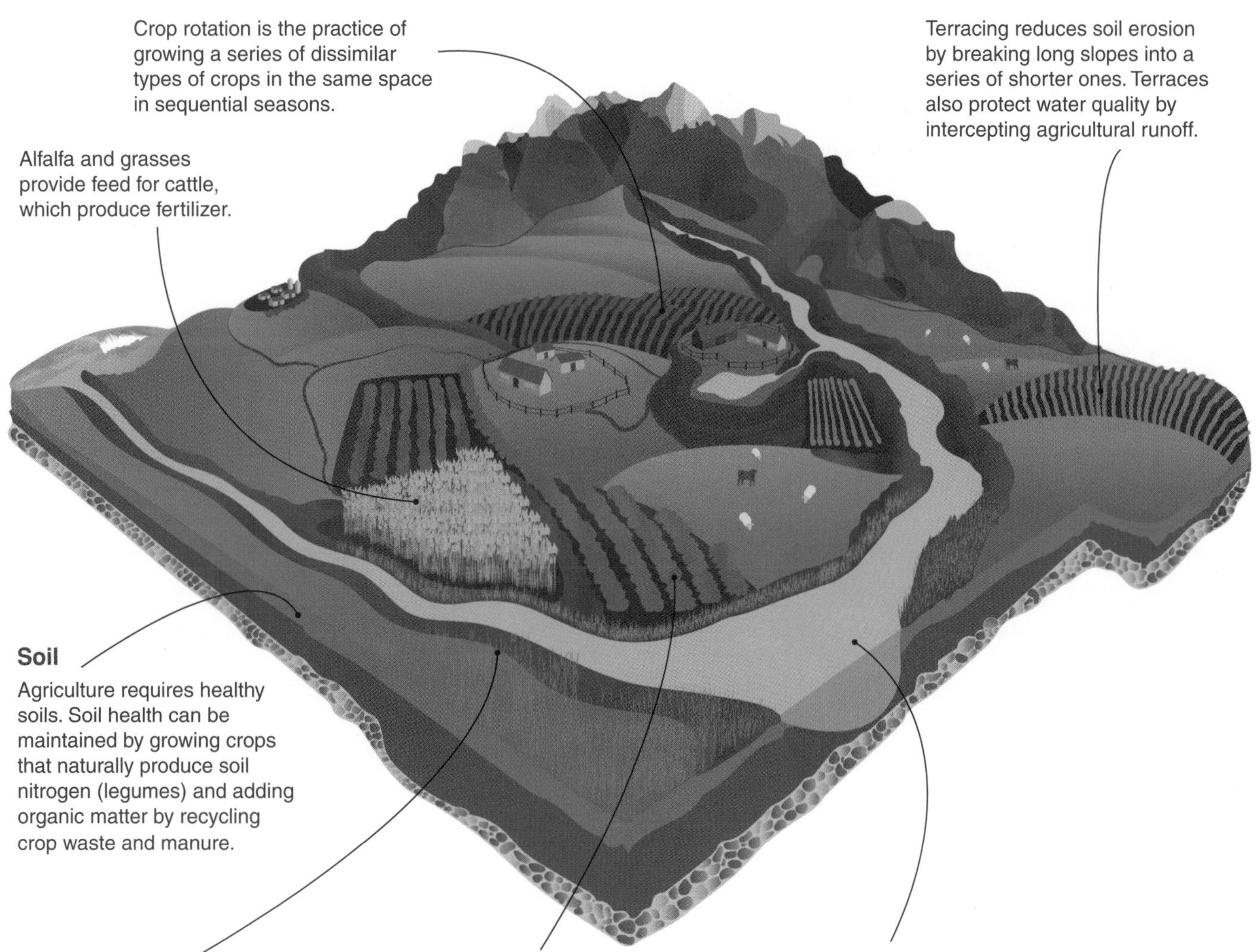

1. What is sustainable agriculture? ______________________________

____

____

____

ISBN: 978-1-98-856632-0

Many sustainable practices don't yet include the use of high yielding genetically engineered organisms, such as rice and wheat. GMOs that can maximize yield with minimum resource use or in marginal growing environments will be an important option if the world is to feed its rapidly growing population.

Mineral resources, such as rock phosphate and calcium sulfate, supply many of the nutrients needed to maintain agricultural production. Peak phosphorus is expected in 2030. After this, we will need to find new ways to produce phosphorus for fertilizers, such as reclaiming it from plant and animal matter.

Sharon Loxton

Nitrogen fertilizers require ammonia which is made from nitrogen and hydrogen via the Haber process. This requires large amounts of energy and hydrogen, both of which usually come from fossil fuels. To make fertilizers truly sustainable, renewable energy sources and hydrogen supplies are needed.

2. Explain how sustainable agriculture manages each of the following resources to meet its goals of long term sustainability:

(a) Biodiversity: ______

(b) Water: ______

(c) Soil: ______

3. Discuss the issues associated with resource use and crop yield in agriculture. Produce a reasoned argument as to the best combination of agricultural practices to feed the growing human population over the next 30 years:

______

ISBN: 978-1-98-856632-0

Farming and tillage

- Tillage is the mechanical agitation of the ground by plowing and overturning the soil. It has several benefits including the aeration of the soil, mechanical destruction of weeds, and plowing the nutrients in green crops into the ground ready for the next crop.
- Despite advantages, there are several disadvantages to tillage, including the exposure of soil to the wind, increasing erosion, and loss of water. One method of reducing soil erosion is the no-tillage system (right and below) in which the residue of the previous crop is left on the surface and seed is planted beneath the ground with special machinery.

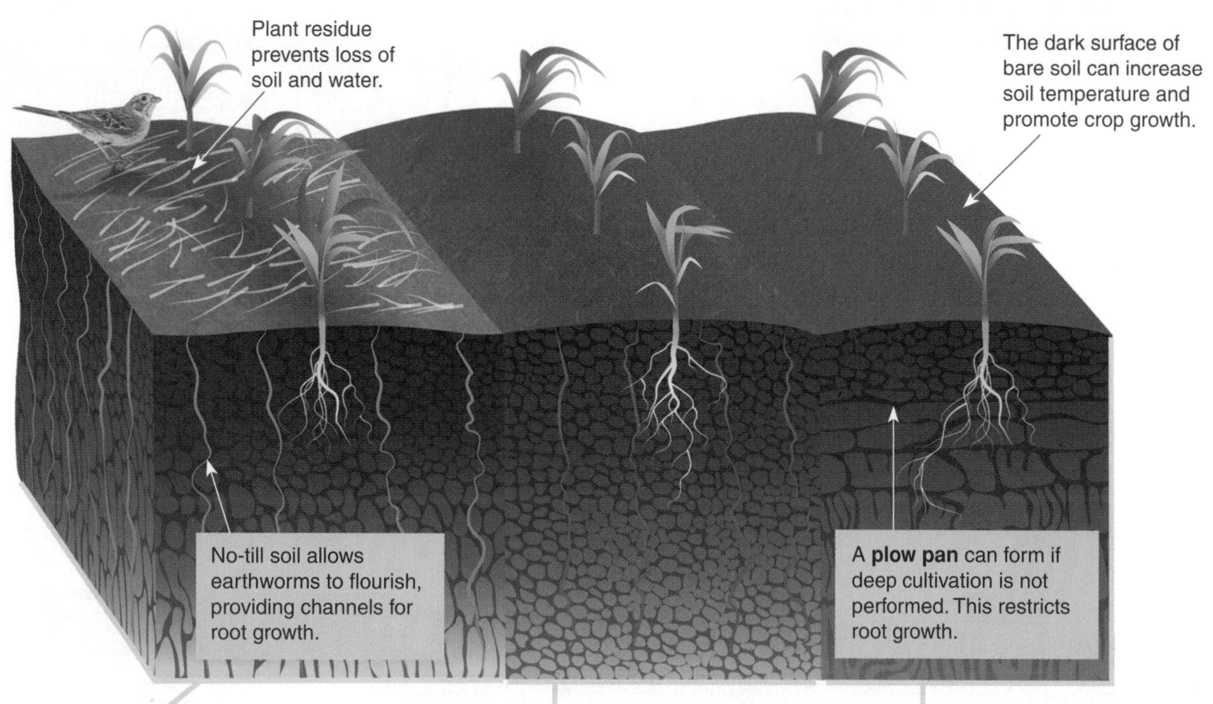

No-tillage systems

The vegetation remaining after harvest is mowed, rolled, or sprayed to begin its break down. Seeds are planted into the ground with seed drills. Residue from the previous harvest helps to reduce loss of water and soil, and prevents weeds becoming established. No-tillage is an extreme form of conservation tillage.

Conservation tillage

Conservation tillage reduces disturbance and retains crop residues. Up to 50% of the crop residue is plowed and buried but the soil is not inverted. Seed is planted into the soil beneath the residue. Conservation tillage reduces overall fuel use and labor costs, and increases carbon storage in the soil.

Intensive tillage

Up to 90% of crop residue is plowed and buried. Fields are tilled with machinery to break up soil and produce a smooth surface for planting. This disturbance to the soil can help if soils are wet or compacted but leads to greater loss of soil carbon and reduced biological activity. After planting, cultivators and herbicides are used to prevent weeds growing.

4. (a) Describe the main difference between no-till and tillage farming methods: ____________________

(b) Contrast the effort required for no-till and intensive tillage methods and suggest when each of these methods might be advantageous.

91 Reducing Soil Erosion

Key Question: How does soil erosion occur and how can different agricultural methods reduce soil erosion?

Soil is important for plant growth. Soil contains various minerals and materials that help it to retain water and remain bound together. Conservation tillage in some form is now the most common practice when preparing soil for planting, largely replacing less sustainable intensive tillage systems in the United States. Globally however, overgrazing in particular has led to increasing desertification, especially in the world's drylands. Loss of covering vegetation increases the loss of water and soil. This in turn reduces the growth of vegetation, creating a cycle that leads to further land degradation (below).

Soil erosion and water loss

- The positive (reinforcing) feedback loop caused by the loss of vegetation cover can quickly cause land to become unproductive, especially in harsh environments such as the semi-arid rangelands of the south and mid-western United States (right).
- Overgrazing by livestock removes plant cover and increases evaporation from exposed soils. Rangelands can quickly turn into semi-arid deserts as the soils dry out and plant growth is reduced. During the Dust Bowl era of the 1930s vegetation loss was caused by removing native prairie plants and leaving the land without cover. The resulting dust storms swept the region from Texas to Nebraska.

USDA

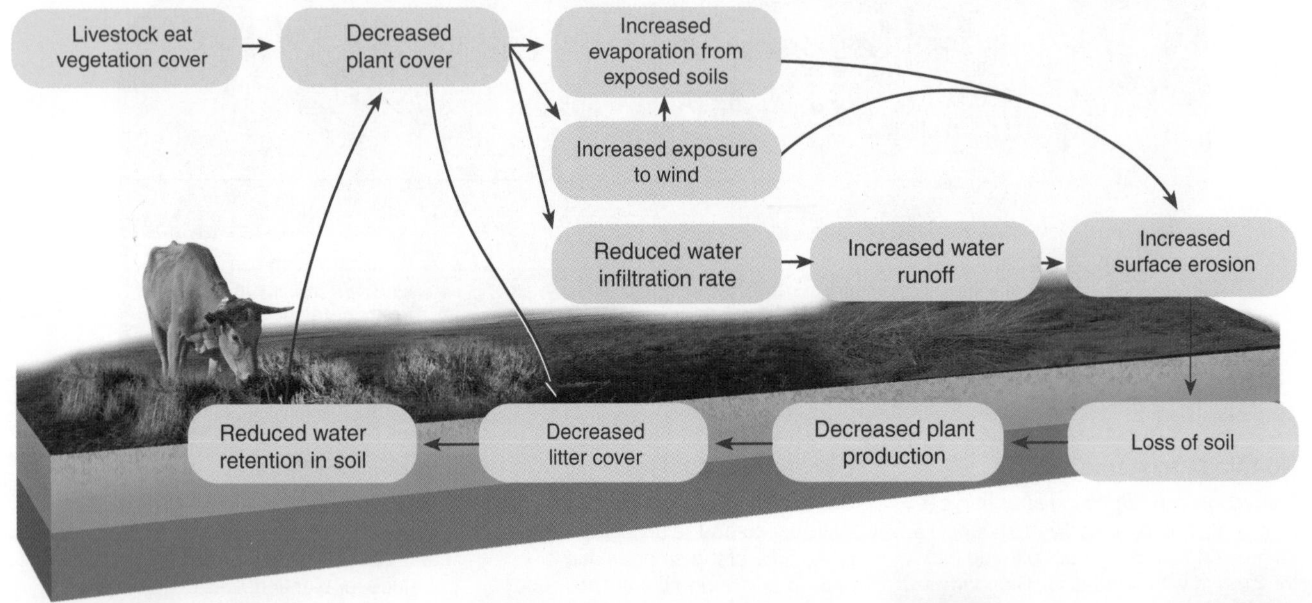

USDA

The Dust Bowl in the 1930s was a result of drought and the removal of vegetation. Soils lying fallow (without crop cover) dried out and blew away, ruining over 14 million hectares of farmland.

Texas long-horned cattle Nebraska

Overgrazing has detrimental effects on grasslands, opening space for invasion by weeds and increasing susceptibility to erosion by removing grass cover and trampling seedlings.

Erosion of soil in forests can result from deforestation. The tree roots maintain soil structure. Without them, the soil washes away leaving bare earth and unstable ground, as in the stream pictured above.

1. How does decreased plant cover lead to increased soil erosion? ______________________

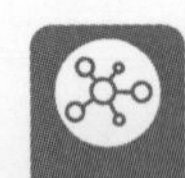

63

ISBN: 978-1-98-856632-0

Methods to reduce soil erosion

- Large volumes of topsoil can be lost through wind or rain after plowing and planting, before there is sufficient crop growth cover to protect it. Even when a crop is fully established, there may still be exposed ground from which soil can be lost. Planting techniques such as minimum tillage farming, terracing, contour plowing, and intercropping can reduce the exposure of soil.

Crops are often planted parallel to the slope of the land so that machinery can move through them easily. This orientation produces channels down which water can easily flow, taking valuable top soil with it.

USDA

Plowing and planting across, rather than down, slopes produces contours that slow water runoff and reduce soil loss from erosion by up to 50%. Water has more time to settle into the soil, reducing the amount of irrigation required.

Terracing converts a slope into broad strips, slowing or preventing water and soil runoff and reducing erosion. This technique is commonly used in paddy fields. Terraces also help to control flooding downstream.

USDA

Windbreaks reduce soil erosion by reducing wind speed close to the ground. They also reduce water loss, and so lower irrigation demands. Windbreaks placed near drainage ditches help to reduce erosion because the tree roots stabilize soil at the edge of the ditch.

Wawny

Agroforestry is a combination of agriculture and forestry. Crops or stock are raised on the same land as a stand of woody perennials. Biodiversity levels are often higher than in conventional agricultural systems, and soil loss is reduced compared to open planting.

Cropping system	Average annual soil loss (t/ha)	Percent rain runoff
Bare soil	41.0	30
Continuous corn	19.7	29
Continuous wheat	10.1	23
Rotation: corn, wheat, clover	2.7	14
Continuous grass	0.3	12

Cunningham- Saigo

Soil erosion is significantly reduced when the vegetative cover over the soil is maintained (above). Continuous cover can be achieved by using machinery to plant crops directly into the soil, along with fertilizers and pesticides, beneath the existing ground cover.

2. Why is it important to reduce soil loss as much as possible? ______________________

3. How does terracing and contour plowing reduce soil loss compared to plowing parallel to the slope?

4. Study the data in the table above right. Which crop has the greatest soil loss per hectare. Why do different crops and cropping systems have such different soil loss values?

ISBN: 978-1-98-856632-0

92 Aquaculture

Key Question: Is aquaculture a sustainable method of obtaining fish?

There is clear evidence that many of the world's most prized fisheries are being overfished. Fisheries such as Atlantic bluefin tuna, North sea cod, and Atlantic salmon have been overfished precisely because they are prized fisheries, the fish are valuable because people like to eat them, and they were once relatively easy to catch. However, as fish stocks have declined, people have realized that solutions are needed to ensure the fisheries survive, both for the environment and for the economy. Fish farming has been seen as one way to reduce the number of fish caught in the wild while increasing the total number of fish produced. Aquaculture includes not just fish farming but the farming of any marine species, including mussels and prawns. It is a highly contentious issue, with arguments both for and against it.

Fish farming: A solution to the problem?

- Human demand for fish has outpaced the rate at which those fish can replace themselves. Fish farming is a way to produce fish and other marine species without harvesting wild populations. For example, the Atlantic salmon has been so overfished that wild caught salmon is no longer a viable fishery. Instead, Atlantic salmon are farmed in large sea pens.
- Around 2.5 million tonnes of salmon are produced from farms a year, compared to less than 3000 tonnes caught in wild. Returns like these from commercial fish farms reduce the need to catch wild fish and allow wild stocks to recover.
- Fish farming does not have to rely on specific locations. Atlantic salmon, native to the North Atlantic, are farmed in Chile, Canada, Norway, Russia, the UK, and Australia. Similarly Chinook (king) salmon, native to the North Pacific, are farmed in New Zealand and Chile. New Zealand is the world's largest producer of Chinook salmon, producing more farmed salmon than the rest of the world's entire catch.
- Fish farming is highly efficient. In the wild, a salmon might need 10 kg of food for every 1 kg of body weight. Farmed fish require just 4 kg of food per kg of body weight. Much of this food includes fish meal.
- The increase in fish farming has not caused an increase in the catch of fish for fish meal. Instead, the fish meal required for fish farming has come from fish meal that was once fed to livestock such as pigs and poultry, which now use other feeds types such as grain.

Fish farming: An unsustainable disaster?

Chinook salmon

- Most fish farming is carried out in sea cages rather than containment facilities. This means waste from the fish farm enters the local ecosystem directly. Fish are held at high density in the pens and produce a large and concentrated amount of waste, including feces and food waste. In sites without adequate currents, these wastes can build up in the area, polluting the water and causing disease in the farmed fish and in local populations of marine animals. Heavy metals may also accumulate in the environment and in the fish, creating a hazard for human consumption.
- Disease can be a problem in cages, spreading quickly through the high density population. Antifouling, antibacterial, and antiparasitic chemicals are used to reduce disease.
- Escapes from the cages are common, especially in high seas. If the fish being farmed are not native, they can compete with native fish. Farmed fish also have lower genetic diversity than wild fish, so a large escape could decrease the overall genetic diversity of a wild population.
- Many of the farmed fish species are carnivorous and so are fed fish meal and oils in order to produce fish high in omega-3 fats (not made by fish but taken in with their normal diet). A large percentage of the commercial fish take is dedicated to catching bait fish such as sardines specifically for fish meal. What's more, 80% of all fish oil produced is used in the aquaculture sector. This has the potential to drive these forage fish to extinction.

1. Identify some advantages and disadvantages of fish farming. Use the data plotted on the opposite page to help you:

(a) Advantages: ______________________________

____

____

____

____

____

ISBN: 978-1-98-856632-0

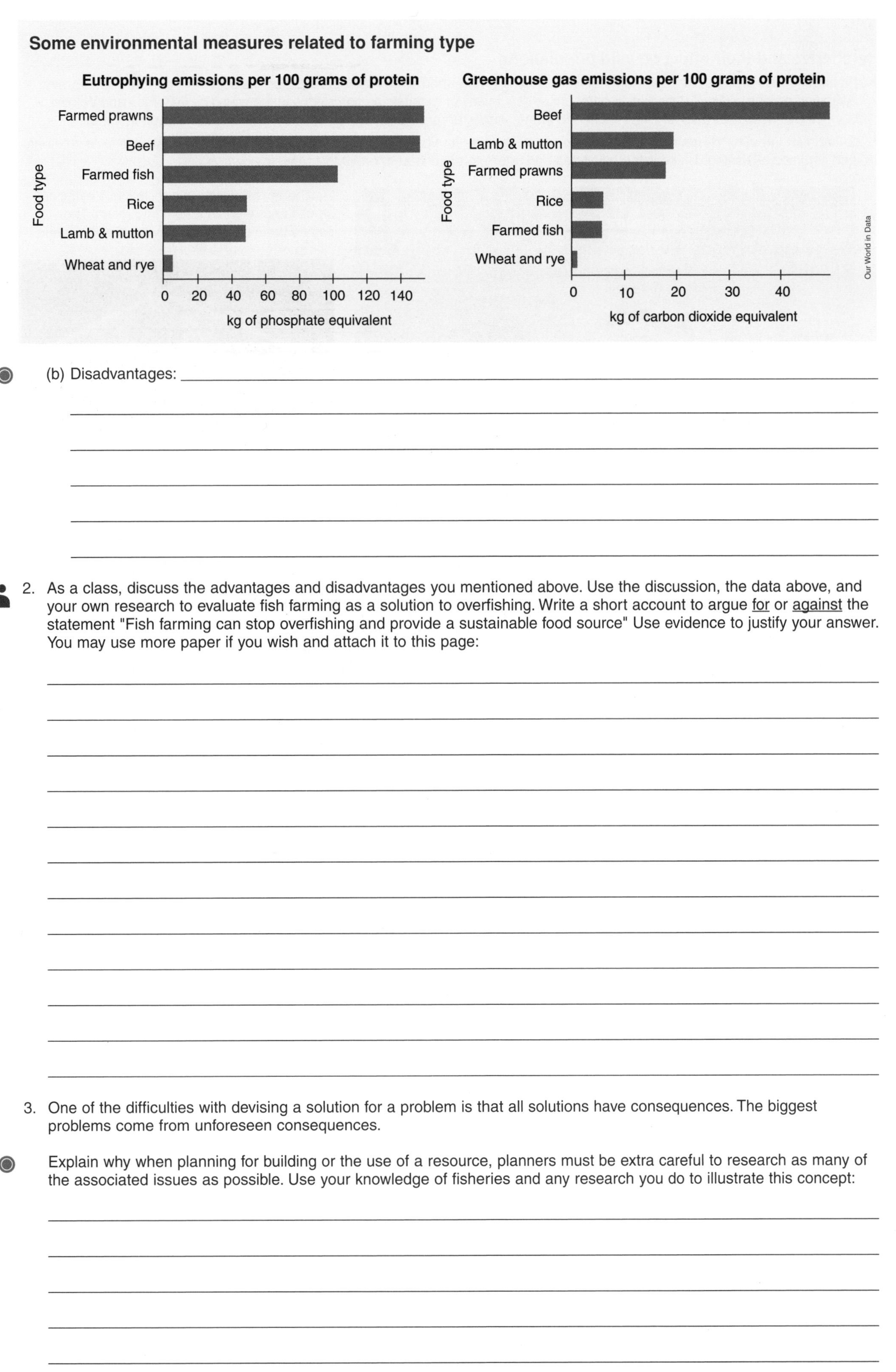

(b) Disadvantages: ______________________________

2. As a class, discuss the advantages and disadvantages you mentioned above. Use the discussion, the data above, and your own research to evaluate fish farming as a solution to overfishing. Write a short account to argue for or against the statement "Fish farming can stop overfishing and provide a sustainable food source" Use evidence to justify your answer. You may use more paper if you wish and attach it to this page:

3. One of the difficulties with devising a solution for a problem is that all solutions have consequences. The biggest problems come from unforeseen consequences.

Explain why when planning for building or the use of a resource, planners must be extra careful to research as many of the associated issues as possible. Use your knowledge of fisheries and any research you do to illustrate this concept:

ISBN: 978-1-98-856632-0

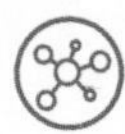

Hatcheries and their effect on wild populations

- Fish hatcheries are operations for the artificial breeding and rearing of fish species. In some cases, this is part of a fish farming operation producing fish for market. In other cases, it is a way of maintaining fish stocks in the wild. The U.S. Fish and Wildlife Service oversees the National Fish Hatchery System, which rears a variety of fish species to maintain wild populations.
- Salmon and trout hatcheries are an important part of the program because of the importance of these fish species in recreational and commercial fishing. These fish grow at sea and return to their natal streams to spawn (below).

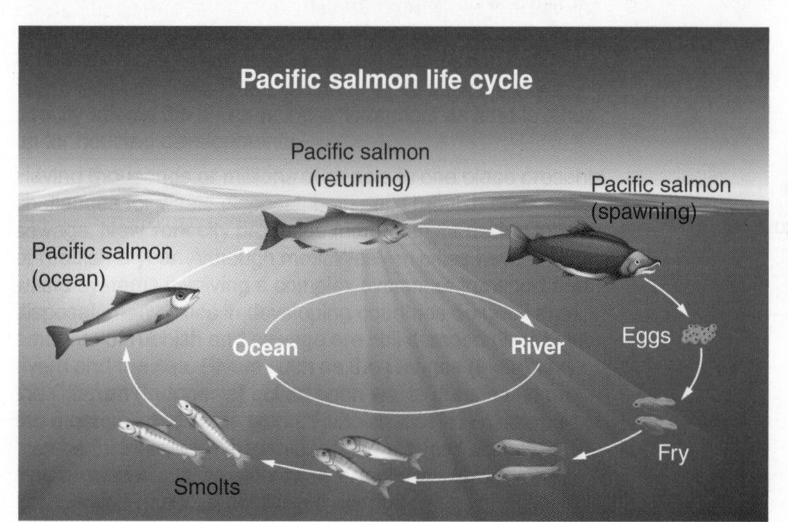

Hatcheries intervene in the life cycle by raising smolts and releasing them into rivers. The smolts then follow the life cycle of wild salmon.

Adult salmon in holding pen

- There is a certain amount of evidence that, unless managed very carefully, hatchery releases of salmon into the wild can actually do more harm than good to the population. It is simplistic to assume that if wild stock numbers are declining, the population can be rebuilt simply by introducing more young.
- Rebuilding a natural population must account for other factors involved in its decline, such as habitat loss and catch rate.
- Increasing the population with an oversupply of young can affect the carrying capacity of the environment. The behavior of hatchery young is different of those hatched in the wild, which affects their long term survival (Fig. 1 below).
- One of the major problems with hatchery released salmonids is that they cannot imprint on the river where they hatched (as they do not have one). This affects their return from sea and productivity tends to decline as the fraction of hatchery spawners in the population increases (Fig. 2 below). This is true for all species of salmonids studied.

Fig. 1: Snake River Chinook smolt to adult survival

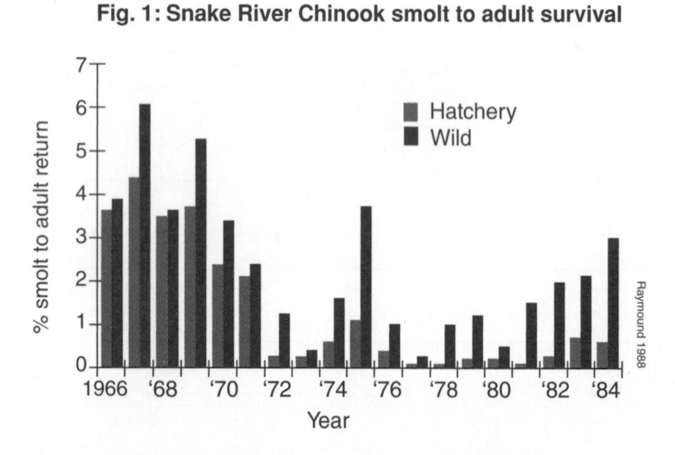

Fig. 2: Offspring produced in the wild and the proportion of hatcher-origin spawners

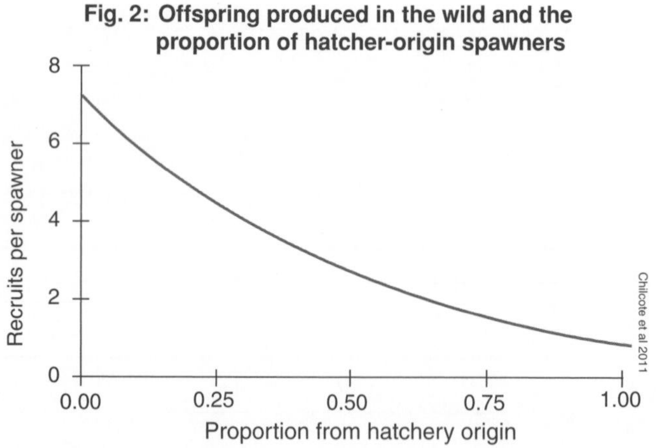

4. (a) What is the purpose of salmon hatcheries? ______________________________

   (b) Do hatchery reared salmon survive as well as wild hatched salmon? ______________________________

   (c) How do hatchery salmon compare to wild salmon in the production of offspring? ______________________________

   (d) Why is releasing hatchery reared salmon a simplistic way to restore fish stocks? ______________________________

ISBN: 978-1-98-856632-0

93 Sustainable Forestry

Key Question: How can forestry become more sustainable? The idea of sustainable forestry followed acknowledgement of the damage done by unrestricted logging of old growth forests. Changes in consumer behavior, including the reuse of lumber from demolition, can help to mitigate the impact of humans on forests, but this must be combined with more sustainable forestry practices. For forestry to be sustainable, demand for lumber must be balanced by tree regrowth. Sustainable forestry allows timber demands to be met without over-exploiting the timber-producing trees. Different logging methods are used depending on the type of trees being logged. This prevents disruption of the services that forests provide, including providing shelter for wildlife, reducing water runoff and flooding, and moderating local climate.

Sustainable methods of forestry

Selective logging

A mature forest is examined, and trees are selected for removal based on height, girth, or species. These trees are felled individually and directed to fall in such a way as to minimize the damage to the surrounding younger trees. The forest is managed in such a way as to ensure continual regeneration of young seedlings (reforestation) and provide a balance of tree ages that mirrors the natural age structure of the forest.

Forestry integrated pest management (forestry IPM) has an important role in sustainable forestry, allowing pests and diseases to be managed to an economically acceptable level.

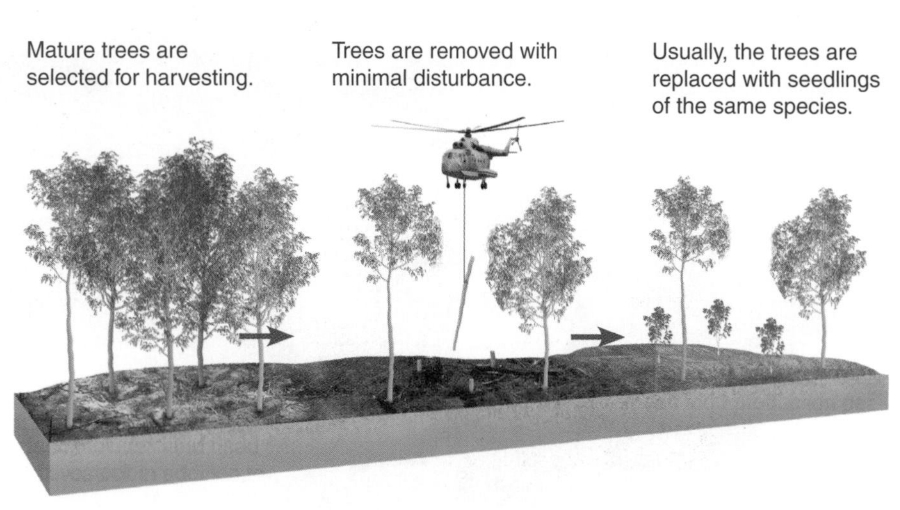

Strip cutting

Strip cutting is a variation of clearcutting. Trees are clearcut out of a forest in strips. The strip is narrow enough that the forest on either side is able to reclaim the cleared land. As the cleared forest reestablishes (3-5 years) the next strip is cut.

Strip cutting allows the forest to be logged with minimal effort and damage to forest on either side of the cutting zone, while at the same time allowing the natural reestablishment of the original forest. Each strip is not cut again for around 30 years, depending on regeneration time.

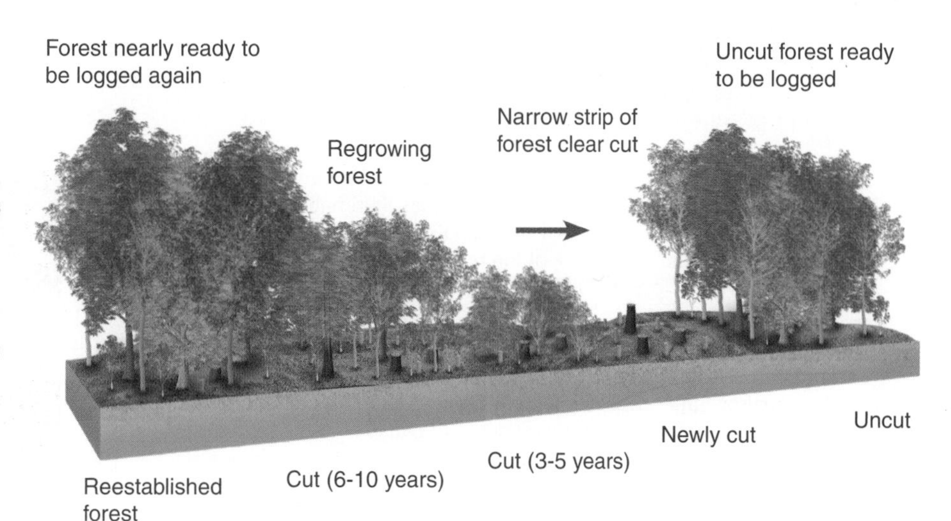

1. Identify advantages and disadvantages of each of the logging methods above:

ISBN: 978-1-98-856632-0

STB-1 7.F
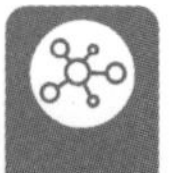

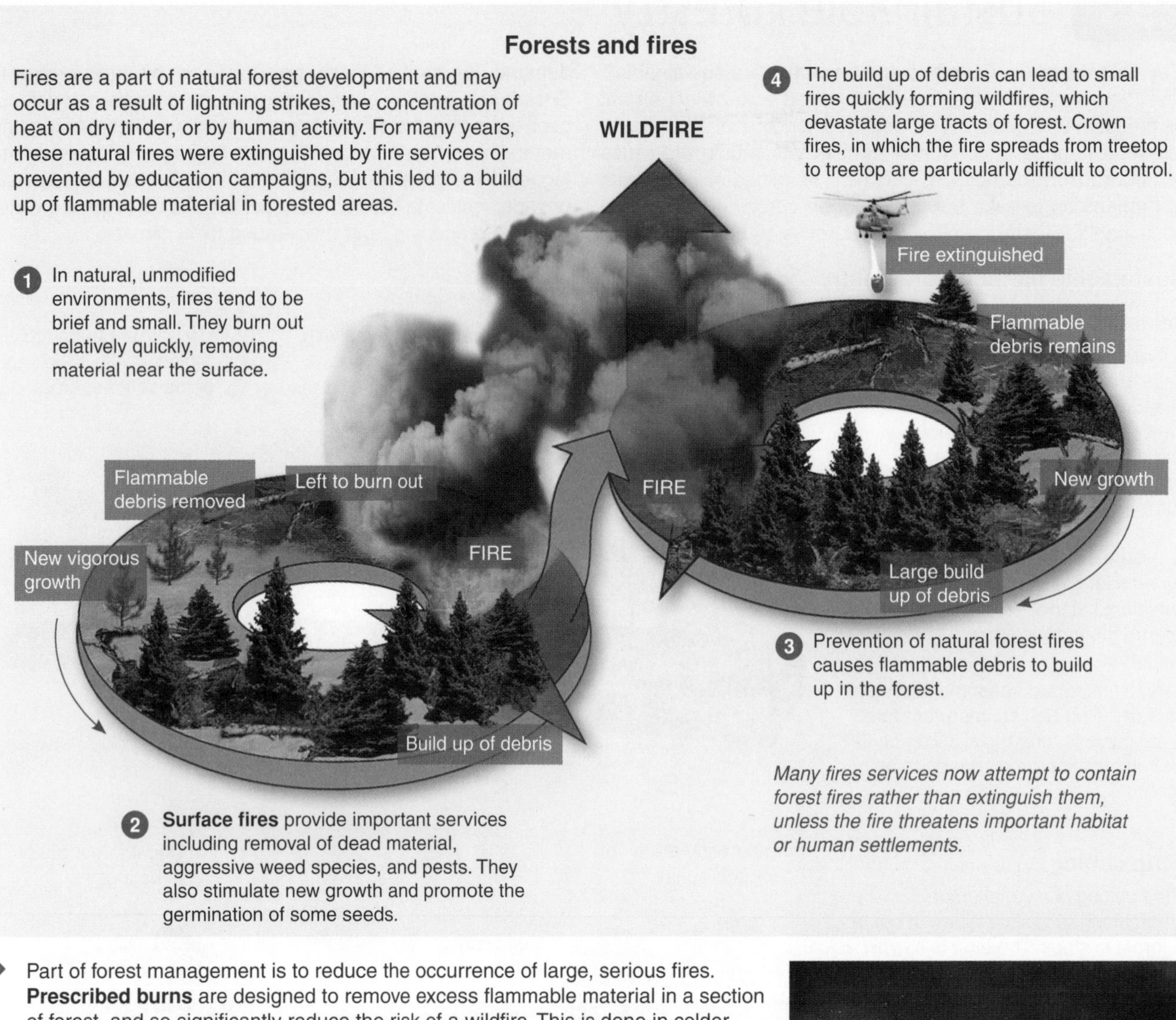

- Part of forest management is to reduce the occurrence of large, serious fires. **Prescribed burns** are designed to remove excess flammable material in a section of forest, and so significantly reduce the risk of a wildfire. This is done in colder seasons when there is a lower risk of the burn becoming uncontrollable. The controlled burns also help to stimulate new growth in the following season.
- Prescribed burns are carried out to prevent small surface fires from becoming crown fires or out of control wildfires. Surface fires burn debris close to the ground and can be of benefit to a forest. Crown fires are large, extremely hot forest fires that often destroy large trees and forests. Ground fires are fires that burn material underground (such as peat) but may emerge to cause surface fires.

2. Distinguish between, ground fires, surface fires, and crown fires: ____________________

3. Some people argue that conservation of forests includes reducing any fires to prevent damage to the forest. Others argue that prescribed burns simulate natural fires and prevent larger more dangerous fires. Justify the use of prescribed burns in the forestry setting. You may include the relevance of local ecology (local adaptation to fire) if you wish:

ISBN: 978-1-98-856632-0

94 Personal Progress Check

Answer the multiple choice questions that follow by circling the correct answer. Don't forget to read the question carefully!

1. The overuse of a shared resource, due to self interest rather than the common good, and leading to its collapse is called:
   (a) The Collapse of the Common
   (b) Resource depletion
   (c) The Tragedy of the Commons
   (d) Individual Resource Attainment

2. A common resource can be classified as:
   (a) Both rival and nonexcludable
   (b) Rival or nonexcludable
   (c) Rival and excludable
   (d) Rival or excludable

3. From the table shown below the most effective use of irrigating a crop appears to be:
   (a) Flood irrigation
   (b) Drip irrigation
   (c) Sprinkler irrigation
   (d) Perforated pipe irrigation

Treatment	Yield (t/ha)
Flood irrigation	24.52
Drip irrigation	45.25
Sprinkler irrigation	34.20
Perforated pipe irrigation	36.65

4. Regulation of clearcutting in public forests can:
   (a) Provide income for the State through taxes and permits.
   (b) Provide oversight to ensure sustainable practices.
   (c) Provide income and jobs for workers.
   (d) All of the above.

5. Environmental benefits of clearcutting include:
   (a) It can mimic natural events and reduces the amount of time logging teams are in a forest.
   (b) It removes only the damaged trees and provides gaps for new tree growth.
   (c) It provides small clearings that allow more sunlight into the forest to accelerate tree growth.
   (d) It removes invasive trees species leaving room for natives.

6. Which is true about farmed fish?
   (a) They never escape from cages onto the wild.
   (b) They are more genetically diverse than fish of the same species in the wild.
   (c) They have no impact on the quality of the water where they are raised.
   (d) Disease can spread rapidly through the population due to high population density.

7. Which of the following best illustrates the pesticide treadmill?
   (a) A chemical process used to manufacture pesticides
   (b) Biomagnification of pesticides in the tissues of primary and secondary consumers.
   (c) Increased pesticide use is needed to control resistant pests.
   (d) Removal of pesticide residue by repeated washing.

8. Which of the following represents the greatest potential risk of using biological controls?
   (a) The control agent attacks both the target species and beneficial and/or native species.
   (b) The control agent attacks a different pest species.
   (c) Repeated introductions are needed to prop up the control agent's population
   (d) Application and use of the control agent are more costly than using conventional pesticides.

9. Which of the following farming practices is consistent with integrated pest management?
   (a) Crops are sprayed with pesticide at set intervals to ensure pests are kept to a minimum.
   (b) Pests are controlled with a combination of biological, chemical, and mechanical means.
   (c) Pesticides, herbicides, and liquid fertilizer are applied in a single integrated application.
   (d) Areas needing pest control are identified by drone and relayed to computers for targeted spraying.

10. A forested area was converted to an urban area. Which of the following water related effects are likely to happen because of this:

	Runoff	Flood intensity	Groundwater recharge
(a)	Increase	Decrease	Increase
(b)	Decrease	Increase	Increase
(c)	Increase	Increase	Decrease
(d)	Decrease	Decrease	Increase

11. Reducing urban runoff can be done by:
   (a) Increasing the area of permeable paving.
   (b) Increasing the capacity of the stormwater drainage system.
   (c) Reducing the amount of public transport use, especially trains.
   (d) Increasing the camber of the road to assist with water flow from the surface.

12. The Green Revolution is responsible for:
   (a) Increased dependence of farmers on pesticides.
   (b) Increased use of mechanical farming, including tractors and harvesters.
   (c) Increased crop yield.
   (d) An increase in the number malnourished people.

ISBN: 978-1-98-856632-0

13. Refer to the graph of change in cereal production and land use in the United States below:
    (a) Is directly linked to the amount of land used.
    (b) Is directly linked to population growth.
    (c) Has increased the same amount year on year.
    (d) Has increased at a roughly exponential rate.

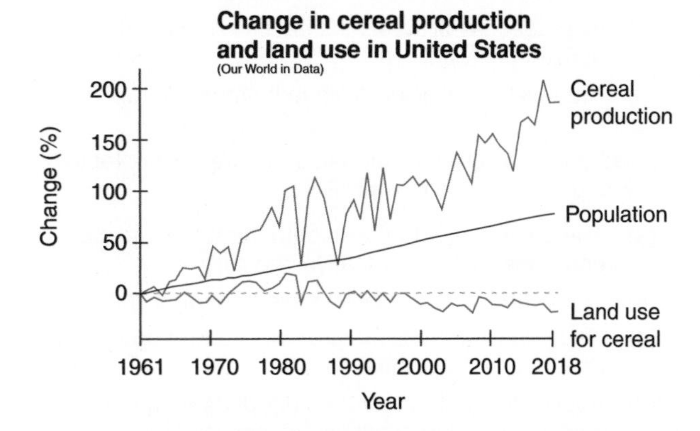

14. Genetic engineering of crops:
    (a) Has decreased crop yields because of a lack of genetic diversity.
    (b) Is a process of careful selection and breeding of crop plants over many generations.
    (c) Has caused a decline in the number of plant species grown as crop plants.
    (d) Has the potential to increase nutritional value and yield in crops.

15. A 50 hectare (Ha) farm is suited for both growing corn and farming beef. Which of the following farming regimes would produce the most calories per hectare for human consumption?

	Hectares for farming beef	Hectares for growing corn
(a)	0 Ha	50 Ha
(b)	13 Ha	37 Ha
(c)	30 Ha	20 Ha
(d)	50 Ha	0 Ha

16. For the same 50 Ha farm, which regime will produce the most greenhouse gas emissions?

	Hectares for farming beef	Hectares for growing corn
(a)	0 Ha	50 Ha
(b)	13 Ha	37 Ha
(c)	30 Ha	20 Ha
(d)	50 Ha	0 Ha

17. The risks of subsurface mining include:
    (a) Risk of tunnel collapse.
    (b) Lung damage through dust inhalation.
    (c) Build up of explosive gases.
    (d) All of the above.

18. Refer to the graph below. Overall, fisheries catches have remained steady or even slightly declined over the last decade. Reasons for this might include:
    (a) Fishing vessels aren't trying hard enough to catch fish any more.
    (b) Fish populations are declining and aquaculture production is increasing.
    (c) Climate change means the fishing seasons have shortened so there isn't enough time to catch fish.
    (d) Aquaculture has taken up space at all the best fishing grounds so has increased at the expense of conventional fishing.

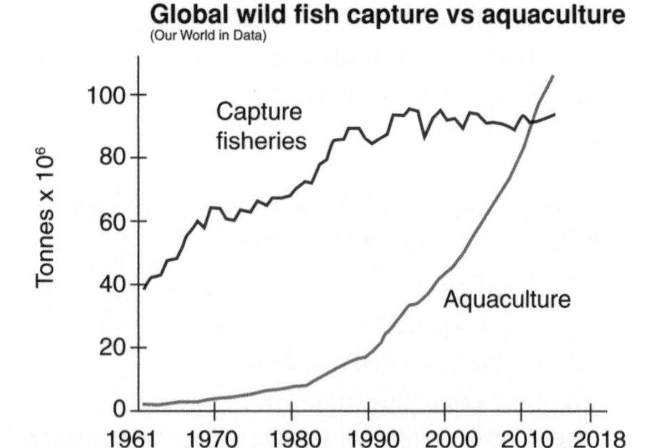

19. The process of mountaintop removal can be best described as:
    (a) The removal of trees from mountain tops during a logging operation.
    (b) The burying of toxic waste at high elevation, effectively removing the mountain from a functioning ecosystem.
    (c) The use of heavy equipment to move overburden downhill during a mining operation.
    (d) The reduction in height of mountains due to glacial movements.

20. Urban areas:
    (a) Are places where there are more than 1000 people per square mile.
    (b) Are places where the majority of the world's food is produced.
    (c) Have less of the population than rural areas.
    (d) Cover 80% of the United States.

21. Which of the following is not typically a feature of sustainable agriculture:
    (a) No tillage
    (b) Crop rotation
    (c) Use of genetically engineered crop varieties.
    (d) Use of inorganic fertilizers.

22. Soil erosion as a result of agriculture can be reduced by:
    (a) Contour cultivation.
    (b) Mixed cropping.
    (c) Conservation tillage.
    (d) All of the above.

ISBN: 978-1-98-856632-0

23. The diagram below shows a simplified map of a region where two possible areas could be surface-mined for coal. Each site presents its own environmental problems. For each site, describe the environmental problems mining might cause. Propose solutions that will minimize the impact of these problems on the environment and the people in the nearby town. Decide which site you would mine and give reasons.

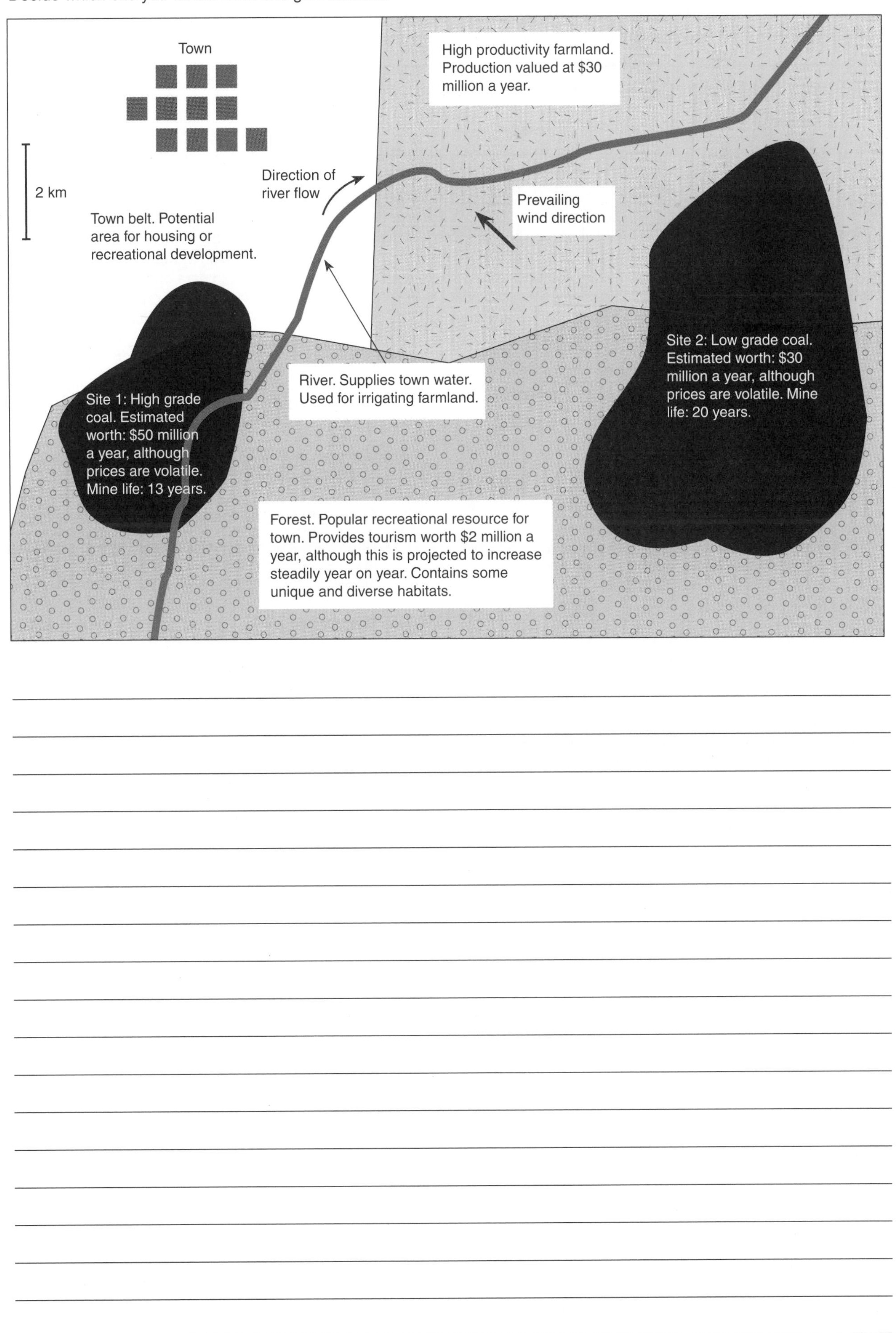

ISBN: 978-1-98-856632-0

6. Energy Resources and Consumption

Developing understanding

Content: This unit examines human use of renewable and nonrenewable sources of energy and the impact of this use on the environment. The consumption of energy and the type of energy resources used depends on level of economic development and (to an extent) on the geological history of the region, which determines the resources that are locally available.

Skills: In this unit, you can practice identifying where natural energy resources occur globally. You should be able to describe different energy sources, distinguish between renewable and nonrenewable sources, and evaluate their relative merits. Text and data analysis are an important part of this chapter. You may want to consult the glossary and conversion charts at the end of the book to help you with vocabulary and the units used to express energy production and use.

6.1 Renewable and nonrenewable resources .... activities 96 - 97

☐ 1. Identify differences between nonrenewable and renewable energy sources and describe examples in each category.

6.2 Global energy consumption .... activity 98

☐ 2. Describe trends in global energy consumption and account for any changes evident over the last 200 years or so. Interpret data on global energy consumption and explain any patterns you observe.

6.3 Fuel types and uses .... activities 99 - 101, 106

☐ 3. Identify types of fuels and their uses to include peat, coal, oil, natural gas, and plant biomass such as wood. Which of these are fossil fuels and how do they compare in terms of the energy they provide and the emissions they produce?

☐ 4. Distinguish between types of coal and describe the factors during formation that have contributed to their particular qualities. How is coal used to make electricity and what are its advantages and disadvantages as a fuel source.

☐ 5. Describe how oil and natural gas are extracted and used and compare their advantages and disadvantages.

6.4 Distribution of natural energy resources .... activities 100 - 101

☐ 6. Describe the global distribution of available natural energy resources, such as coal and oil. Explain why the pattern of energy resource distribution is not uniform.

6.5 Fossil fuels .... activities 95, 99 - 102

☐ 7. Describe what is involved in the combustion of fossil fuels and explain how this chemical reaction is used in power generation. Use an energy chain to describe the energy transformations involved in generating electricity from different types of energy sources.

☐ 8. Explain the methods used to extract fossil fuels. Explain why less accessible resources become more economically viable as supplies of fossil fuels decline.

☐ 9. Describe the advantages and environmental impacts of different methods of fossil fuel extraction. Describe and evaluate the environmental risks associated with extracting non-conventional fossil fuels.

6.6 Nuclear power .... activities 103 - 105

☐ 10. Describe the process of fission. Where does the heat come from in the process and how is it used to power a turbine and generate electricity?

☐ 11. Explain what radioactivity is, its uses (including in nuclear power plants and in radiometric dating), and the problems associated with its use. In what way is nuclear power a clean energy? In what way is it not?

☐ 12. Use case studies to describe the short and long term effects of nuclear energy on the environment.

6.7 Energy from biomass .... activity 106

☐ 13. Describe the environmental effects of using biomass to generate power. Compare different types of biomass fuels in terms of their relative costs and benefits.

6.8 Solar energy .... activities 107 - 108

☐ 14. Use examples to describe how solar energy can be used to generate power. Include reference to photovoltaic solar cells, and active and passive solar energy systems.

☐ 15. Describe the benefits of solar power generation, its costs, and its effects on the environment.

6.9 Hydroelectric power .... activities 109 - 110

☐ 16. Describe the principles of hydroelectric power generation. Compare and contrast systems for using the energy of water to generate power to include impoundment and run-of-the river systems, as well as tidal and wave power systems.

☐ 17. Describe the benefits of hydroelectric power generation, its costs, and its effects on the environment.

6.10 Geothermal energy .... activity 111

☐ 18. Describe the use of geothermal energy in power generation. What are the costs and benefits of geothermal energy, what limits its use, and what are its environmental effects?

6.11 Hydrogen fuel cell .... activity 112

☐ 19. Describe the use of hydrogen fuel cells in power generation. Describe the environmental benefits of fuel cells and suggest why the technology has not been widely adopted.

6.12 Wind energy .... activity 113

☐ 20. Describe how wind energy is used in power generation and describe its benefits and environmental effects.

6.13 Energy conservation .... activity 114

☐ 21. Describe methods for conserving energy on both small and larger scales (e.g. around a home, in industry, and in public transportation and building design). What contribution does energy conservation make towards meeting the world's future energy demands?

95 Using Energy Transformations

Key Question: How do power plants use kinetic and potential energy to produce electricity?

Most commercial electricity is generated by transforming kinetic energy (the energy of movement) into electrical energy. This is usually achieved by using kinetic energy to turn a turbine attached to a magnet or electromagnet housed inside a large set of wire coils (or vice versa) (the generator). Moving the magnet through the coils produces electricity by a process called electromagnetic induction. The difference between most forms of electricity generation is the method employed to turn the turbine. Energy comes in many forms, but can be separated into two major categories: potential (stored) energy and kinetic energy. Energy can be transformed easily between these forms. A rock at the top of a hill has potential energy. Giving it a push so that it rolls down the hill converts the potential energy into kinetic energy, along with some sound and heat. Energy is lost from a system (normally as heat due to friction) whenever energy is transformed from one form into another. The efficiency of a system is improved by reducing these energy losses. Generally, the fewer steps involved in energy transformation, the less energy will be lost from the system.

A generalized power plant

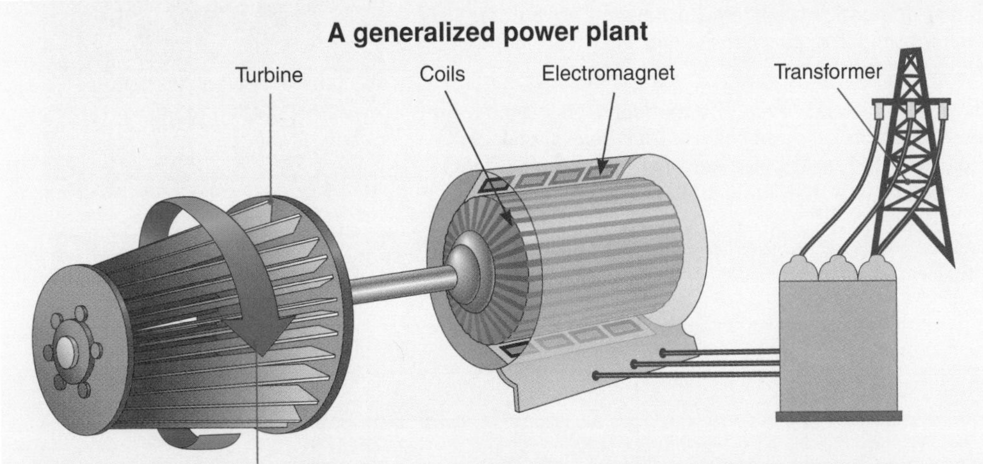

The method used to turn or drive the turbine is what distinguishes the power plant. Hydroelectric power plants use falling water, thermal plants use steam, and wind turbines use wind.

The capacity of an electricity generation plant refers to its instantaneous power output. For example, a plant rated at 1000 MW has the ability to produce 1000 megawatts (1000 megajoules per second) of electricity at any one point in time.

Photovoltaics

Photovoltaic cells (or solar cells) are increasingly being used to produce electricity on a small scale.

The solar cell is able to produce electricity directly from the Sun's energy without the need for a turbine.

Gravitational potential energy: water in dam

Kinetic energy: water moving through a dam

Kinetic energy: water turning a turbine

Electrical energy: induction from a turning coil in a dam

Heat energy: heat loss caused by resistance

An energy chain can be used to describe where the energy used to generate electricity comes from and where it goes to. The number of steps in the chain depends on the type of electricity generation and the number of energy transformations involved.

1. Describe the process by which electricity is commercially generated: ______________________

____

____

____

____

2. Explain why no form of electricity generation can ever be 100% efficient: ______________________

____

____

____

ISBN: 978-1-98-856632-0

INVESTIGATION 6.1: Home electricity survey

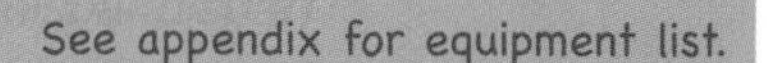
See appendix for equipment list.

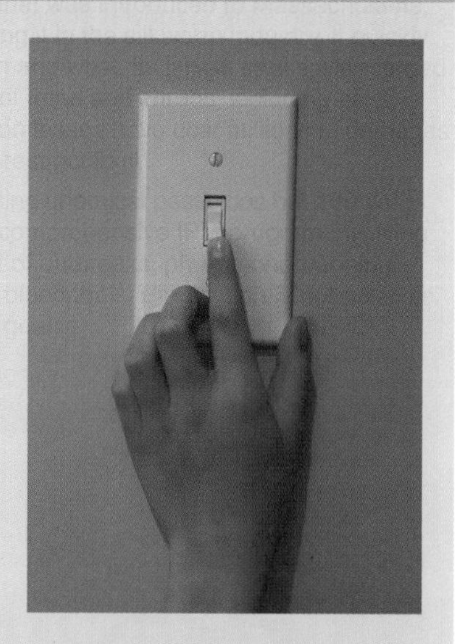

1. Virtually every home appliance we use requires electricity, from microwave ovens and dishwashers to televisions and computers. All these appliances use electricity at different rates. This is shown on the device as its wattage or power. A watt (W) is the use of 1 joule (J) of energy per second. A joule is the SI measure of energy. It is defined as the energy transferred when using a force of 1 newton to move an object 1 meter (or one newton meter). Another way of viewing it is that it takes 4.2 joules to raise the temperature of 1 mL of water by 1°C. A kitchen kettle rated at 2000 W will take 21 seconds to raise the temperature of 1 L of water by 10°C.
2. Most electrical appliances have their wattage printed on them, usually near the power cord. Light bulbs normally have the wattage printed on the top (in older incandescent bulbs) or near the bottom (in newer LED bulbs). They normally also have the voltage and the current (V and I). These multiplied together will give the wattage (approximate for AC appliances).
3. Your home will be filled with appliances, even the mundane ones you forget about such as light bulbs and electric toothbrushes. Pick five appliances that you or your household use the most often and list them in the table below. Find their wattage and fill out the table below:

Appliance	Watts	Hours used per day	Energy used per day (J)

4. Electricity is priced using a unit called the kilowatt hour (kWh). One kWh is one kilowatt sustained for one hour, or the use of 1000 J/s for one hour, which equals 3600 kJ (1000 J x 60 seconds x 60 minutes). Find your household's electricity bill for the previous month (you may need permission from your parents or caregiver) and determine how much electricity in kWh was used in that month. You may find that it is divided into different parts, such as heating and general use. If you can, try and find how much electricity was used on heating and on general use. List these in the space below.

   Total electricity: ____________________

   Heating: ____________________

   General use: ____________________

5. Use the information above to work out the amount of energy in kilojoules used:

   Total electricity: ____________________

   Heating: ____________________

   General use: ____________________

6. Based on your data from number 3, is the energy used by your household about what you expected? Explain:

____

____

3. Use the following conversion factor to work out the amount of carbon dioxide equivalent your household produces based on the electricity it uses: 1 kWh = 7.07×10^{-4} tonnes CO_2 (1 tonne = 1000 kg).

____

____

4. How could this CO_2 production be reduced? ____________________

____

ISBN: 978-1-98-856632-0

96 Nonrenewable Energy Resources

Key Question: What are nonrenewable resources, what types are there, and where do they come from?

The Earth contains enormous energy resources, which can be obtained relatively easily and used to provide energy we can use. The most commonly used of these resources are the fossil fuels, i.e. coal, oil, and natural gas. These can be burned to produce heat energy or refined to supply a variety of energy or material needs. As well as fossil fuels, radioactive minerals can be mined and concentrated, and the energy they produce harnessed to provide electrical energy. The world's total energy use is around 160,000 TWh but the global distribution of this energy use is not uniform. For example, the world's 20 wealthiest countries constitute less than 20% of the world's population but use more than half the world's commercial energy supply. In contrast, many poorer nations still lack reliable or easily accessible energy resources.

Nonrenewable energy resources from the Earth's crust

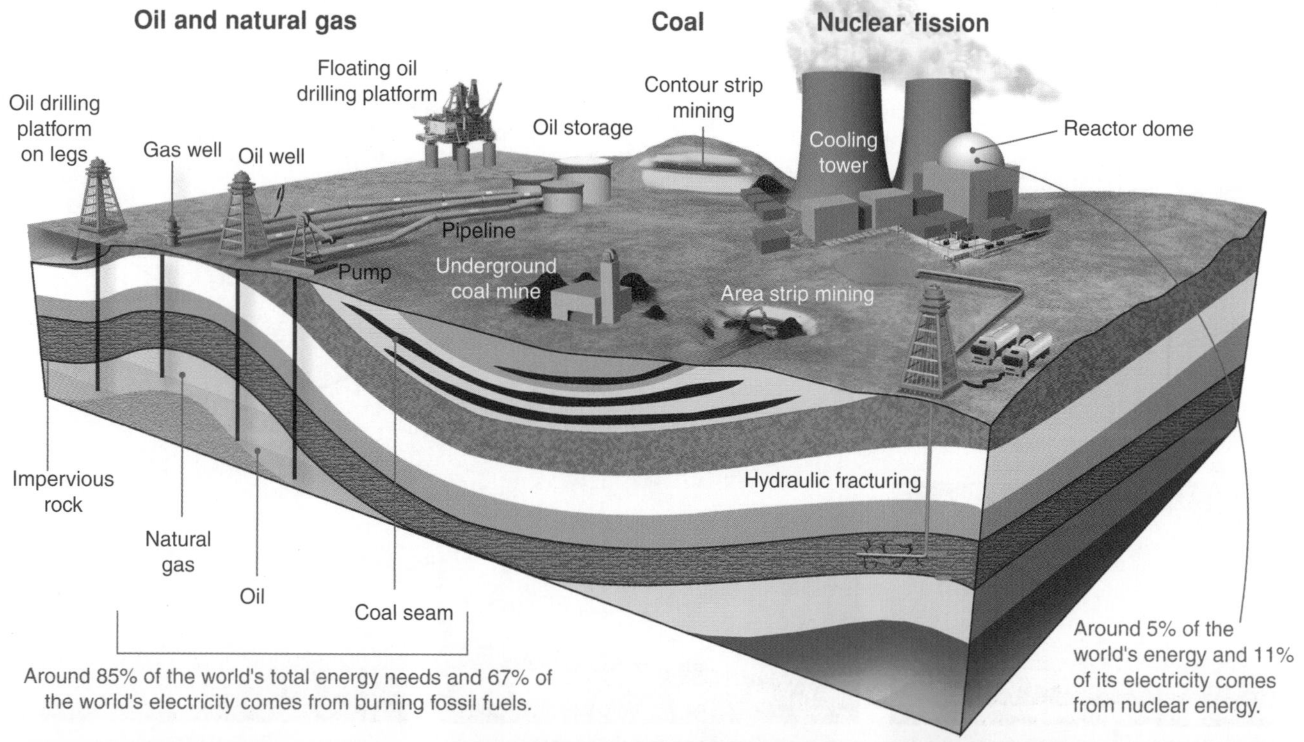

Around 85% of the world's total energy needs and 67% of the world's electricity comes from burning fossil fuels.

Around 5% of the world's energy and 11% of its electricity comes from nuclear energy.

A nuclear power plant uses uranium-235 or plutonium-239 as fuel in a controlled nuclear fission reaction to release energy for propulsion, heat, and electricity generation. Nuclear power does not release CO_2, but safe storage and disposal of nuclear waste remains a challenge.

Coal can be easily extracted from seams found near the surface. This causes a large amount of disruption to the landscape. Coal from deeper seams can be extracted by underground mining, which causes little surface disruption provided there is no land subsidence.

Coal and oil are extremely energy dense. They are also highly portable, stable, and relatively safe to work with under everyday conditions. This makes them the ideal choices for use as fuels because they don't need heavy unwieldy containers or special safety equipment to be stored.

1. What is meant by the term "fossil fuel"? ____________________

____

____

2. Why are fossil fuels so useful as fuels and what problems might be involved in replacing them? ____________________

____

____

____

ISBN: 978-1-98-856632-0

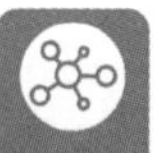

97 Renewable Energy Resources

Key Question: What are renewable resources and what types are there?

A renewable energy resource is one where energy can be extracted repeatedly without its source ever being depleted. Renewable energy resources have been used by humans for centuries, the most common being water wheels and windmills providing rotational energy to mills and small factories. Both these technologies have been modernized and scaled up as hydroelectric dams and wind turbines.

Fossil fuels are polluting, supplies are limited, and their extraction is environmentally damaging, so the development and improvement of renewable energy technologies is an increasingly high priority. Some renewable energy technologies are in use already and many can be scaled down easily to provide portable energy, such as solar cookers or solar panels. However renewable energies have their own problems to do with space, noise, and use of rare or toxic minerals, as well as the cost of operation and length of life.

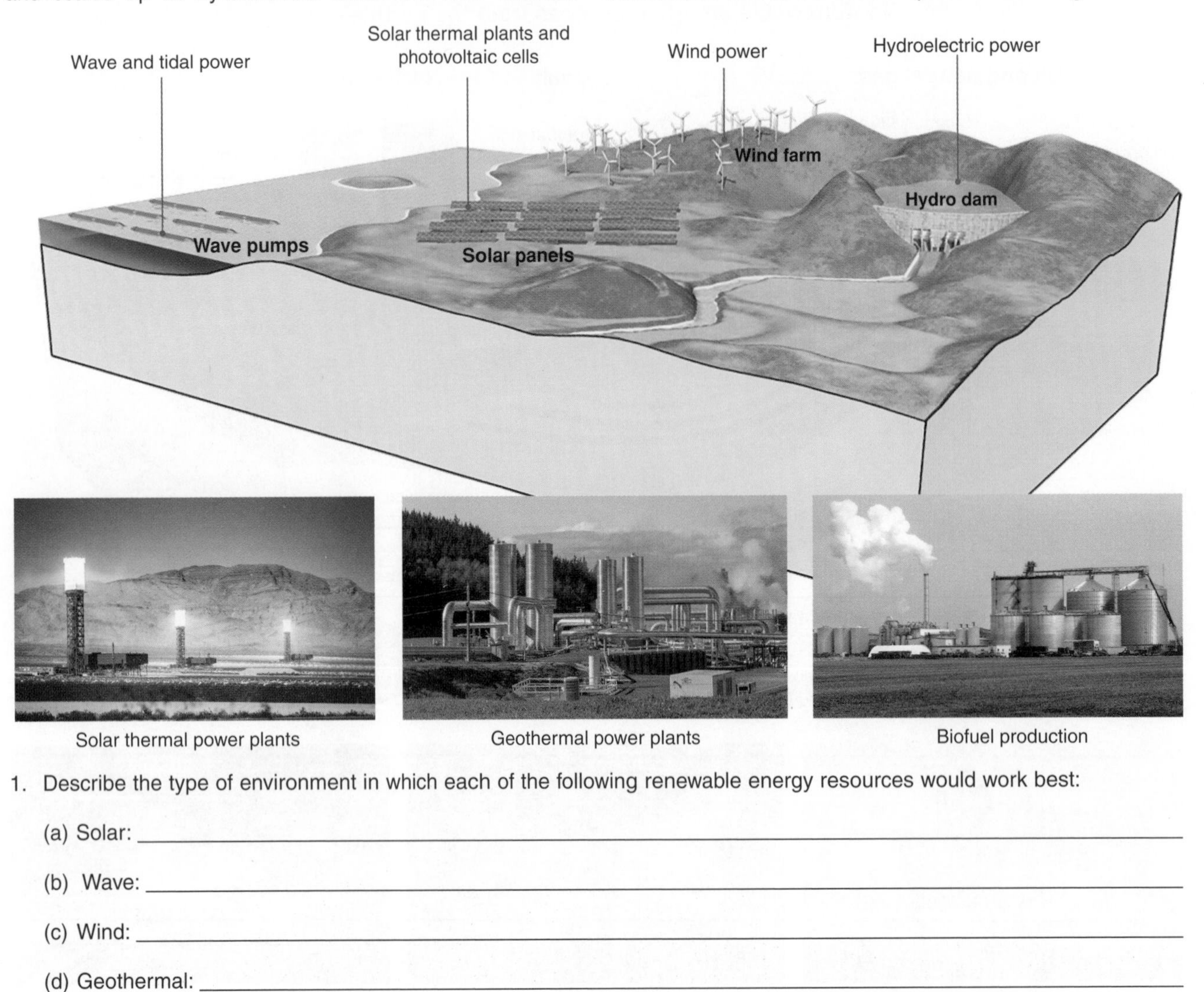

Solar thermal power plants

Geothermal power plants

Biofuel production

1. Describe the type of environment in which each of the following renewable energy resources would work best:

   (a) Solar: ______________________

   (b) Wave: ______________________

   (c) Wind: ______________________

   (d) Geothermal: ______________________

   (e) Hydro: ______________________

   ____

2. Explain why renewable energy sources are likely to become predominant in the future: ______________________

____

____

____

____

____

____

____

____

ISBN: 978-1-98-856632-0

98 Global Energy Consumption

Key Question: What are the trends in human energy use?

Human history is linked closely with our ability to harness and transform energy. The energy a person could harness 20,000 years ago was around 20,000 J per day. Today the average human uses more than 200 million joules per day. This energy use is not evenly distributed, however. People in developed countries use more than people in undeveloped countries, the wealthy use more than the poor, and industry uses more than households. The primary sources of the energy used also varies regionally based on the availability of the resources, their ease of use, and the political and ideological influences affecting a country. The graphs below show various aspects of global energy use. Germany is used as an example of the development of a typical industrialized nation (bottom right).

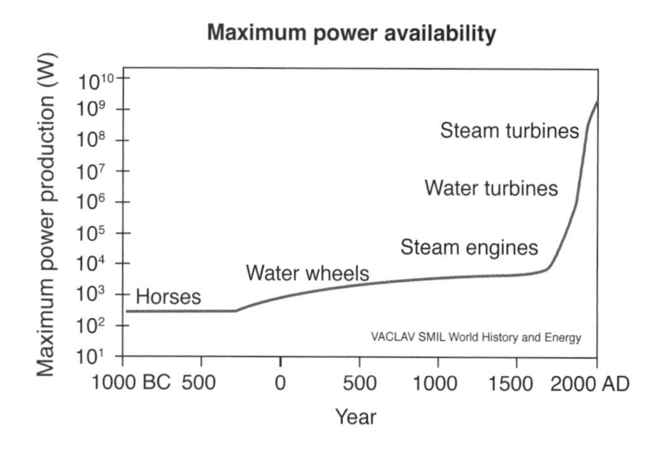

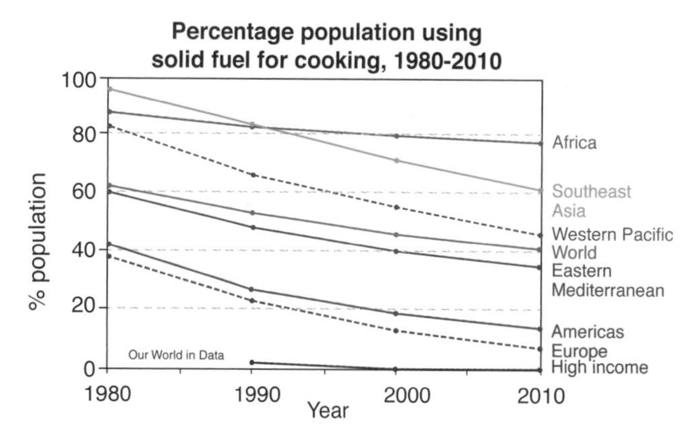

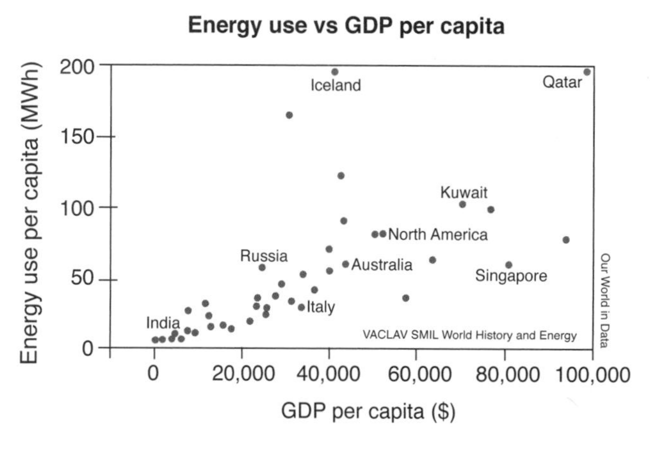

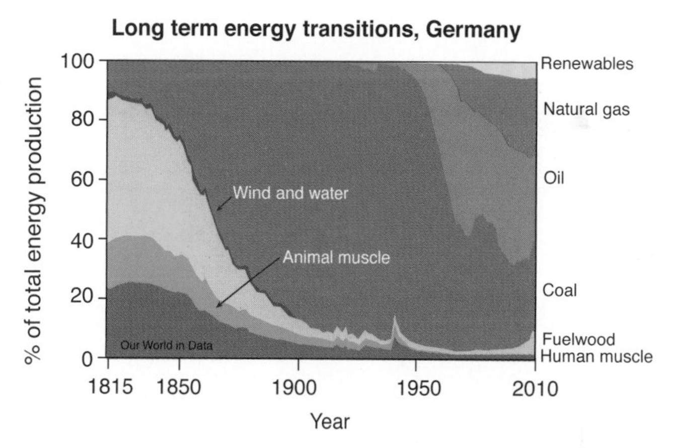

1. The data below shows the world energy consumption divided into different energy resources. First complete the calculations to obtain the cumulative data by adding together the values as indicated. The first two rows have been completed for you. Plot the data in the shaded columns as a cumulative graph, similar to the one for energy transitions in Germany (above). Identify the contributions of each energy resource using labels or a key.

Year	Biofuels (TWh)	Coal (TWh)		Oil (TWh)		Natural gas (TWh)		Other (TWh)	Total (TWh)
	1	2	1+2	3	1+2+3	4	1+2+3+4	5	
1800	5556	97	5647	0	5647	0	5647	0	5647
1850	7222	569	7791	0	7791	0	7791	0	7791
1880	6944	2542		33		0		0	
1900	6111	5728		181		64		17	
1920	6944	9833		889		233		64	
1940	7222	11,586		2653		875		192	
1960	8889	15,442		11,097		4472		689	
1970	9444	17,065		26,664		9615		1279	
1980	10,000	20,857		35,605		14,237		2459	
1990	11,111	25,818		37,812		19,485		4282	
2000	12,500	27,422		43,058		23,991		5454	
2010	11,667	41,985		48,869		31,567		6955	
2018	11,111	43,869		54,220		38,489		9375	

ISBN: 978-1-98-856632-0

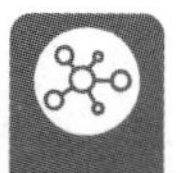

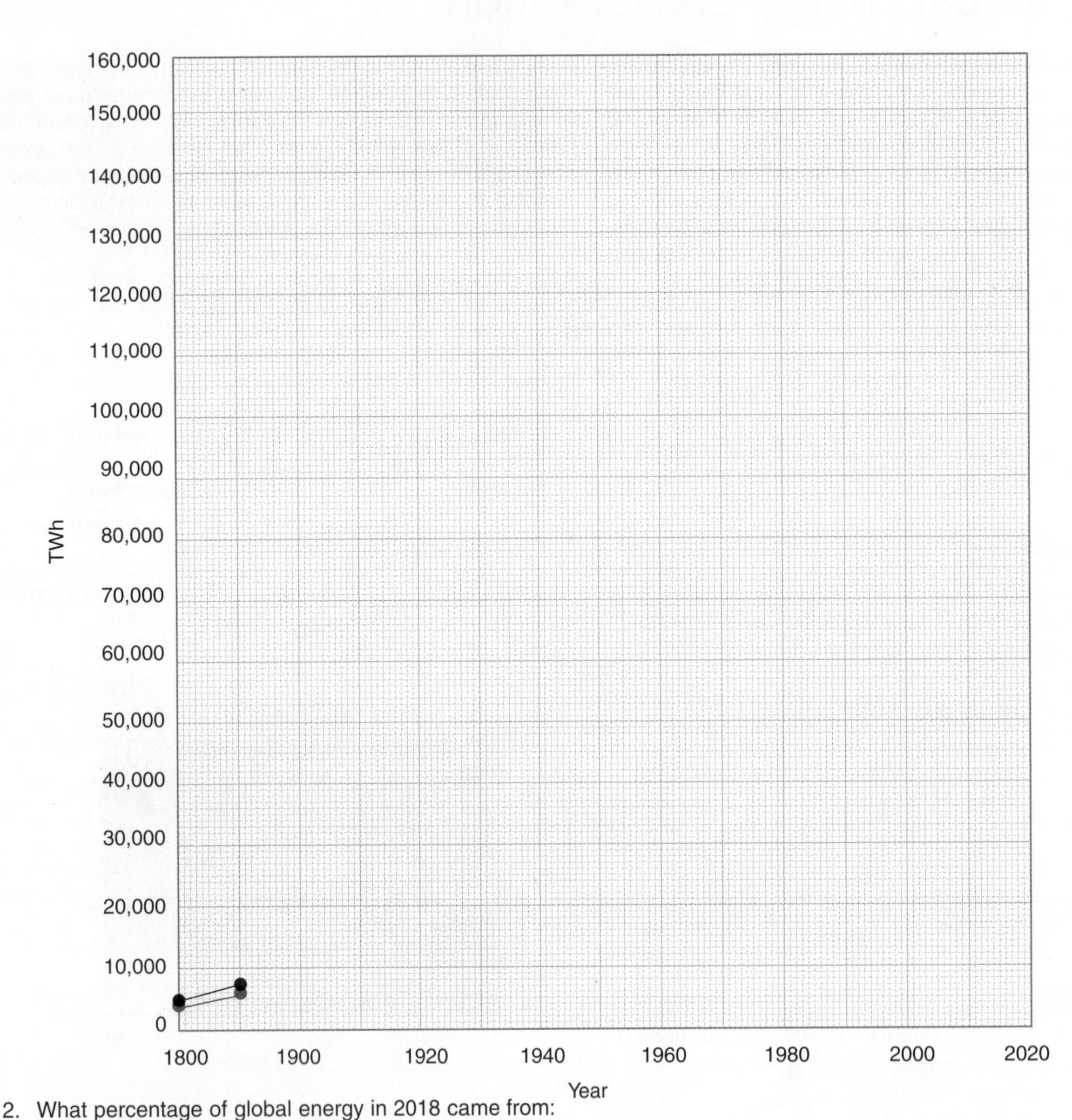

2. What percentage of global energy in 2018 came from:

   (a) Coal: ______________________ (c) Natural gas: ______________________

   (b) Oil: ______________________ (d) Other sources (renewables except biofuels): ______________

3. Calculate the total amount of energy used globally in:

   (a) 1900: ______________________ (b) 2018: ______________________

   (c) How many times more energy was used in 2018 than in 1900? ______________________

4. Describe the transition of a country's fuel use as it progresses to a fully industrialized one: ______________________

5. Why would Europe and the Americas have a much lower solid fuel use for cooking than other regions?

ISBN: 978-1-98-856632-0

99 Fossil Fuels

Key Question: What are fossil fuels, why do we use them, and what happens when they burn?

Fossil fuels are formed from the organic remains of once living organisms. The type of fuel is related to the type of organism that died. Coal and peat form from the buried remains of plants that lived in swamps about 300 million years ago. Oil and natural gas form from the buried remains of plankton that lived about 200 million years ago.

Not quite the perfect fuel

- The perfect fuel would be one you never have to replace, can be used to power any type of machine, no matter how much energy it demands, is easily transportable, safe, and produces no emissions or waste at all. Obviously this kind of fuel doesn't yet exist, but we do have fuels that fit a number of these categories.
- Fossil fuels represent the concentrated energy that was in millions of living organisms when they died. This energy can be released simply by burning the fuel in air. Fossil fuels are mostly just carbon (about 90% for anthracitic coal) and when carbon burns in air, carbon dioxide and heat are released.

Fossil fuels can be used for anything from home heating to fueling the massive engines of ships.

$$C + O_2 \longrightarrow CO_2 + \text{heat}$$

- Oil is a mixture of hydrocarbons (these are organic compounds consisting entirely of hydrogen and carbon). When these burn they produce carbon dioxide and water:

$$C_8H_{12} + 11O_2 \longrightarrow 8CO_2 + 6H_2O + \text{heat}$$

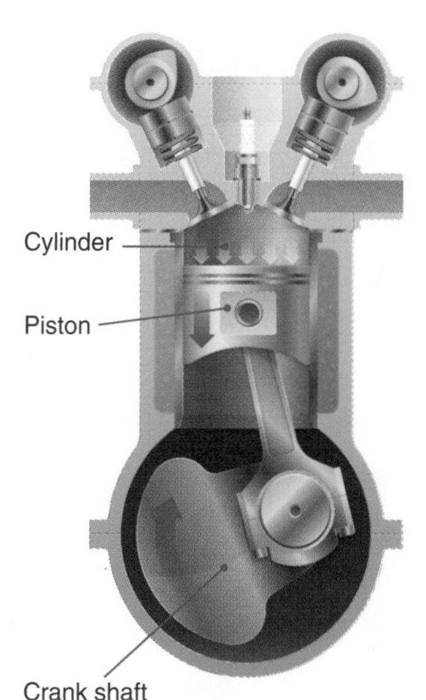

- The heat released can be used to do work. Fossil fuels are quite versatile and can be used in many applications where heat is needed. Oil in particular can be refined into many types of fuels with properties suited to specific applications.
- Gasoline is a mixture of short chain hydrocarbons (e.g. isooctane, top right). In an internal combustion engine, fuel is injected into the cylinder and ignited (left). The explosion forces the piston down. This helps turn the crank shaft and so produces a rotating shaft. In this case, heat is a waste product.
- A jet engine (bottom right) ignites kerosene based fuel to produce exhaust. The exhaust turns a turbine connected to a fan that provides air for the combustion of the fuel. The high pressure gases produced by the burning fuel provide the thrust to push the aircraft forward.

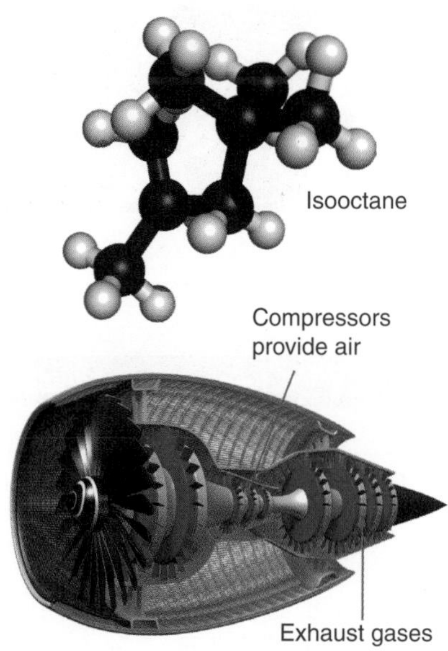

- The major disadvantage of carbon based fuels is associated with the air pollution they produce. Even under ideal conditions, carbon based fuels still produce carbon dioxide, which adds to the greenhouse effect in the atmosphere, warming the Earth. Under conditions of limited oxygen, carbon based fuels combust incompletely, producing carbon monoxide, which is toxic, and soot which is a contributor to smog, particulate pollution, and lung disease.

1. How are fossil fuels formed? ______________________________

____

____

2. How do fossil fuels satisfy the requirements of a fuel? ______________________________

____

____

3. What are some disadvantages of fossil fuels? ______________________________

____

____

ISBN: 978-1-98-856632-0

100 Coal

Key Question: How and why is coal used as a fuel?

Coal is formed from the remains of terrestrial plant material buried in vast shallow swamps during the Carboniferous Period (359 to 299 mya) and subsequently compacted under sediments to form a hard black material. Burning coal accounts for about one third of the world's energy production and is used for domestic and industrial purposes. Coal reserves are estimated at 1.1 trillion tonnes, but removing it from the ground requires large amounts of energy and causes immense disturbance of the surrounding landscape. Burning coal produces vast quantities of greenhouse gases and pollutants, contributing to smog and global warming.

Using coal for electricity

- Coal is pulverized and used to fuel thermal power stations. A 1000 megawatt coal fired power plant uses about 9000 tonnes of coal a day. Globally, coal fired power plants emit 10 Gt of CO_2 a year, or about 20% of global emissions. Unsurprisingly, they are the single largest source of human produced greenhouse gas emissions. A schematic for a coal fired power plant is below:

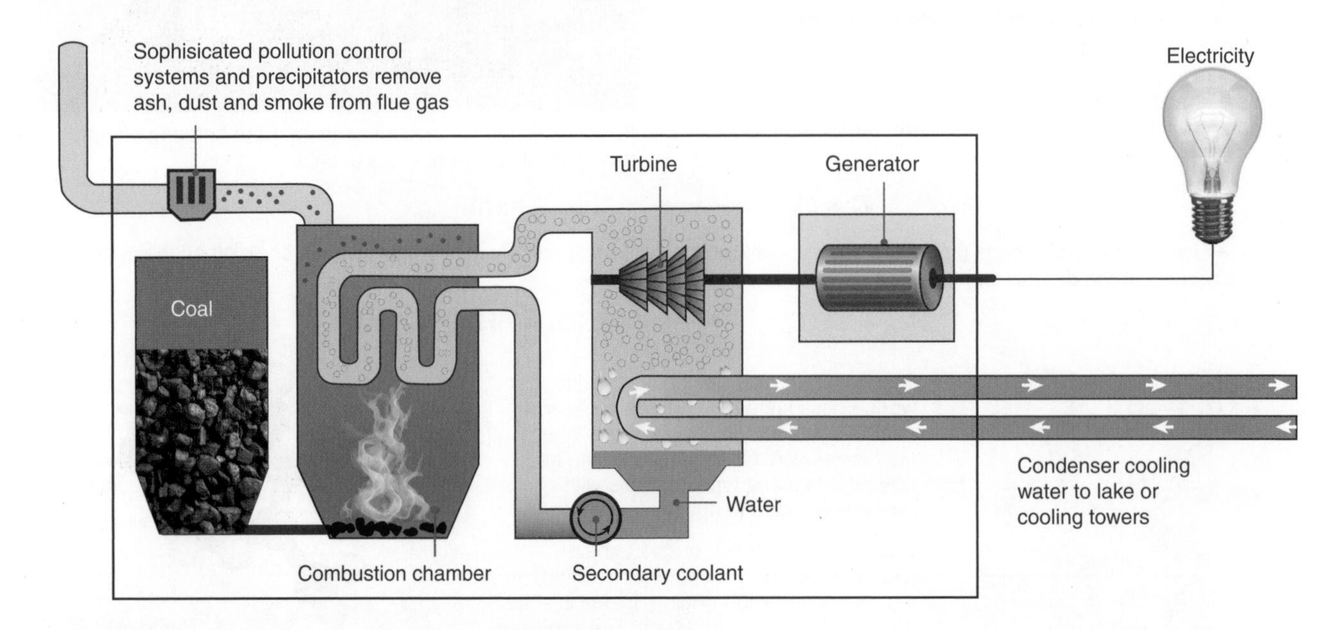

Advantages and disadvantages of coal	
Advantages	**Disadvantages**
Relatively easy to extract when near to surface.	High CO_2 production when burned
High net energy yields.	High particle pollution from soot
Can be used to produce syngas (synthesis gas, a fuel-gas mixture) and converted to other fuels (e.g. gasoline).	Low grade coals produce high pollution and contribute to acid rain
Important in industry as coke (reducer)	High land disturbance through mining
Huge supplies	

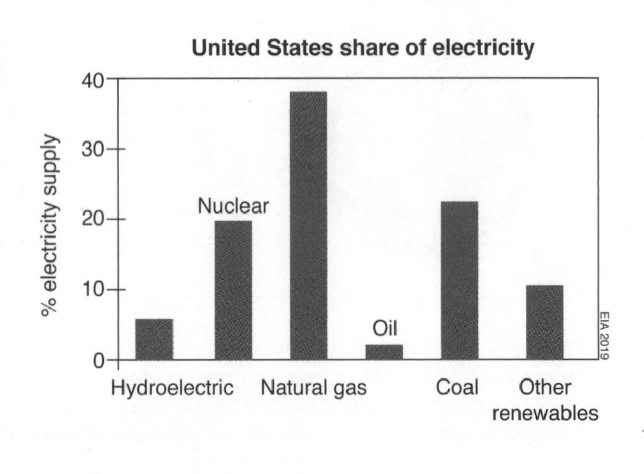

1. (a) What percent of electricity is produced using coal in the United States? ______

   (b) The world uses about 8.5 billion tonnes of coal a year. How long will the estimated global coal supply last?

   ______

2. Describe the basic workings of a coal fired power plant: ______

ISBN: 978-1-98-856632-0

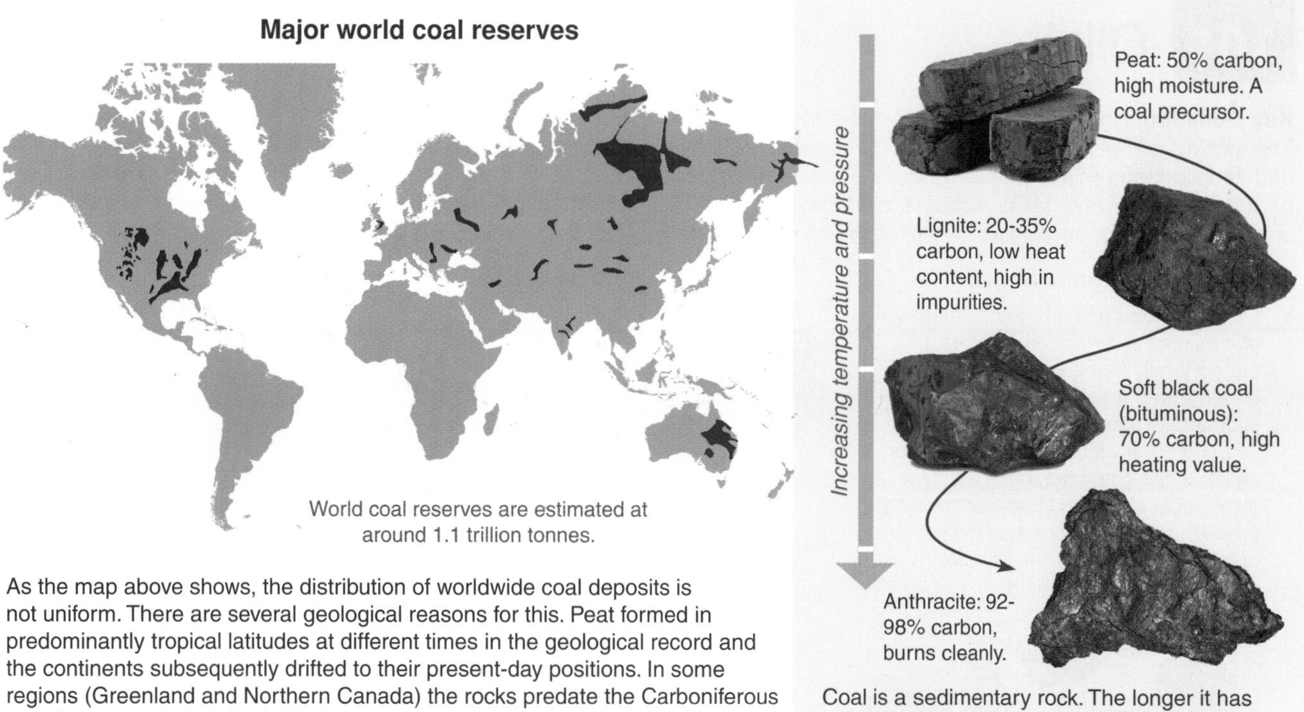

World coal reserves are estimated at around 1.1 trillion tonnes.

As the map above shows, the distribution of worldwide coal deposits is not uniform. There are several geological reasons for this. Peat formed in predominantly tropical latitudes at different times in the geological record and the continents subsequently drifted to their present-day positions. In some regions (Greenland and Northern Canada) the rocks predate the Carboniferous and these continental shields lacked the terrestrial plant life needed to form major coal deposits. In other regions (e.g. the Amazon basin in South America), coal-bearing rocks are buried so deeply, they are not accessible.

Coal is a sedimentary rock. The longer it has been buried and compressed, the better it is as a fuel. Peat still has a high moisture content. It is not coal, but is part of the coal "family".

3. Describe the advantages and disadvantages of using coal: ______

4. Explain why anthracite is a better fuel than peat: ______

5. Give one reason to account for the non-uniform distribution of coal globally: ______

6. In 1988, the United States' EPA conducted a detailed study of 20 potentially toxic substances from coal burning electric utilities. It concluded that, with the possible exception of mercury, there were no compelling health risks from burning coal. In many developing countries, emissions from burning coal are a serious problem for health due to exposure to arsenic, fluorine, radioactive particles (uranium and thorium), and carcinogenic organic compounds.

   Discuss the EPA's statement above. Explain why burning coal in the United States presents little or no health risk, whereas developing countries experience many health problems from burning coal. Use more paper if you wish.

   ______

ISBN: 978-1-98-856632-0

101 Oil

Key Question: How and why is oil used as a fuel?

The world's oil reserves formed from the remains of algae and zooplankton (animal plankton) that settled to the bottom of shallow seas and lakes about the same time as the coal forming swamps existed. These remains were buried and compressed under layers of nonporous sediment. The process, although continuous, occurs so slowly that oil (like coal) is essentially nonrenewable. Crude oil can be refined and used for an extensive array of applications including fuel, road tar, plastics, and cosmetics.

Oil and natural gas

- Oil and natural gas are both composed of a mixture of hydrocarbons and are generally found in the same underground reservoirs. Natural gas is generally defined as a mixture of hydrocarbons with four or fewer carbon atoms in the chain (as these are gaseous at standard temperatures and pressures). Oil is defined as the mixture of hydrocarbons with five or more carbon atoms in the chain.

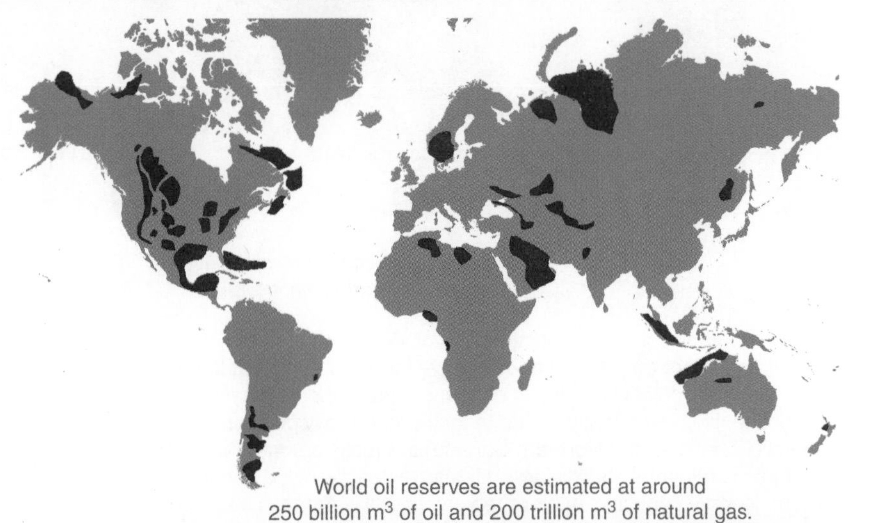

World oil reserves are estimated at around 250 billion m^3 of oil and 200 trillion m^3 of natural gas.

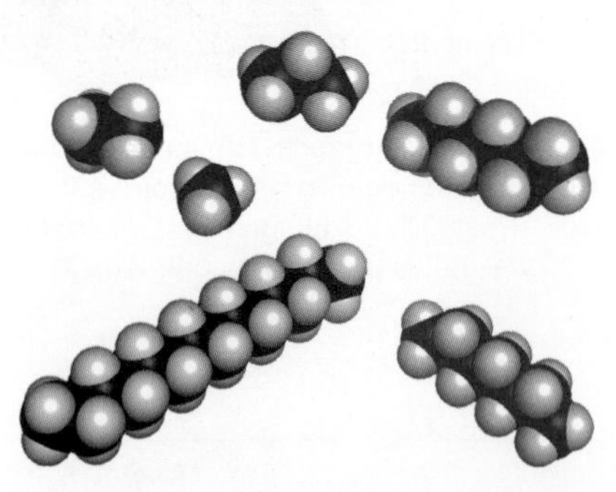

- Oil can be used as a fuel for power plants but this is usually left over from the refining of crude oil. More commonly, natural gas is used. Natural gas can be used in combined cycle power plants. Instead of just combusting the natural gas to heat water to steam to drive a turbine, the combustion process itself is used to drive a primary turbine via the expansion of hot gases. This provides more efficient electricity generation.

Oil	
Advantages	**Disadvantages**
Large supply	Many reserves are offshore and difficult to extract
High net energy gain	High CO_2 production
Can be refined to produce many different fuel types	Potential for large, widespread environmental damage if spilled
Easy to transport	Rate of use will use up reserves in the near future

1. Describe the difference in the composition of natural gas and oil: ______

2. Describe how oil is formed and why this makes it non-renewable: ______

3. Describe some of the advantages and disadvantages of using oil as a fuel: ______

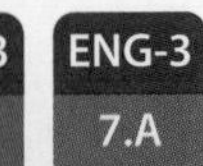

ISBN: 978-1-98-856632-0

Oil production, transport and refining

Natural gas is often found in the same reservoirs as oil. Drilling rigs require specialized facilities to store the gas. Because of this, much natural gas is either vented, or reinjected to maintain pressure in the reservoir.

Transport of natural gas requires specialized equipment. Liquid natural gas (LNG) tankers are able to cool the gas to -162°C and transport it as a liquid (saving space). Gas can also be piped to shore if facilities are nearby.

USDE

Oil can be found in materials that make conventional extraction methods impossible. These **non conventional oils** (e.g. oil shale) are often mined in the same way as coal and then crushed and heated to release the oil.

Crude and heavy oils require refining before use. Crude oil is separated into different sized fractions by a distillation tower. Heavy oils may be heated under pressure to break them into smaller more usable molecules.

Oil is refined in a distillation tower by **fractional distillation**. The tower is around 400°C at the bottom, but cools towards the top to less than 100°C. Crude oil is pumped into the bottom of the tower and evaporates. The oil vapor cools and condenses as it travels up the tower. Long chain hydrocarbons condense near the bottom while short chain hydrocarbons condense near the top.

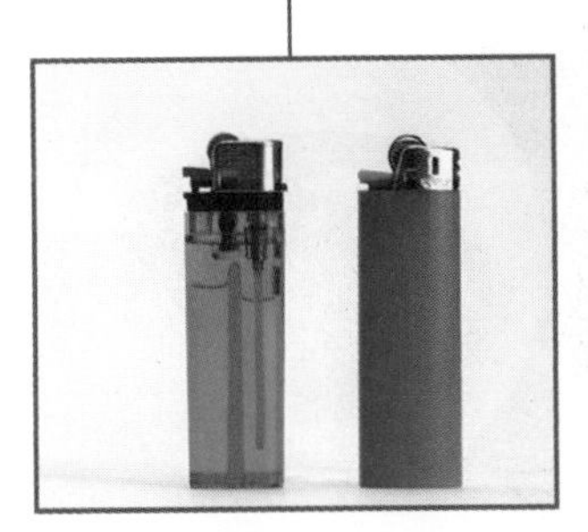

Short chain hydrocarbons find use in portable lighters. Butane is commonly used in cigarette lighters and camp stoves. Propane is commonly used for larger barbecue grills.

Petrol and diesel are formed from hydrocarbons with between 6 and 12 C atoms. They provide a high energy, easily combustible fuel that, being a liquid, is easily stored and transported.

Mid length hydrocarbon chains (about 15 C atoms) are used as jet fuel. They are less volatile and less flammable than shorter chain hydrocarbon fuels while providing high energy per unit volume.

Long chain hydrocarbons may be heated to split them into shorter chains (to boost the fractions of petrol and diesel produced), or used in lubricating oil, heavy fuel oil, waxes, and tar.

4. Explain how crude oil is refined: ______________________________

5. Investigate the use of refined fuels and then explain why short chain hydrocarbons, such as propane and butane, are used in gas stoves and portable lighters whereas longer chained hydrocarbons are used in vehicles:

ISBN: 978-1-98-856632-0

102 Oil Extraction

Key Question: How is oil extracted from the ground?

Because oil can be found in so many different kinds of sediments or deposits, many different techniques are required to extract it. Conventional oil can be pumped directly from the reservoir, but other non-conventional oils, such as heavy crude, oil sands, and oil shales require quite different extraction techniques. These are often energy intensive, reducing the net energy gain. 2020 estimates put conventional oil reserves at 1.5 trillion barrels and non-conventional oil reserves at around 3 trillion barrels.

Oil and natural gas extraction

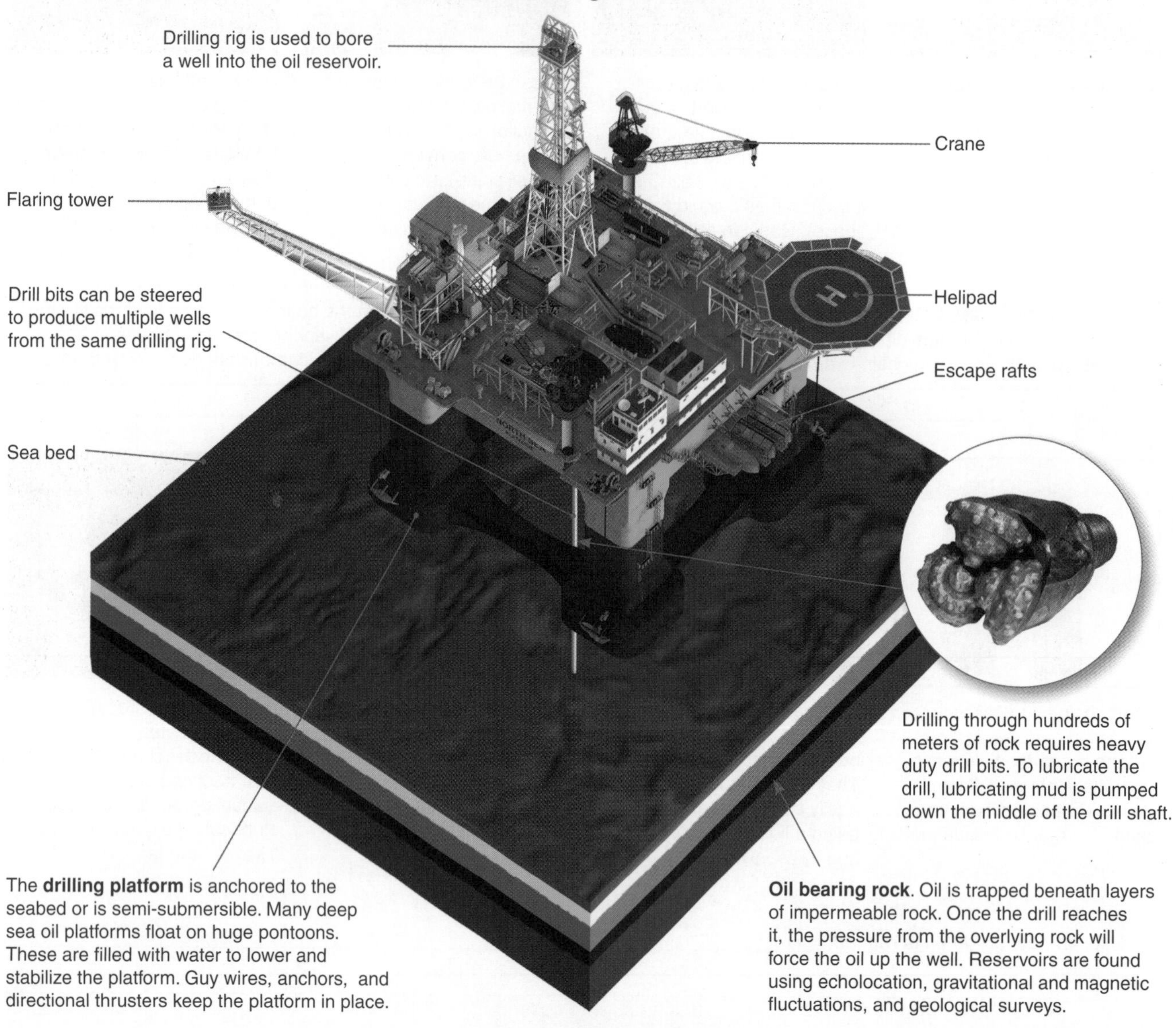

Oil shales and oil sands

Oil shale is shale that contains a solid bituminous material called kerogen. The rock is mined by open pit mining and the oil extracted by heating the shale and washing the oil out. This process is very energy intensive and its carbon footprint is much larger than that of conventional oil extraction. However, global reserves are large at ~1.6 trillion barrels (proven). Potential reserves may be several time more than this.

Oil sands are loose sands and sandstones that are saturated with bitumen. The sands are mined by open pit mining and the oil is extracted in a similar way to shale oil. Again, the process has a large carbon footprint but the reserves are substantial (more than 170 billion barrels in the US).

1. Briefly describe the process of extracting crude oil: ______________________________

____

____

____

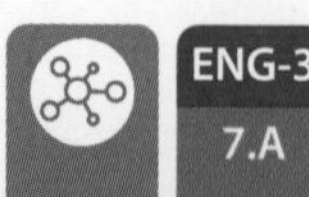

ENG-3

7.A

ISBN: 978-1-98-856632-0

Hydraulic fracturing

- The increasing price of a barrel of oil at the beginning of this century created more interest in extracting oil and natural gas from sediments that were once uneconomic to mine. Some geological formations may contain large amounts of oil or natural gas, but due to low pressure or impermeable rock, e.g. shales, these have poor flow rates. A process called **hydraulic fracturing** (fracking) is used in order to increase the flow rate in these environments.

1. A well is bored into the layer containing the oil or gas.
2. The well is lined with concrete and steel casings.
3. The well is then drilled horizontally, up to 1500 m from the vertical well.
4. A perforation tool is inserted into the well and explosives are used to fracture the rock.
5. Fluid, which is 99.5% water and 0.5% additives, is pumped into the well to increase flow and keep the fracture open.
6. Gas and oil then flow back up the well. Water (flowback) is recovered and stored in lined pits for later treatment.

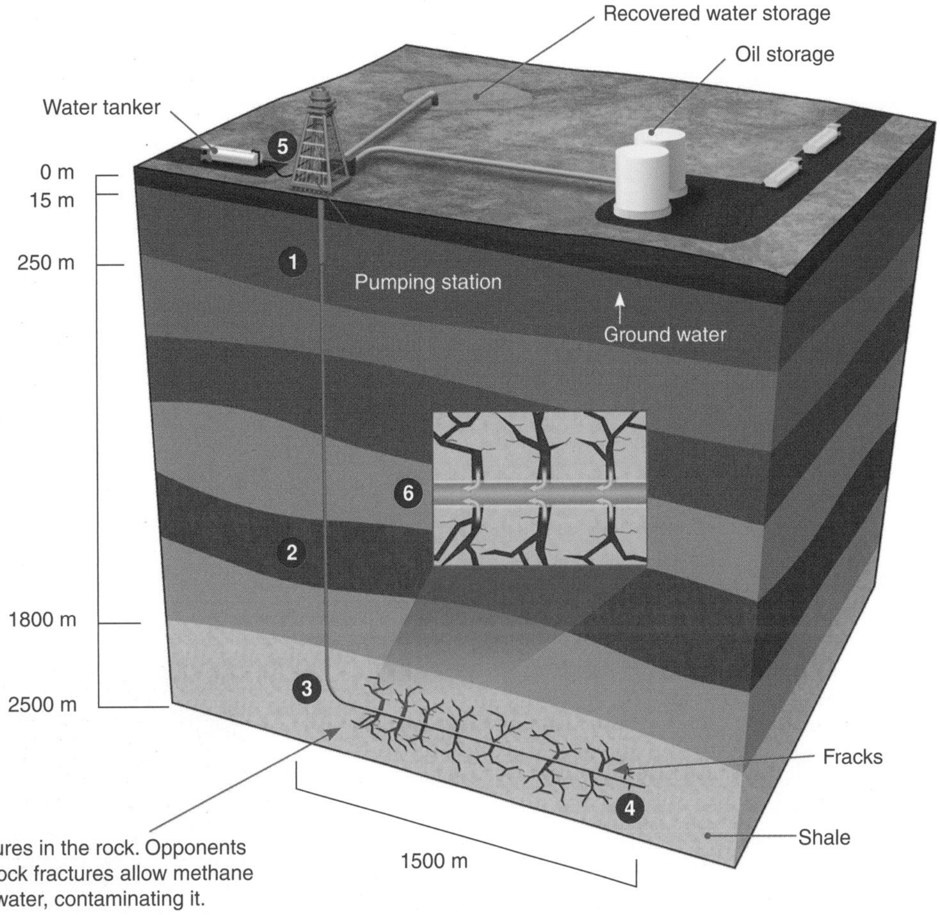

Recovered water storage
Oil storage
Water tanker
0 m
15 m
250 m
Pumping station
Ground water
1800 m
2500 m
Fracks
Shale
1500 m

Hydraulic fracturing causes fractures in the rock. Opponents of hydraulic fracturing claim the rock fractures allow methane and flowback to leak into groundwater, contaminating it.

2. The world uses 101 million barrels of oil per day. Assuming no more oil reserves are located, calculate:

   (a) How many years conventional oil supplies will last based on current consumption: ____________________

   (b) How many years non-conventional oil supplies will last based on current consumption: ____________________

3. Describe the difference between conventional and non-conventional oils: ____________________

4. Explain how hydraulic fracturing increases the flow rate of natural gas or oil: ____________________

5. Describe the environmental concerns associated with hydraulic fracturing: ____________________

ISBN: 978-1-98-856632-0

103 Nuclear Power

Key Question: How is nuclear power used to generate electricity and what are its benefits and drawbacks?

Nuclear power plants produce about 5% of the world's usable energy supply but 11% of the world's electricity supply because virtually all of them are used for electricity production. Nuclear fission reactors are currently the only reactor type used to produce commercial electricity, although there are a number of reactor designs. Nuclear power stations for electricity generation were developed in the 1950s but they lost popularity for a time during the 1970s and 80s following two high profile accidents. Until the Fukushima disaster in 2011, nuclear power was again gaining popularity as a way to reduce CO_2 emissions from power generation. However the disaster served as a reminder of the potential hazards of nuclear power. Many countries have now stopped developing nuclear power plants and are shutting down those that are operational. Germany will shut down all nuclear power plants by 2022. Some scientists worry that shutting down nuclear power plants will lead to a rise in greenhouse gas emissions because renewables are not ready to meet the shortfall.

Nuclear fission

Nuclear fission is a type of radioactive decay and can be spontaneous or **induced** (right). Induced fission usually occurs in the controlled conditions of a nuclear reactor or the somewhat less controlled conditions of a nuclear weapon.

Uranium subjected to fission produces around three million times as much energy as an equal mass of coal.

Uranium-235 makes up 0.7% of uranium ore. It is enriched to 3.5% for use in fuel rods. Once spent it makes up just 1% of the uranium in the fuel rod.

In an induced fission reaction, a neutron is absorbed by a uranium-235. The briefly excited uranium-236 splits in two, forming two similar sized nuclei and releasing free neutrons.

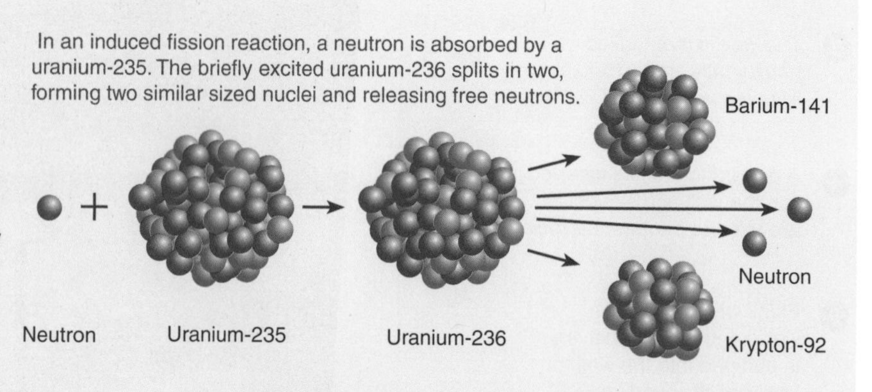

- When uranium-236 splits and releases neutrons, those neutrons can be absorbed by nearby uranium-235 atoms which then split and release neutrons and so on in a chain reaction. With each fission reaction, energy is released as heat. This heat is used to boil water to produce steam to drive a turbine.
- So much heat is produced that poorly managed nuclear fuel can become hot enough to melt.
- The power output of the nuclear reactor depends on the rate at which the nuclear chain reaction proceeds. It is adjusted by controlling how many neutrons are able to produce more fission reactions. Control rods that are made of a neutron poison are used to absorb neutrons. Absorbing more neutrons in a control rod means that there are fewer neutrons available to cause fission, so pushing the control rod deeper into the reactor will reduce the reactor's power output and extracting the control rod will increase it.

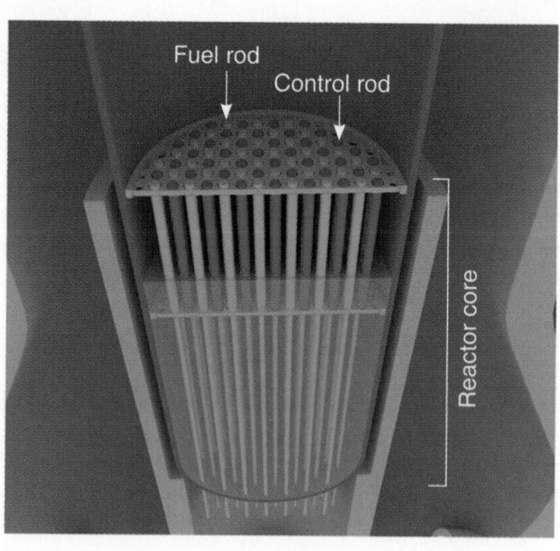

1. (a) Explain where the energy for nuclear power plants comes from: ____________________

(b) Explain how the nuclear reaction is controlled: ____________________

2. Explain how the electricity is produced in nuclear power plants: ____________________

ISBN: 978-1-98-856632-0

The nuclear power plant

- A nuclear power plant consists of a **reactor building**, **powerhouse**, and **cooling tower**(s). The reactor building houses the reactor core, which consists of a series of nuclear fuel rods set between removable control rods.
- Heat produced in the reactor is passed through a heat exchanger to heat water to steam which drives the turbines and generator. Steam then passes into a condenser cooled by water pumped from the cooling tower.

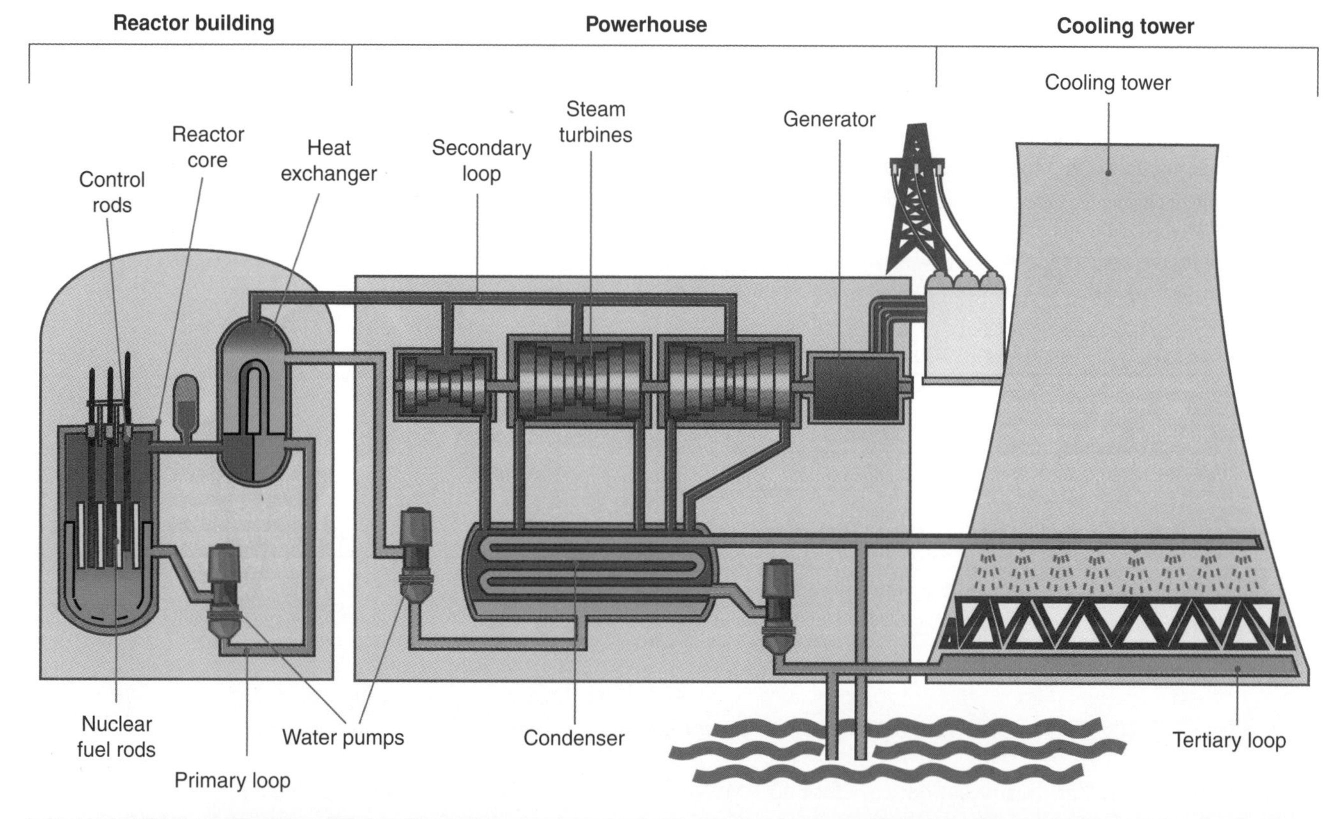

Nuclear power generation	
Advantages	**Disadvantages**
Large potential fuel supply	High start up costs
Little fuel is needed so supplies last a long time	Disposal of waste presents major technical and environmental problems
Low air pollution (low CO_2 emissions)	Risk of catastrophic environmental disaster if accident occurs
Little land required	Technology can be adapted to develop nuclear weapons
Large amount of energy generated	Potential terrorist target

3. Explain how the radiation produced by the reactor core is prevented from contaminating the rest of the power plant:

4. Explain the purpose of the water pumps in a nuclear power plant?

5. How might nuclear reactors help reduce future greenhouse emissions?

6. Is nuclear power renewable or nonrenewable?

ISBN: 978-1-98-856632-0

104 Radioactivity

Key Question: What is radioactivity and how can it be used? Radioactivity is the emission of high energy particles or ionizing radiation from an unstable atom (radioactive decay). The emission of these particles results in the change of the atom from one element into another. Radioactive isotopes (atoms with the same number of protons but different numbers of neutrons) can be useful for a number of different things. Some are used to date rocks, fossils, and organic matter, others are used in medicine for cancer treatment. Each radioactive isotope has a characteristic half-life.

Radioactivity and half-lives

- The radioactivity of a sample of radioactive material decreases over time. The half-life of an isotope is the time taken for the radioactivity of a sample to decrease by half, or the time taken for half of the atoms in a radioactive material to decay.
- For some isotopes this is very short, seconds or up to weeks. For others it may be millennia or even eons.

Isotope	Half-life
Uranium-238	4.5 billion years
Uranium-235	700 million years
Potassium-40	1.3 billion years
Plutonium-239	24,000 years
Carbon-14	5740 years
Cesium-137	30 years
Strontium-90	29 years
Cobalt-60	5.3 years
Iodine-131	8 days

Decrease in radioactivity over time

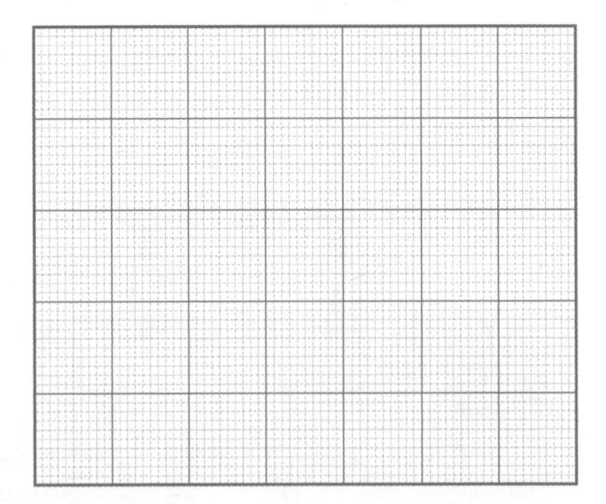

INVESTIGATION 6.2: Using M&M's® to model half-lives See appendix for equipment list.

1. Work in pairs for this investigation. Place 100 M&M's® in a lidded container and shake them up.
2. Pour them out onto a plate and remove the M&M's® with the M facing up. These represent decayed atoms. Record the number of M&M's® left (M facing down) in the table below. This is round (half-life) #1.
3. Put the remaining M&M's® back into the container and repeat the procedure. Repeat this until there are no more M&M's®.
4. Calculate mean values for the class and enter these in the final row.

Round number											
M&M's® left											
Class average											

1. Plot a line graph of the decay of M&M's® on the grid above right. Plot the number of M&M's® remaining on the y axis, and the number of half-lives (rounds) on the x axis. Join the points to form an approximate decay curve.

2. (a) As a class, average the number of M&M's® left after each round.

   (b) Using the class average, how many rounds did it take for the number of M&M's® to fall to one quarter the original?

   ___

   (c) Using the class average, how many rounds did it take for the number of M&M's® to fall to one sixteenth the original?

   ___

   (d) You left a bag of 100 M&M's® with a friend who decided to eat them using the procedure above. Every 2 minutes from when they started your friend carried out the procedure (eating the decayed atoms). When you came back there were 6 M&M's® left.

   How long before your return did your friend start eating the M&M's®? ___

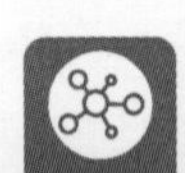

ENG-3
2.B

ISBN: 978-1-98-856632-0

Nuclear waste and radioactivity

- The composition of the fuel rods used in nuclear power plants depends on the type of reactor. A typical pressurized water reactor uses a fuel rod composed of mainly uranium-238 with about 7% uranium-235.
- Once the fuel is spent (no longer usable), the proportion of uranium-235 has fallen to about 1% and the rods also contain the decay products of the uranium isotopes. The fuel is still radioactive and produces heat, but the atoms are no longer concentrated enough to produce a chain reaction. The fuel rods are therefore placed into storage ponds for several years to remove the decay heat, and further reduce their radioactivity.
- The fuel can then be recycled and the uranium recovered, reconcentrated, and reused. This is a difficult and expensive process so in most cases it is easier and cheaper to simply mine more uranium.

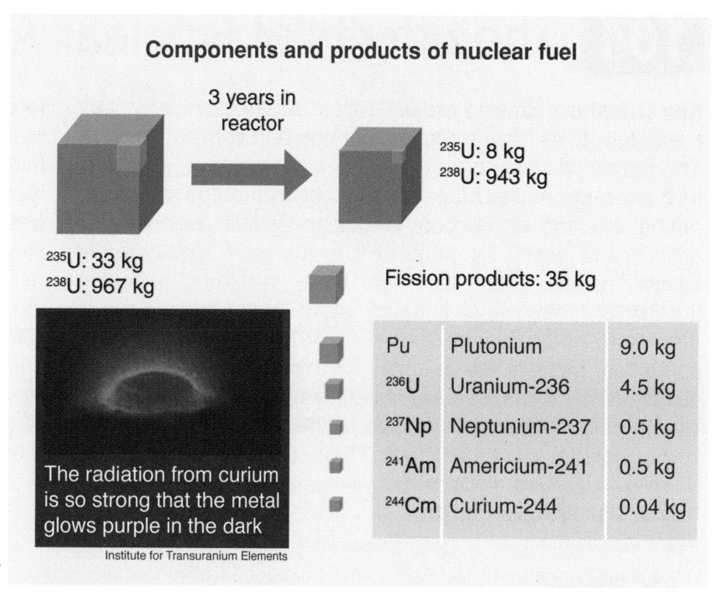

The radiation from curium is so strong that the metal glows purple in the dark

Measuring radioactivity

- There are three common units for measuring radioactivity and its effects. It is important to understand them so that you can understand information presented about radioactivity, such as in graphs.
- The three units are the becquerel (Bq), the gray (Gy), and the sievert (Sv).
  - Becquerels describe the number of atom decays over time. 1 Bq = 1 decay per second.
  - The gray describes the amount of energy from ionizing radiation absorbed per kilogram. 1 Gy = 1 joule absorbed per kg (1 J/kg).
  - The sievert takes into account the type of radiation (e.g. alpha, beta, gamma, or x-ray), the amount of energy the radiation produces, and which part of the body is exposed. It measures the potential health risk of a radiation dose. 1 Sv is quite a lot of radiation, so microsieverts (μSv) are normally used. Radiation damages DNA by breaking the bonds in DNA (below).

Sieverts	Annual dose of radiation relative to background	Biological effects of exposure to radiation dose
0.006	1	Normal annual dose (mostly from natural radiation)- no effect
0.01	2	Whole body CT scan (multiple x-rays) - no detectable effect
0.05	8	Total maximum annual dose for a worker in a radiation area. Slightly higher chance of some form of cancer (but statistically extremely low) compared to no exposure.
0.1	16	Small risk of cancer but still very low.
0.4	64	Radiation poisoning (if received quickly)
2	320	Radiation poisoning (if received quickly)
4	640	Mostly fatal
8	1300	Always fatal (and normally quickly)

3. (a) The radioactivity of a sample of cobalt-60 was measured. Many years later it was found to have dropped to 1/8 of the original radioactivity. How many years had passed?

   ____

   (b) Which of the isotopes in the table on the previous page would be useful for dating the rocks of the Earth? ________

   ____

4. Explain how ionizing radiation damages DNA and what the consequences of this might be: ______________________________

   ____

   ____

   ____

5. Explain why radioactive waste must be stored safely away from the natural environment: ______________________________

   ____

   ____

   ____

   ____

ISBN: 978-1-98-856632-0

105 The Effects of Nuclear Accidents

Key Question: How do we deal with the risks associated with the radioactivity inherent to nuclear power plants?

The major disadvantage of current nuclear power plants is that when the nuclear fuel is no longer useful it is still highly radioactive and dangerous. Disposing of this spent fuel is difficult and costly, so most of it is stored in underground vaults. These produce their own set of problems, including the risk of groundwater contamination. A second problem is the nature of the fission chain reaction. Unless it is carefully controlled, there is the potential for things to go wrong very quickly. Nuclear reactors are not nuclear bombs, nor can they ever explode in such a way due to the low concentration of fissile material in the fuel rods. Their real danger lies in the fact the fuel produces heat and remains hot even when the reactor is shut down. Unlike a coal or oil fired power plant, fuel cannot be removed and must be constantly kept cool via a flow of water. If the water flow stops, two catastrophic scenarios can occur. The water around the fuel can turn to steam very rapidly and cause a steam explosion that can damage the reactor and containment vessel, and/or the fuel can melt (a meltdown) at which point controlling the chain reaction becomes impossible and again the reactor can be seriously damaged. A damaged reactor can leak radioactive material into the environment. Due to the radiation in the core, disassembling a damaged reactor is an extremely difficult and dangerous task.

1979: Three Mile Island

The Three Mile Island nuclear power plant consisted of two reactor units. Unit 2 opened in 1978, at a cost of about $1 billion. A series of malfunctions, design flaws, and operator errors eventually led to the partial meltdown of the Unit 2 reactor core on March 28, 1979.

Cascading chain of events

1. The accident started with the simple issue of water being forced into an air line during the routine clearing of a filter. In response, computers shut down pumps in the secondary loop which took steam from the heat exchanger to the turbine, cooling the core at the same time. Auxiliary pumps were unable to pump water because valves that should have been open had been closed.
2. The loss of cooling water caused the reactor to overheat and the internal pressure to increase. A pressure relief value malfunctioned and allowed primary coolant to leak. Operators misinterpreted the cause of this and switched off coolant pumps in the primary loop.
3. This caused a decease in coolant around the core, which partially melted down. It was not until more than two hours after the start of the accident that the coolant loss was stopped and water was recirculated around the core.
4. Contaminated coolant and gases escaped from the core, contaminating the containment building. A small amount of radioactive material escaped from the containment building but not enough to cause any significant environmental effects.

- Unit 2 reactor was shutdown permanently, after being active for just 13 months. The cleanup ended in 1993 at a cost of $1 billion. Associated property damage was estimated at about $2 billion.
- The entire Three Mile Island plant is now closed. Unit 1 closed in 2019 due to financial reasons.

Effects of Three Mile Island

Although radiation did leak from the plant this was not due to a containment breach, rather from steam and water released due to a faulty valve. An estimated 2 million people were exposed to radiation, but the average dose equated to about 1% of the annual dose of natural background radiation, and about 16% of the dose of a chest X-ray. The maximum dose a person could have received would have been around twice the annual dose of natural background radiation.

The real effects of the Three Mile Island accident were not environmental, but psychological and political. The public became aware of how unpredictable nuclear power could be.

1. Summarize the causes of the Three Mile Island accident: ______

2. What were the effects of the Three Mile Island meltdown? ______

3. Do you think the cost of building of Unit 2 justified? ______

ISBN: 978-1-98-856632-0

2011: Fukushima Daiichi

- On March 11 2011, multiple reactor failures occurred at the Fukushima Daiichi nuclear power station, 220 km north of Tokyo, Japan, following a magnitude 9.0 earthquake and 10 m high tsunami.
- The three functioning reactors shut down immediately after the earthquake. Diesel generators provided electricity to circulate coolant but were flooded by the tsunami. Without coolant, the reactor cores overheated and melted down. Heat generated by the nuclear fuel caused reactor water to boil to steam, exposing the fuel rods to air and producing hydrogen gas.
- Venting the gas from each of the three separate reactor containment vessels led to explosions that destroyed the outer reactor buildings. It was not until the end of September 2011 that the three reactor cores were brought to below 100°C.

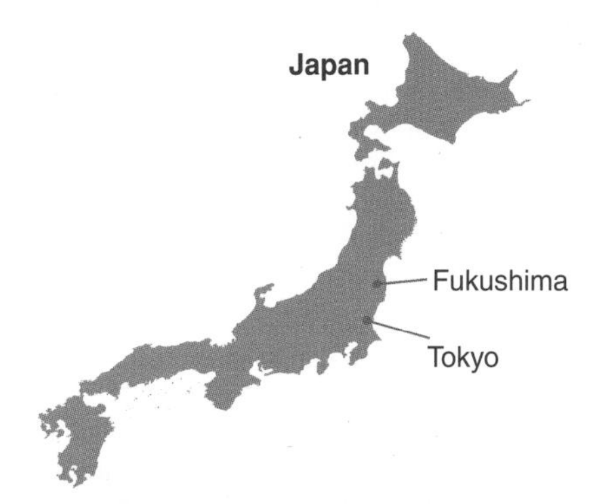

Reactor 3: Partial core meltdown. Hydrogen explosion destroyed the top half of the building and damaged the water supply for reactor 2. Containment vessel damage caused leakage of radioactive material.

Reactor 2: Full core meltdown. Hydrogen explosion from leaking gas destroyed the upper part of the outer building. Damage to the containment vessel caused thousands of liters of radioactive coolant water to leak out.

Reactor 1: Full core meltdown. Hydrogen explosion from vented gas destroyed the outer building. Containment vessel was undamaged.

Turbine buildings

Sea wall

Sea

Fukushima Daiichi reactors 1-4

Reactor 4: Fire in nuclear fuel storage pond. Spent fuel was partially exposed. Coolant leaked after ice damage to pipes.

Cause of the disaster

Although it was initiated by the earthquake and subsequent tsunami that flooded the backup generators, the full extent of the disaster at Fukushima Daiichi has been attributed to human error and a lack of safety systems. Investigations found the following key points:

- A failure to develop basic safety requirements.
- Lack of preparation and the mindset to respond efficiently to a disaster.
- Failure by regulators to properly monitor nuclear safety.
- Tepco (the company running the station) failed to report changes to the emergency coolant systems, and failed to properly act on warnings that the generators were susceptible to flooding.

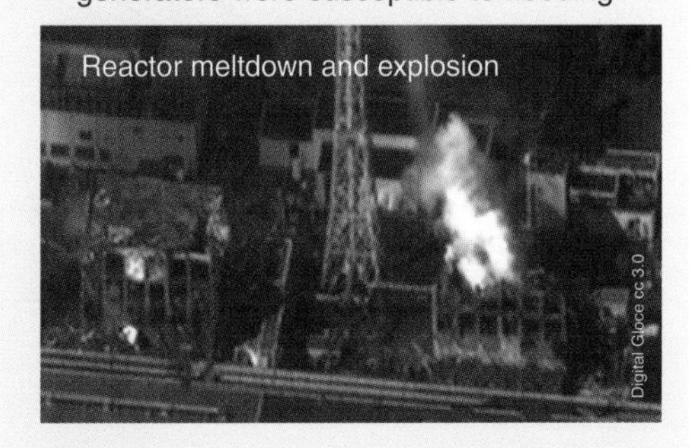

Reactor meltdown and explosion

Cleanup

- The devastation caused by the tsunami has made the cleanup difficult and it could take decades. The need to decommission four damaged reactors makes the task complex and extremely difficult.
- Nearly 1.2 million tonnes of radioactive water used for coolant still needs decontaminating. Proposed plans may see the water released into the ocean or left to evaporate over several years
- Remote control cranes are being installed to remove the radioactive material inside the damaged containment buildings.
- Contaminated soil from the surrounding land has been dug up and removed to safe storage.
- The estimated cost of the cleanup is around $76 billion, although this is only part of the hundreds of billions of dollars needed for the cleanup and recovery due to the earthquake and tsunami.
- About 371 km^2 has been designated an exclusion zone. As the cleanup continues, some of this land is being opened up again.

Inspection for fuel assembly removal (2013)

ISBN: 978-1-98-856632-0

Environmental effects of the Fukushima Daiichi disaster

- The long term effects of the Fukushima Daiichi disaster are still being studied. High levels of radioactive particles were vented into the atmosphere but ~80% of this fell into the sea. Similarly, radioactivity leaked into the water also ended up in the sea. Continued monitoring indicates that radioactivity in the area is now mostly below safe levels, although there are still a number of "hotspots" where radiation levels are elevated. There have been no radiation-linked deaths from the disaster.
- Between March 21 and mid-July 2011 about 2.7×10^{16} Bq of cesium-137 leaked into the sea, representing the largest ever individual leak of radioactive material. This radiation has been dispersed due to the high solubility of cesium and the strong currents in the area. Although radioisotopes from Fukushima have been detected in fish across the Pacific Ocean, this is mostly due to the use of very sensitive equipment, and radionuclide levels are well below safety limits.
- One benefit of the radiation release from Fukushima into the sea is that new regulations were placed on catches of Pacific bluefin tuna, and scientists were able to use the radioisotopes in them to track their migrations across the ocean.
- Recorded biological effects from the radiation released include:
  - A study of populations of the pale grass blue butterfly from various places around Japan found a number of mutations in the populations closest to Fukushima including abnormal legs and wing shapes, dented eyes, and changes to color and spot patterns on the wings.
  - Studies of Japanese macaques in the exclusion zone around Fukushima have shown clear differences in body mass in macaques born before and after the disaster. Macaques are also showing abnormally low blood counts related to high muscle radiocesium.

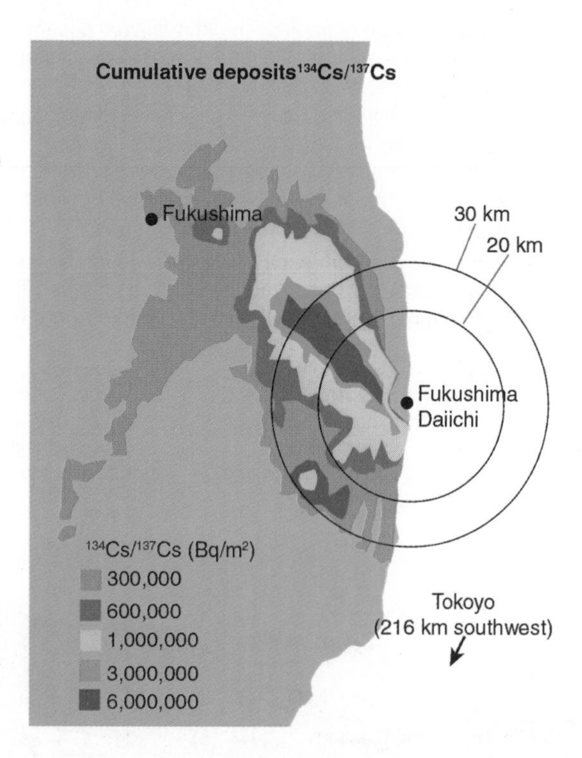

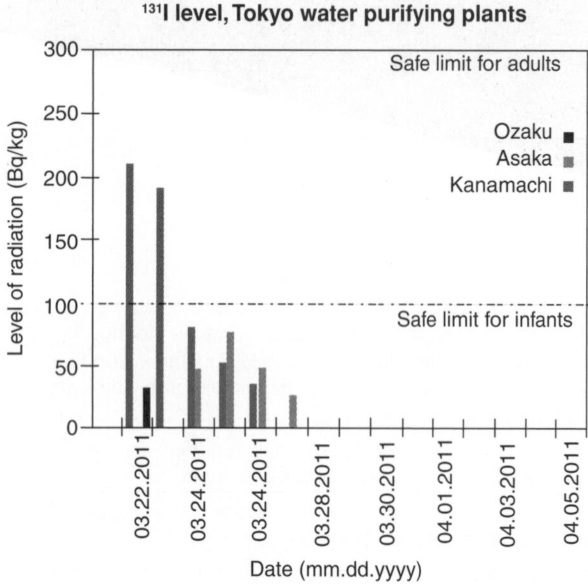

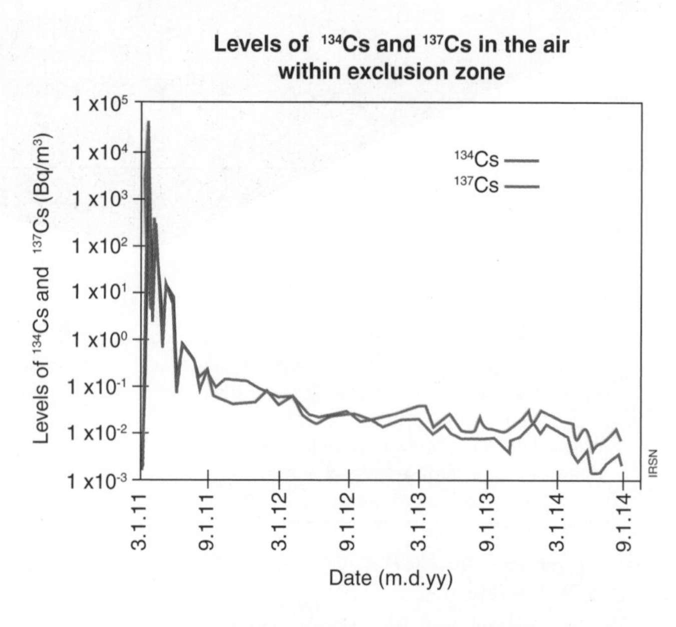

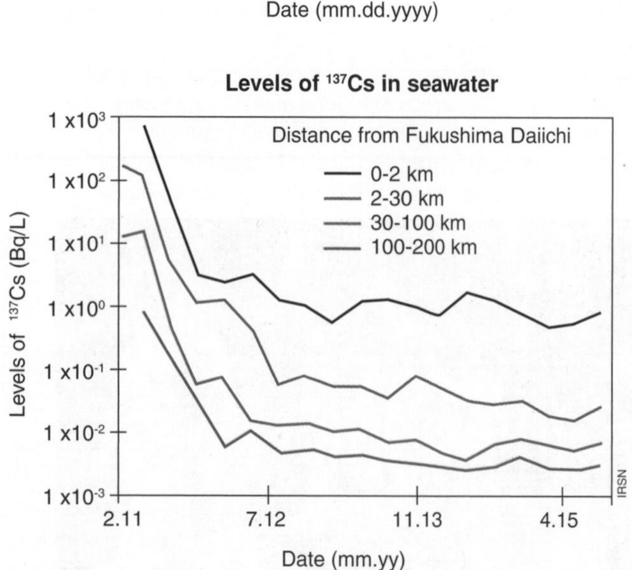

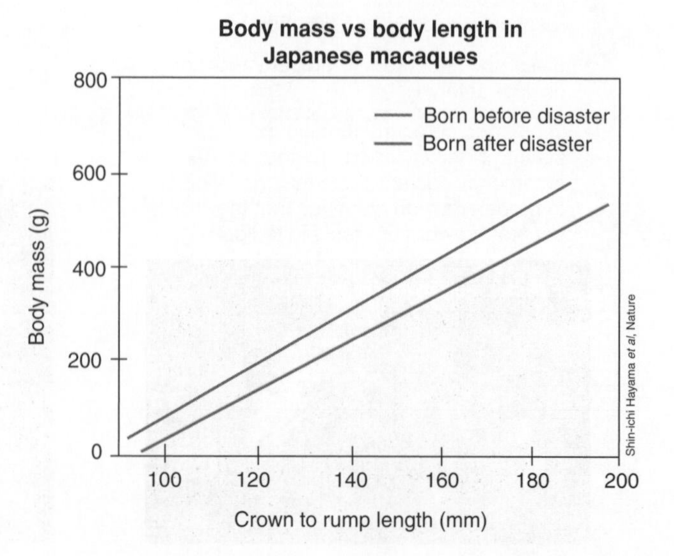

ISBN: 978-1-98-856632-0

4. (a) Describe the events that led to the three reactor meltdowns at Fukushima Daiichi: ______

(b) Explain what caused the explosions in number 1, 2, and 3 reactor buildings: ______

(c) Explain why the events at Fukushima Daiichi have been called a man-made disaster: ______

(d) Describe the clean up of Fukushima Daiichi: ______

5. Describe the trend in radioactivity resulting from the release of material from Fukushima Daiichi and give a possible explanation for it:

6. Describe evidence that radiation released from Fukushima Daiichi has affected nearby animal populations:

7. The majority of the radiation from Fukushima Daiichi leaked into the sea. Explain why this is not as big a problem as the radiation that leaked onto the land?

8. Describe one environmental benefit of this disaster: ______

ISBN: 978-1-98-856632-0

1986: Chernobyl

On 26 April 1986, the number 4 reactor at the Chernobyl nuclear power plant exploded. Ironically, the explosion occurred during a safety test. The test was designed to evaluate the turbine's ability to supply electricity to the coolant pumps in the event of a reactor shut down and loss of power. It was assumed that as the turbine spun down (due to a lack of steam) it could be used to generate electricity to cover the 1 minute gap between the loss of power and the emergency diesel generators running up to full speed.

Cascading chain of events

1. The reactor was set to half its usual power output to begin the test, but the test was delayed by several hours. As a result, xenon levels in the reactor increased, creating unsuitable conditions for the test. This was either not realized or ignored.
2. As the test proceeded, the power output of the reactor was reduced. Unexpectedly, it then fell below the level needed for the test. To try to raise the power output, all but six of the control rods were removed from the core. Again, the unbalanced state of the core was ignored.
3. Pumps circulating coolant and steam to the turbine were turned off. Immediately, the reactor output rapidly increased, boiling the water in the core to steam. An emergency shut down was initiated. However as the control rods moved back into the core, the graphite tips actually *accelerated* the reaction.
4. The expanding steam jammed the control rods in place before they were fully inserted. An initial steam explosion blew the lid off the reactor, exposing the superheated interior to the air. This caused the larger explosion which destroyed the core and ejected large amounts of radioactive material into the atmosphere.

Cause of the accident

The investigation into the disaster found that the failure of the test and the subsequent explosion were due to:

- The postponement of the test by several hours so that senior operators were no longer on site.
- Extremely small operational safety margins and a lack of regard for safety.
- Inexperienced operators being in control of the test.
- Human error.
- Poor design of the reactor control rods.
- Poor design for overall control of the nuclear reaction.

Cleanup

- The Chernobyl explosion is the worst nuclear accident in history. The cleanup of the Chernobyl site, at least in the early stages, can probably best be described as monumental and even heroic, and involved more than half a million people.
- The radiation on top of the reactor building, near the ventilation stack (right), was so high it destroyed the circuits of robots that were initially used to try to clear the debris. Eventually workers were needed to clear the debris. They could work for only 90 seconds at a time and nearly 5000 people were needed for the job. Once the radioactive debris was cleared, a huge concrete sarcophagus was built around the building.
- The surrounding land up to 30 km from the power plant was evacuated and remains an exclusion zone due to radioactive isotopes in the soil. Soil was turned over and buried, along with parts of nearby forests.
- The sarcophagus around the number 4 reactor was built as an emergency containment and not designed as a permanent measure. In 2008, building began on the New Safe Confinement (NSC) structure (above and below). This was slid into place over the old sarcophagus. The structure was completed in 2018 at a cost of around \$2 billion. Underneath it, the number 4 reactor can finally be decommissioned and made safe using remote controlled machinery.

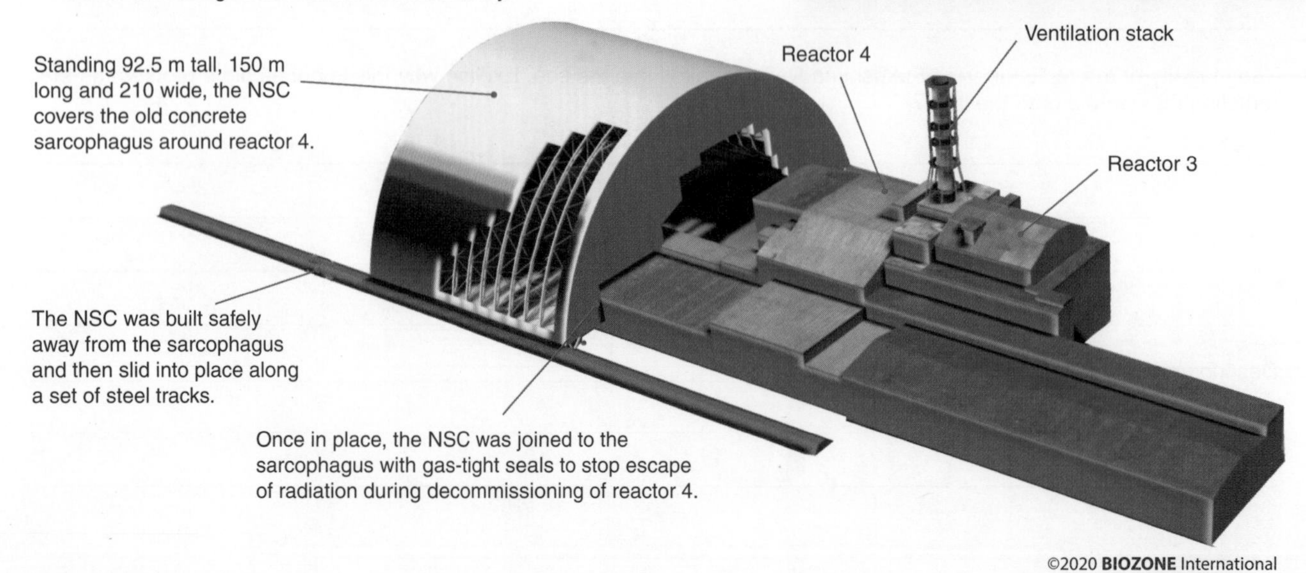

ISBN: 978-1-98-856632-0

Environmental effects of the Chernobyl accident

- Radioactive particles released by the explosion fell across a large area surrounding the plant, killing much of the nearby forest. In particular, an area of pine forest (later known as the Red Forest) received an extremely large dose of radioactive particles. The pine forest was bulldozed and buried after the pines died. Winds blew radioactive material over a large part of Europe. Radioactivity in surrounding waterways fell rapidly due to dilution and deposition, but wildlife around the area have suffered higher than normal rates of mutation, with many animals dying from thyroid disease. Much of the radioactivity is now concentrated in the soil.
- Major radionuclides released by the explosion were iodine-131, cesium-134 and 137, and plutonium isotopes.
- The exclusion zone around the power plant has become a wildlife refuge due to the evacuation of residents immediately following the disaster. Ecological succession has returned much of the land to forest or open meadow.
- It will take many generations before the area around Chernobyl will be safe for long term habitation by humans. The radioactive material in the destroyed reactor will remain dangerously radioactive for possibly another 20,000 years (but will likely be removed or well protected by that time). Because of the dynamic environment, pockets of the surrounding land are highly radioactive, while others are less so.

Chernobyl viewed from the abandoned city of Pripyat

Vegetation overgrows recreational area in Pripyat

Radiation due to cesium-137

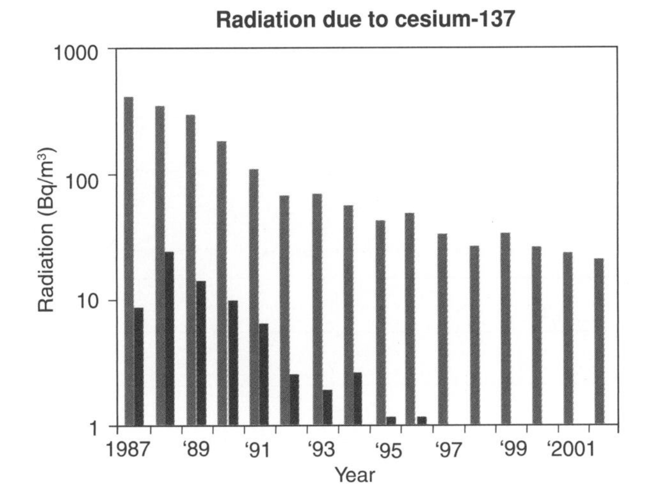

Kiev reservior (117 km from Chernobyl)
Kahova reservior (700 km from Chernobyl)

Radiation due to strontium-90

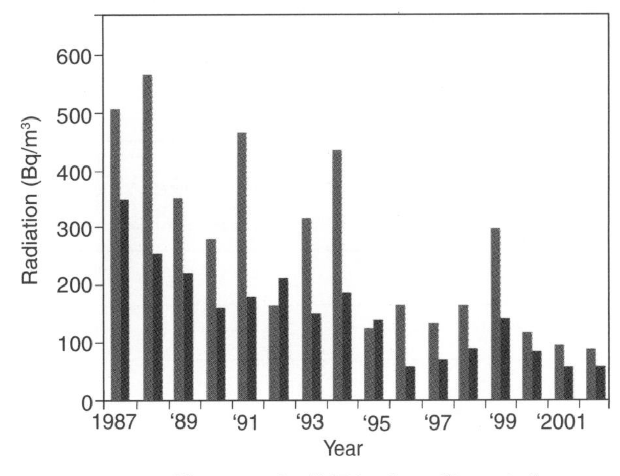

Kiev reservior (117 km from Chernobyl)
Kahova reservior (700 km from Chernobyl)

Cesium activity in muscles of roe deer (southern Germany)

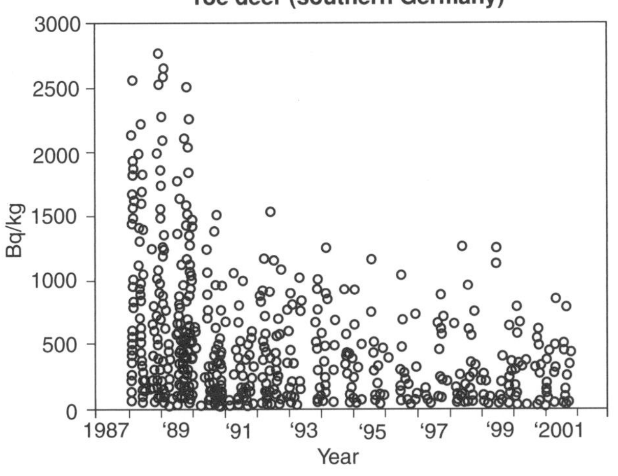

Radioactivity in fish from the Kiev reservoir

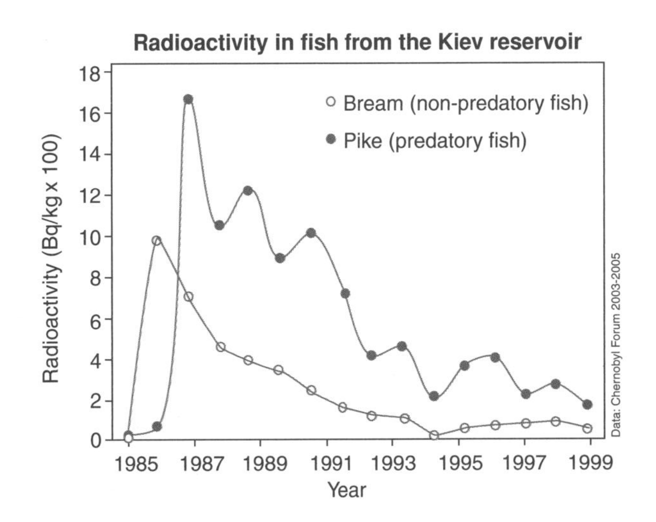

Data: Report of the UN Chernobyl ForumExpert Group "Environment" (EGE) 2005, unless indicated otherwise

ISBN: 978-1-98-856632-0

9. (a) What caused the accident at Chernobyl?

(b) Describe the clean up of Chernobyl:

(c) Explain why the Chernobyl accident released so much more radiation than the Fukushima disaster:

10. Describe the trend in radioactivity resulting from the release of material from Chernobyl:

11. Explain why the levels of radioactivity in pike in the Kiev reservoir are higher than those of bream:

12. Explain where the cesium in roe deer has come from. How does this show radiation was not limited to the exclusion zone around Chernobyl?

13. Water dilutes the radioactivity of radionuclides. Why then would the radiation levels in reservoirs be higher than might be expected?

ISBN: 978-1-98-856632-0

Comparing nuclear disasters

Radiation released (PBq)

Three Mile Island (0.62)
No known health effects
INES* level 5

Fukushima (770)
Long term health effects unknown
INES level 7

Chernobyl (5200)
Over 6000 cases of thyroid cancer.
4000+ deaths from radiation exposure.
INES level 7

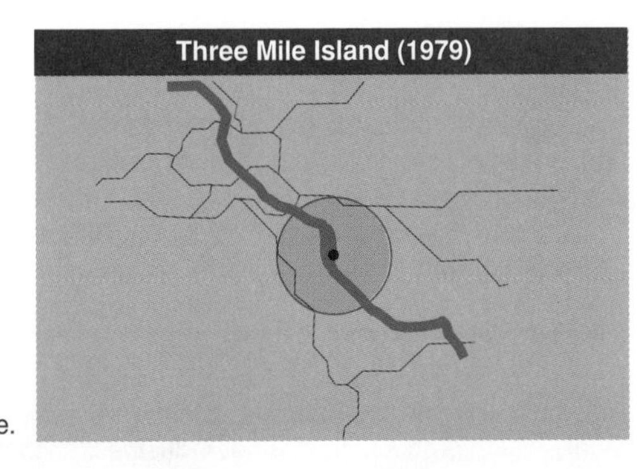

8 km voluntary evacuation zone affecting 140,000 people.

Deaths resulting from accident: 0

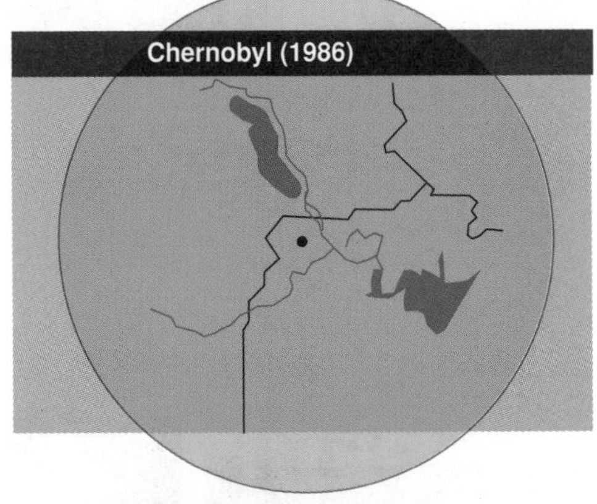

30 km mandatory evacuation zone affecting 230,000 people.

Deaths resulting from accident: 30
Related deaths: ~4000+

Fukushima Daiichi (2011)

20 km mandatory evacuation zone affecting 80,000 people.

Deaths resulting from accident: 1
Related deaths: ~2200

*International Nuclear and Radiological Event Scale. It is a tool for communicating the safety significance of nuclear and radiological events to the public.

Is nuclear power dangerous?

- Disasters like Chernobyl and Fukushima show what can happen when a nuclear reactor is not carefully controlled. Dangerous radioactive isotopes including iodine-131, cesium-134 and 137, and strontium-90 were released into the environment.
- Iodine-131 can be absorbed into the thyroid, causing thyroid cancer. However its half-life is only 8 days and its presence in the environment is short (only about 3 months).
- Cesium-134 and cesium-137 have longer half-lives, (cesium-134 ~2 years and cesium-137 ~30 years). They can accumulate through biomagnification and concentrations increase up the trophic levels (biomagnification). They too can cause cancer.
- Strontium-90 has a half-life of about 29 years. It and cesium-137 are the major contributors to radionuclide contamination around Chernobyl and Fukushima.
- Despite these long term problems, deaths from nuclear disasters are actually the lowest of any form of electrical generation per terrawatt-hour of electricity produced.

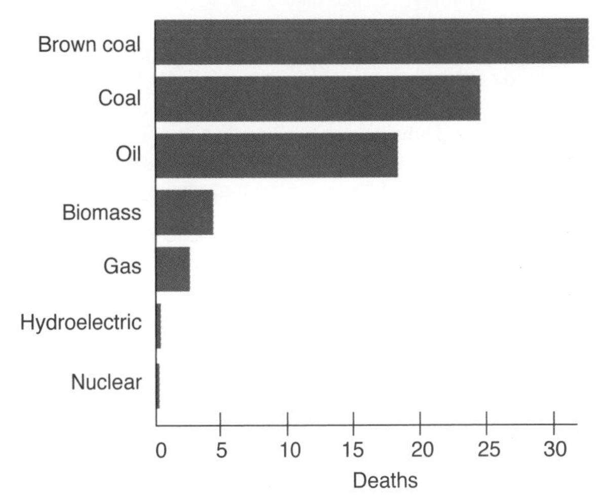

14. "*Nuclear power provides clean, cheap and safe electricity.*" Discuss the merits of this statement:

ISBN: 978-1-98-856632-0

106 Energy from Biomass

Key Question: How do we obtain energy from biomass and what are the effects of this?

Biomass is any material derived from a living organism, e.g. animal waste or wood from plants. Fuels made from biological processes have been used for many years. In many regions of the world, dried animal dung is still used to fuel fires. More recently there has been a move to produce more commercial quantities of renewable biofuels for use in transport and industry. Biofuels include ethanol, gasohol (a blend of petrol and ethanol), methanol, and biodiesel made from a blend of plant oils and traditional diesel oil. Biogas (methane) is an important renewable gas fuel made by fermenting wastes in a digester. Although these fuels come from renewable material, their large scale use is problematic.

Biomass

- Biomass fuels include almost any solid form of biomass, such as wood and wood pellets, crop residue, and even dried animal waste. It can include biomass grown specifically for fuel or, more commonly, waste products from other industries, such as corn husks or wood chips from the timber industry.
- The problem with biomass as a fuel is that it burns much faster than it is produced (it may take ten years for a tree to grow, but less than a day to burn it as fuel). As a result, biomass power plants are relatively small and limited to the waste material they can acquire. What's more, much of this material is not concentrated (e.g. compare the energy in 1 kg of wood compared to 1 kg of coal) so biomass power plants are not particularly efficient at producing electricity.

Wood waste

Tetris L CC3.0

Biofuels

- Biofuels are made from processing biomass. The most common types are bioethanol (95% of the world's ethanol is produced biologically) and biodiesel. Like simple biomass, biofuels are renewable, but are limited by the rate of production and use.
- Biofuels can be divided into generations depending on how the fuel is produced.

Sugarcane

1st generation biofuels include those grown on typical arable lands explicitly for the production of fuel, but they are often food crops. They include sugarcane and corn. As such, they often displace food crops.

Legume crop residue

2nd generation biofuels are produced from crop by-products (cellulose biomass instead of sugars or oils). Biomass may be gasified to produce syngas, or pyrolyzed (decomposition by heat).

Photobioreactor for algal culture

IGV Biotech CC 3.0

3rd generation biofuels are still mostly experimental. They are mostly based around algae, which contain high levels of lipid oils. The algae could be grown in bioreactors (above) or on waste water ponds.

Photoelectric cell

MisterRichValentine CC 3.0

Instead of destroying biomass to produce energy, **4th generation biofuels** use living material to produce energy directly. Note the H_2 and O_2 released in the photoelectric cell above. These are still at an experimental stage.

1. The table below shows the capacity and heat rate of several power plants. The heat rate is the amount of energy used (given in MBtu or one thousand British Thermal Units) per megawatt-hour of electricity produced. The heat rate is the inverse of the efficiency, so a plant with a lower heat rate is more efficient.

Plant	Code	Primary fuel	Capacity (MW)	Heat rate (MBtu/MWh)
Agua Mansa Power Plant	AM	Natural gas	61	9.7
Clearwater	CW	Natural gas	49	8.2
El Nido	EN	Biomass	13	21.7
DTE Stockton	DTES	Biomass	45	13.9
Mt Poso Cogeneration	MPC	Biogas	44	16.3
Sunshine Gas Producers	SGP	Landfill gas	23	12.1
Indigo Generation	IG	Natural gas	135	10.2

(a) Which type of power plant has the greatest capacity (on average)? ______

(b) Which type of power plant is the least efficient (on average)? ______

(c) Explain why burning biomass is a useful but inefficient way to produce electricity: ______

______

______

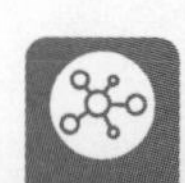

ENG-3
7.B

ISBN: 978-1-98-856632-0

Corn ethanol: Is it actually worth it?

- Ethanol is an important industrial chemical. It has properties that make it useful in both food production and industry. Ethanol has been proposed as a replacement for fossil fuels such as gasoline because it burns well as a fuel, it can be converted to other chemicals, it is easy to produce in large quantities, and it can be produced from plant material.
- At the beginning of this millennium, ethanol was heavily promoted as a carbon neutral, high energy liquid fuel and the best alternative to gasoline. Corn use for ethanol production in 2001 was around 7.5% of the US corn harvest. More than 90% was used to feed people and livestock.
- In 2010, the US government provided US$5.68 billion in subsidies to meet its mandate that biofuels make up 10% of the fuel for the US passenger vehicle fleet. By 2018, corn ethanol production increased to around 60 billion liters and consumed 40% of all corn grown internally.
- The corn ethanol industry, which requires 13 million hectares of land, competes directly with the food and livestock feed industries. This has resulted in a rise in food prices.
- The Congressional Research Service has reported that even if the entire US corn crop was used to produce ethanol for transport, it would only provide 18% of the country's transport fuel needs. To do so, however, would be disastrous for many countries because the United States produces 40% of the world's corn. 70% of global corn imports come from the United States.
- The carbon neutrality of corn ethanol is also disputed. It requires large amounts of fuel to grow, harvest, transport, and distill the crop. Ethanol also contains only two thirds the energy of the equivalent volume of gasoline.
- As an alternative, corn waste after harvest could provide up to 1.27 billion metric ton of useful waste and produce 30% of the US transport fuel needs. However, this would use the organic material that is normally plowed back into the land as fertilizer. This would have implications for soil fertility and increase dependence on inorganic fertilizers, which are costly to produce and create problems of water contamination.

Ethanol plant

USDA

2 (a) Is corn a 1st or 2nd generation biofuel? ___________________________

(b) Is the corn residue left after harvesting a 1st or 2nd generation biofuel? ___________________________

3. The grain required to produce 100 L of ethanol can feed a person for a year. Around 49 billion liters more ethanol was produced in the US from corn in 2018 than in 2001. How many people could this have fed?

____

4. Explain why ethanol production from corn is not a viable alternative fuel: ___________________________

____

____

____

____

____

5. Suggest why 3rd generation biofuels are still in the developmental stage, with virtually none in commercial production:

____

____

____

6. Describe how biofuels can form part of the solution to reducing CO_2 emissions? ___________________________

____

____

____

____

ISBN: 978-1-98-856632-0

107 Solar Energy

Key Question: How can the Sun's energy be used to produce electricity and what are its costs and benefits?

The energy reaching the Earth from the Sun is in the order of trillions upon trillions of joules per day, far more than all of humanity uses in an entire year. This energy can be harnessed in many ways for heating or to create electricity. Currently, most large scale methods of generating electricity from sunlight are **solar thermal**, in which sunlight is concentrated to heat a fluid, which will turn water to steam to drive a turbine. Photovoltaic cells (solar panels) are becoming more popular as their cost goes down and their efficiency increases. Importantly, the solar panels can be used on almost any scale without a loss of efficiency, making them useful for home installation as well as large scale power plants.

Solar thermal systems

- One way to produce electricity from solar energy is to concentrate sunlight to produce heat that can turn water into steam to turn a turbine. The two most common methods to do this are the central receiver system and the distributed receiver system.

A **central receiver system** uses mirrors, called heliostats, to focus the Sun's rays onto a central tower. The focused light is used to heat water, pumped into the central tower, to steam. The steam drives a turbine to create electricity. The Ivanpah solar thermal power facility shown above has three receiver units, each capable of producing about 130 MW of electricity.

Distributed receiver systems use parabolic troughs to focus light into a thin beam. The beam of light heats oil in a pipe running along the focal point of the trough. The oil is used to heat water to steam to drive a turbine. The SEGS above generates about 354 MW of electricity and is the second largest solar facility in the world, after the Ivanpah facility.

Photovoltaic systems

- Photovoltaic (PV) cells are able to convert sunlight directly into electricity. Electricity is produced when a photon of light hits a semiconducting material (such as silicon) and knocks an electron loose. The electron is captured and made to travel in one direction around a circuit, producing direct current electricity.
- PV cells are becoming more popular as their efficiency increases and their cost decreases. Many Antarctic research stations are now powered at least partially by PV cells.
- A major development in PV technology was the introduction of bifacial PV cells. These are able to gather light directly from the Sun on the upper face, and reflected light on the lower face, increasing the cell's efficiency by about 11%.

USAF

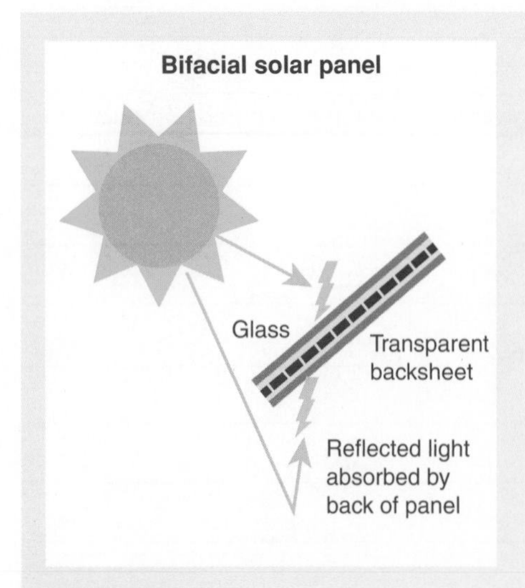

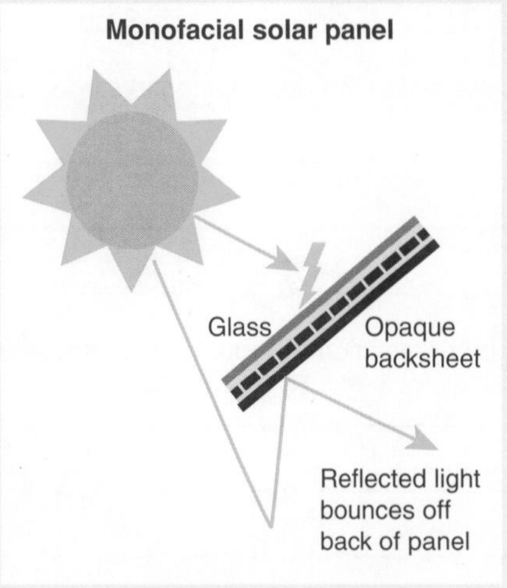

Bifacial solar cells have a clear backing so need to be mounted off the surface to absorb the reflected light.

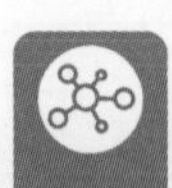

ENG-3
5.C

ISBN: 978-1-98-856632-0

The costs of solar power

Solar power generation	
Advantages	**Disadvantages**
PV cells can be scaled up or down as needed. Small photovoltaic cells are portable and can power many applications	Ground shaded by large solar panels
Low or no CO_2 emissions	Back up and warm-up systems required (usually gas)
Relatively high net energy gain	Large land area needed for commercial scale production
Unlimited energy source during fine weather	High sunshine hours required
Solar cookers are transportable and simple to use	High start up costs

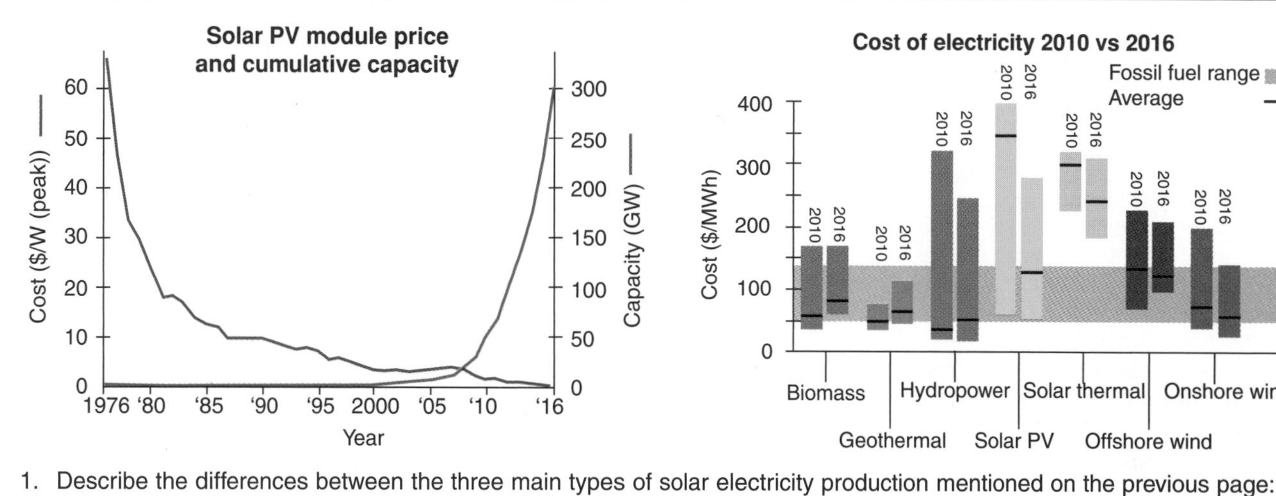

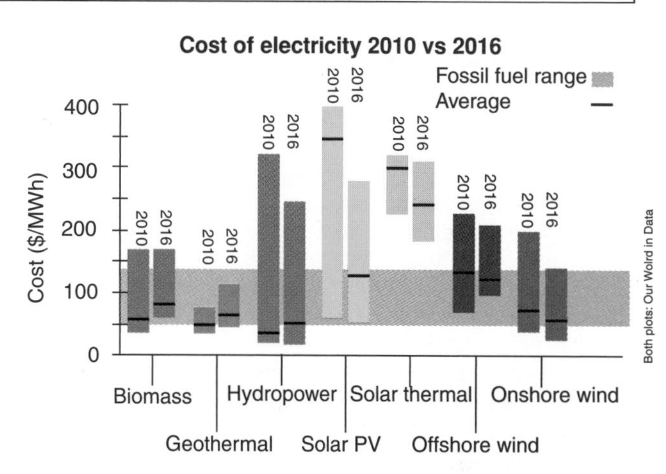

1. Describe the differences between the three main types of solar electricity production mentioned on the previous page:

2. When central receiver systems were first developed they caused the deaths of numerous birds. Why might this have happened? Hint: solving the problem involved random facing of the mirrors when the facility was offline.

3. Why are gas warm-up systems needed for central and distributed receiver systems?

4. (a) What is the trend in the cost of PV cells?

   (b) What is the trend in global installed capacity?

   (c) Explain these trends:

5. (a) Which renewable energy source has had the greatest drop in cost since 2010?

   (b) What might this mean for the future uptake of this technology?

ISBN: 978-1-98-856632-0

108 Investigating Solar Houses

Key Question: How is solar energy used to heat houses?
Solar heating can be divided into passive and active. Passive heating is the most common and the simplest. No external sources are needed to move heat about, but must be designed well to obtain the best effects. Active solar heating uses external energy (e.g. pumps) to help circulate heat from heat collectors. Computer programs are used to model these systems and improve their efficiency.

- **Passive solar heating** is becoming more common in houses. It can efficiently heat a home without electrical input or equipment for moving heat around. The design and placement of the house is important when using passive solar heating. Houses placed with their main windows facing south in Northern Hemisphere and north in the Southern Hemisphere gain large amounts of solar energy during the day. Double glazed windows and insulation help to store this energy to keep the house warm at night.
- **Active solar heating** uses pumps to circulate heat gathered from a rooftop collector to various parts of a house. Pumps may circulate water through a tank to provide hot water or through a heat exchanger to feed radiators.
- The latest solar technology includes **direct solar steam generation**. Nanoparticles convert solar energy directly to heat. When immersed in water and exposed to light they instantly vaporize the water to produce steam. This technology has been applied to sterilization of water, food, and equipment in places with no electricity.

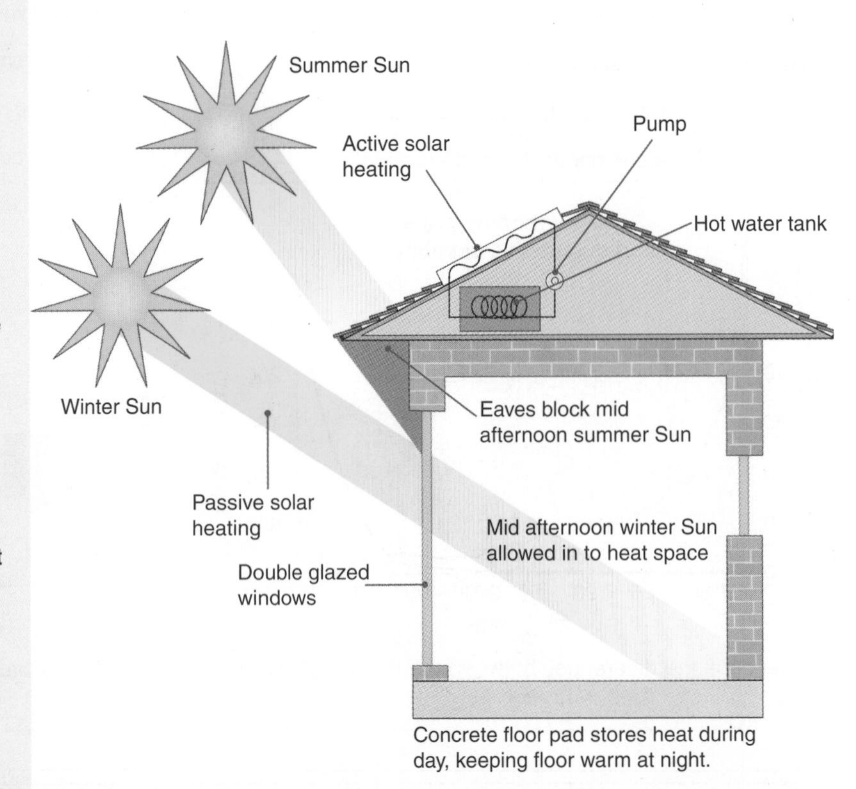

INVESTIGATION: 6.3 Solar heating houses

See appendix for equipment list.

1. This activity requires the free program Energy 2D, downloadable from https://energy.concord.org/energy2d/ or from the link in the **BIOZONE Resource Hub**.
2. Open the Energy 2D program. Go to the **Examples** dropdown menu and look for **Building energy analysis**. There are five solar heating examples listed. Click on the first example: **Solar heating: Gable roof**.
3. You should see the image shown on the right.
4. If you click on **Run** at the bottom of the screen you should see sun rays moving straight downwards. Isotherm bars show how heat is being transferred.
5. Note how the thermometers behave. You can move them about by clicking and dragging them.
6. Left click on the blue area. You can now use Q and W to change the angle of the Sun's rays. Note how the thermometers behave as the angle of the rays change so that light is shining in the windows.
7. Once you have explored this model return to **Examples > Building energy analysis** and click on **Solar heating: Shed roof**. This shows a second type of house design with larger windows.
8. Again you can click **Run** and change the angle of the Sun's rays. Again note how the thermometers behave.
9. Again after you have explored the shed roof model return to **Examples > Building energy analysis** and click on **Solar heating: Two stories**.
10. Again you can click **Run** and change the angle of the Sun's rays. Again note how the thermometers behave.
11. For any of these models you can change parts of the house by clicking and dragging the shapes, e.g. making bigger or smaller windows.

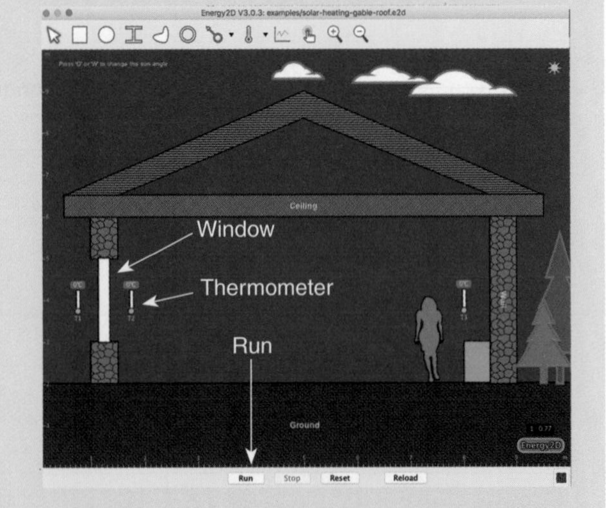

ISBN: 978-1-98-856632-0

1. Explain the difference between passive and active solar heating: ______

2. How does the shape of the house and position of windows affect how the house heats up or cools down based on the angle of the Sun's rays?

INVESTIGATION: 6.4 Solar power

See appendix for equipment list.

1. Returning to the Energy 2D program again, open the program and this time under **Examples** find **Industrial Applications** and then **Solar thermal power plant**.
2. Click **Run** to see how the power plant works. You can again change the angle of the Sun by pressing Q or **W**.
3. Note how the thermometer behaves and how the mirrors must adjust to continue to focus on the power tower.
4. After running the simulation for a minute stop it and click **Reset**. Now add a cloud by clicking on **Insert> cloud**. Right click on the cloud and click **Properties**. In the **Speed** field type 0.005.
5. Run the simulation. Does the cloud affect how the power tower heats up? You can add more clouds and spread them out to see how this affects the power tower.

3. What effect does cloud cover have on the solar power tower? How does this affect where they can be built?

4. Discuss how a house could meet all its energy demands from solar energy: ______

ISBN: 978-1-98-856632-0

109 Hydroelectric Power

Key Question: How can electricity be generated from water? What are the environmental effects of a large scale dam?

Hydroelectricity accounts for around 20% of global electricity production. Electricity is produced by utilizing the gravitational potential energy of water stored in reservoirs behind dams. As water falls, directed along pipes into the powerhouse, the potential energy is converted into kinetic energy, which turns turbines to generate electricity. The larger the volume of water and the further it has to fall, the greater the amount of energy it contains. Larger dams can therefore produce larger amounts of electricity. The generation of the electricity itself produces no emissions, but dam construction requires massive amounts of energy and labor and often requires river diversions. The construction of large hydroelectric dams is controversial because creating a reservoir behind the dam often inundates towns and land. Dams constructed inefficiently can also fill up with silt and gradually reduce in their generation capacity.

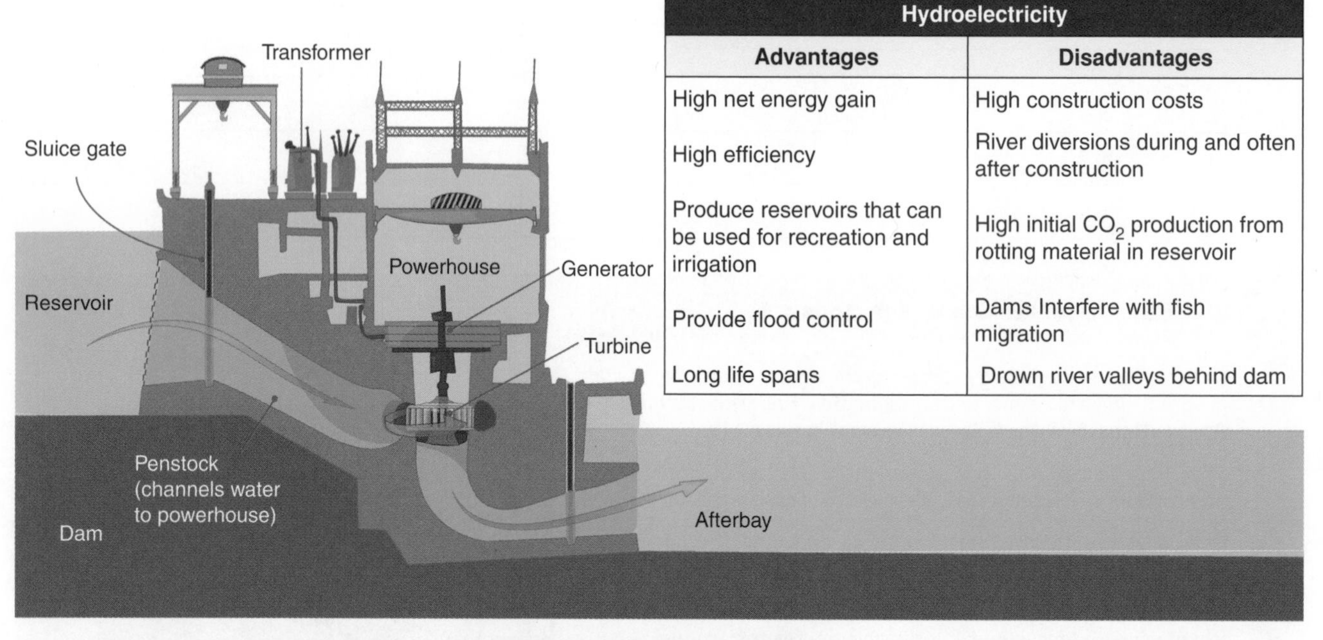

Hydroelectricity	
Advantages	**Disadvantages**
High net energy gain	High construction costs
High efficiency	River diversions during and often after construction
Produce reservoirs that can be used for recreation and irrigation	High initial CO_2 production from rotting material in reservoir
Provide flood control	Dams Interfere with fish migration
Long life spans	Drown river valleys behind dam

Using hydroelectric power

Hoover Dam, Colorado River NV/AZ

The mass of water and the distance it falls are important in determining the amount of electricity that can be produced. The power (the energy produced per second) produced by a hydroelectric power plant can be approximated from the mass of water flowing past the turbine and the height of its fall.

Chief Joseph Dam, Columbia River, WA

Water doesn't have to be stored in a dam for a hydroelectric power plant to work. Water can be directed to flow past the turbine and simply use the force of the flowing water (called **run-of-the-river**). The dam is usually there to divert water towards the intake or powerhouse or to store water in case of lower river levels.

Dlouhé stráne pumped storage plant, Czech Republic

Pumped storage is a useful way of storing excess energy in hydroelectric plants. During off-peak times, water flowing through the plant is used to pump water to a higher storage pond. During high demand, this water can be run through a separate powerhouse to provide extra electricity to the local grid.

1. (a) Explain how hydroelectric dams are used to generate electricity: ______________________

____

____

____

(b) Describe the relationship between water volume, height of the dam and electricity production:

____

____

ISBN: 978-1-98-856632-0

The power (in watts) that can be delivered by a hydroelectric power plant when water is stored in a dam can be calculated using the equation right. Where water is not stored in a dam and a run-of-the-river turbine is used, the equation for power produced depends on the radius of the water intake and the velocity and density of the water.

Image: A Francis turbine being installed at the Grand Coulee Dam, US. Francis turbines are the most common water turbine is use.

$$P = h \times g \times Q \times \eta$$

P = power (watts W),
h = height (m),
Q = flow rate (kg/s),
g = the strength of gravity (9.8 N/kg),
η = efficiency of the power plant (%).

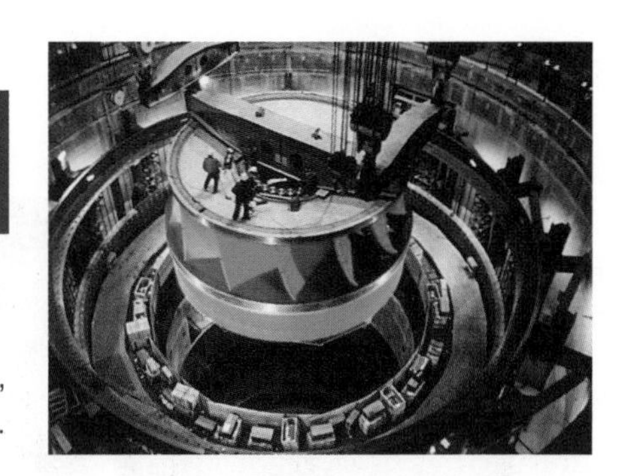

2. (a) Calculate the maximum power produced by a power plant with a water fall of 30 m and a flow rate of 10,000 kg/s:

(b) If the efficiency of the plant is 80%, what is the actual power produced?

(c) Why is efficiency important?

3. (a) Explain how pumped-storage hydroelectric power can help electricity production during periods of high demand:

(b) Explain why pumped-storage hydroelectric power is an efficient use of electricity resources:

4. Explain why run-of-the-river type power plants are subject to highly variable power output:

5. Using specific examples, describe some advantages and disadvantages of large scale hydroelectric dams:

ISBN: 978-1-98-856632-0

Issues with hydroelectric power

The Yangtze River

All images NASA except where indicated

1987

2006

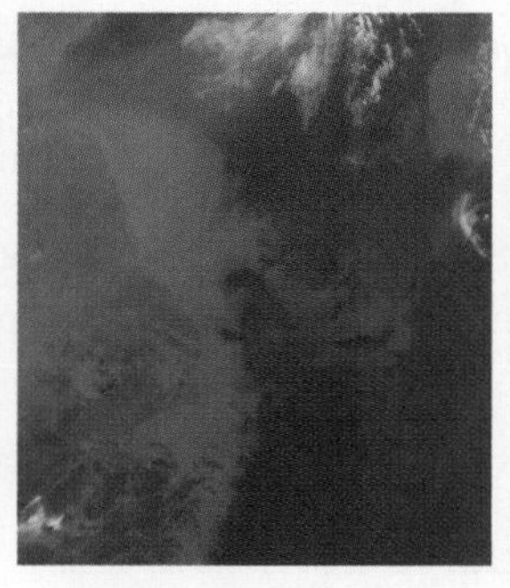
Silt from Yangtze River

BS Thurner Hof
Siberian crane

The Three Gorges Dam (above) on the Yangtze river, China, is 2.3 km wide and 101 m high, with a reservoir 660 km long. It has a generation capacity of 22,500 MW. The construction of the Three Gorges Dam caused the river water level to rise by 100 m, and required the relocation of 1.2 million people.

Dams reduce flood risk by regulating downstream water flows. However, they also prevent deposition of fertile silts. Flooding land behind the dam to create a reservoir seriously disrupts the feeding areas of wading birds.

The Colorado River

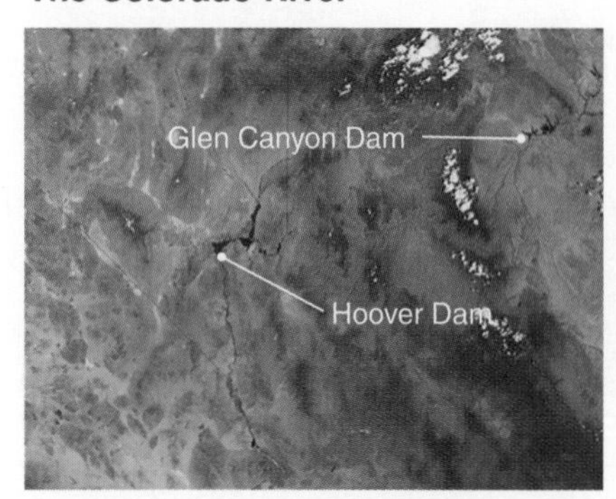

A number of dams have been built on the Colorado River, which runs from Colorado to Mexico. The two largest hydroelectric dams on the river are the Glen Canyon Dam and the Hoover Dam. Together these dams have a generation capacity of over 3000 MW and provide irrigation and recreation for thousands of people. Both dams control water flow through the Colorado River and were controversial even before their construction.

The construction of **Glen Canyon Dam** effectively ended the annual flooding of the Colorado River. This has allowed invasive plants to establish and has caused the loss of many camping beaches as new silt is trapped behind the dam. The reduced flow rate of the river has severely affected native fish stocks. Controlled floods held in 1996 and 2004 have had beneficial effects on the downstream ecosystems.

Hoover Dam, which impounds Lake Mead, has a generation capacity of over 2000 MW. Water from Lake Mead serves more than 8 million people in Arizona, Nevada, and California. The dam has had a major effect on the Colorado delta, which has reduced in size from around 800,000 hectares to barely 73,000 hectares. Native fish populations have also been reduced.

6. Using relevant examples, provide an evaluation of the following statement: "*Hydroelectric power produces clean, environmentally friendly electricity*":

ISBN: 978-1-98-856632-0

110 Wave and Tidal Power

Key Question: Can the energy in tides and waves be used to provide a viable source of electricity?

An enormous amount of energy is stored in the world's oceans. Twice daily, tides move huge volumes of water up and down the coasts of the continents, while billions of joules of energy are transferred when waves meet the shore. Many of the world's energy problems could be solved if this energy could be harnessed, but there are many problems involved in doing this. Machinery to harness tidal or wave energy requires certain shoreline contours and seabed features, and regular swells. It must also be able to withstand constant immersion in seawater and the relentless and often unpredictable movement of the sea. Many designs have been proposed to exploit various types of seawater movement. While some have shown promise, most have not proved economic and there are also concerns over effects on marine life and shorelines. For these reasons, ocean power is unlikely to contribute much to future world energy needs.

Using tidal flows

- Tidal barrages have the potential to produce vast amounts of electricity. However, they are expensive to build, require several meters of tidal difference, and potentially destroy the estuaries across which they are built.

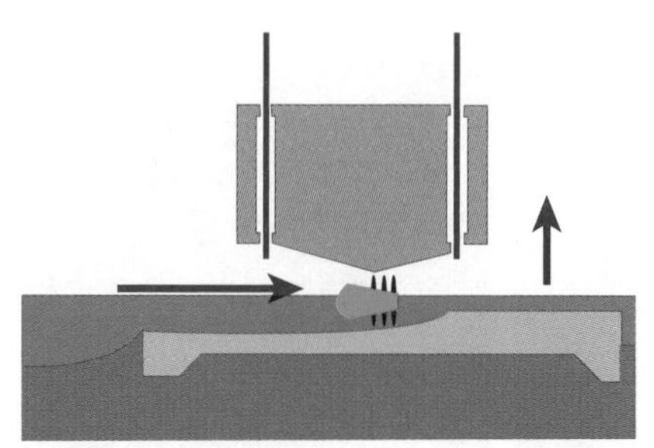

There are various tidal barrage designs. In ebb generation, the gates are opened to let the tide flood in.

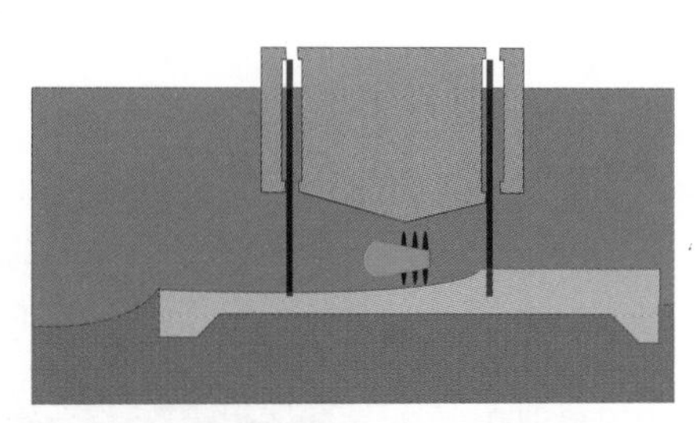

The gates are closed at the tide's highest point to contain the greatest volume of water.

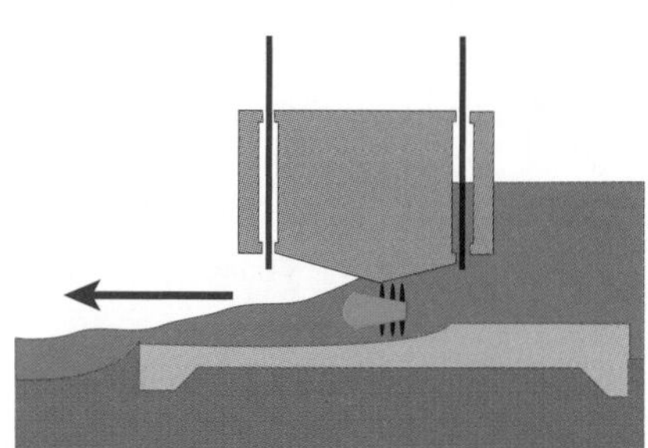

The gates are opened at low tide and the water flowing through drives the turbines in the same way as a hydroelectric dam.

Aerial view of the tidal barrage on the Rance River

The Rance Tidal Power Station in France began operation in 1966. It has a peak output of 240 MW.

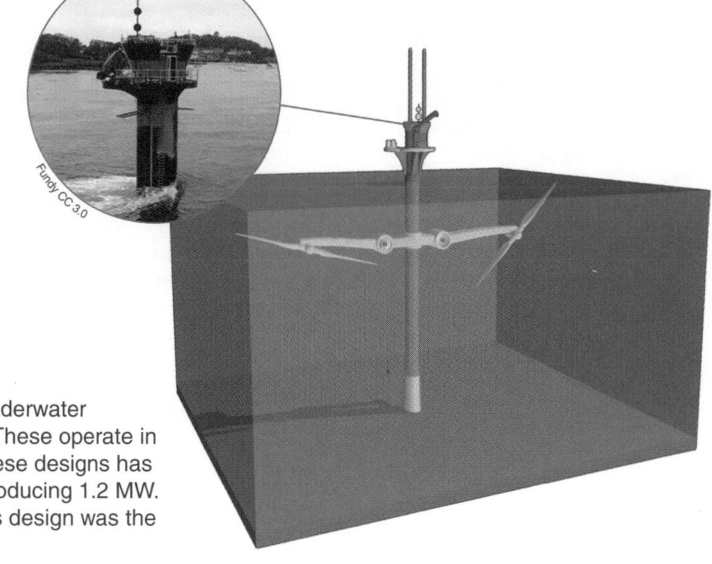

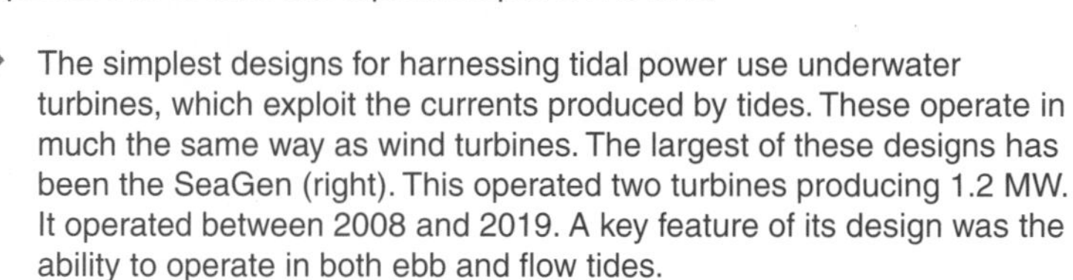

- The simplest designs for harnessing tidal power use underwater turbines, which exploit the currents produced by tides. These operate in much the same way as wind turbines. The largest of these designs has been the SeaGen (right). This operated two turbines producing 1.2 MW. It operated between 2008 and 2019. A key feature of its design was the ability to operate in both ebb and flow tides.

1. Explain the potential benefits of harnessing ocean power: ______

2. Why are there so many different types of design for exploiting wave and tidal power? ______

3. What kind of challenges do underwater turbines like the SeaGen face compared to wind turbines? ______

ISBN: 978-1-98-856632-0

Wave power

- Producing electricity from wave movement is extremely difficult. Developers must take into account wave height and period. These vary almost continuously, sometimes subtly and sometimes by extremes. Alongside this is the need to design equipment that can withstand the extreme environment, which includes saline water, debris, and continual pounding by waves.
- Designs vary enormously. It may be that a standard design is not possible because of the many diverse marine situations.

- The Pelamis wave energy generator (right and photo below far right) was a design in which several large tubes were connected together. The movement of the tubes drove internal generators that produced electricity. The system operated from 2004 to 2014.

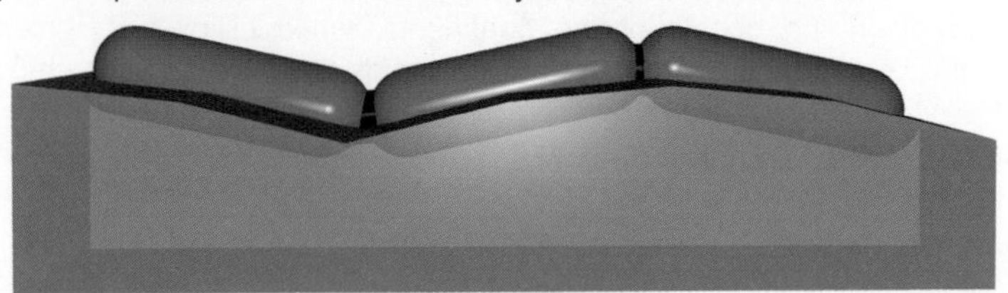

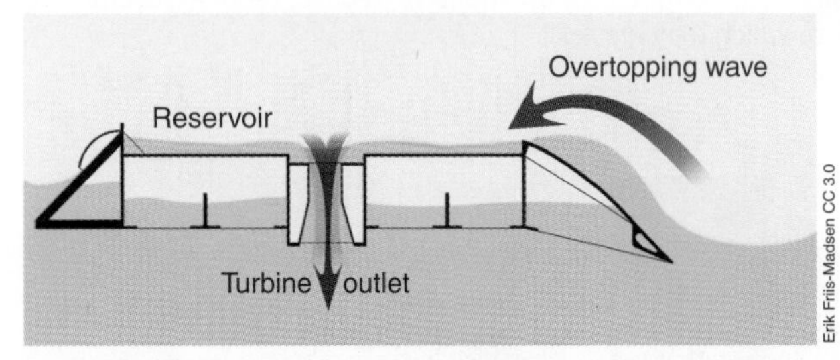

Wave Dragon

Pelamis

- The Wave Dragon (above and near right) directs waves to overtop the front slop. Water then flows out the bottom, driving a turbine. This device is still undergoing testing.

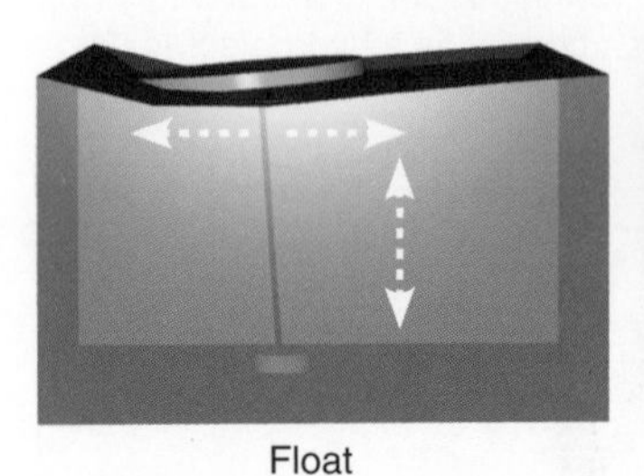

Float

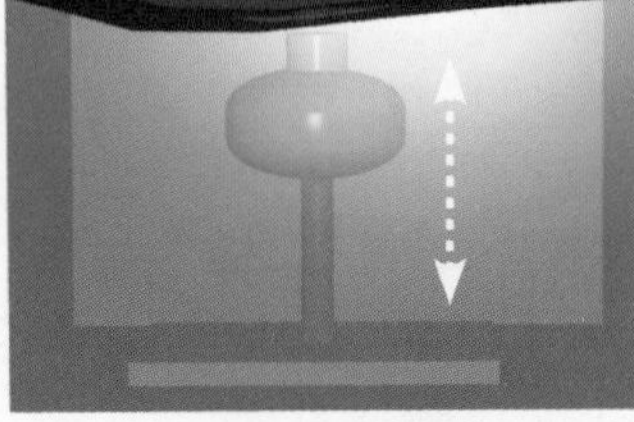

Underwater buoy

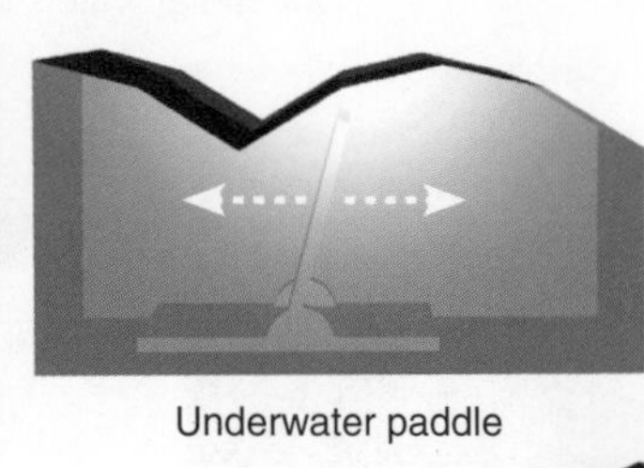

Underwater paddle

- Some devices are anchored to the sea floor and use the movement of waves to move a float or paddle back and forth, driving a small turbine of a generator. Other devices float on the surface and use a internal piston to drive a turbine. These floating devices can make use of both the roll and heave of waves, making them somewhat more efficient. Testing of these devices is still ongoing.

4. What are some potential disadvantages of using the oceans to produce electricity? ______________________

5. Describe the technical problems associated with producing energy from the sea: ______________________

6. Why is ocean power unlikely to ever produce much of the world's energy? ______________________

ISBN: 978-1-98-856632-0

111 Geothermal Power

Key Question: How is the heat in the Earth exploited to produce electricity?

Geothermal power stations operate where volcanic activity heats groundwater to steam. Bores drilled into the ground release this steam and transfer it via insulated pipes to a separator where the dry steam (steam without liquid water) is separated and directed to turbines. Wet steam and waste dry steam are then condensed to water and injected back into the geothermal reservoir to maintain the pressure and groundwater supply. This management practice is essential to prevent land subsidence and depletion of the reservoir. Geothermal power stations often operate close to full capacity, providing a base load, which other power sources top up. Globally, installed capacity is around 15 GW.

The geothermal power plant

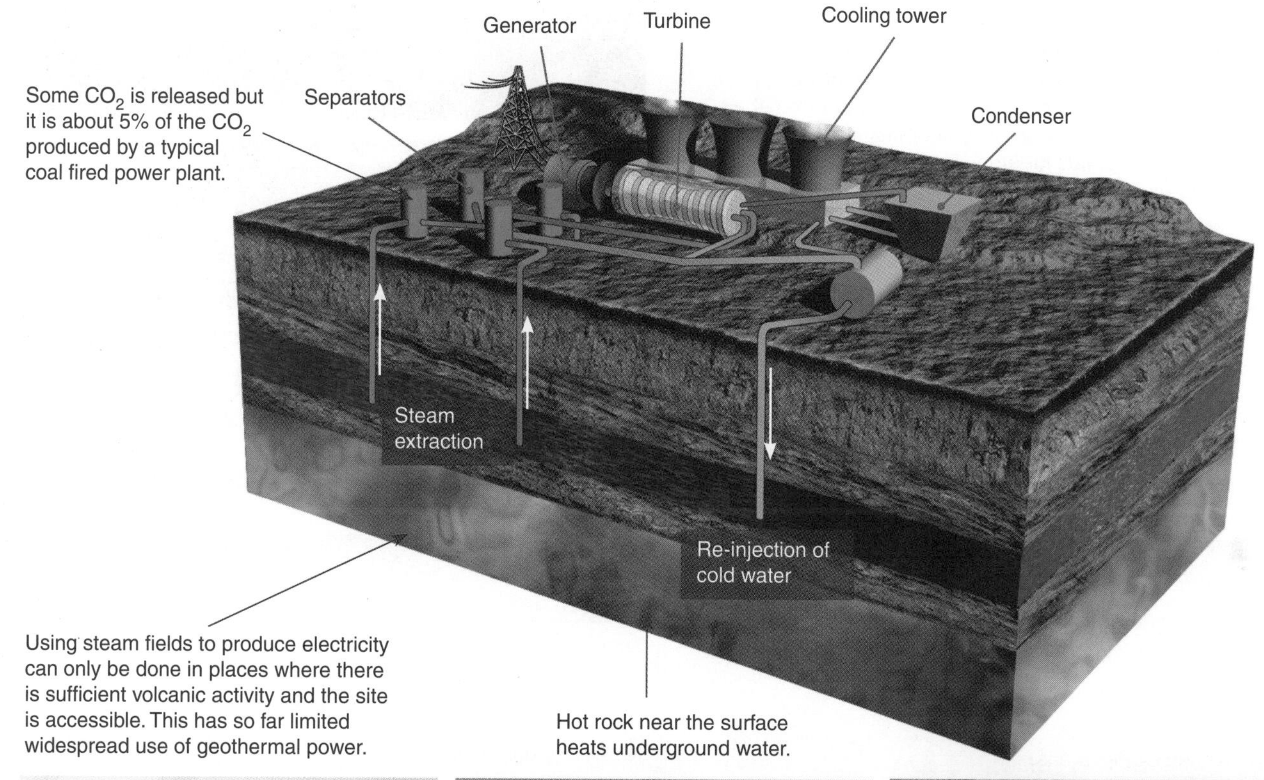

Wairakei geothermal area, New Zealand

Flash steam geothermal plant, Iceland

Wairakei geothermal power station, NZ

QFSE Media CC 3.0

Geothermal energy is produced by the fission of radioactive material deep in the Earth. This causes an enormous amount of heat, which heats groundwater close to the surface, producing a geothermal reservoir. The geothermal activity is usually visible at the surface as geysers and boiling mud (above left).

Geothermal power stations often provide base load supplies. This is the minimum continuous electrical supply for an area and is supplied by power stations that can operate constantly at near full capacity. A newer and now more common type of geothermal plant is the binary cycle plant (above center). Here low temperature water (~57°C) is passed by a secondary (binary) fluid with a very low boiling point. The fluid flash-vaporizes to gas and is used to drive a turbine. Geothermal fields (above right) are often large and steam must be sent along specially designed pipes that can expand and contract up to several meters in various weather conditions.

1. Explain how a geothermal power station works: ______________________________

____

____

____

2. Explain why geothermal power plants can be used as baseload supplies: ______________________________

____

____

ISBN: 978-1-98-856632-0

Other uses of geothermal energy

- Below about 3 m, the ground temperature is relatively stable and similar to the average air temperature. This stable temperature is exploited by **geothermal heat pumps**, which are now installed in many houses (top right).
- These use a small pump to circulate fluid inside pipes from the roof and floor space of a house into the ground. In summer, this transfers heat from the house to the ground, cooling the house. In winter, it transfers heat from the ground into the house. Geothermal heat pumps do not have to be used in geothermal areas, they simply use the relatively constant temperature of the ground.
- Geothermal power is only around 20% efficient when used to produce electricity. However, waste hot water from the power plant can be used to heat other industrial operations, such as heating ponds for producing tropical shrimp in temperate environments (bottom right).
- Geothermal energy is useful for direct heating and only needs electricity to run pumps to move water or fluid about. As a result, this kind of heating can extract 4-5 times more energy from the ground that was used to run the pump.
- This kind of heating is often used in heating geothermal hot pools. Water can be pumped into a heat exchanger deep in the ground and heated by hot rocks, before being pumped into a pool. Other hot water pools simply pump hot water directly from the ground to the pool.

KPryor

Geothermal Power	
Advantages	**Disadvantages**
Moderate to high net production of usable energy	Few suitable sites
Low - moderate CO_2 emissions	Easily depleted if not carefully managed
Low cost (in suitable areas)	Noise and odor pollution
Low environmental impact if managed correctly	Land subsidence possible

3. Explain why geothermal electricity is currently only viable in a few places on Earth: ______________________

4. Explain why geothermal reservoirs used for electricity production must be carefully managed:

5. Describe some uses for geothermal energy other than generating electricity: ______________________

ISBN: 978-1-98-856632-0

112 Hydrogen Fuel Cells

Key Question: How do hydrogen fuel cells work and can they be a viable alternative source of electricity?

A hydrogen fuel cell uses the oxidation of hydrogen to produce electricity. Fuel cells have been in use for decades, but since the beginning of this century development has accelerated, especially in relation to powering vehicles. Because fuel cells use an external fuel supply, their operation is only limited by the amount of available fuel.

The hydrogen fuel cell

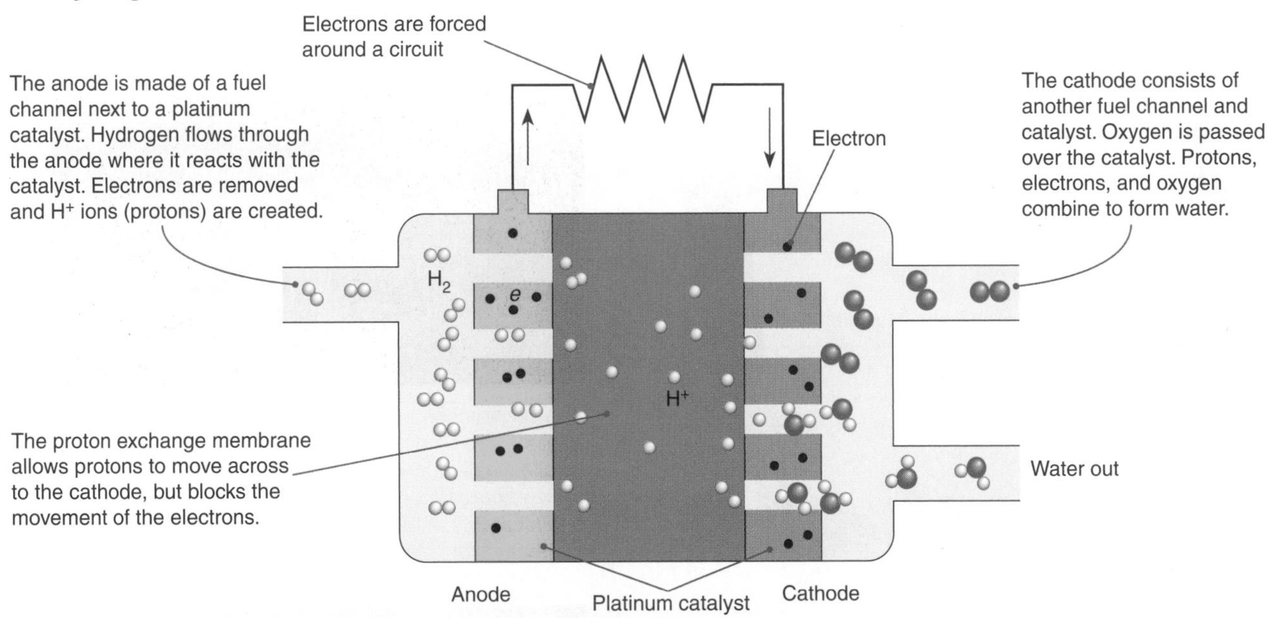

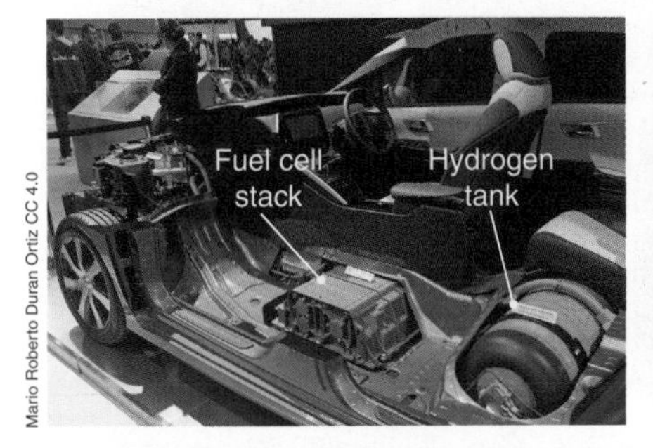

The only emissions from hydrogen fuel cells is water. A fuel tank holding the hydrogen fuels the fuel cell which produces electricity for an electric motor. This makes fuel cell based vehicles a good alternative to conventional combustion engine vehicles.

At the moment most of the hydrogen for fuel cells is produced by steam reforming from natural gas. The rest is produced using electrolysis. This could be sustainable if the energy used to do this is produced using sustainable sources (such as solar PV).

Hydrogen fuel cell vehicles currently suffer from a lack of infrastructure (few places to fuel them). Fueling is similar to a normal car and takes about the same time which is one of the great appeals of these vehicles. The range of a full tank is about the same as a conventional car.

1. Explain how a hydrogen fuel cell produces electricity? ______

2. (a) Explain why fuel cell power vehicles are not yet a fully carbon neutral solution: ______

(b) How could they become carbon neutral? ______

ISBN: 978-1-98-856632-0

113 Wind Power

Key Question: What are the advantages and disadvantages of using wind to produce electricity?

Wind power has been used for centuries to provide the mechanical energy to pump water. Today it is mainly used to produce electricity. Wind power is becoming increasingly reliable and cost effective as the technology develops and turbines are able to operate in a range of conditions and wind speeds. Globally, wind power is steadily increasing in generation capacity, but wind is a variable energy provider. Fluctuations in power availability begin to become perceptible when it makes up more than 20% of a nation's power output, meaning output cannot be matched to changes in demand. To increase the use of wind power better systems for managing and distributing electricity will be required.

Wind turbine

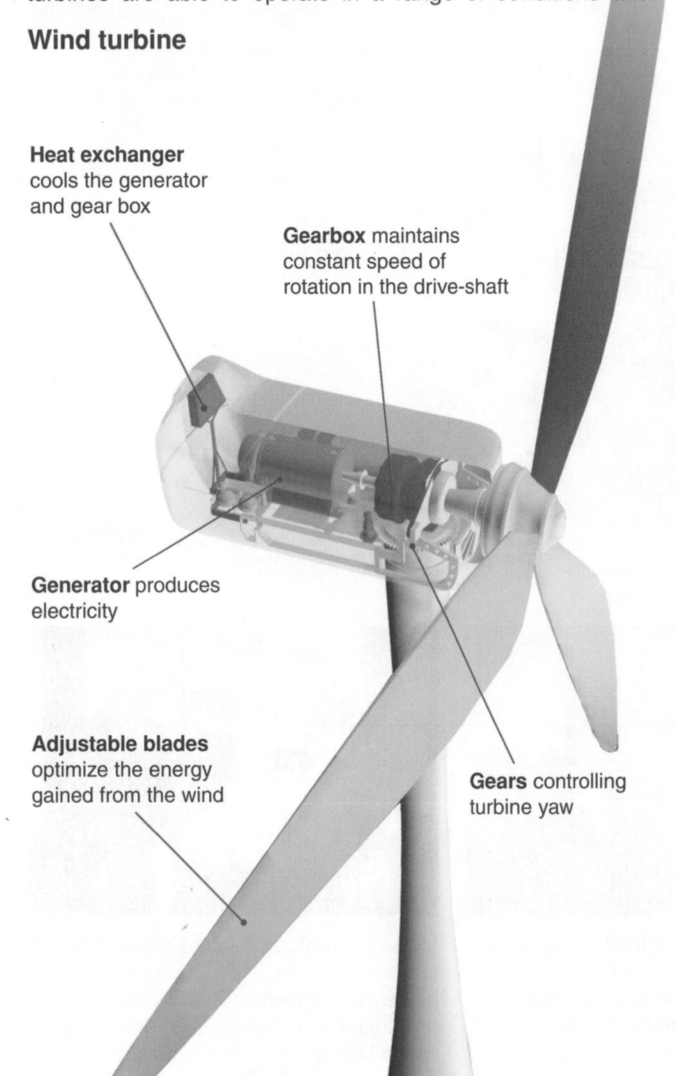

Wind farms often cover large areas of land but turbines can be designed to operate at sea and, on a smaller scale, along highway edges. Turbines range in size from just a meter across, to the world's current largest at 260 m tall and 220 m in diameter, with a generation capacity of 12 MW.

At the end of 2018, the power output from wind turbines was around 5% of the global production of usable energy. Electricity generation from wind has been rising rapidly in recent years as the technology is refined. Global installed capacity is more than 600 GW.

- The power available to a wind turbine can be approximated from the density of the air acting on the turbine blades and its speed:

$$P = \pi/2 \times r^2 \times v^3 \times \rho$$

- P = power (watts W), r = radius of blades, v = wind velocity (m/s), ρ = air density (kg/m^3).
- The efficiency η reduces the amount of power produced. Wind turbines all have a maximum rated output independent of the wind power. This is called the capacity factor (cf), which equals the % of time the turbine is actually producing power (about 40% of the time).

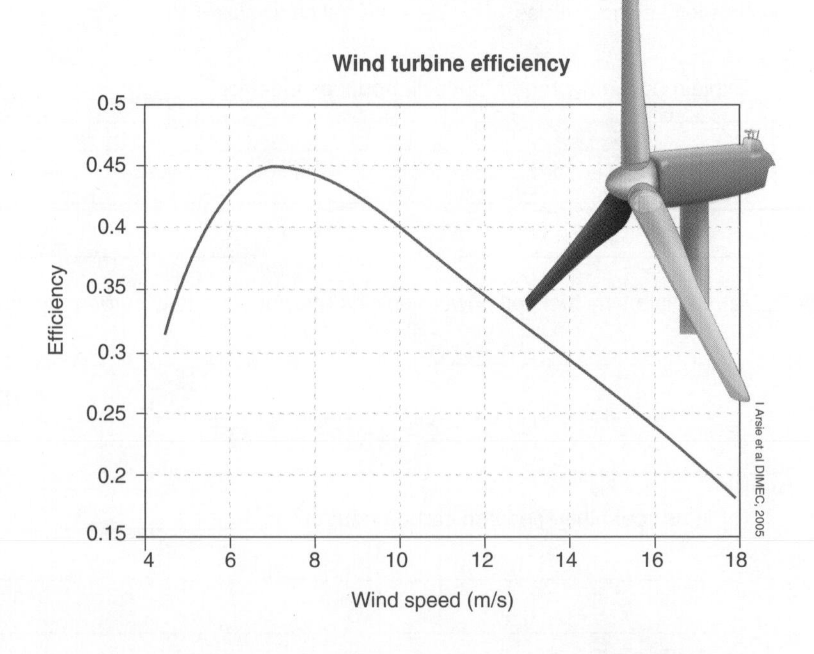

ISBN: 978-1-98-856632-0

Environmental effect of wind turbines

- Over their entire life cycle wind turbines produce some of the lowest greenhouse gas emissions of any electricity production facility. This includes mining of minerals, manufacture and installation, and life time use.
- In the same way as solar power plants, wind farms require large open spaces and so they tend to in be rural areas. This has led to what is often called "industrialization of the country" and "energy sprawl". This includes the spreading of access roads and transmission networks, all of which affect the visual appeal of the areas around wind farms.
- There is documented evidence of wind farms affecting flying animals, especially where they are placed at the top of hills. Birds and bats following the contours of these hills are struck by the turbine's blades and killed.
- The blades have a service life of between 10 and 20 years and are generally made of fiberglass or (increasingly) carbon fiber, and there is no easy way of recycling these. When their lifespan ends, the blades must be disposed of in landfills.
- Because wind turbines sit on single tall towers well above the ground, the area underneath them is minimally affected. Therefore if they are sited on agricultural ground the land can continue to be used for agriculture (right).

Wind Power	
Advantages	**Disadvantages**
No emissions	Production of visual and noise pollution
Little ground disturbance during or after construction	Requires steady winds
Compact and transportable to most locations	Can interfere with the flight paths of flying animals
Can be located in many areas (even at sea)	Much of actual cost to user is repaying start up costs.
Cost certainty. Operating cost is not affected by fuel prices	Back up systems are required in low winds

1. A major problem with generating electricity is the effect of the facility on the environment. Describe how wind power solves some of these problems. What problems does it create?

2. Explain why increasing uptake of wind power will require better management of the electrical grid:

3. A typical wind turbine produces around 2.3 MW. The average house uses 30 kWh per day. Calculate the following:

   (a) The minimum number of wind turbines required to power a town of 20,000 households:

   (b) The total cost of the wind turbines in 3(a) above at a rate of $1000 per kilowatt installed:

4. (a) Calculate the potential power available to a wind turbine with a 95 m diameter operating in wind speeds of between 8 and 12 m/s (air density is 1.2 kg/m^3):

   (b) What is the actual power output of the turbine at that wind speed?

ISBN: 978-1-98-856632-0

114 Energy Conservation

Key Question: How can our energy use be reduced?

An increasing population and demand for technology continually increase global energy requirements. Traditionally, the solution to this demand has been to produce more usable energy (build more power plants). As the economic and environmental costs of this option increase, it becomes more and more important to increase the efficiency of energy generation and use. Energy efficiency involves improving products or systems so that they do more work and waste less energy, conserving energy overall. General improvements in efficiency and overall reductions in energy consumption can be achieved by improving the energy efficiency of processes, appliances, materials, and vehicles, increased use of public transport, and simply reducing individual energy use.

Energy efficient houses

- Most of the energy used in domestic or commercial buildings is for heating, air conditioning, and lighting. Most buildings are highly energy inefficient, leaking energy as heat. New technologies and products enable the construction of energy efficient buildings (below) or **superinsulated** homes, saving the homeowner money and reducing carbon dioxide emissions.
- Superinsulated homes are often constructed from straw bales or advanced insulation materials. They are designed to leak no heat, and gain heat from intrinsic heat sources (such as waste heat from appliances or the body heat of the occupants).

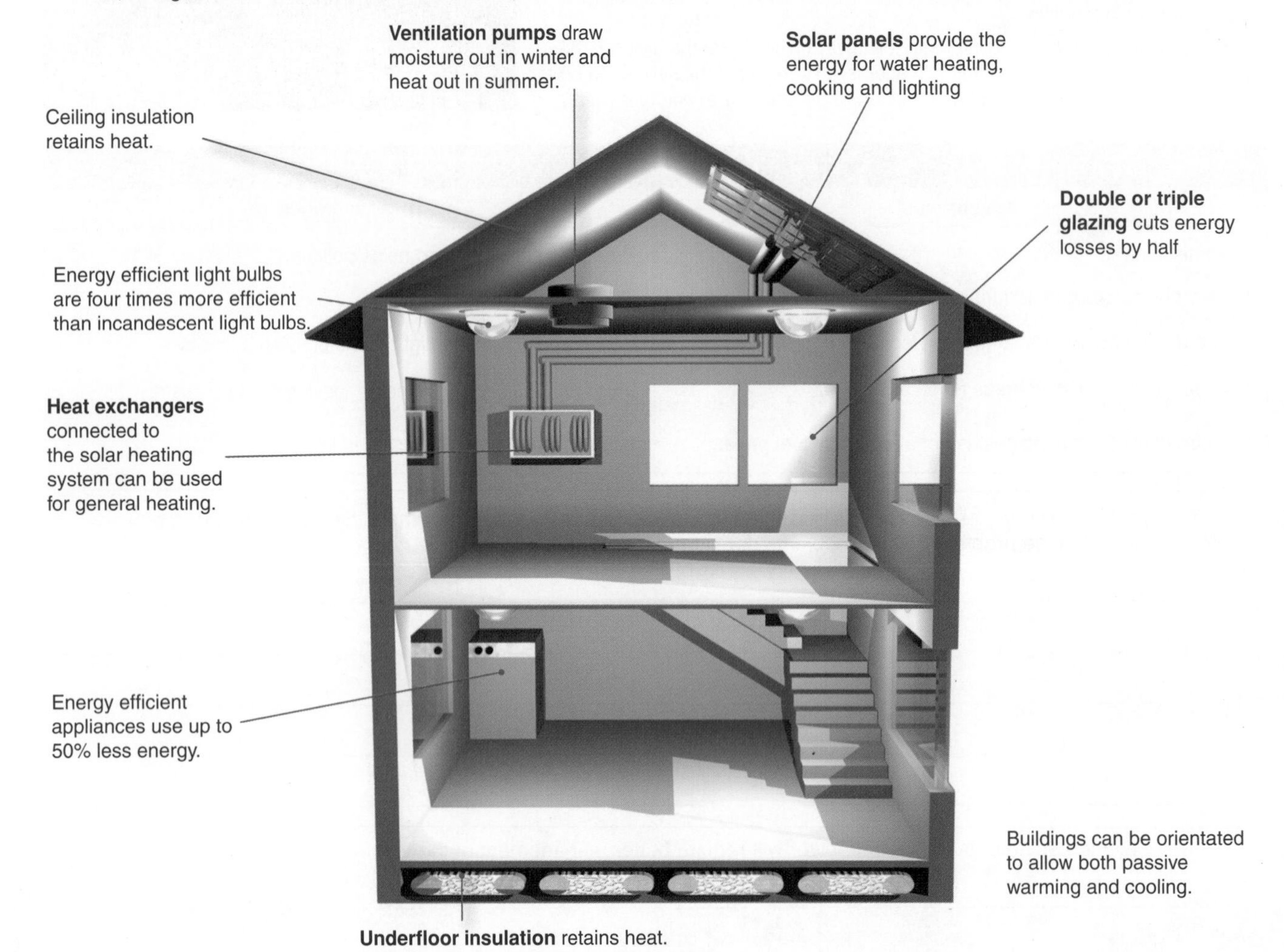

1. Explain how a superinsulated house works: ______________________

2. Explain why simply building new power stations is no longer seen as an acceptable solution to increased energy demands:

____

ISBN: 978-1-98-856632-0

Energy efficiency in transportation

- 25% of the world's global energy is used for transportation. Around 80% of this is wasted because it cannot be used by internal combustion engines. Fuel efficiency has become increasingly important for car manufacture. There are many reasons for this, including growing consumer awareness of the effect of emissions, greater demand for value for money in fuel consumption, and stricter regulations on vehicle emissions.
- The Corporate Average Fuel Economy (CAFE) standards, first enacted in 1975, are regulations to improve the fuel economy of cars and light trucks sold in the US. Standards for fuel economy are set, which manufacturers must obtain. These have increased year after year. The average miles per gallon (MPG) target in 2025 will be just slightly less than double the target set in 2013 for most cars. Penalties are applied if a vehicle does not meet the standard for the year it was first built.
- CAFE has provided the incentive for developing energy-efficient vehicles using lighter, stronger materials, improved aerodynamics, and greater fuel efficiency. As a result fuel economy has been steadily improving since the early 2000s.

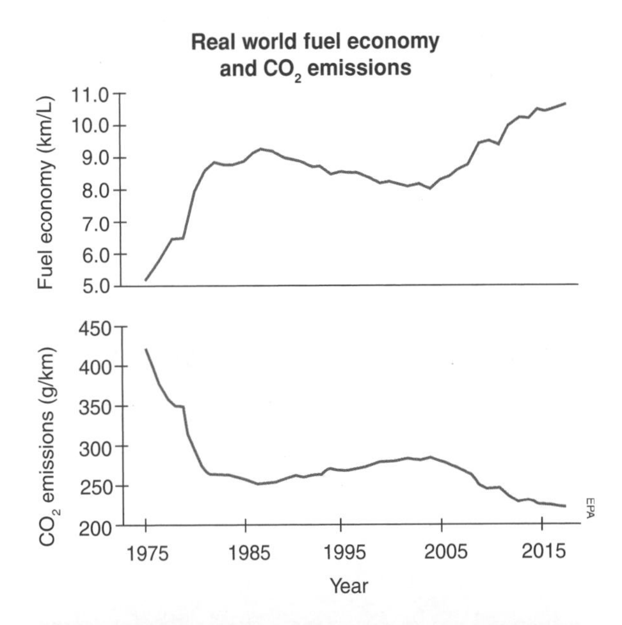

Hybrid and electric vehicles

- Hybrid vehicles use a combination of an internal combustion engine and electric batteries for propulsion. Energy savings are made by capturing the energy released during braking, storing energy in the batteries, using the electric motor during idling and slow driving, and using both the petrol and electric motors for peak power needs (which reduces fuel consumption).
- Electric cars are improving rapidly and the distance range of their batteries is rapidly approaching that of a conventional car. However they still suffer from a long change time (fast chargers has reduced this to about 30 minutes for 80% charge).

- Additionally there is no convention on the recycling or disposal of the batteries, which have a lifespan of 10-20 years.

Comparing efficiencies

- The total transport efficiency of a vehicle depends on its fuel efficiency and the number of people it is transporting. Buses often carry less than half their capacity while private cars use less fuel per kilometer. Rail is the most efficient public transport. Enhancements in ticketing software and airplane capacity allow most flights to be almost full, with high passenger numbers.

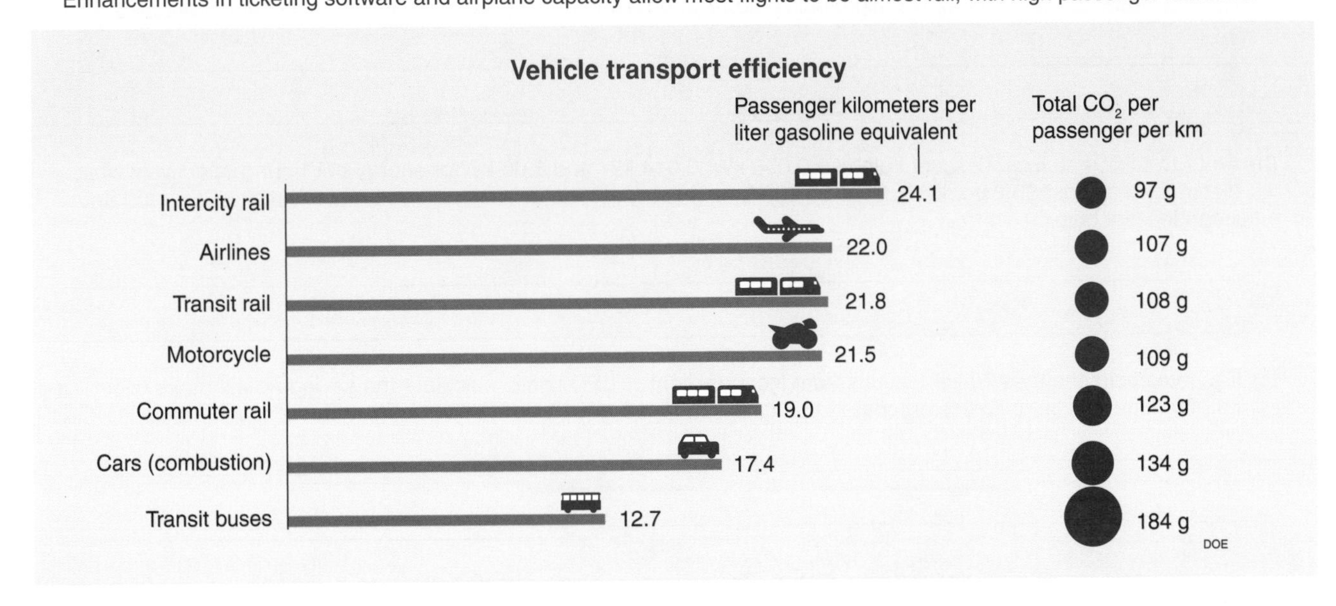

3. Describe the role of CAFE in vehicle fuel efficiency: ______________________________

____

____

4. What other factors have helped increase fuel efficiency? ______________________________

____

ISBN: 978-1-98-856632-0

Household lighting

- One of the best examples of improving efficiency to save energy is the replacement of incandescent light bulbs in the home with LED light bulbs. LED bulbs are vastly more energy efficient than incandescent bulbs, converting 95% of the electricity they use to light (as opposed to about 10% in incandescent bulbs). They also last far longer. Considering the number of lights bulbs used in houses throughout the world the energy saving just in producing light is in the order of terrawatthours a year.
- Many countries are now phasing out incandescent bulbs. This has not been without problems. Although the price of LED continues to fall, they originally cost many times more than an incandescent bulb. There were also problems with the ability to dim LED bulbs. Many people were concerned with the mandated phase out of incandescent bulbs, calling it "light bulb socialism".

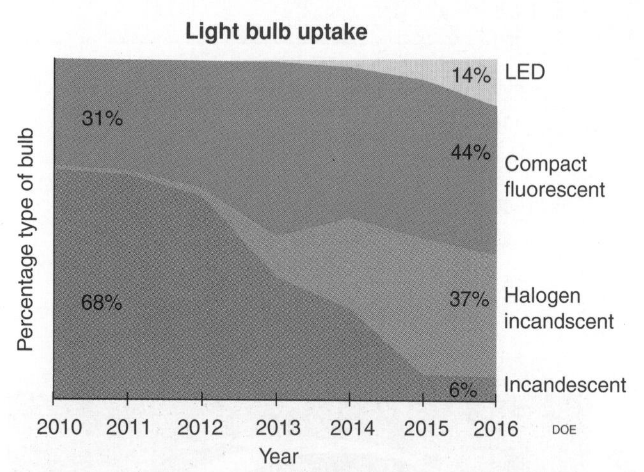

Energy efficient light bulbs are rapidly becoming the major part of the light bulb market. Incandescent bulbs, on the other hand are no longer a significant part of the market.

	Lumens				
	250	400	700	900	1100
Incandescent	25 W	40 W	60 W	75 W	100 W
Halogen	18 W	28 W	42 W	53 W	70 W
Compact fluorescent	6 W	9 W	12 W	15 W	20 W
LED	4 W	6 W	10 W	13 W	18 W

This table shows the light output (measured in lumens) of various light bulb types compared to their wattage. Incandescent bulbs last about 1000 hours compared to the 10,000 hours of a compact fluorescent light (CFL) and 50,000 hours of a LED light.

5. What are some advantages and disadvantages of electric vehicles? ___

6. (a) An LED light bulb typically costs around $5 while a CFL costs $3 and an incandescent bulb $1. Over 50,000 hours of light bulb use, calculate the cost of light bulbs alone when using an LED bulb, a CFL or an incandescent bulb:

   (b) An LED, CFL, and incandescent bulb use 0.006 kW, 0.014 kW and 0.06 kW of energy per hour respectively while electricity may cost $0.2 per kWh. Over 50,000 hours, calculate the cost of running an LED bulb, a CFL, and an incandescent bulb:

   (c) If a household changes 20 light fittings from incandescent to LED lights, calculate the savings it will make over 50,000 hours of light bulb use compared to if it had changed to CFLs or remained incandescent light bulbs:

7. How many times more efficient at producing 1100 lumens of light are LED bulbs compared to other light bulb types:

8. Why do you think people are sometimes worried about problems such as "light bulb socialism'? ___

ISBN: 978-1-98-856632-0

115 Personal Progress Check

Answer the multiple choice questions that follow by circling the correct answer. Don't forget to read the question carefully!

Refer to the following energy sources for question 1 to 5

A. Nuclear fission
B. Solar
C. Wind
D. Hydroelectric

1. Process that produces long lived radioactive isotopes:
   (a) A (b) B (c) C (d) D

2. Electricity produced from the movement of water:
   (a) A (b) B (c) C (d) D

3. Energy source that can be converted directly to electricity using PV cells:
   (a) A (b) B (c) C (d) D

4. The energy source that is non-renewable:
   (a) A (b) B (c) C (d) D

5. The energy source that can be used both passively and actively for space heating:
   (a) A (b) B (c) C (d) D

Refer to table 1 for question 6 - 8

Table 1

Fuel	Energy per kg (MJ/kg)	Energy per liter (MJ/L)
Anthracite coal	30 MJ/kg	43 MJ/L
Gasoline	44 MJ/kg	34 MJ/L
Dry wood	19 MJ/kg	10 MJ/L
Natural gas	46 MJ/kg	0.036 MJ/L

6. Which fuel has the great energy density?
   (a) Anthracite coal
   (b) Gasoline
   (c) Dry wood
   (d) Natural gas

7. Which fuel requires the least mass to produce 100 MJ of heat energy?
   (a) Anthracite coal
   (b) Gasoline
   (c) Dry wood
   (d) Natural gas

8. Which fuel is renewable?
   (a) Anthracite coal
   (b) Gasoline
   (c) Dry wood
   (d) Natural gas

9. CAFE standards are regulations to:
   (a) Reduce traffic congestion
   (b) Increase fuel economy in the country's vehicle fleet
   (c) Decrease the price of fuel for vehicles
   (d) Maintain fuel economy over time

10. A radioactive material has a half-life of 35 years. How many years will pass before the radioactivity drops to 25% of the original radioactivity?
    (a) 35 years
    (b) 70 years
    (c) 105 years
    (d) 140 years

11. Which of the metals below is considered an energy source?
    (a) Copper
    (b) Iron
    (c) Uranium
    (d) Cobalt

12. Which of the following correctly describes a fossil fuel:
    (a) Is a fuel made from dinosaur bones
    (b) Is renewable because it is naturally occurring
    (c) Is non-renewable because it take tens of millions of years to form
    (d) Burns to release oxygen

13. Identify the coal type with the highest carbon content.
    (a) Anthracite
    (b) Bituminous coal
    (c) Lignite
    (d) Peat

14. A light bulb that is 90% efficient will use 1 joule of energy to produce how much light energy?
    (a) 1.1 joules of light energy
    (b) 0.9 joules of light energy
    (c) 0.9 joules of heat energy
    (d) 0.1 joules of light energy

15. Solar power plants that focus light on to a tower containing water to produce steam need which of the following?
    (a) Flat non-tracking mirrors aimed at the top of the tower.
    (b) Flat solar tracking mirrors that direct sunlight towards the top of the tower.
    (c) A flat solar tracking grid of photoelectric cells.
    (d) A passive system where building design alone absorbs enough solar energy to heat the water.

16. Hydroelectric power plants use pumped storage to do which one of the following?
    (a) Produce excess energy by using extra pumps to move more water past the turbines.
    (b) Store energy by pumping water from the river downstream back into the reservoir.
    (c) Produce more energy by pumping water to other power plants.
    (d) Store energy by pumping excess water to a high level reservoir during times of low demand.

ISBN: 978-1-98-856632-0

Use the information below for questions 17 and 18

The process below occurs in a thermal power plant, such as a natural gas fuel plant. The efficiency of each step is:

Production of steam in boiler	→	Steam turning turbine	→	Turbine driving generator to produce electricity
60%		80%		85%

17. The overall efficiency of the process is:
    - (a) 25%
    - (b) 41%
    - (c) 76%
    - (d) 225%

18. If the plant uses 20 MJ of energy what will the electrical energy output be?
    - (a) 5 MJ
    - (b) 45 MJ
    - (c) 8.2 MJ
    - (d) 15.2 MJ

19. Which of the following statements describes the process of turning geothermal energy into electricity?
    - (a) Hot water from under the ground is used to turn turbines and produce electricity. Hot water is the returned to the ground.
    - (b) Heat from deep in the ground is used to heat boilers which produce the steam to turn a turbine and produce electricity. Waste steam is returned to the boiler.
    - (c) Water is circulated through pipes buried in the ground. The water is turned to steam by geothermal heat. The steam is used to turn a turbine to make electricity.
    - (d) Steam from the ground is directed through insulated pipes to turbines, which turn the generators. Waste water and steam is injected back into the steam field.

20. Which of the following fuel types is the most energy efficient when used to power cars?
    - (a) Hydrogen fuel cells
    - (b) Electric batteries charged from mains supply
    - (c) Gasoline
    - (d) Diesel

21. Which of the following would affect the amount of solar energy available for use in a solar power plant?
    - (a) The latitude
    - (b) The time of day
    - (c) The season
    - (d) All of the above

22. Which of the following statements about passive solar heating is true?
    - (a) Uses building design elements to capture and retain heat from the sun to warm a building.
    - (b) Uses pumps to capture and circulate solar energy about the building, but uses no internal heating components.
    - (c) Is the slow steady heating of the Earth's surface by the Sun.
    - (d) Is only viable in extremely sunny areas such as deserts.

Refer to table 2 for question 23

Table 2

Fuel	Energy per kg (MJ/kg)
Anthracite coal	30 MJ/kg
Natural gas	46 MJ/kg
Enriched uranium	3,900,000 MJ/kg

23. What mass of coal needs to be burned to produce the same energy as released by the fission of 1 kg of enriched uranium?
    - (a) 130 tonnes
    - (b) 90.7 tonnes
    - (c) 130 kg
    - (d) 90.7 kg

24. A light bulb rated at 13 W is left on for 4 hours. Given that it is 90% efficient at producing light, the light energy produced will be which of the following?
    - (a) 1870 J
    - (b) 4680 J
    - (c) 168,480 J
    - (d) 187,200 J

25. Which of the following statements about the production of electricity using water (hydroelectricity) is true?
    - (a) It is very efficient because there are few steps in the process so most of the energy in the water is converted to electricity.
    - (b) Is very inefficient because most of the energy is lost as friction of the water against the penstock walls.
    - (c) Is very efficient because water is renewable.
    - (d) Is very inefficient because it is dependent of the available water.

26. Which of the following releases the least amount of carbon dioxide per unit of energy?
    - (a) Coal
    - (b) Oil
    - (c) Natural gas
    - (d) All of these produce the same amount of carbon dioxide

27. Antarctic research stations have started using solar photovoltaic cells to provide power. The best angle of these relative to the horizon would be:
    - (a) 0°
    - (b) 45°
    - (c) 66°
    - (d) 90°

28. Which of the following correctly shows the energy change in a photovoltaic cell (PV) and a solar oven

	PV cell	Solar oven
(a)	Solar → electricity	Solar → electricity
(b)	Solar → thermal	Solar → electricity
(c)	Solar → electricity	Solar → thermal
(d)	Solar → thermal	Solar → thermal

ISBN: 978-1-98-856632-0

29. A town's local thermal power plant is due to be replaced by solar PV and wind turbines. The power plant is rated at 80 MW and currently meets the needs of a town of 64,000 households (each household uses 30 kWh per day). The utilities to replace the power plant include solar PV cells and wind turbines rated at a maximum of 4 MW output with a diameter of 105 m, but these must be placed on hillsides remote from the town. The number of households is expected to grow by 2.5% every year for the next ten years. The cost of installing the wind turbines is about $1000 per kilowatt and the cost of installing the solar PV cells is about $1800 per kilowatt.

Electricity source	Hectares per megawatt
Coal	4.9
Gas	5.0
Solar (PV 90°)	17.6
Wind	28.6

- The energy produced by a photovoltaic cell can be approximated using the angle of the sunlight above the horizon.

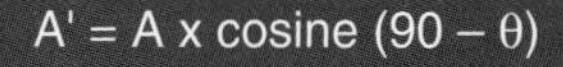

$$A' = A \times \text{cosine } (90 - \theta)$$

- A = the solar energy when the sun is directly overhead,
  A' = the amount of solar energy actually received,
  θ = the angle of the Sun in the sky at noon (0° = the horizon, 90° = directly overhead).
- This gives the maximum possible energy gain provided the solar panel is pointed directly at the Sun.

- The power available to a wind turbine can be calculated using the equation below.

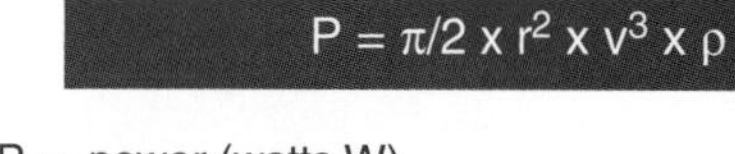

$$P = \pi/2 \times r^2 \times v^3 \times \rho$$

- P = power (watts W),
  r = radius of blades,
  v = wind velocity (m/s),
  ρ = air density (kg/m^3).
- The efficiency of the wind turbine depends on wind speed but is about 30%.

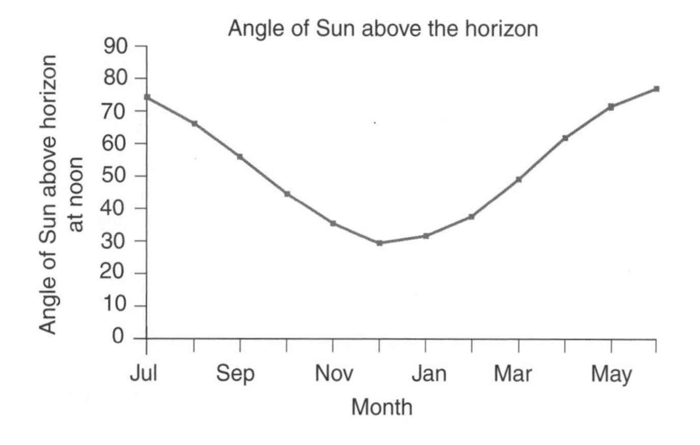

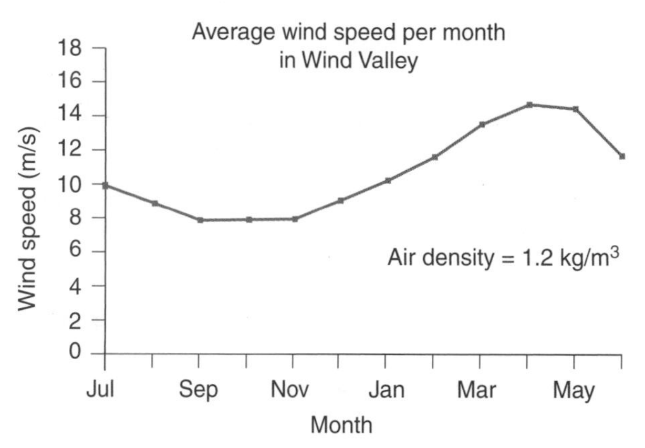

(a) Calculate the energy needs of the town now and in 10 years time: ____________________________________

(b) How is it best to power the town? What combination of solar and wind will meet the growing demands? You must factor in availability, efficiency, cost, and space needed for the new power supplies. Show your calculations and use them to justify the cost of installation. You may use extra paper if required. Attach any extra paper to this page.

ISBN: 978-1-98-856632-0

7. Atmospheric Pollution

Developing understanding

Content: This unit explores the sources and effects of air pollution. Air is a natural resource that crosses the boundaries of different ecosystems, so air pollution in one region is not confined but can spread to affect other regions. The Clean Air Act regulates the emission of air pollutants that affect health. These can come from natural sources or as a result of human activities. Once the sources of air pollutants are identified, measures can be taken to improve air quality.

Skills: This unit emphasizes skills in comparing and predicting patterns and trends in data and explaining how these illustrate environmental concepts. You will practice drawing conclusions based on data analysis and proposing evidence-based solutions to problems. An understanding of how environmental legislation is applied to achieve specific outcomes is central to this chapter.

7.1 Introduction to air pollution .... activity 116

☐ 1. Explain what is meant by air pollution. Identify types and sources of pollutants, both natural and those that result from human activities, such as the combustion of fossil fuels.

☐ 2. What is the role of the Clean Air Act and how is it administered? Describe its achievements and provide evidence to support your statements.

☐ 3. Describe evidence to illustrate the contribution of human activity to air pollution. What happens to air quality when human-generated sources of pollutants decrease?

☐ 4. List the air pollutants produced by the combustion of fossil fuels to include both gases and particulates. Distinguish between primary and secondary pollutants and their origins.

7.2 Photochemical smog .... activity 117

☐ 5. Describe the components of photochemical smog, its general causes, effects on health, and the environmental factors that affect its formation and severity.

☐ 6. In more detail than above, explain how the secondary pollutants that make up photochemical smog form in the presence of sunlight. Explain why levels of nitrogen oxides peak in the morning but ground level ozone peaks in the afternoon.

☐ 7. Identify the sources of VOCs in the atmosphere and explain their role in the formation of photochemical smog. Describe the effect of reducing the levels of nitrogen oxides and VOCs on levels of photochemical smog.

7.3 Thermal inversion .... activity 118

☐ 8. Describe the causes of thermal inversion and its effects on the normal temperature gradient through the atmosphere. Explain how thermal inversions trap pollutants and cause a deterioration in air quality.

7.4 Atmospheric CO_2 and particulates... activity 119

☐ 9. As you saw earlier, not all air pollution is the result of human activity. Describe natural sources of carbon dioxide and particulates in the atmosphere to include respiration, decomposition, natural combustion (wildfires), volcanic eruptions, and dust storms.

☐ 10. Volcanic activity and wildfires are natural sources of both gas and particulate air pollutants, sometimes in very extensive volumes. Describe some of the problems with the pollutants released during these natural events, including their effects of regions well outside the immediate zone of the event.

7.5 Indoor air pollutants........................ activity 120

☐ 11. Distinguish between outdoor and indoor air pollution. Identify the types and sources of common indoor air pollutants, distinguishing between gases and particulates, and between natural sources, human-made sources, and the products of combustion.

☐ 12. Conduct your own investigations of the particulate pollution in different regions of your school environment. Explain your results in light of the characteristics of the environment in the different regions you sampled.

☐ 13. Describe the characteristics of the natural pollutant radon. Explain how it enters indoor spaces, where it is most concentrated, and the effects of exposure on human health.

7.6 Reducing air pollution .... activities 121-122

☐ 14. Identify the three broad ways in which air pollution can be reduced and explain how each practice achieves its aims.

☐ 15. Identify some of the technological solutions to the air pollutants released by gasoline and diesel vehicles. Include reference to vapor recovery nozzles on gasoline pumps and catalytic converters in vehicle exhaust systems and explain how each of them works to reduce pollution.

☐ 16. Identify some of the technological solutions to the air pollutants released in industrial exhaust streams, including from coal-fired power stations. Include reference to electrostatic precipitators, and wet and dry scrubbers, and explain how each of them works to reduce pollution.

7.7 Acid rain .... activity 123

☐ 17. Explain what is meant by acid deposition. Describe its components and its causes, both natural and anthropogenic (human-made).

☐ 18. Describe the effects of acid deposition on the environment, including on soils, water bodies, living organisms, and human-made structures. Explain why the impact of acid deposition can vary regionally depending on local geology.

7.8 Noise pollution .... activity 124

☐ 19. Explain what is meant by noise pollution and describe human activities that cause it. How is noise level evaluated and what is important about its scale of measurement.

☐ 20. Describe the effects of noise pollution on human health and on the animals in natural ecosystems. Explain how noise pollution can interfere with the sensory systems animals use to communicate, hunt, and navigate.

116 Introduction to Air Pollution

Key Question: What components make up air pollution and where does it come from?

Air pollution is defined as the presence of compounds in the air at levels that pose a health risk. Some natural processes, including volcanic eruptions and wildfires, contribute to air pollution, but human activity is the main cause. Air pollution tends to be concentrated around areas of high population density because transportation and industrial processes are common sources of pollutants. Air pollutants can be divided into primary and secondary pollutants. **Primary pollutants** (e.g. vehicle exhaust gases) are emitted directly from the source. **Secondary pollutants** (e.g. acid rain) form in the atmosphere when primary pollutants react with atmospheric components. Air pollution occurs indoors too. Enclosed spaces such as cars, homes, schools, and offices may have higher levels of harmful air pollutants than the air outdoors.

Types and sources of air pollutants

Air pollutants can be either gases or particulates (solids suspended in the air). Some pollutants, such as smoke, are a mix of both. Different types of air pollutants have different levels of toxicity. Some common ones, and their sources, are shown below.

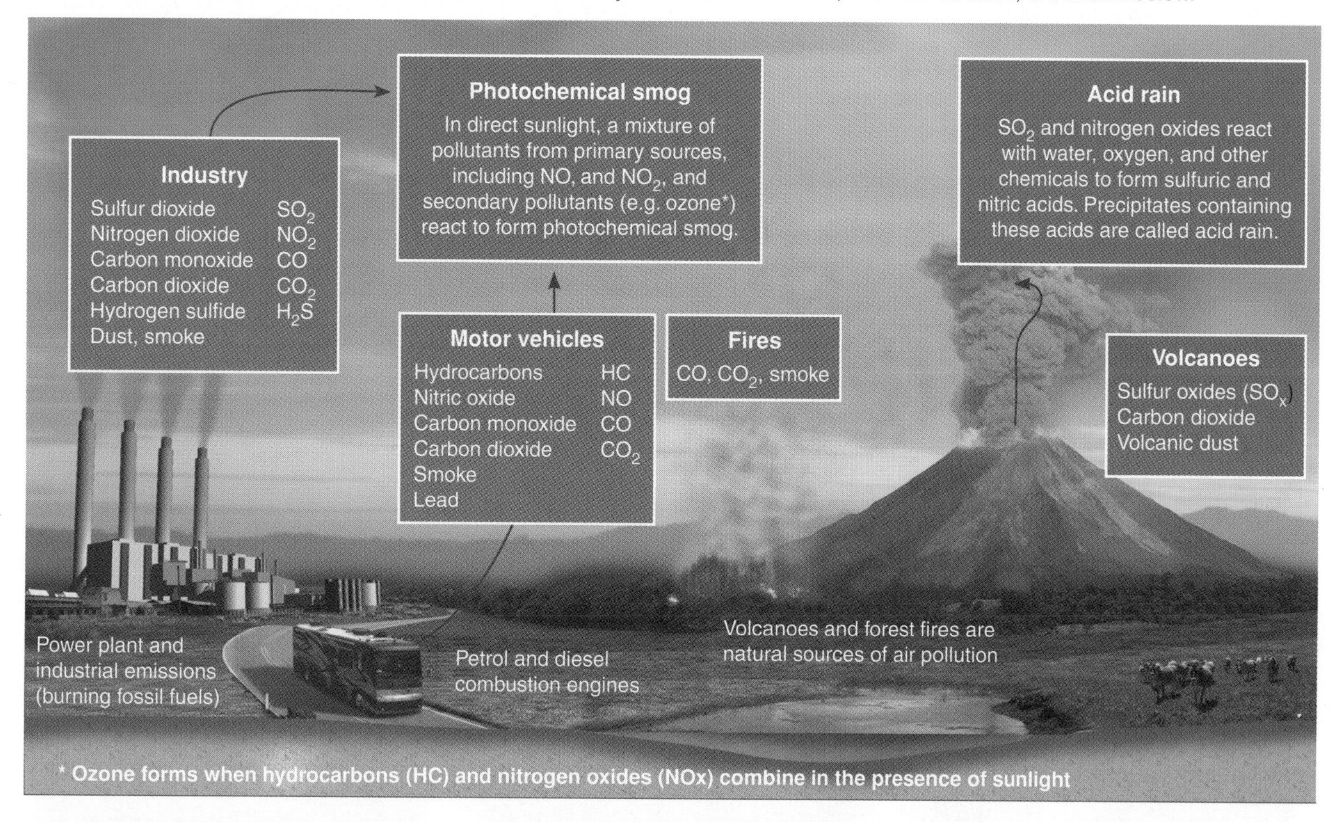

Fossil fuels (e.g. coal) are burned to make electricity, power industrial processes, and fuel vehicles. Coal-fired power stations (above) generate over 30% of the world's electricity and contribute significantly to air pollution. When coal is burned (a process called combustion) pollutants (carbon dioxide, sulfur dioxide, nitrogen oxides, toxic metals, and particulates) are all released into the atmosphere.

Wknight94 cc 3.0

Many fossil fuels contain sulfur impurities. When they are burned, the sulfur is oxidized to sulfur dioxide. Coal-fired power stations as well as volcanic eruptions (above) release large quantities of sulfur dioxide and this can affect air quality and contribute to acid rain. Sulfur dioxide can cause coughing, wheezing, or a shortness of breath when breathed in. Long term exposure causes respiratory illness.

More people own private vehicles than ever. Vehicles are a large contributor of air pollutants, so the level of air pollution from vehicles has been increasing. Cars produce carbon monoxide, hydrocarbons, and nitrous oxides. These pollutants contribute to poor air quality and are linked with numerous health issues. Improved technologies are helping to reduce these harmful emissions.

ISBN: 978-1-98-856632-0

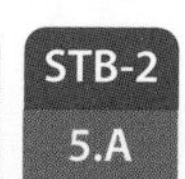
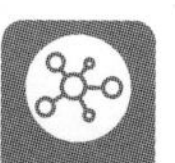

The Clean Air Act

- The Clean Air Act (1963) is a United States federal law designed to control air pollution on a national level. The act is administered by the Environmental Protection Agency (EPA). It has undergone a number of amendments since it was first introduced.
- One of its achievements has been banning the use of lead in gasoline in on-road vehicles. Lead, as tetraethyl lead (TEL), was added to gasoline to improve engine performance.
- In the late 1940s, it was discovered that lead from gasoline was accumulating in the environment. Researchers found that TEL was harmful to humans even at low levels. Children are especially at risk of lead poisoning because their brains are still developing and this makes them more sensitive to the effects of lead.
- In 1973, the EPA began reducing the level of TEL in gasoline and it was banned in the US in 1996.
- The use of lead in other products (paints, cans, pipes) has also been banned. The major sources of lead emission today are from ore and metal processing and emissions from lead-containing aviation fuel.

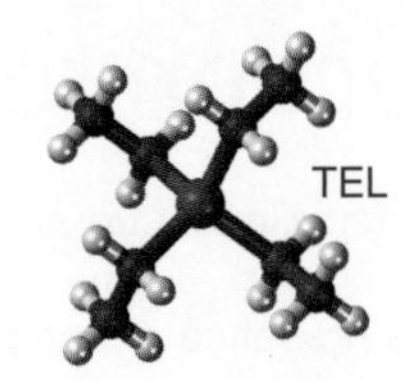

ymto public domain

Lead air quality (1980-2014)
Annual maximum 3-month average

Lead concentration ($\mu g/m^3$)

0, 2, 4, 6, 8, 10

National standard $15 \mu g/m^3$

1980, 1982, 1984, 1986, 1988, 1990, 1992, 1994, 1996, 1998, 2000, 2002, 2004, 2006, 2008, 2010, 2012, 2014

Source US EPA

1. Describe the difference between primary pollutants and secondary pollutants and give examples of each:

2. Why does air pollution tend to be highest in and around cities?

3. What is the purpose of the Clean Air Act?

4. (a) Describe the trend in atmospheric lead since 1980:

   (b) What do you think have been the main contributors to this trend? Explain your reasoning:

   (c) Explain why there is still lead in the atmosphere:

ISBN: 978-1-98-856632-0

How did Covid-19 help reduce air pollution levels?

- At the beginning of 2020, a pandemic was declared as the Covid-19 virus spread throughout the world. Many countries went into lockdown to stop its spread, and millions of nonessential workers stayed at home for several weeks or months. The graph below shows the effects of the lockdown on levels of the air pollutant PM 2.5 in 10 major cities.
- PM 2.5 (Particulate Matter 2.5) refers to particles or droplets in the air that are 2.5 microns or less in diameter. PM 2.5 is produced by vehicles, from operations where fuels such as wood, heating oil or coal are burned, and from forest and grass fires. Fine particles also form from the reaction of gases or droplets in the atmosphere from sources such as power plants.
- Particulate matter is harmful because it can be inhaled into the lungs. Long term exposure can cause cardiovascular and respiratory (breathing) diseases as well as increasing the risk of lung cancer.
- In many cities it is common to see people wearing face masks to protect themselves when air pollution levels are high (right).

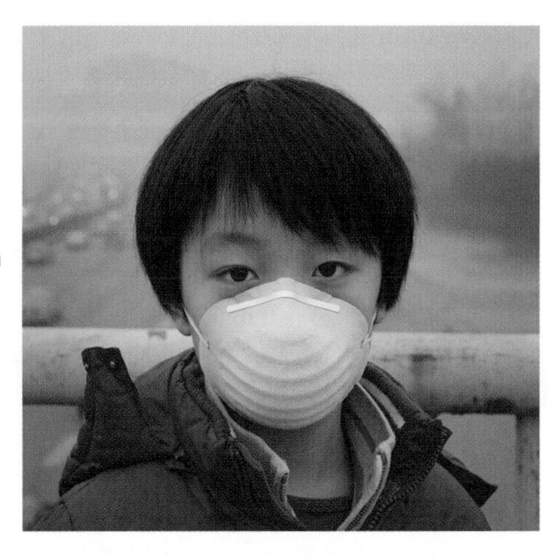

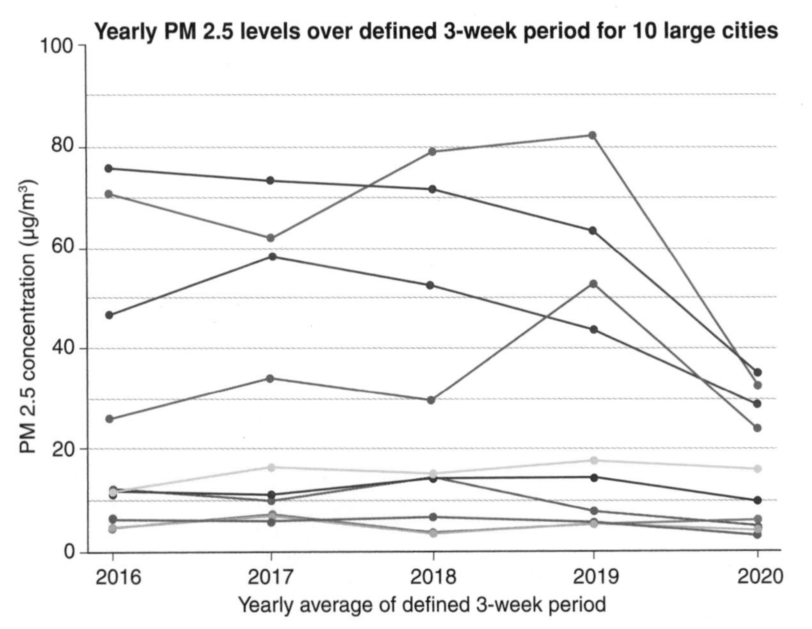

Key	City	Date	Shift
●	Seoul	26 Feb – 18 Mar	↓ -54%
●	Wuhan	3 Feb – 24 Feb	↓ -44%
●	Mumbai	23 Mar – 13 Apr	↓ -34%
●	Delhi	23 Mar – 13 Apr	↓ -60%
●	Rome	9 Mar – 30 Mar	↓ -19%
●	Madrid	23 Mar – 13 Apr	↓ -11%
●	London	23 Mar – 13 Apr	↓ -9%
●	Sao Paolo	23 Mar – 13 Apr	↓ -32%
●	New York	23 Mar – 13 Apr	↓ -25%
●	Los Angeles	23 Mar – 13 Apr	↓ -31%

Adapted from IQAir (2020) COVID-19 air quality report.
*Note that Rome and Madrid track very closely until 2019-2020

5. (a) Study the graph of PM 2.5 levels above. Briefly describe the general trend between 2019 and 2020:

____

____

____

(b) Suggest what caused this trend: ____

____

____

____

(c) Predict what you think would have happened to air pollution levels when the lockdown ended: ______________

____

____

(d) From this study, suggest one way in which large cities could reduce their level of air pollution: ______________

____

____

____

ISBN: 978-1-98-856632-0

117 Photochemical Smog

Key Question: What causes photochemical smog? What are its effects and how can we reduce it?

Smog (a joining of the words **sm**oke and f**og**) is a type of air pollution. There are two types of smog: winter smog and summer smog. Summer smog is also called photochemical smog and forms mainly in the warmer months. Nitrogen oxides (NO_x) from vehicle emissions or pollutants from coal fired industrial processes react in the atmosphere in the presence of sunlight to form the secondary pollutants that make up photochemical smog. This is a serious problem in many large cities around the world and it can cause many health problems. It mainly affects the respiratory (breathing) system. Emphysema, asthma, chronic bronchitis, lung infections, and cancers are caused by, or made worse from, exposure to photochemical smog. Eye and nose irritation, birth defects and low birth weights are also linked to prolonged exposure to photochemical smog.

Smog day and sunny day (Fanhe, China)
Tomskyhaha CC 4.0

How does photochemical smog form?

- The largest contributor to photochemical smog is vehicle emissions (exhaust fumes). Photochemical smog tends to form in the morning in large cities because vehicle emissions are high as a result of large numbers of people traveling to work.
- The nitrogen oxides produced by the car engines enter the atmosphere where, in the presence of sunlight, they react with volatile organic compounds (VOCs), specifically hydrocarbons, to form photochemical smog (diagram below). VOCs are found in the atmosphere as a result of human activity (e.g. burning fossil fuels) and from naturally occurring processes (e.g. produced by plants as signaling molecules). A feature of VOCs is that they have a high vapor pressure resulting from a low boiling point. This feature causes VOCs to evaporate (liquid → vapor) or sublimate (solid → vapor) at room temperature (so they easily form vapor).
- Nitrogen oxides may also react with sunlight to produce single oxygen atoms (O). These then combine with molecular oxygen (O_2) to produce ozone (O_3). Whereas NO_2 levels peak in the morning, ozone production peaks in mid-late afternoon after the morning exhaust fumes have had time to react in the sunlight. The ozone in photochemical smog is called ground level ozone because it is located relatively close to the ground. This distinguishes it from stratospheric ozone, which is formed naturally when sunlight energy splits molecular oxygen (O_2 + sunlight → O + O then O + O_2→ O_3). Ground level ozone is regarded as a pollutant. Other chemicals present in photochemical smog are nitric acid, aldehydes, and PANs (peroxyacyl nitrates).

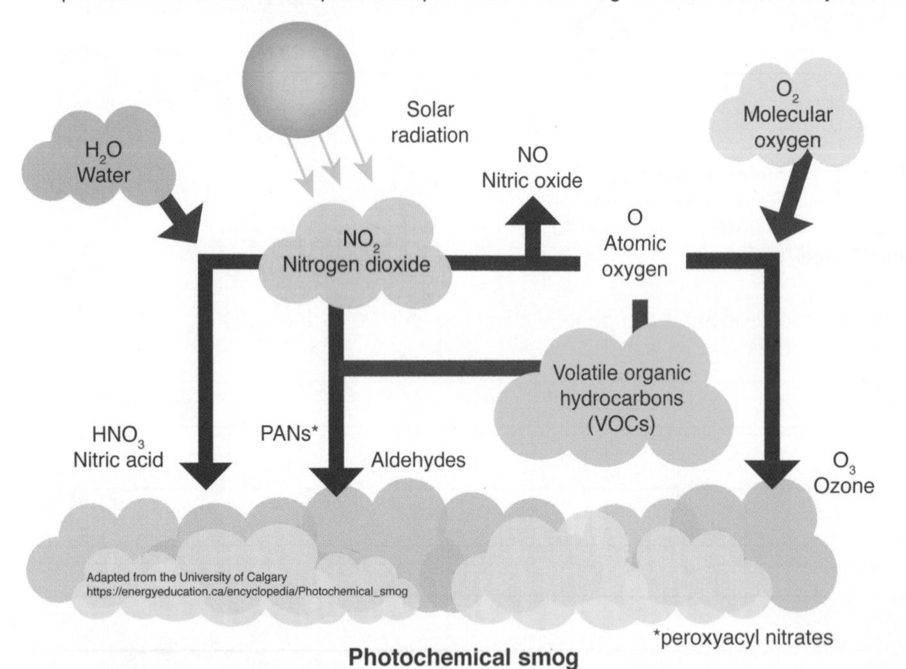

*peroxyacyl nitrates

Photochemical smog

Photochemical smog over Mexico, 2010
Fidel Gonzalez cc 3.0

1. Suggest why most cities experience lower levels of smog in the weekend compared to weekdays: __________________

2. Use the diagram above to outline how nitrogen oxides form the air pollutants in photochemical smog: __________________

ISBN: 978-1-98-856632-0

118 Thermal Inversion

Key Question: What is a thermal inversion and what is its relationship with air pollution?

As you saw in chapter 4, atmospheric temperature decreases with increasing altitude. For example, the temperature at sea level is higher than at the peak of a tall mountain. Temperature inversion is the opposite of this, in which a layer of warm air sits on top of a layer of cooler air. The layer of warm air is called the inversion layer. When it forms over a city, smoke and other air pollutants can be trapped under it. Pollution can then become concentrated because it cannot rise to a higher altitude and be dispersed. A concentration of pollutants under a thermal layer may cause health issues.

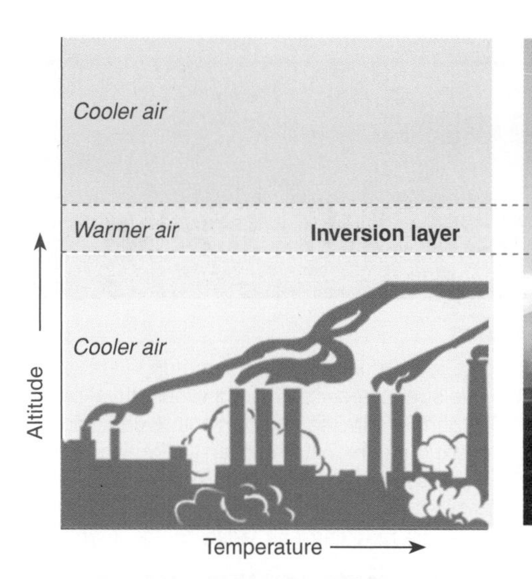

Rising smoke (arrowed) is trapped by the inversion layer in Lochcarron, Scotland.

How do thermal inversions form?

- During the day, energy from the Sun heats up the Earth's surface. Heat is slowly released from the land and the warm air rises because of its lower density. As it rises, the warm air cools and becomes more dense. It falls back towards the ground and displaces warm air closer to the ground generating a convection (heat transfer) motion.
- At night, with no sunlight to continue to heat the Earth's surface, the ground becomes cool. On a clear night, cooling can happen very quickly. As it cools, the ground takes the heat from the air close to it, cooling the air closest to the ground. The ground layer of air is now cooler than the layer of air above it and a thermal inversion is formed. Fog often forms at the base of the inversion layer. The thermal inversion is usually corrected when the Sun rises and begins to reheat the Earth's surface.
- The example described above is called a ground inversion, but turbulence, subsidence, and frontal inversions are possible too.
- The inversion layer acts as a type of cap, trapping pollutants and stopping them from being dispersed. The increased concentration of pollutants can cause respiratory and other health effects. One study in Hanoi City (Vietnam) showed that hospital visits for respiratory and cardiovascular problems increased significantly when thermal inversions were present.

1. Why do pollution levels increase when a ground inversion layer is present? ______________________________

____

____

2. In the space below draw two simple diagrams (representations) showing a profile of relative temperature change through the atmosphere under normal conditions and when there is a thermal inversion present. Label layers as appropriate:

ISBN: 978-1-98-856632-0

119 Natural Causes of Air Pollution

Key Question: What are some of the natural sources of carbon dioxide and particulates in the atmosphere?

Natural processes and activities can cause air pollution. Natural sources are small contributors to total air pollution levels, but they can have significant impact in the short term, often within a localized region. Carbon dioxide and particulate matter are two natural pollutants of significance. Their natural sources are described below.

Natural sources of carbon dioxide and particulates

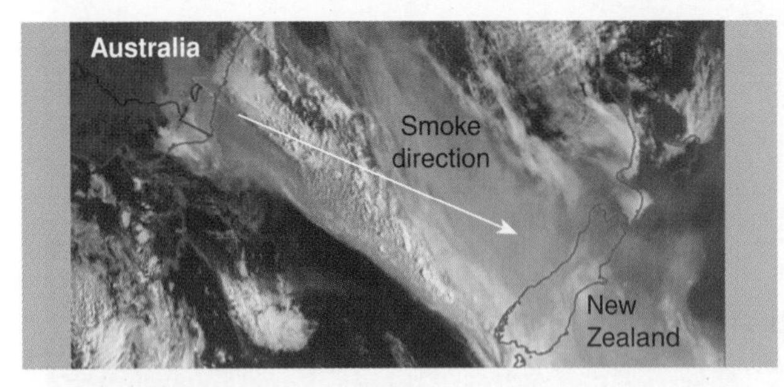

Wildfires and bushfires

Wildfires (bushfires) are large uncontrolled fires. They can be started by lightning strikes, although many start as a result of human actions. As they burn, they release large amounts of CO_2, smoke, and particulates into the air. Regions close to the fires are most affected by the pollutants, but winds can carry smoke large distances. Smoke from the 2019-2020 Australian bushfires affected air quality in New Zealand, 2,000 km away.

Dust storm in Iraq

Dust (sand) storms

Dust storms (also called sandstorms) are common in areas with low precipitation levels (e.g. deserts). Strong winds drive loose particles of sand into the air, increasing particulate pollution. Some dust storms are huge, measuring over 1.6 km high. The Sahara Desert has always experienced dust storms, but they have increased 10 times as much since the 1950s. Dust from a large storm in the Sahara may carry as far as central Europe.

Sarychev Peak erupts in 2009. Air traffic was disrupted.

NASA

Volcanic eruptions

Volcanic eruptions release a number of pollutants including sulfur dioxide, hydrogen chloride, carbon dioxide and ash (particulate matter). Once it enters the atmosphere, volcanic emissions can be carried very long distances. The material from an eruption can cause respiratory problems, eye injuries and even death. People wear masks and protective gear to stay safe.

Decomposing apple

SallyV CC4.0

Metabolic processes

Living organisms carry out some metabolic (biochemical) processes that release carbon dioxide into the atmosphere. Both plants and animals carry out cellular respiration, a process used to generate energy. Carbon dioxide is a by-product of this reaction. During decomposition organic substances are broken down into smaller molecules. Carbon dioxide is released as a result of this.

How do we know what gases are produced by volcanoes?

- Specialist equipment is used to measure the quantity and composition of gases emitted from a volcano.
- Measurements can be ground based (an instrument is located on the volcano) or remote (measurements are made by from the air using aircraft or satellites).
- The information collected can tell us if the levels of gases around a volcano (and its surrounding area) are safe for humans.
- The photo on the right show a multiGAS measuring instrument on the crater of Mount St. Helens (USA). It measures water vapor, carbon dioxide, sulfur dioxide, and hydrogen sulfide in gas plumes.

Peter Kelly, USGS

1. Why do you think natural sources contribute only a small amount to total long term air pollution? ______________________

____

____

2. When might researchers use remote methods to measure volcanic emissions? ______________________

____

____

ISBN: 978-1-98-856632-0

120 Indoor Air Pollution

Key Question: What are indoor air pollutants and what effect can they have on health?

Often, when we think of air pollution, we think of problems we see outside, such as smog in cities. However, air pollution can also occur indoors when pollutants accumulate inside homes, schools, workplaces, and vehicles. Pollutants can concentrate quickly inside so that the air indoors can contain higher concentrations of pollutants than outside. There are many sources of indoor air pollution (below) and many have harmful health effects if present in high enough concentrations. Indoor pollutants can be human-made or natural, and the type of air pollutants present differs depending on a building's use (e.g. commercial or domestic). Indoor pollution varies between countries depending on income level and technological development. Indoor pollution is generally a bigger problem in low income countries where open fire is used to cook indoors.

Common indoor pollutants in our homes

Mold and mildew can grow in poorly ventilated spaces. Inhalation of these can cause breathing problems, including asthma.

Tobacco smoke contains particulate matter and dozens of toxic products including formaldehyde, carbon monoxide, hydrogen cyanide, and nitrogen oxides. Many countries have banned smoking indoors to stop non-smokers being exposed to second-hand smoke.

Open fires are commonly used for cooking and heating in developing countries. Homes are often poorly ventilated, so smoke, particulates, and CO can reach very high levels. Even in developed countries, gas cookers and heaters release CO, NO_2, and particulates.

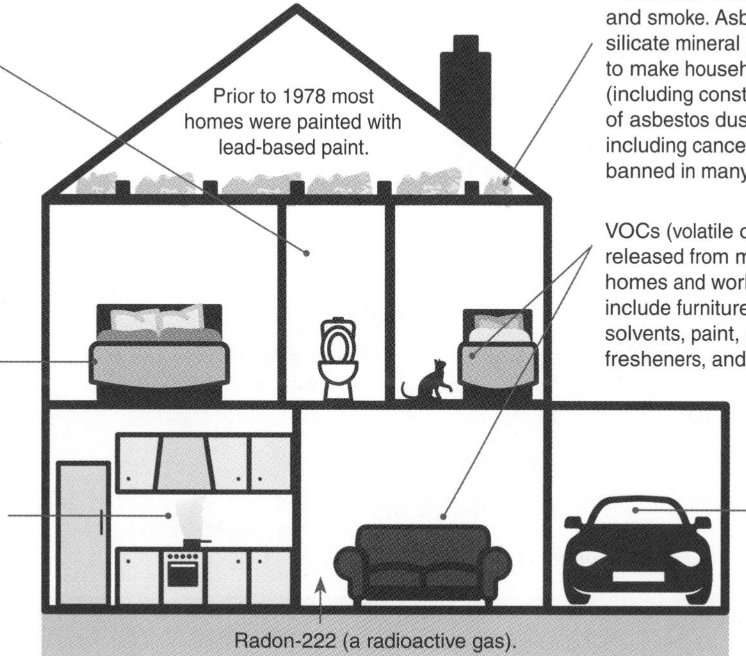

Particulate material includes asbestos, dust, and smoke. Asbestos is a human-made silicate mineral product and was widely used to make household and industrial products (including construction materials). Inhalation of asbestos dust causes lung diseases, including cancer. It is still used in the US, but banned in many other countries.

VOCs (volatile organic compounds) are released from many products found in our homes and workplaces. Common sources include furniture, carpets, cigarettes, solvents, paint, glue, cleaning products, air fresheners, and photocopiers.

Sulfur dioxide and carbon monoxide (CO) are present in car emissions. Breathing in high concentrations of CO reduces oxygen availability to cells. CO is an asphyxiant (deprives someone of oxygen).

Radon-222

Radon-222 is a naturally occurring radioactive gas. It is produced as an intermediate product when uranium decays to lead. It is present in soils and rocks, and mostly enters buildings from the soil through small cracks and spaces in a building's walls or foundations. It may be present in groundwater too. All buildings contain some radon, but levels are highest in lower levels (e.g. basements). In normal circumstances, radon is the single largest contributor to a person's background radiation dose.

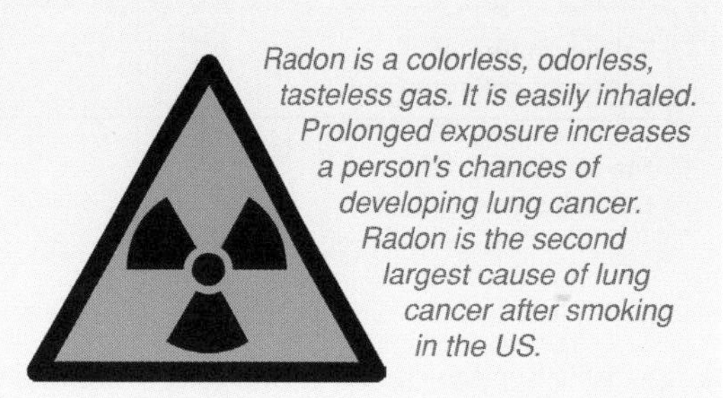

1. A list of indoor pollutants is provided below. Categorize their source as human-made, natural, or products of combustion. *Radon, carbon monoxide, dust, mold, asbestos, smoke, VOCs, nitrogen oxides, formaldehyde, mildew.*

Human-made	Natural	Combustion

2. Explain why a person could be exposed to high levels of radon without knowing it: ______

ISBN: 978-1-98-856632-0

3. Suggest why premature deaths from indoor air pollution are higher in developing countries than in developed countries:

INVESTIGATION 7.1: Measuring particulates in air

See appendix for equipment list.

Work in pairs or small groups to investigate the amount of particulate matter present in your school environment. Each group should test a different area of the school. Sampling areas could include hallways, stairwells, library, cafeteria, classrooms, administration area, nurse's office, or just inside the main building entrance. Place at least one air trap outside as a comparison.

1. Write your sampling location on the back of a piece of grid paper (14 squares x 14 squares). Measure the size of 1 square and record it below in the yellow cell.
2. Make an air trap by attaching the grid paper to a piece of thick card or a plastic plate using tape or binder clips. Make sure that the grid squares are not obscured when you attach it to the backing.
3. Use a plastic knife or a spatula to evenly cover the grid with a relatively thick layer of petroleum jelly (e.g. Vaseline®). Make sure that you can still see the grids.
4. Take your air trap to your sampling site. You can either attach it to a wall with tape or Blu-tack, or leave it on a flat surface (e.g. table). Place a note next to it stating this it is an experiment in progress, please do not touch!
5. After 24 hours go back and collect your sampling card.
6. Use a stereomicroscope or hand held magnifying glass to count the number of particles collected. Record your results and the results of other groups in the table below.
   Note: If a particle spans two or more squares, only count it once.

	Sampling location						
1 square =							
Total number of particles collected							
Mean number of particles per square							

4. (a) Which indoor area had the lowest number of particles?

   (b) Which indoor area had the highest number of particles?

   (c) Suggest a reason for the these results:

   (d) How did the indoor results compare to the outdoor results? Give a possible explanation for any differences:

ISBN: 978-1-98-856632-0

121 Reducing Air Pollution

Key Question: What methods can be used to reduce air pollution and are they effective?

In the US, the Clean Air Act was amended in 1970 to limit emissions from stationary and mobile sources (vehicles). At the same time, the National Ambient Air Quality Standards (NAAQS) were established. The purpose of this was to address the public health and welfare risks posed by widespread air pollutants. Other major amendments occurred in 1977 and 1990. New standards meant that ways had to be developed to reduce emissions. These generally fall into three categories; regulatory practices, conservation practices, and the use of alternative fuels.

Marc St. Gil EPA public domain

USDE Public Domain

Regulatory practices

The US Environmental Protection Agency (EPA) establish health-based national air quality standards for common pollutants. Each state is responsible for implementing strategies to achieve these standards. For toxic pollutants or acid rain, the EPA may also monitor compliance in addition to setting limits. The image above shows a factory in Houston burning car batteries in 1972. The EPA shut this factory down in 1975.

Conservation practices

Reducing or conserving the use of fossil fuels reduces air pollution. There are a number of ways to achieve this:

- Riding a bicycle or walking instead of traveling in a vehicle.
- Using public transport or carpooling to minimize vehicle emissions.
- Using energy efficient light bulbs and appliances, and turning off lights and appliances when they are not in use conserves electricity.

Alternative energy and fuel sources

Many processes still rely on combustion of fossil fuels, which is a major source of air pollutants. Solar cells, hydroelectricity, and wind farms produce electricity without emitting pollutants. Alternative fuels, called biofuels, can be used to replace gasoline in vehicles. Biofuels are made from renewable food crops such as corn or soya, or cellulose (e.g. forestry waste). Their use reduces air pollutant emissions, but reduces crop biomass available as food, and it can drive up the price of food.

1. Explain the role of the US EPA in reducing air pollution levels: ______________________

____

____

____

2. Why do you think it is important to use a combination of all three practices described above to reduce air pollution?

____

____

____

____

3. The graph on the right shows levels of atmospheric NO_2 in the US between 1980-2018. Use this data to evaluate the success of national initiatives to reduce NO_2 pollution:

____

____

____

____

____

____

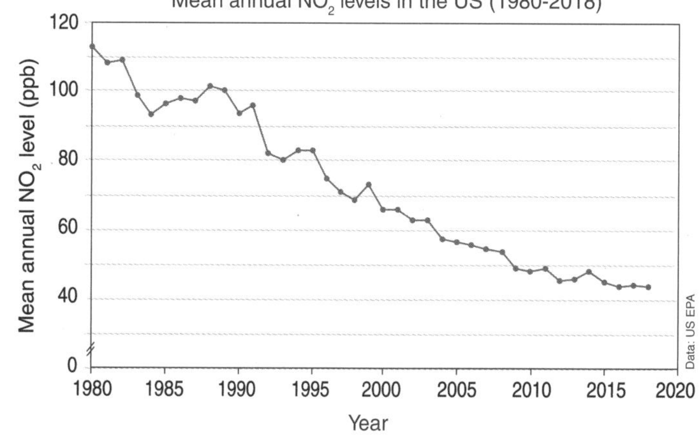

ISBN: 978-1-98-856632-0

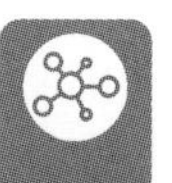

122 Using Technology to Reduce Air Pollution

Key Question: How can technology be used to reduce air pollution and how effective are the different options?

Ideally, stopping or limiting the production of emissions is the best way to deal with air pollution. Another way is to remove the pollutants at the source before they can be released into the atmosphere. There are many ways technology is currently used to reduce air pollution and to help maintain acceptable standards of air quality.

Reducing air pollutants associated with industry

Industrial processes produce a large number of different pollutants, so a number of methods are often used to clean up their gas discharges. Electrostatic precipitators and scrubber systems are both commonly used to remove contaminants from coal burning power plants, although this is not their only use. For example, electrostatic precipitators are used to sample biological airborne particles, such as viruses, for analysis, capture, and inactivation. Similarly, wastes collected from scrubbers can have commercial value (e.g. limestone-based scrubbers in coal-fired power plants can produce synthetic gypsum for use in drywall manufacture).

Electrostatic precipitators

- An electrostatic precipitator (ESP) is a filtration device that removes fine particles, such as dust and smoke, from an exhaust gas stream before it is released to the environment.
- An ESP uses static electricity to remove particles from a gas stream (see the diagram, right).
- During the process, the "dirty gas" passes through two electrodes. One of the electrodes is negatively charged. Smoke particles in the gas obtain a negative charge as they pass by it.
- A second electrode is positively charged. When the negatively charged dust particles in the gas pass by, they are attracted to the positively charged electrode and stick to it.
- Once the gas has passed through both electrodes it is "clean" and can be discharged.
- The method is very effective, removing 99% of particulate matter from a waste gas stream.

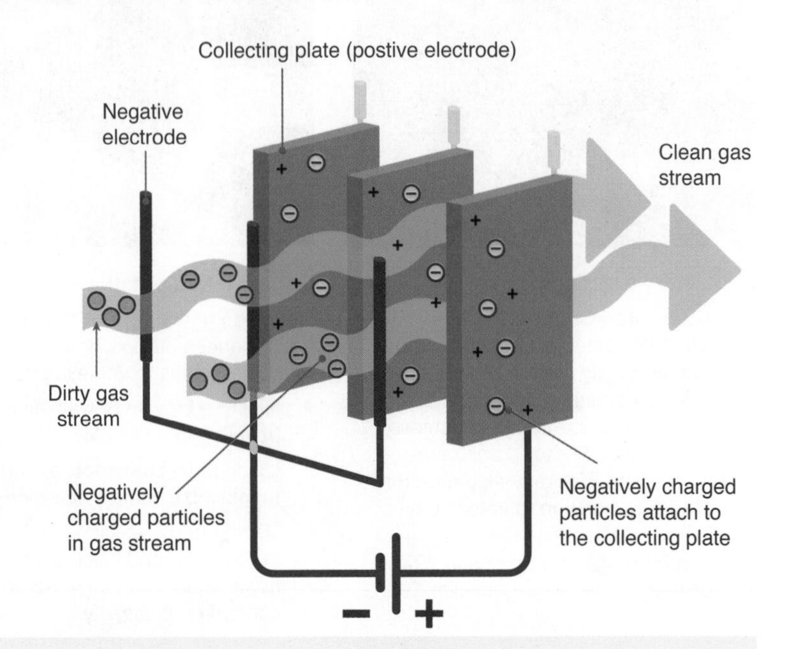

Scrubber systems

Scrubber systems are used to remove particulates and/or gases from industrial gas flue streams. There are two general types, wet scrubbers and dry scrubbers. Wet scrubbers saturate the waste stream with moisture to remove particles, whereas dry scrubbers typically use dry reactants to clean the gas stream. In both systems, the captured waste must be safely disposed of.

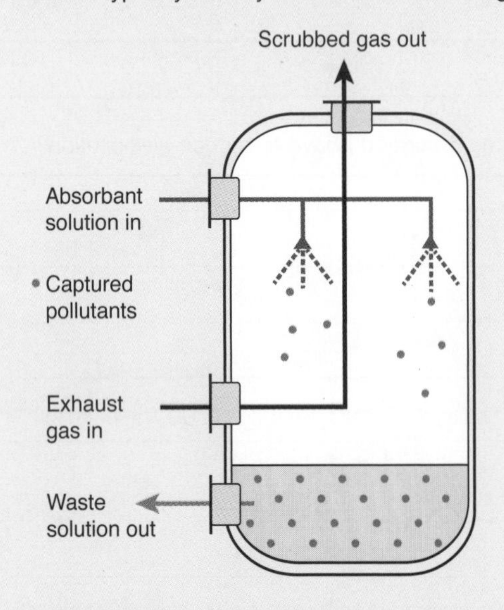

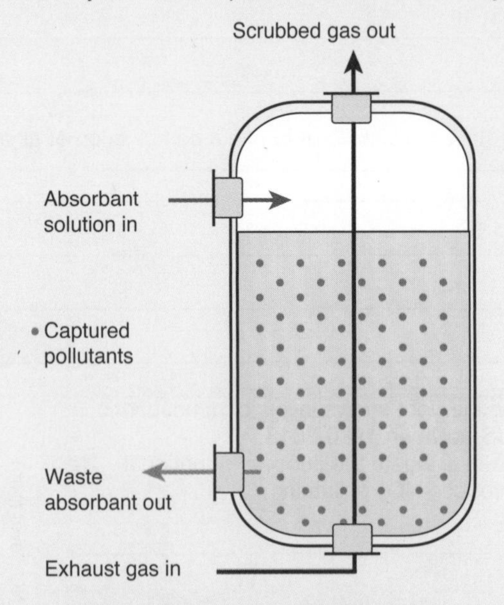

Wet scrubbers remove pollutants from gas flue streams by spraying liquid onto the gas. The water spray collects the dust and particulate matter, and it falls to the bottom of the scrubber. The clean gas stream is passed out.

Advantages: • Can handle moist streams • Good SO_2 removal • Cools hot gases • Handles flammable dusts safely.

Dry scrubbers work in a similar way to wet scrubbers, but spray fine (usually dry) absorbent reagents to remove pollutants. Dry scrubbers are often used to remove acids from combustion sources.

Advantages: • Can neutralize corrosive gases • Cost effective • Spent media can be a source of revenue.

ISBN: 978-1-98-856632-0

Reducing air pollutants associated with vehicles

In big cities, vehicles are a major contributor to air pollution levels. Recall earlier that when the number of vehicles on the roads dropped during the Covid-19 lockdowns, air pollution fell significantly. It makes sense to try to reduce air pollution produced by vehicles as much as possible. Two common methods are described below.

Vapor recovery nozzle

Vapor guard prevents vapors escaping into the environment.

Holes in the nozzle capture gasoline vapors, and the vapor is returned to the storage tank. The hose nozzle makes a tight connection with the fill pipe on the vehicle's fuel tank.

Gasoline vapors accumulate in vehicle fuel tanks above the liquid level. When the tanks are filled, the rising liquid forces these vapors to rise, the vapors flow around the nozzle into the air. Today, vapor recovery nozzles are fitted to gasoline pumps to recover (capture) the vapors. Vapors are drawn in through holes in the side of the nozzle and travel through special hoses back to the main storage tank. The system is highly effective, preventing the escape of around 95% of gasoline vapors.

Catalytic converter

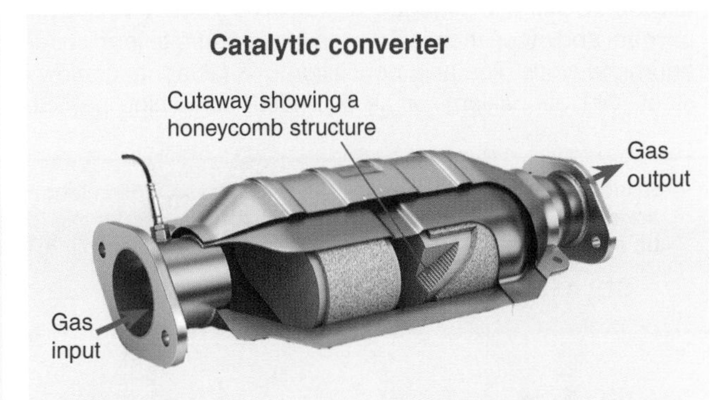

Catalytic converters are devices in the exhaust systems of gasoline and diesel fueled cars. The incomplete combustion of fuel and the reaction of nitrogen at high temperature with oxygen produces hydrocarbons and harmful gases (CO and NOx). Metal catalysts in a catalytic converter convert these into less harmful products through a series of reduction-oxidation (redox) reactions.

Oxidation reactions: Carbon monoxide (CO) is oxidized and converted to carbon dioxide (CO_2). Oxygen combines with hydrocarbons to produce water and carbon dioxide.

Reduction reaction: Nitrogen oxides are reduced to nitrogen gas (inert) and oxygen gas.

1. Briefly summarize how electrostatic precipitators and scrubber systems work to clean up gas streams:

2. The graph on the right shows the effectiveness of scrubbers on removing sulfur dioxide produced by coal fired power plants.

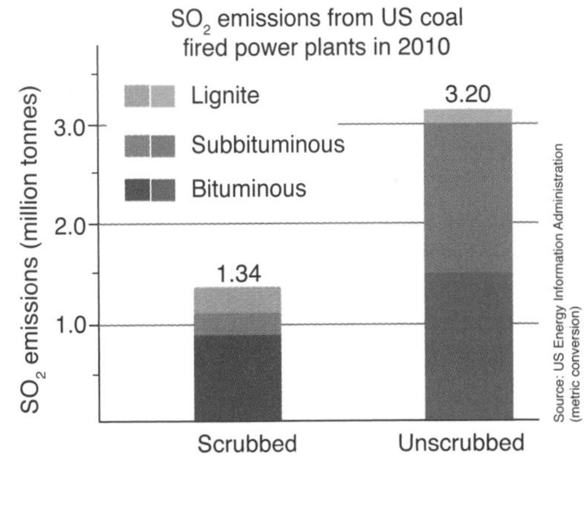

(a) The numbers at the top of each column show the total SO_2 emissions from three types of coal. Calculate the percentage decrease in SO_2 emissions when a scrubber is used:

(b) Based on your calculation, explain if you think scrubbers are an effective solution to reduce SO_2 emissions:

ISBN: 978-1-98-856632-0

123 Acid Rain

Key Question: How does acid rain form and how does it harm the environment?

Acid rain is also called acid deposition. It occurs when sulfur dioxide (SO_2) and nitrogen oxides (NO_x) react with water, oxygen, and other chemicals in the atmosphere to form sulfuric and nitric acids. The acid deposition can fall as rain, snow or sleet (wet deposition), or as dry, sulfur-containing particles.

A small proportion of the SO_2 and NO_x that contributes to acid rain is from natural activity (e.g. volcanoes), but most comes from human activity (below). Pollutants formed in one region can be carried long distances by wind, and fall as acid deposition somewhere else. For example, emissions from the US produce acid deposition in Canada, and activities in China cause acid rain in Japan.

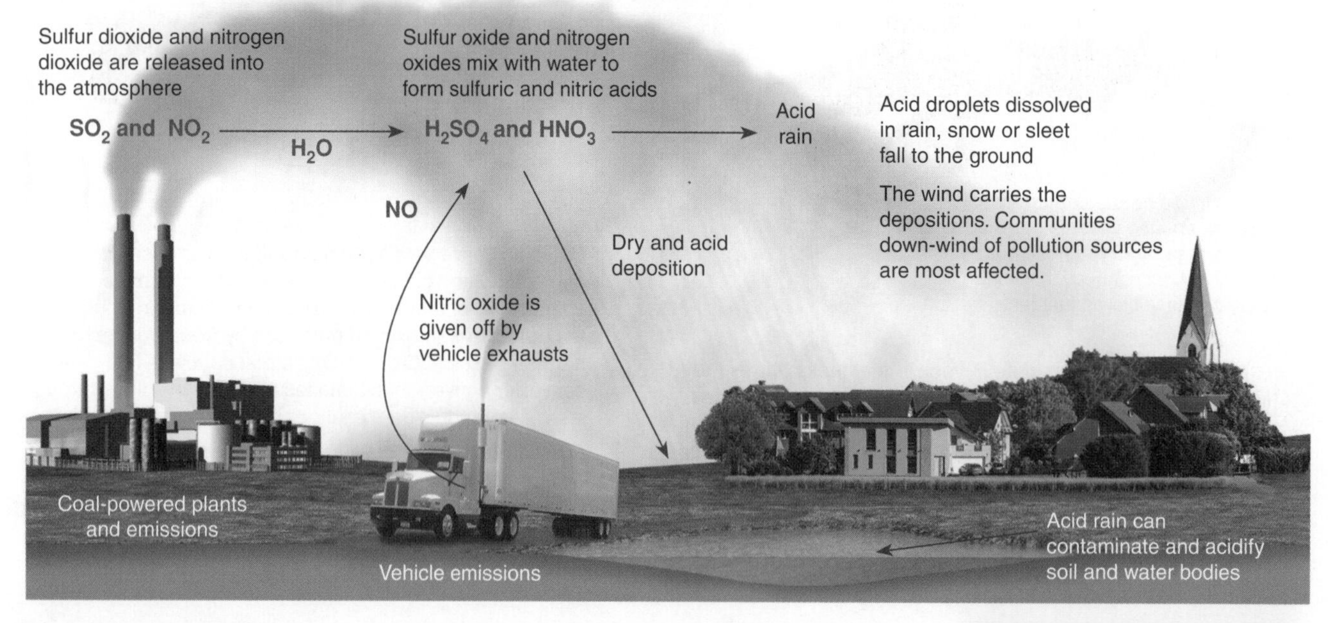

What does acid rain do?

Acid rain damages human-made structures and natural systems.

- Many historic buildings and statues are made from marble or limestone and are dissolved due to chemical weathering over time when they come into contact with acid rain. The damage to buildings and monuments can be serious.
- Acid rain acidifies land and water, and can harm natural systems. As acidic water flows through soil, aluminum (toxic to plant growth) in clay is mobilized, and nutrients and minerals are transported into waterways. The waterways become more acidic and many organisms cannot tolerate the changes. For example, it is common to see large numbers of dead or dying trees in areas affected by acid rain, and the young of many animal species are often harmed by lower pH or higher aluminum levels. At higher elevations, acid fog can damage trees, leaving the leaves dying or dead and no longer able to photosynthesize.
- Some areas are more sensitive to the effects of acid rain than others. Resistance depends on the amount of alkali material present in soil and bedrock. Regions with bedrock containing fewer alkali components are less able to reduce acidity than regions with a higher level of alkali components.

This statue's facial features have been dissolved by acid rain.

Dead trees caused by acid fog.

1. The pH of some common substances are shown below.

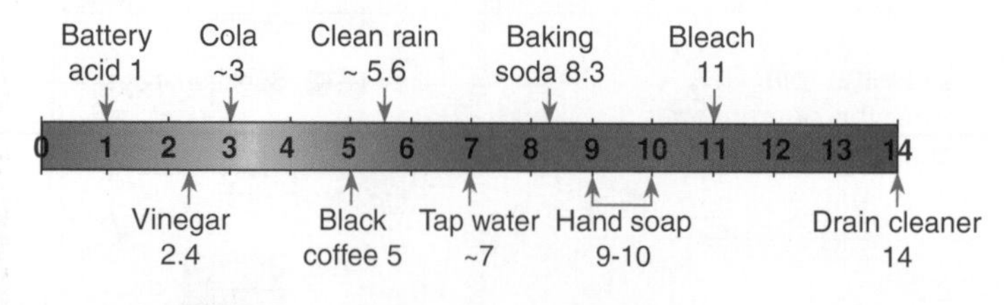

(a) What do you think the pH of acid rain might be? ____________________

(b) Now research and write down the actual pH of acid rain. Was your guess right? ____________________

2. Explain why acid rain affects regions that are a considerable distance from the source of the pollutants: ____________________

____

____

____

ISBN: 978-1-98-856632-0

124 Noise Pollution

Key Question: What are the sources of noise pollution and how does noise pollution harm humans and other animals? Not all pollution is caused by chemicals. Have you ever found it hard to get to sleep because a neighbor is having a loud party or you can't study because of roadworks? These are examples of noise pollution. Noise pollution is defined as any unwanted or disturbing sound that is at a level high enough to cause physiological stress or hearing loss. As the human population has grown, so has the amount of noise we make, so the harm caused by noise pollution is more widespread.

Sources of noise pollution

Urban areas are noisy places. Noise pollution can be hard to escape because it comes from many sources. Transportation, sirens, construction, road works, industrial activity, and domestic and leisure activities all create noise pollution. This can lead to stress, insomnia and in some cases mental illness.

Noise can still be a problem away from cities. Farm machinery can produce constant low frequency noise. This can be dangerous to the person controlling the equipment and irritating to people further away. This bird scarer (above) produces a very loud irregular bang, which can startle people and livestock.

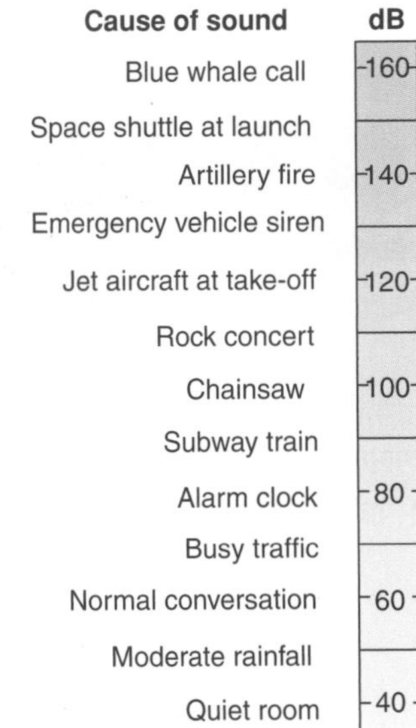

Noise pollution can damage an animal's hearing and affect its ability to communicate, hunt, and find mates. In some instances migratory routes are altered. Many bird species avoid noisy areas on their migration routes. Their migration route, and sometimes their final destination, may be altered.

Ship's engines, oil drills, and sonar devices create noise pollution in the ocean. Sonar can be as loud as 235 decibels and travel long distances underwater. It interferes with the echolocation and communication of whales, making it difficult for them to navigate, and may cause strandings.

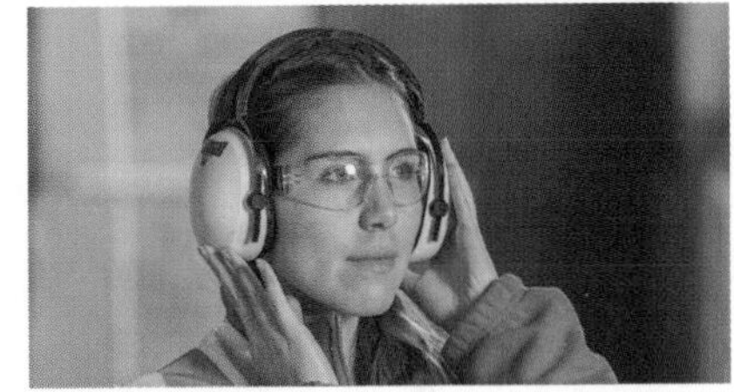

Sound is measured in decibels (dB). It is a logarithmic scale, so 30 dB is 10 times more powerful than 20 dB. Sounds over 85 dB can cause noise induced hearing loss (NIHL). Protective equipment (ear plugs or ear muffs) are worn by people working in high risk situations to protect their hearing.

1. (a) In your classroom, or at home, sit for five minutes and identify any sources of noise pollution you can hear:

___

___

___

(b) Choose one example from your list and then do some research to find out how it could be harmful to (i) humans or (ii) other animals. Describe the evidence supporting a claim of harm (or no harm if this applies):

___

___

___

___

___

ISBN: 978-1-98-856632-0

125 Personal Progress Check

Answer the multiple choice questions that follow by circling the correct answer. Don't forget to read the question carefully!

1. Which US Government agency is responsible for implementing and monitoring the Clean Air act?:
   (a) National Oceanic and Atmospheric Administration (NOAA)
   (b) United States Geological Survey (USGS)
   (c) United States Department of Agriculture (USDA)
   (d) United States Environmental Protection Agency (US EPA)

2. The Clean Air Act was first passed in:
   (a) 1963
   (b) 1965
   (c) 1977
   (d) 1990

3. Most air pollution is the result of:
   (a) Volcanic eruptions
   (b) Burning fossil fuels
   (c) Wild fires
   (d) Mining activity

4. Pollutants emitted directly from a source are called:
   (a) Primary air pollutants
   (b) Secondary air pollutants
   (c) Photochemical smog
   (d) Acid rain

5. Pollutants formed through reactions in the atmosphere are called:
   (a) Primary air pollutants
   (b) Secondary air pollutants
   (c) Photochemical smog
   (d) Acid rain

6. Pollution hanging over urban areas that causes reduced visibility is called:
   (a) Air pollution
   (b) A temperature inversion
   (c) Smog
   (d) Light pollution

7. The image above is showing:
   (a) Acid rain
   (b) Smog
   (c) Low cloud
   (d) A thermal inversion

8. The pattern of air layers in a thermal inversion is:
   (a) Warm-cold-colder
   (b) Warm-cold-warmer
   (c) Cold-warm-colder
   (d) Cold-warm-warmer

9. How is air pollution movement affected during thermal inversion?
   (a) There is no difference in its movement
   (b) Pollution moves very slowly away from the affected area.
   (c) Pollution moves very quickly away from the affected area.
   (d) Pollution is drawn to the affected area.

10. The main health effect of photochemical smog is:
    (a) Eye irritation
    (b) Nose irritation
    (c) Birth defects
    (d) Breathing (respiratory) problems

11. Dust, ash and pollen are examples of which type of air pollutant:
    (a) Particulate matter
    (b) Ground level ozone
    (c) Nitrogen oxides
    (d) Smog

12. Which of these was banned from gasoline in the 1970s?
    (a) Cadmium
    (b) Arsenic
    (c) Mercury
    (d) Lead

13. An example of a primary pollutant is:
    (a) Photochemical smog
    (b) Ozone forming in the atmosphere
    (c) Nitrogen dioxide released by a car
    (d) Acid rain

ISBN: 978-1-98-856632-0

14. Which of the following is NOT a primary pollutant?
    (a) Sulfur dioxide
    (b) Nitric oxides
    (c) VOCs
    (d) Nitric acid

15. Which two molecules are the main components of acid rain?
    (a) Sulfuric acid and nitric acid
    (b) Nitric acid and VOCs
    (c) Sulfuric acid and carbon monoxide
    (d) Carbon monoxide and nitric acid

16. Acid rain can damage:
    (a) Drinking water
    (b) Buildings and monuments
    (c) Aquatic organisms
    (d) All of the above

The next two questions relate to the structure shown below.

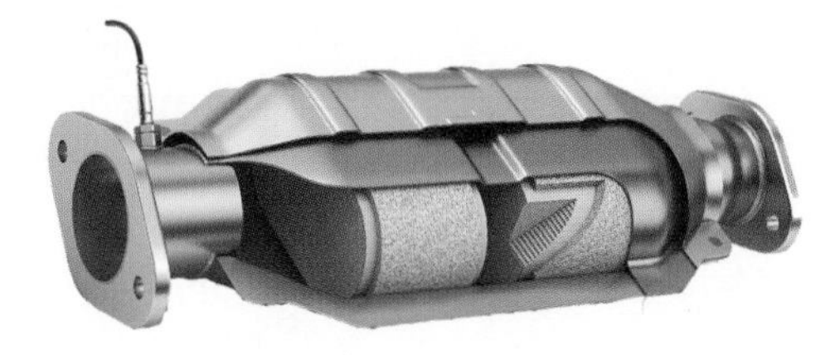

17. The image above is of an air pollution prevention mechanism found in vehicles. What is its name?
    (a) Electrostatic precipitator
    (b) Dry scrubber
    (c) Vapor recovery nozzle
    (d) Catalytic converter

18. Which pair of harmful pollutants present in car exhaust emissions does the structure above convert?
    (a) Lead and carbon monoxide
    (b) Carbon monoxide and nitrogen oxides
    (c) Carbon dioxide and particulates
    (d) Carbon monoxide and sulfur dioxide

19. Electrostatic precipitators remove which type of pollutant:
    (a) VOCs
    (b) Particulate matter
    (c) Carbon monoxide
    (d) All of the above

20. Scrubber systems capture:
    (a) Radioactive material from soil
    (b) Carbon monoxide from chimney flues
    (c) Particulate matter from gas streams
    (d) Particulate matter from water flows

21. Indoor air pollution is often a bigger problem in:
    (a) High income, technologically developed countries
    (b) Low income, technologically undeveloped countries
    (c) Densely populated countries
    (d) None of the above, it is the same in all countries

22. In developing countries the main source of indoor pollution comes from:
    (a) Pets
    (b) Mold and fungi growth
    (c) Presence of lead-based paint
    (d) Open sources of heating and cooking

23. This gas is colorless, odorless, and decreases the body's ability to transport oxygen:
    (a) Carbon monoxide
    (b) Carbon dioxide
    (c) Radon
    (d) Nitrogen dioxide

24. This decay product of uranium is a common indoor pollutant:
    (a) Polonium-218
    (b) Lead-206
    (c) Radon-222
    (d) Thorium-230

25. After cigarette smoking the next largest cause of lung cancer in the US is:
    (a) Prolonged exposure to asbestos
    (b) Prolonged exposure to carbon monoxide
    (c) Prolonged exposure to radon
    (d) Prolonged exposure to particulate matter

26. How many times more powerful is a noise with a 100 dB rating than a noise with a 50 dB rating?
    (a) 10 times
    (b) 1000 times
    (c) 10,000 times
    (d) 100,000 times

27. At or above this decibel level, hearing loss can occur:
    (a) 25 dB
    (b) 55 dB
    (c) 85 dB
    (d) 115 dB

28. High levels of noise pollution can:
    (a) Alter the migration patterns of birds
    (b) Disorient whales causing them to beach
    (c) Make animal communication more difficult
    (d) All of the above

ISBN: 978-1-98-856632-0

29. Acid rain is harmful to many plant and animal species.
In this section, you will design an investigation to test the effect of acid rain on the growth of seedlings.

i. State the hypothesis for your experiment
ii. Describe the method you would use to test your hypothesis
iii. Identify dependent and independent variables, controlled variables, and experimental control.

NEED HELP? see Activity 175

Use the spaces below to plan and design your experiment. You can draw diagrams and use extra paper if needed.

ISBN: 978-1-98-856632-0

8. Aquatic and Terrestrial Pollution

Developing understanding

Content: This unit examines the types and impacts of pollutants arising from human activities. In this unit, you will come to understand how pollutants affect the environment and human health, and look at the role of legislation in reducing pollution and regulating water quality. Current environmental concerns globally include increasing generation of waste (including e-waste) and the emergence and spread of new diseases (including Covid-19).

Skills: This unit emphasizes skills in thinking critically about environmental problems and their potential solutions. Quantitative skills are important too, as applied to first or second-hand data.

8.1 Sources of pollution .... activity 126

☐ 1. Identify sources of pollution, distinguishing between point source and non-point sources of pollutants.

8.2 Human impacts of ecosystems activities 127 - 134

☐ 2. Describe how pollution affects organisms with different tolerance levels for pollutants, including corals.

☐ 3. Describe the sources and environmental impacts of different pollutants on aquatic environments. Include reference to oil spills, nutrient pollution and oceanic dead zones, heavy metal contamination of water bodies, ocean litter, sediment pollution, and pollution by methylmercury. Where appropriate, discuss the economic impact of pollution, including clean-up costs. Describe and explain oxygen sag curves for aquatic systems.

8.3 Endocrine disruptors .... activity 135

☐ 4. Explain types of endocrine disruptors, their sources, and their effects on the health of humans and other animals.

8.4 Human impacts on wetlands and mangroves .... activity 136

☐ 5. Recall the features of wetland ecosystems and the ecosystem services they provide. Describe the impacts of human activity on wetlands and mangrove ecosystems, including threats from commercial aquaculture development, pollution, construction of dams, and overfishing.

8.5 Eutrophication .... activity 137

☐ 6. Explain the causes and consequences of nutrient enrichment on aquatic ecosystems,. Describe the characteristics of eutrophication and how trophic state is categorized and identified (oligotrophic vs eutrophic).

8.6 Thermal pollution .... activity 138

☐ 7. Describe the causes and consequences of thermal pollution, including the effect of increased temperature on dissolved oxygen content. Recall how tolerance for abiotic factors varies for different species and apply this understanding to thermal tolerance.

8.7 Persistent organic pollutants .... activity 139

☐ 8. Describe the effects of persistent organic pollutants (POPs) on ecosystems. Include reference to their capacity for bioaccumulation and capability for long distance transport.

8.8 Bioaccumulation and biomagnification .... activity 139

☐ 9. Distinguish between bioaccumulation and biomagnification. What type of pollutants are most likely to accumulate in tissues and concentrate in food chains and why?

8.9 Solid waste disposal........................ activity 140

☐ 10. Describe methods for the disposal of municipal solid waste (MSW), including the design and features of sanitary municipal landfills. Explain problems with MSW disposal, including the accelerating problem of e-waste.

☐ 11. Describe the environmental effects of solid waste disposal with reference to waste disposal by incineration, problems with illegal dumping, and increasing ocean plastic pollution.

8.10 Waste reduction methods .... activities 141 - 143

☐ 12. Describe and evaluate changes to current practices that could reduce waste generation. Include reference to reusing and recycling materials (especially e-waste), composting, and landfill mitigation strategies.

8.11 Sewage treatment .... activity 144

☐ 13. Explain the crucial importance of sewage (wastewater) treatment. Describe best practices in sewage treatment including important features of primary, secondary, and tertiary treatment processes.

8.12 Lethal Dose 50% (LD_{50}) .... activity 145

☐ 14. What is meant by lethal dose 50% (LD_{50})? Explain how and why LD_{50} is used in the study of toxic substances.

8.13 Dose response curve .... activity 145

☐ 15. Explain the purpose of dose response curves and evaluate their use in providing information on a substance's toxicity.

8.14 Pollution and human health .... activity 146

☐ 16. Identify human health issues that are linked to pollution. Explain why cause and effect relationships can be difficult to establish for environmental pollutants that affect health.

8.15 Pathogens and infectious disease.................................. activities 147 - 151

☐ 17. Identify different types of pathogens, including viral, bacterial, protistan, and fungal pathogens. Explain how different pathogens cause disease, how they are transmitted, and factors important in how they cycle through the human population. Include reference to the diseases plague, tuberculosis, malaria, West Nile virus, SARS, MERS, Zika virus, cholera, and Covid-19.

☐ 18. Explain the role of socioeconomic factors and climate in the spread of disease and in the occurrence of endemic diseases such as malaria. Describe the role of vectors in the spread of disease and explain how patterns of disease occurrence may change as climate warms.

☐ 19. Evaluate the threat of emerging diseases with reference to the current Covid19 pandemic. What is the impact of pandemics on the environment and on global economies?

126 Sources of Pollution

Key Question: What is the difference between point source pollution and non-point source pollution?

Land and water can become polluted by human activities. Most pollution from human activity occurs in or around urban and industrial areas and regions of industrialized agriculture (below). Pollution sources may be categorized as **point source** or **non-point source**. Point source refers to a single, identifiable source of a pollutant (e.g. an effluent outfall) whereas non-point sources are diffuse and so can be harder to identify because they enter the environment via a number of routes. Pollution affects the physical, chemical, and biological components of ecosystems.

Human sources of land and water pollution

Point source pollution

Point source (PS) pollution is any contaminant that enters the environment from a single source. Factories and sewage treatment plants are two common types of point sources. Waste may be discharged through smokestacks, discharge pipes, or drainage ditches. Sometimes the waste (effluent) is discharged directly into the environment without treatment, and sometimes it is partly treated before being discharged. For example, sewage plants historically would complete a first stage treatment of human waste and discharge partially treated effluent into a river or the ocean. Failure of sewerage infrastructure, e.g. during heavy rain, is a common cause of point source discharge of untreated sewage. Point source pollution can be relatively easy to control because the source is easily identified.

Non-point source pollution

Non-point source (NPS) pollution comes from many different sources including land runoff, precipitation, atmospheric deposition, or seepage. As rainfall or snowmelt moves over and through the land it picks up pollutants and deposits them in a different place (often water bodies). Have you ever noticed colorful rings in a car park puddle after it has rained? This happens because the rain has run across the asphalt and the engine oil from cars collects in puddles. Other common pollutants include fertilizers, herbicides and insecticides, oil and chemicals from urban runoff, or sediment transported from eroded land. It can be much harder to find and control non-point source pollution.

1. Describe the causes and consequences of point source and non-point source pollution: ______________________

____

____

____

____

ISBN: 978-1-98-856632-0

127 Tolerance Range in Aquatic Communities

Key Question: How can species tolerance for pollutants be used as an indicator of environmental health?

The ability of species to survive within a certain range of abiotic factors also applies to environmental pollutants. One measure of ecosystem health is to measure the variety of organisms within the ecosystem. A high diversity of species indicates high environmental quality, low diversity equates to environmental stress. Certain species, called **i**ndicator species, are typical of ecosystems in a particular state of health (e.g. polluted or clean). Some species are sensitive to pollutants and will be absent even at very low pollutant levels. Other species can tolerate higher levels of pollutants.

Pollution tolerance

The diagram below shows the response of freshwater organisms to two different environmental factors: dissolved oxygen (dark blue line) and pollutant levels (red line). Note the change in the species assemblage in response to the changing concentration of contaminants with distance from the discharge. We will look at the effect of dissolved oxygen demand in another activity.

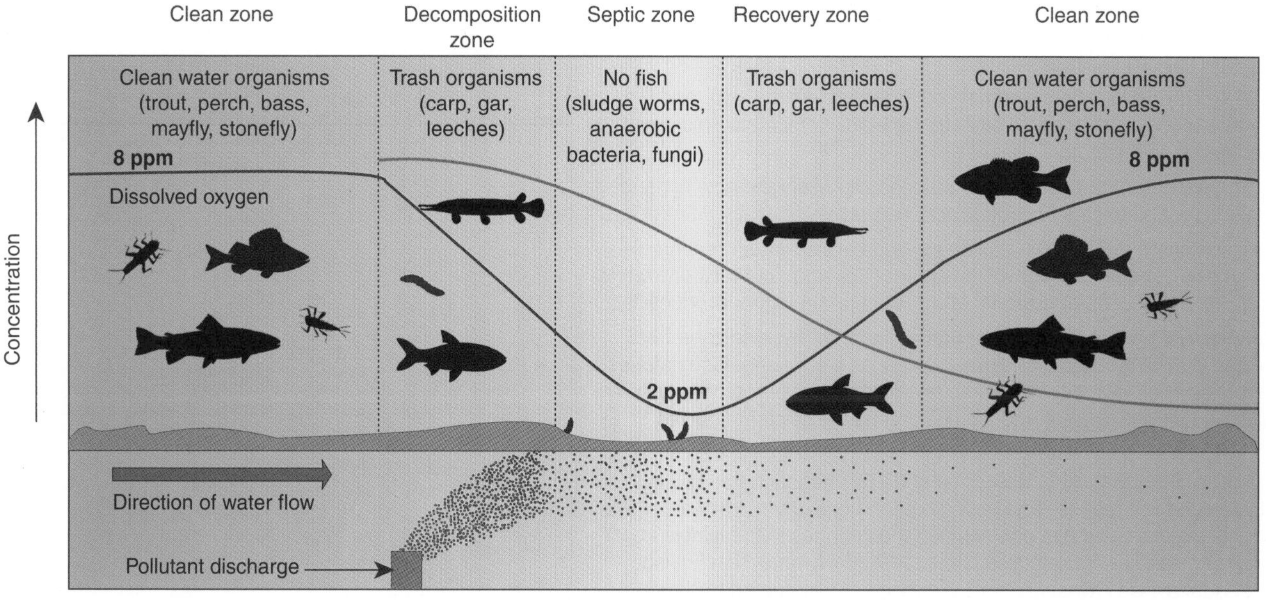

Coral reefs have tolerance levels too

- Coral reefs are colonies of marine invertebrates. Most corals have a symbiotic relationship with algae living within the coral structure. The algae supply the coral with 90% of its energy.
- Like any living organism, coral is affected by abiotic factors. If coral becomes stressed, the algae are expelled from the coral (coral bleaching). This makes the coral more vulnerable to other environmental stressors. Increased temperature, increased pollution, sediment run off, exposure to too much sunlight, and extreme low tides can cause coral bleaching. Destructive fishing practices (e.g. trawling and dredging) break pieces off the reef causing damage.

1. Use the diagram above to explain why there is a change in species composition when a pollutant enters a water body:

____

____

____

____

____

2. What does coral bleaching indicate about the environment in which the coral is growing? _______________

____

____

____

ISBN: 978-1-98-856632-0

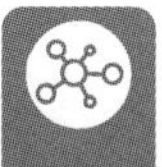

Case study: The Clean Water Act and ecological recovery

In 1948, regulations were passed to control the discharge of pollutants into water bodies in the US. In 1972, the act underwent significant changes and became known as the Clean Water Act (CWA). The CWA governs water pollution in the US.

The Illinois Waterway is a case study for the positive ecological effects of environmental legislation. The Illinois Waterway is an extensive area consisting of Lake Michigan and several rivers (right). It experienced prolonged degradation as a result of two events. The first was when the 45 km Chicago Sanitary and Ship Canal opened in 1900. The canal carried sewage away from Chicago's water supply (Lake Michigan) so the water supply would not be polluted. This was achieved by reversing the flow of the Chicago River so instead of flowing into Lake Michigan, it followed the canal into the Des Plaines River and finally emptied into the Illinois River. The second event was the introduction of common carp into the Illinois River in 1887.

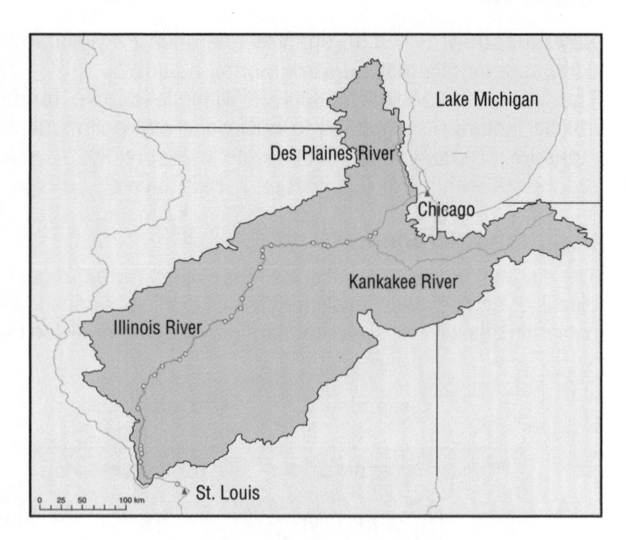

In 1908, commercial fish yield peaked at record levels. Carp made up more of the catch than all other fish species combined. This was attributed to two factors:

- The water that previously drained into Lake Michigan now expanded the river floodplains providing more habitat.
- The effluent discharges depleted oxygen in the water creating a hypoxic zone near the discharge point (Chicago), but further away it had a beneficial "fertilization" effect, generating higher productivity.

However, as the floodplains were drained and the hypoxic zone from sewage discharge began to expand, changes were seen. Fish catches fell and species diversity measures revealed higher proportions of pollution-tolerant species and the disappearance of other species. These measures indicated unhealthy waterways.

The Long-Term Electro-Fishing Project (LTEF) began in the 1950s. It was designed to monitor and understand the ecology of the waterways. Its longevity means it has documented the changes in the Illinois Waterway after the introduction of the CWA. Early analysis showed water quality was lowest closest to Chicago and improved further away. Near Chicago, species diversity measures were lower and the proportion of invasive fish relative to native fish was higher.

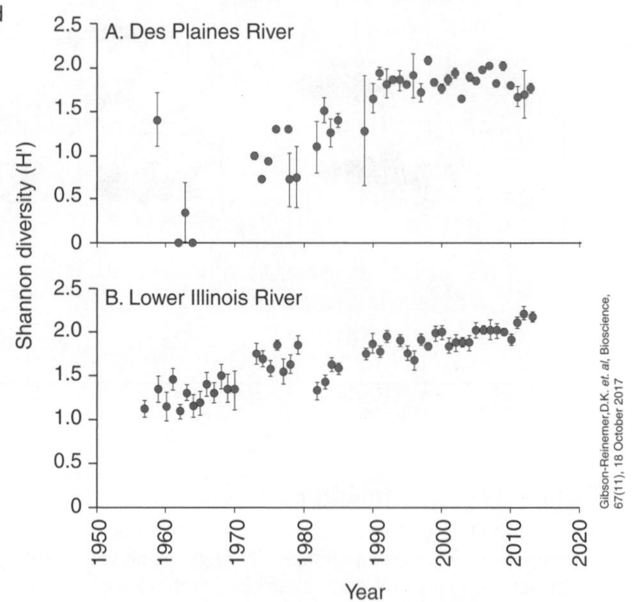

Above: Species diversity measures (Shannon index) in the Des Plaines River (A) and Lower Illinois River (B) from 1957-2013. Error bars = standard error.

The CWA forced authorities to improve water quality. In 1983, the Tunnel and Reservoir Plan was implemented to comply with CWA standards. It created a huge network of bedrock tunnels to capture sewer overflow so it could undergo secondary wastewater treatment. Previously this material would have been released into the Illinois Waterway untreated. The positive effects of this treatment plan were recorded in the LTEF project results (right). Today the carp population is greatly reduced and species richness and diversity measures have improved as a result of the improved water quality.

3. (a) Explain why water quality was lowest closest to Chicago: ______

   (b) How was this was reflected in the aquatic communities of the Illinois Waterway? ______

4. Explain how the application of environmental legislation has had a positive effect on the ecology of the Illinois Waterway: ______

ISBN: 978-1-98-856632-0

128 The Environmental Effects of Oil Spills

Key Question: What are the effects of oil spills on marine life and how do we quantify them?

The 2010 Deepwater Horizon oil spill in the Gulf of Mexico was the biggest and most disastrous oil spill in US history. It released 780,000 m^3 of oil into the Gulf, affected thousands of kilometers of shoreline, and killed tens of thousands of marine and estuarine organisms. The oil killed marshland plants and coastline erosion has increased substantially as a result. Ten years on from the disaster, the spill's long term environmental and economic effects are still being evaluated.

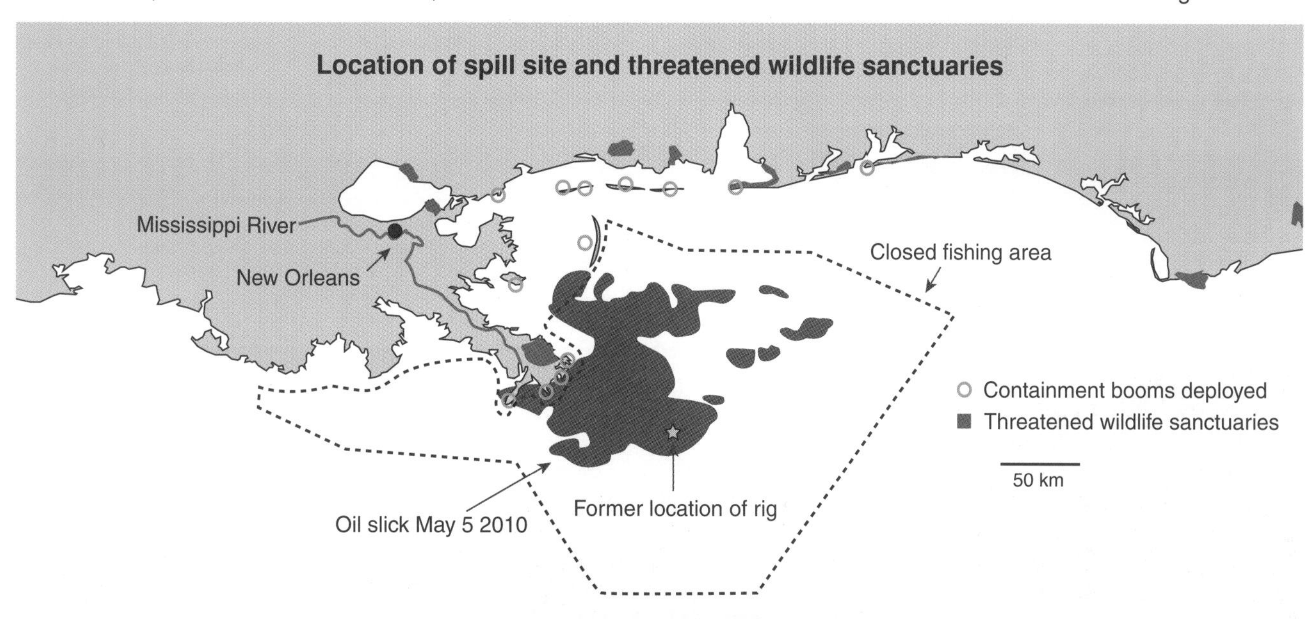

Effects of oil in estuaries and wetlands

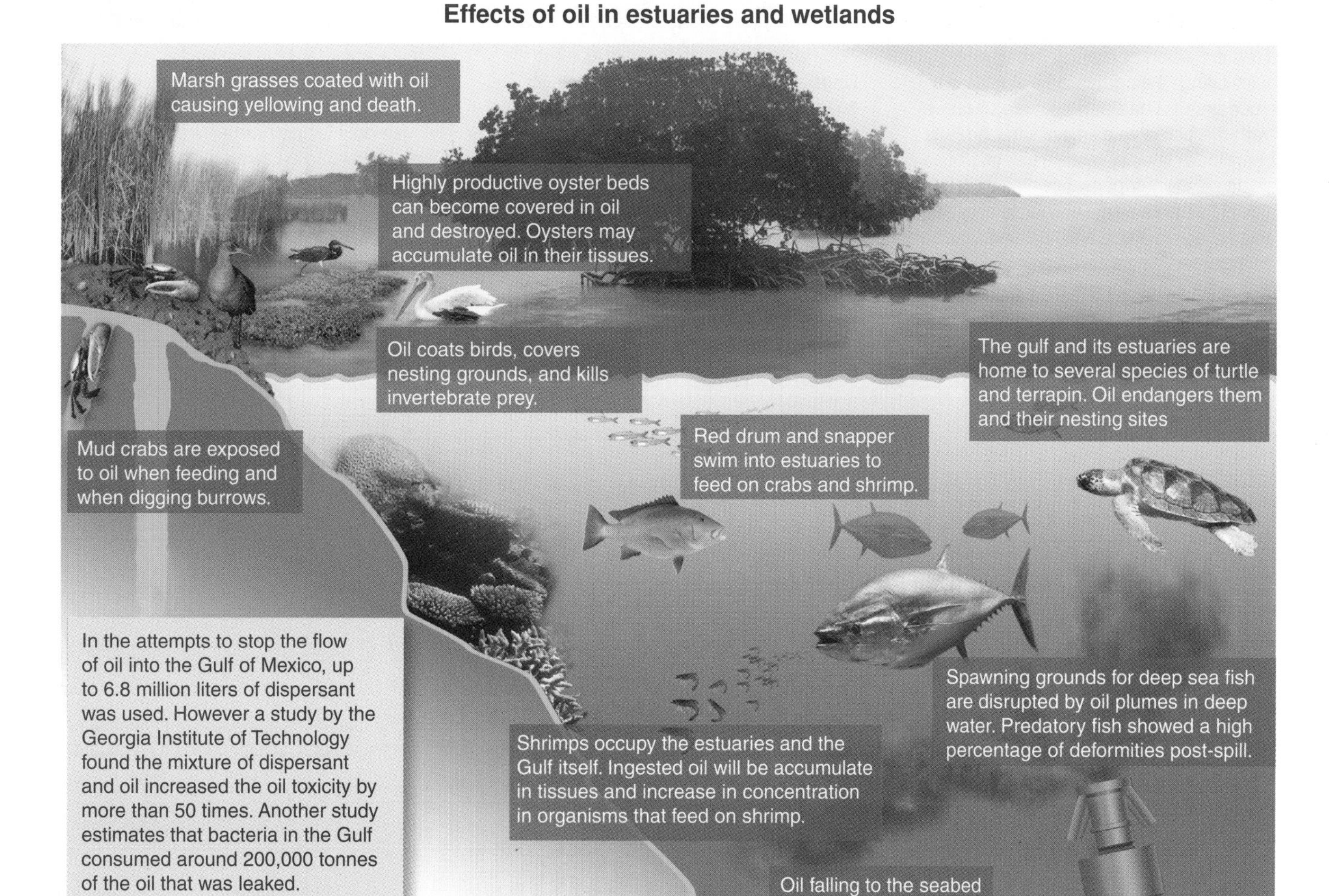

Since the oil spill in April 2010, clean-up teams and researchers have collected data on the affected shorelines of Louisiana, Mississippi, Alabama, and Florida. Approximately 1770 km of shoreline showed oiling, with 354 km heavily oiled. Tarballs continue to wash ashore. Most of the impact has been on marine species, with the effects of petroleum toxicity, dispersant toxicity, and oxygen depletion causing the main damage. A NOAA study in 2012 indicated severe long term environmental effects, including the death of deep sea corals and ongoing effects on the health and reproduction of marine species.

ISBN: 978-1-98-856632-0

Ecosystem recovery time

Historical studies show that the rate of ecosystem recovery after an oil spill depends on the habitat, local climate and environmental conditions (such as temperature), and the type of oil spilled. To compare, the Deep water Horizon spill released 780 million L.

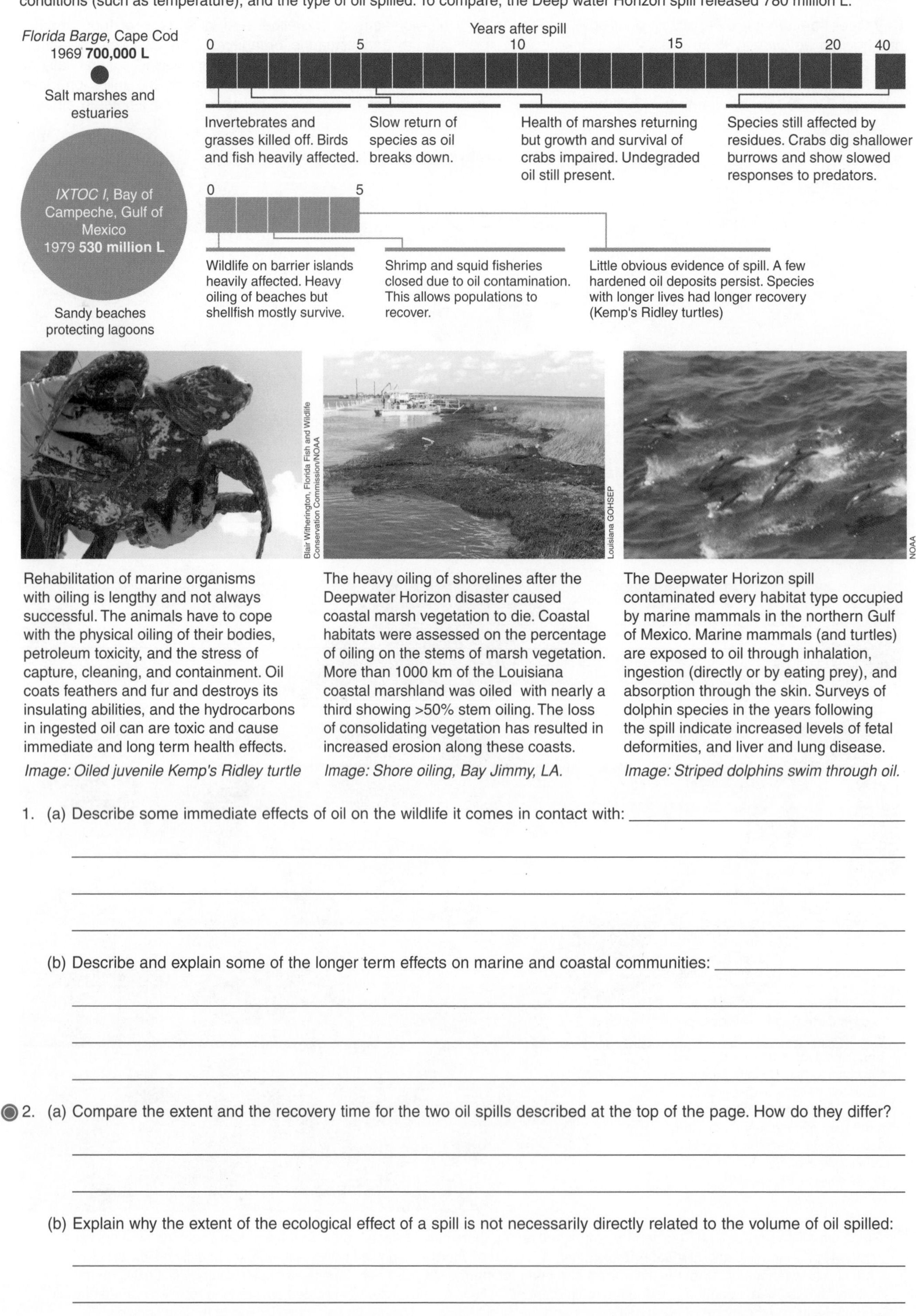

Rehabilitation of marine organisms with oiling is lengthy and not always successful. The animals have to cope with the physical oiling of their bodies, petroleum toxicity, and the stress of capture, cleaning, and containment. Oil coats feathers and fur and destroys its insulating abilities, and the hydrocarbons in ingested oil can are toxic and cause immediate and long term health effects.

Image: Oiled juvenile Kemp's Ridley turtle

The heavy oiling of shorelines after the Deepwater Horizon disaster caused coastal marsh vegetation to die. Coastal habitats were assessed on the percentage of oiling on the stems of marsh vegetation. More than 1000 km of the Louisiana coastal marshland was oiled with nearly a third showing >50% stem oiling. The loss of consolidating vegetation has resulted in increased erosion along these coasts.

Image: Shore oiling, Bay Jimmy, LA.

The Deepwater Horizon spill contaminated every habitat type occupied by marine mammals in the northern Gulf of Mexico. Marine mammals (and turtles) are exposed to oil through inhalation, ingestion (directly or by eating prey), and absorption through the skin. Surveys of dolphin species in the years following the spill indicate increased levels of fetal deformities, and liver and lung disease.

Image: Striped dolphins swim through oil.

1. (a) Describe some immediate effects of oil on the wildlife it comes in contact with: ____________________

____

____

____

(b) Describe and explain some of the longer term effects on marine and coastal communities: ____________________

____

____

____

2. (a) Compare the extent and the recovery time for the two oil spills described at the top of the page. How do they differ?

____

____

(b) Explain why the extent of the ecological effect of a spill is not necessarily directly related to the volume of oil spilled:

____

____

____

ISBN: 978-1-98-856632-0

129 Dealing with Oil Spills

Key Question: How are oil spills cleaned up?

Oil spills can be extremely difficult to clean up due to the sticky nature of the oil. Heavy crude is one of the most difficult substances to clean as it forms thick, viscous slicks that are difficult to disperse. The environment also plays a major role in the clean up. Warm temperatures contribute to the evaporation of large quantities of volatile compounds from the oil and allow bacteria to quickly break it down. Wave action helps to oxygenate and degrade the oil. Many techniques and technologies are used during the clean up. These include confining and burning large slicks, using chemical dispersants and sorbents, and cleaning beaches as oil comes ashore.

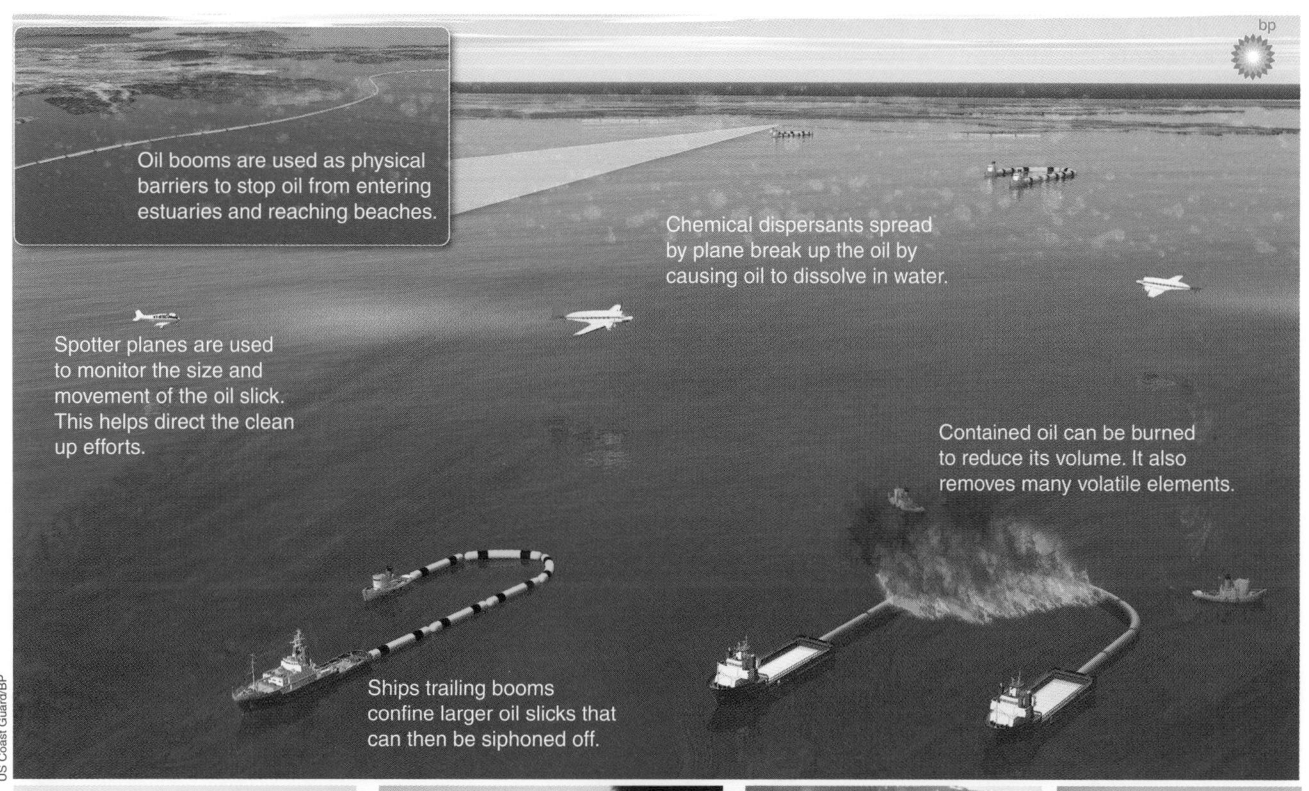

US Coast Guard/BP

Floating booms provide a physical barrier to stop oil movement. They are used to protect sensitive areas. During the Gulf clean-up more than 550 km of booms were used.

Oil captured by skimmer boats is set alight to reduce its volume, although this causes dense plumes of smoke containing large amounts of carbon dioxide.

On accessible beaches, large graders can be used to scrape up large amounts of sand and oil and remove it from the beach. New sand may be brought in to maintain the beach. Hot water and steam can be used to clean beaches and rocks, but it may kill any organisms present.

All images: US Coast Guard

Chemical dispersants are polar molecules with one end attracted to water (hydrophilic) and the other to oil (hydrophobic). The opposing interactions break the oil into small droplets that are more easily dispersed by waves and wind and degraded by bacteria.

Sorbents are used to soak up the oil from a spill. Good sorbents are excellent at soaking up oil but are hydrophobic (don't take up water). Many synthetic sorbents can take up to 70 times their own weight in oil. In large spills they are often used at the end of a clean-up.

Water quality tests are carried out on a regular basis to track the progress of the oil degradation. Bacteria in the Gulf of Mexico waters provide natural bioremediation and quickly began to break down the oil.

Skimmer boats collect oil floating on the surface. This can be burned or siphoned off and processed using centrifuges to separate the oil and water.

ISBN: 978-1-98-856632-0

INVESTIGATION 8.1: Cleaning up oil spills

See appendix for equipment list.

For this activity work in small groups of 3-6. You will be investigating the different techniques used to clean up an oil spill.

1. Pour two liters of tap water into a four liter bucket or container.
2. Mix four tablespoons (about 60 mL) of vegetable oil with four drops of food coloring. The food coloring will not completely mix with the oil. The oil represents the oil in a spill and the food coloring represents the chemicals in the oil.
3. Carefully and slowly pour the oil mixture into the center of the container of water.
4. Cut a craft (popsicle) stick in half so it is roughly 2.5-3 cm long. Place it into the middle of the oil spill. The craft stick represents the ship the oil is spilling from.
5. Your job is to try to clean up the oil within a set time frame. Your teacher will tell you how long you have for clean-up. You have been supplied with a range of clean-up materials to use. These include 3 cm pieces of cotton, cardboard, paper towels and flexible straws. At the end of the clean-up, record the success of each material in the space below.
6. Next add 5-10 mL of a name-brand detergent to the oil in the container. This is simulating adding a dispersant. Use clean materials to try to clean up the remaining oil. Record your observations below.

Clean up material	Material's role	Effectiveness (0-5*)	Observations of clean-up (before dispersant added)	Observations of cleanup (after dispersant added)

*0= not at all effective (no oil was removed), 5= completely effective (all the oil was removed).

1. (a) Were any methods completely effective at cleaning up the oil spill? ______

   (b) What happened when you used dispersant to help clean up the oil? ______

   (c) Explain the role of dispersants in cleaning up an oil spill: ______

2. (a) Were the chemicals (food coloring) easily cleaned up? ______

   (b) Would could this observation mean in the real world? ______

ISBN: 978-1-98-856632-0

Natural degradation of oil

Natural processes break down oil. The mechanisms are summarized below.

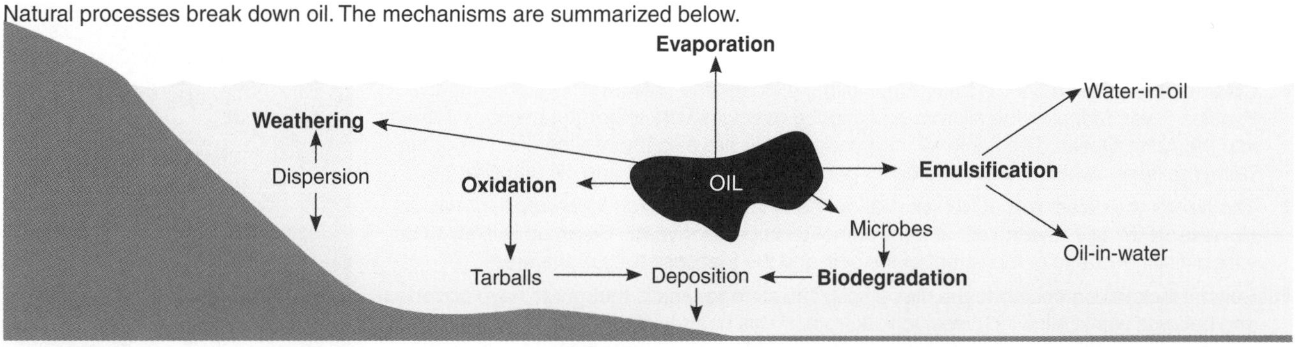

Weathering
Chemical and physical changes causes the oil to become heavier than water. Wave action may help disperse the oil.

Evaporation
Lighter and more volatile molecules in the oil turn into vapor that is lost. A large volume of the oil can be lost in this way.

Oxidation
Oxygen combines with the oil to form water soluble compounds. Tarballs may form and wash up on shorelines.

Biodegradation
Microorganisms break down the oil, working more quickly in warm water. Different types of microbes feed on different oil compounds.

Emulsification
The formation of droplets of oil in water. Generally slows down the process of dispersal by forming "mousse" which may linger for months.

3. Describe the different uses of the floating booms: ____________________

4. Explain why oil collected by skimmers and booms is burned at the surface. What are the negative effects of this?

5. Chemical dispersants have several disadvantages. Look back to the first page of the previous activity and do your own research and then outline some of the environmental problems associated with chemical dispersants for oil spills:

6. Describe the effects of the following natural processes on the oil:

(a) Biodegradation: ____________________

(b) Emulsification: ____________________

(c) Evaporation: ____________________

(d) Oxidation: ____________________

(e) Weathering: ____________________

ISBN: 978-1-98-856632-0

Case study: 2020 Norilsk diesel spill

NASA

- Norilsk is located in Siberia, Russia. On May 29 2020, a fuel storage tank at a local power plant collapsed. Around 21,000 m^3 of diesel oil polluted 350 km^2 of land and rivers feeding into a large freshwater lake, Lake Pyasino.
- Clean up teams used booms to try to contain the diesel and prevent it from entering the Pyasina River. Stopping the oil from entering the river was very important because it drains into the Arctic Ocean. The banks of the Pyasina River are also the calving grounds of the Taimyr reindeer, which are already under pressure from poaching and climate change.
- The size of the diesel spill at Norilsk is about half that of the *Exxon Valdex* spill in Alaska. However, it will still have a serious environmental impact for years. Clean up is likely to be very difficult because of the extent of the spill and the inaccessibility of the area.
- Several factors contributed to the diesel spill. The storage tank is thought to have corroded and become weak, allowing diesel to leak from it. This has resulted in accusations of poor maintenance at the power plant. Norilsk is the world's most northernmost city and is in a continuous permafrost zone. Permafrost is ground that has remained frozen for at least two years. Global warming is accelerating permafrost thaw and it is highly likely that this caused the storage tank to sink, helping to spill the diesel.

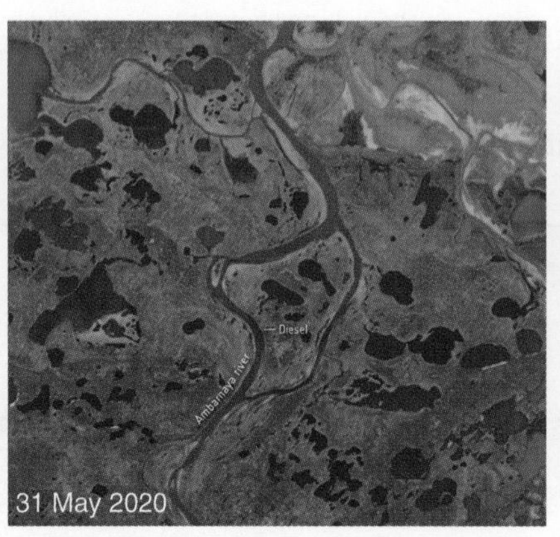

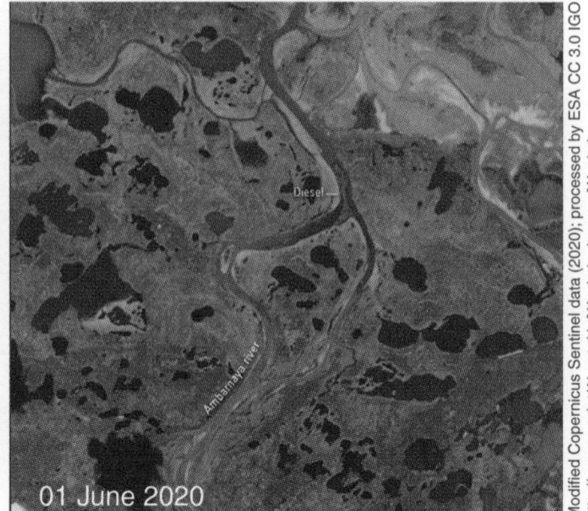

Modified Copernicus Sentinel data (2020); processed by ESA CC 3.0 IGO http://www.esa.int/About_Us/Week_in_images/Week_in_images_1-5_June_2020

The images above were taken from the Sentinel-2 satellite. They show how quickly the diesel (red) traveled along the waterways surrounding the spill site. The photos show diesel oil in the Ambarnaya River. The Ambarnaya River flows into Lake Pyasino (above), a major body of water and source of the Pyasina River.

7. At the time of writing this book the effects of the Norilsk spill were not fully known and clean-up was ongoing. In small groups, research what happened next. How successfully was the spill cleaned up and what have been the immediate and ongoing environmental effects? Summarize your findings below:

8. Global climate change could result in more environmental disasters as permafrost thaws. Propose a solution to prevent more oil spills occurring like the one that happened at Norilsk:

ISBN: 978-1-98-856632-0

130 The Economic Impact of Oil Spills

Key Question: What are the economic effects of oil spills?
Oil spills have an economic cost as well as an environmental cost. The cost of cleaning up an oil spill can be huge. It is estimated BP spent around US$14 billion to clean up the Deepwater Horizon oil spill. The total cost (court fees, clean-up costs, and fines) was US$62 billion. This includes a fine of US$18 billion dollars for breaching the Clean Water Act. Industries and individuals dependent on coastal resources can experience large economic losses after an oil spill. The tourism and fisheries sectors are the most affected.

Preventing oil spills is expensive

- Preventing oil spills from happening is important because oil is extremely damaging to the environment. However, the cost of prevention is high, and the extra costs are eventually passed on to the consumer at the gasoline pump or with price increases for products and services.
- Eventually, the cost of prevention measures becomes too high for the oil company and the consumer. At this point, the cost of the prevention outweighs the benefit of preventing spills.
- For example, when the *Exxon Valdez* oil tanker ran aground near Alaska, 41,000 m^3 of oil spilled into the Prince William Sound. A cost-benefit analysis showed that it cost half as much to clean up the oil spill than to require the use of double hulled oil tankers to reduce the risk of a spill occurring. It was cheaper to clean up the spill than to prevent the spill from happening in the first place. Of course, this does not account for the environmental damage, especially to sensitive species like sea otters.

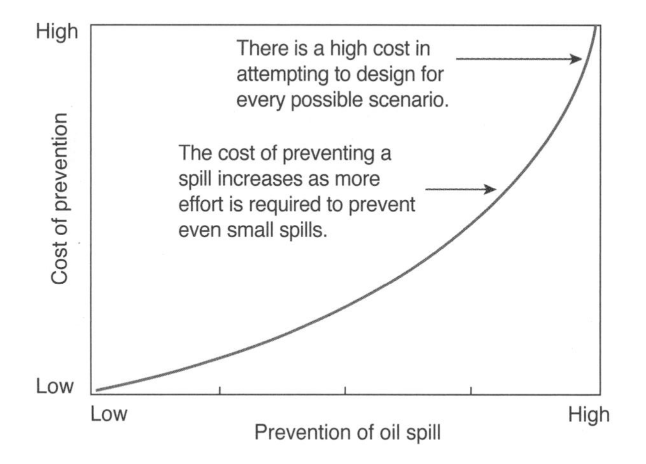

Oil spills and tourism

Many businesses dependent on tourism suffer disruptions and loss of earnings when there is an oil spill. Tourists stop visiting because they can no longer carry out water-based activities such as swimming, boating, fishing, and diving. Accommodation, retail, hospitality and service industries, and attractions are all affected by low visitor numbers. A return to normal trade only occurs once the spill has been cleaned up, and this can sometimes take months or years. The Deepwater Horizon oil spill cost the Gulf coastal economy US$23 billion dollars in lost tourist spending.

An oil spill means no swimming at this beach

infrogmation CC 3.0

Oil spills and fisheries

Oil spills have economic effects on commercial fishery and mariculture (cultivation of marine species) operations.

- Oil can foul (make dirty) or damage expensive fishing or mariculture equipment. Time and money are required to clean the equipment so it can be used again. If it is too damaged, it will need to be replaced.
- Large areas can be cordoned off to contain spills or because clean-up operations are taking place. Access to regular fishing sites is restricted.
- The oil can kill large numbers of commercially fished species. Numbers may decline so much that fishing bans are needed to protect the stock.
- Contaminants accumulate in the fish making it unsafe to eat, so it cannot be sold. The seafood can become tainted and develop a petroleum taste or smell, making it unpleasant to eat.
- The Gulf of Mexico commercial fishing industry is estimated to have lost $247 million as a result of post-spill fisheries closures due to the Deepwater Horizon spill. Thousands of jobs were lost.

1. Read the information on this page and the short article about the economic effects of oil spills on **BIOZONE's Resource Hub**. Your teacher will set you a specified amount of time to carry out a "quick write" activity. Generate as many ideas as you can about the economic costs of oil spills on tourism and fisheries. Record your ideas as bullet points below:

ISBN: 978-1-98-856632-0

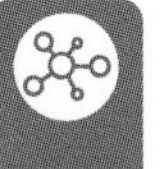

131 Water Quality

Key Question: How do human activities affect water quality? Water quality describes the condition of the water, and quantifies chemical, physical, and biological characteristics. For humans these measurements usually determine if water is suitable for a particular purpose such as drinking or swimming. In a wider context, the quality of water is important for ecosystem health. Over 71% of Earth is covered in water, so water bodies are home to many species. If water quality is poor, the organisms living in the water can be harmed or they may disappear. Over the next few activities you will look at some of the factors influencing water quality, including the role of human activities.

Oxygen sag curves

- Oxygen enters water by diffusion from the atmosphere, aeration (e.g. water falling from a waterfall or moving over rocks), and photosynthesis.
- Dissolved oxygen (DO) is measured in mg/L. A waterway is considered "healthy" and able to support life when the DO is above 5 mg/L, but the level needed for survival varies for different species.
- The DO level decreases when there is an increase in the level of nutrients and organic matter (pollution) in the water. This is because large nutrient loads stimulate algal growth. When the algae die and sink to the bottom they begin to decompose. The decomposition process consumes oxygen, lowering DO levels.
- The measure for oxygen depletion is the biological oxygen demand (BOD) test. BOD measures how much oxygen the organic material is using for its decomposition. The more oxygen that is used, the greater the bacterial activity, and (therefore) the greater the pollution.
- When DO levels fall below a species' tolerance range the organism can become physiologically stressed and will die if unable to move to a more favorable area.
- The relationship between DO and BOD is plotted as an oxygen sag curve. The plot shows how the levels of DO and BOD change with distance from the source of a pollutant (right).

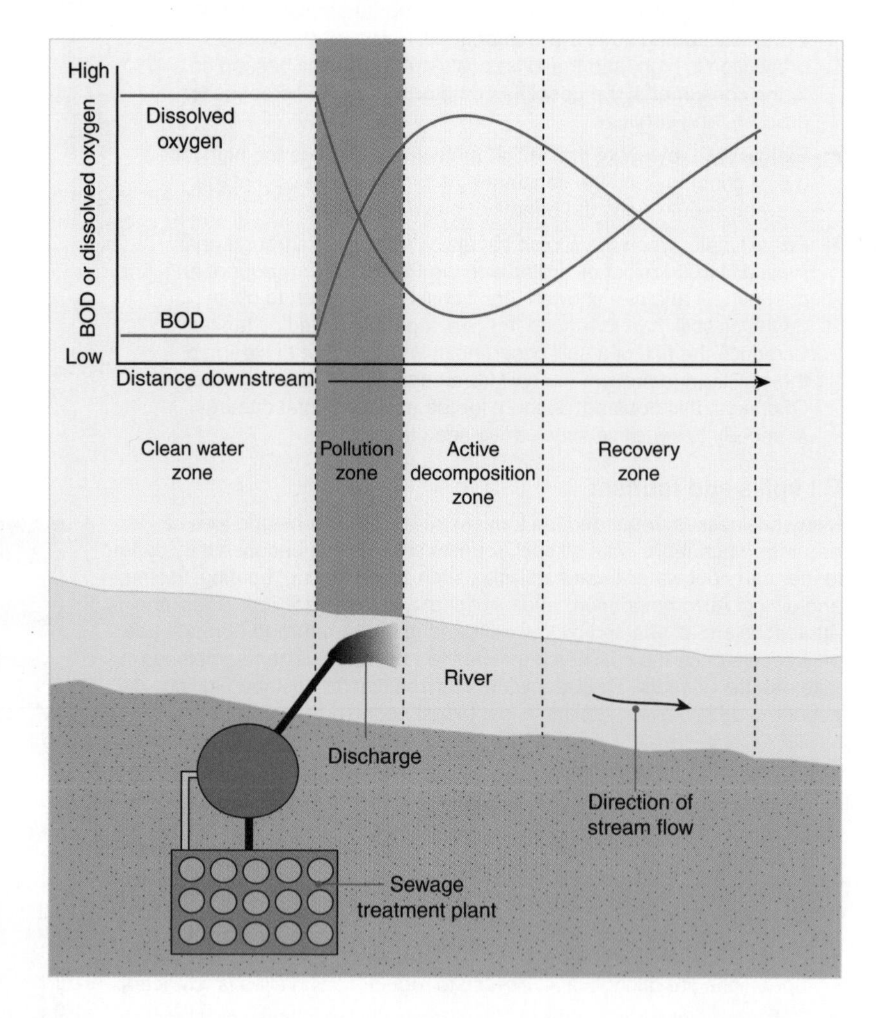

1. (a) What does biological oxygen demand (BOD) measure? ______

(b) Why can it be used as an indicator of pollution? ______

2. Use the oxygen sag graph above to describe the relationship between BOD levels and DO: ______

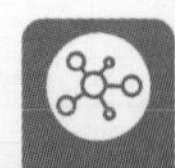
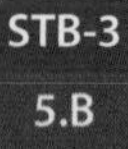
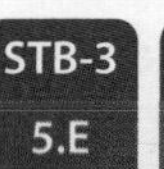
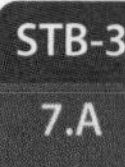

ISBN: 978-1-98-856632-0

3. How could BOD testing be used to identify the source of a pollutant (even when there is no obvious visual source)?

Oceanic dead zones

- When DO levels in the ocean become very low (hypoxic) aerobic (oxygen-requiring life) cannot be supported. A ocean region without marine life is called a dead zone. Organisms that are able to move away (e.g. fish) have left the area and those that cannot move away have died (e.g. corals). Dead zones do occur naturally, commonly seasonally, but an increase in nutrient pollution from human activity has made them more common.
- Dead zones can be classed by duration. Some are temporary, lasting only a hours or days, while others are permanent. Seasonal dead zones occur in the warmer months of the year, because warm water holds less oxygen than cold water.

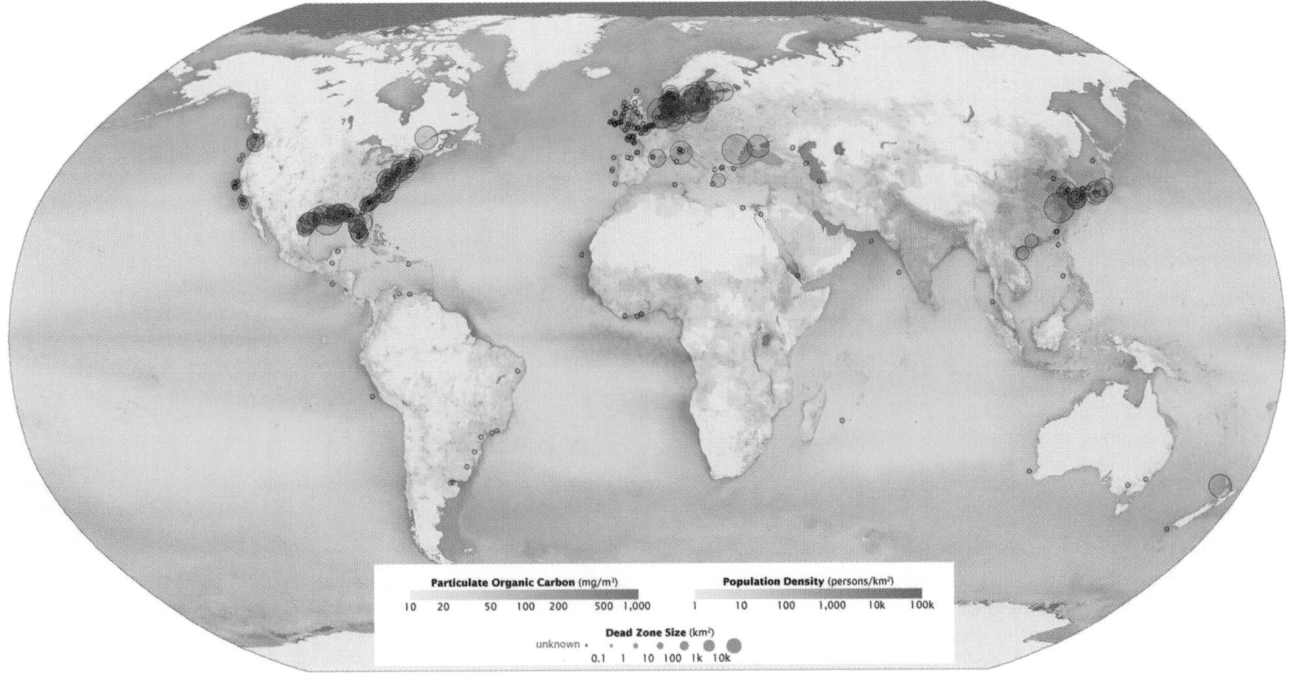

4. What is an oceanic dead zone?

5. The image above shows the location of marine dead zones globally (2008). Red dots indicate where the size of the dead zone is known (see scale), black dots indicate where size of the dead zone is not known. Brown shading indicates population density (population density increases as the shading become darker).

Work in pairs to study the map above. What do you notice about the location of the oceanic dead zones?

ISBN: 978-1-98-856632-0

The Gulf of Mexico dead zone

The image on the right shows how nutrient runoff from farms (green areas) and cities (red areas) in many states drains into the Mississippi River before entering the Gulf of Mexico.

High levels of nitrogen and phosphorus in the runoff along with warm temperatures and plenty of sunlight cause algal growth rates to explode and an oceanic dead zone forms each summer. Scientists have been monitoring the Gulf of Mexico dead zone for over 33 years and its size varies. Increased fertilizer use and high levels of rain and snow melt increase its size. High winds (e.g. from hurricanes) can disrupt algal growth and reduce the size of the dead zone. The dead zone dissipates in the cooler temperatures of fall.

This dead zone is the second largest in the world. The largest is in the Arabian Sea.

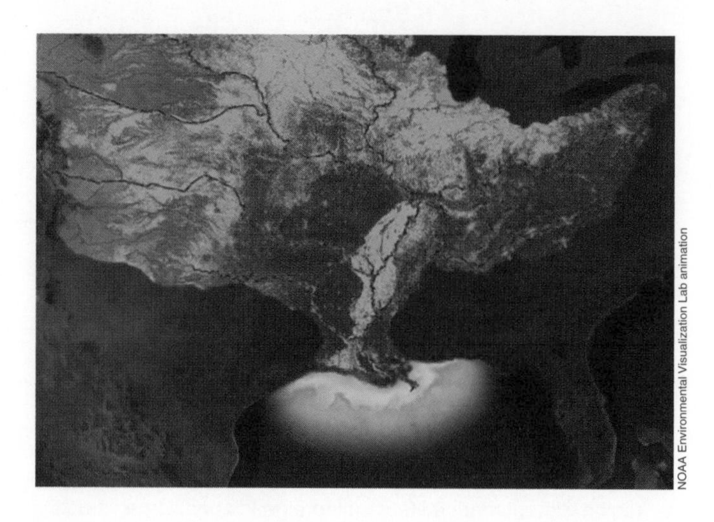

NOAA Environmental Visualization Lab animation

6. Explain the causes of the oceanic dead zone in the Gulf of Mexico: ______

Heavy metal pollutants

- Heavy metals have a relatively high density and are toxic even at very low concentrations. Examples include mercury, cadmium, arsenic, and lead.
- Heavy metals occur naturally in the environment and are used to make many consumer products. They can also be produced as waste products in industrial processes.
- Heavy metals from any of these sources can enter waterways, including groundwater. If they enter drinking water supplies they can then be ingested by humans and livestock. Heavy metals do not break down and are excreted only very slowly, so they accumulate in the tissues of organisms. Over time, heavy metal concentrations can reach levels where they cause harm or even death.
- The World Health Organization (WHO) sets guidelines for heavy metal limits in drinking water, but most countries have additional standards to keep people safe. In the US, The Safe Drinking Water Act (SDWA) of 1974 has specific standards limiting the levels of heavy metals present in drinking water.

This lead service line pipe is used to supply drinking water from a water main to an end user. Lead service lines are the leading contributor of lead contamination in drinking water in many countries because lead leaches from the pipe into the water supply. Replacing the lead pipes with pipes made from other materials is the best way to fix the problem. Doing this is time-consuming and expensive.

7. Describe how heavy metals can get into drinking water: ______

8. In 2014, the city of Flint, Michigan, changed its water supply from Lake Huron and the Detroit River to a new supply from the Flint River. Unfortunately the new water supply exposed 100,000 people to high levels of lead and it was 18 months before the problem was detected. Work in pairs to investigate the Flint water crisis. Identify the cause of the lead contamination and how this affected the Flint community. Summarize your points as bullet points below. You many use more paper if you want. Use the resources on **BIOZONE's Resource Hub** to help you.

ISBN: 978-1-98-856632-0

132 Litter in the Ocean

Key Question: How does ocean litter affect marine life? Marine litter is an enormous problem all around the world. If you have ever walked along a beach after a storm you would have seen litter washed up onto the beach. What you see washed up is only a tiny fraction of what is in the ocean. It is estimated that almost six billion kilograms of litter enters the ocean every year, most of which is plastic. Most litter takes a very long time to break down (plastics can take hundreds of years), so the problem is long lasting. Not only does litter look ugly, but it causes major problems for ocean ecosystems.

Where does ocean litter come from?

Ocean litter is human-created waste that has deliberately or accidentally been released into the ocean. Most if it originates on land, but some comes from activities on the ocean.

- Litter left on the beach is blown into the oceans.
- Litter on the street (dropped deliberately or from overfull trash bins) can be washed or blown into storm water drains. The litter then washes down streams and rivers until it reaches the ocean.
- Recyclable trash is put into a landfill.
- Items flushed down the toilet or present in waste water systems can enter the ocean.
- When people do not have access to waste disposal facilities, waste builds up. Much of it enters waterways and eventually the oceans.
- Waste can be deliberately thrown overboard from boats or it can accidently fall off or be blown off in storms or following maritime accidents (e.g. shipping containers).
- Fishing gear can be lost at sea.

Many different items make up ocean litter, but some items are more common than others. The top 10 ocean litter items found globally during coastal cleanups are: cigarette butts, plastic drink bottles, plastic caps, food wrappers, plastic grocery bags, plastic lids, plastic straws/stirrers, glass bottles, other plastic bags, and foam takeaway containers. Typically plastic items take between 10 and several hundred years to break down.

The oceans concentrate waste into "garbage patches"

Ocean litter accumulates in "garbage patches" within the oceans. The garbage patches form because the surface waters of the oceans circulate in giant whirlpools called gyres. The gyres concentrate floating debris. You can try this yourself by placing some plastic waste in a small pool or large container and swirling the water around.

There are five gyres (below) and each collects litter. The debris ranges in size, from large abandoned fishing nets to microplastics, which are plastic pieces smaller than 5 mm in size. Microplastics are among the most abundant items in ocean garbage patches.

One of the most well known garbage patches is the "Great Pacific Garbage Patch" located within the North Pacific Gyre. It is thought to be around 1.2 million km^2 although its size varies depending on ocean currents and winds.

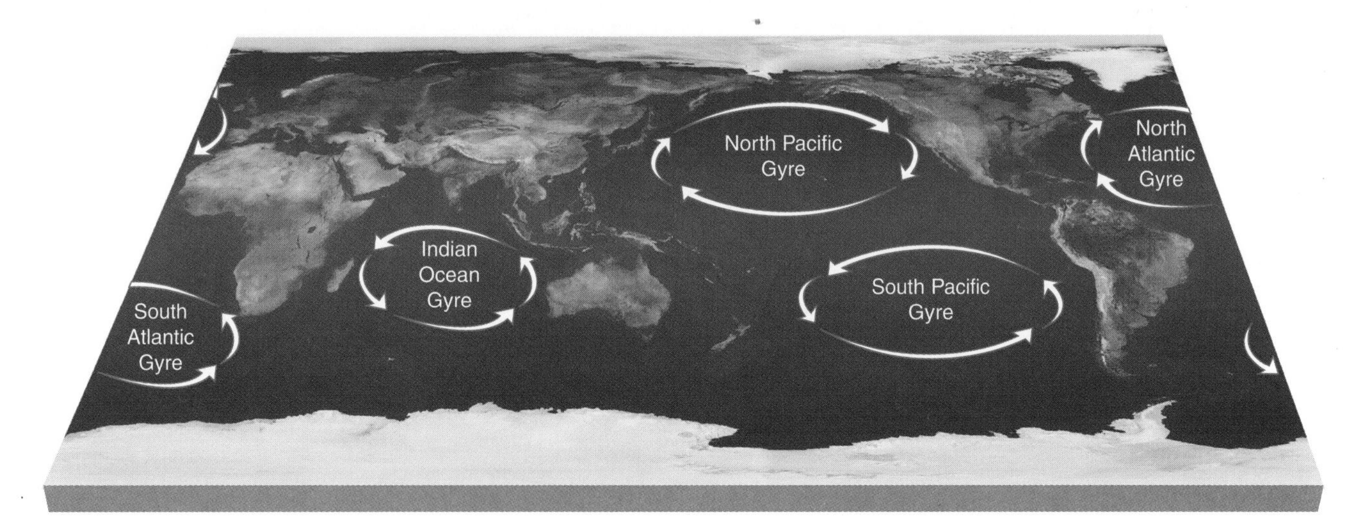

1. Explain how plastic litter disposed of on land can end up in an ocean garbage patch: ______________________

The problem with ocean waste

- Animals become tangled up (entangled) in discarded ropes, fishing nets, and plastic waste. They may lose limbs if the material they are tangled in cuts into them, starve because they can no longer find food, be captured by predators, or suffocate or drown because their movement is restricted or they cannot surface to breathe.
- The break down of some debris releases toxic compounds into the water, or the litter can absorb organic pollutants (PCBs and DDT) from the water. Many organisms ingest these chemicals while they are feeding and can become very sick or die.
- The chemical bonds in plastic are different to the chemical bonds found in nature, so very few organisms (mainly microbes) can degrade plastic. Degradation by UV light is very slow, so plastic stays in the environment for hundreds of years.
- Fish, whales, sea turtles, and birds often mistake plastic waste for food. For example, a floating plastic bag can resemble a jellyfish to a sea turtle. The plastic takes up space in their gastrointestinal tract and the animals starve to death because there is no room left for real food. This problem is distressingly common. For example, almost all of the 1.5 million Laysan albatrosses on Midway Atoll have plastic in their gastrointestinal tract. Approximately one-third of chicks die because their parents feed them plastic, mistaking it for food (right).
- Small microplastics are even more of a problem. The Sun and waves degrade plastic litter into tiny microplastic particles that are easily ingested by animals. Because of their size, they are very difficult to clean up. Microplastics have been detected in deep ocean trenches (and even on top of Mount Everest).

Crab tangled in fishing net

NOAA

This albatross chick had been fed plastic

Chris Jordan

2. Discuss why plastic litter is a particular problem in the oceans: ______________________

3. In 1992, 29,000 rubber bath toys fell off a container ship into the Pacific Ocean. Nicknamed the "friendly floatees", oceanographers mapped their progress across the world's oceans. Use the map (right) to describe the dispersal and longevity of plastic litter:

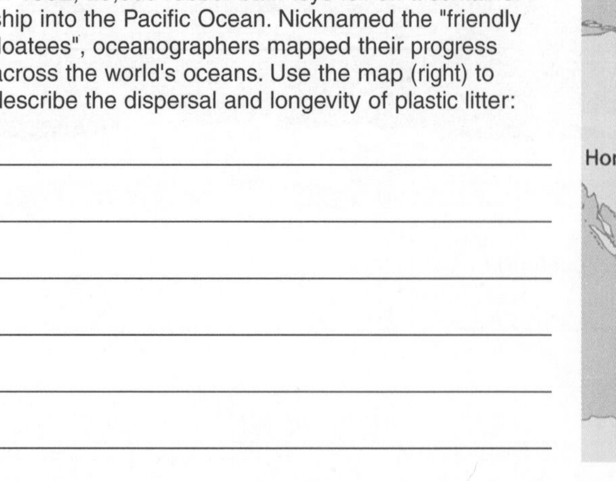

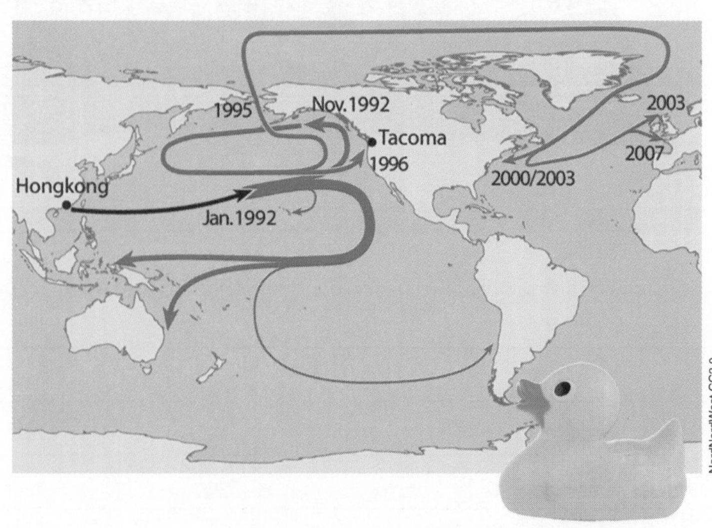

NordNordWest CC3.0

ISBN: 978-1-98-856632-0

133 Sediment and Water Quality

Key Question: How does sediment affect water quality?

One indicator of water quality is turbidity. Turbidity refers to how cloudy the water is, as indicated by the level of suspended particles. Algae, sediment, and organic waste all contribute to turbidity. As turbidity increases, the water becomes cloudier (right). Most water bodies have some level of sediment suspended in them. However, too much suspended sediment can affect water quality and cause problems for the organisms living there. Turbidity can be measured in two ways. One method uses a machine to measure the intensity of light scattered at 90° as a beam of light passes through a water sample. The second method is used for field sampling and uses a black and white Secchi disk. The disk is lowered into the water until it can no longer be seen. The depth at which it just disappears provides an estimate of water clarity (the inverse of turbidity).

The effect of turbidity on photosynthesis

As turbidity increases, it is harder for sunlight to penetrate the water, so light does not reach as far down. This reduces the ability of aquatic plants and algae to grow at depth because they rely on sunlight for photosynthesis. Plant growth rates drop, and so too does the amount of oxygen produced, so the levels of dissolved oxygen (DO) also fall. As we have seen earlier, a certain level of DO is required to support life. If the levels fall too low, organisms will either leave the area or die.

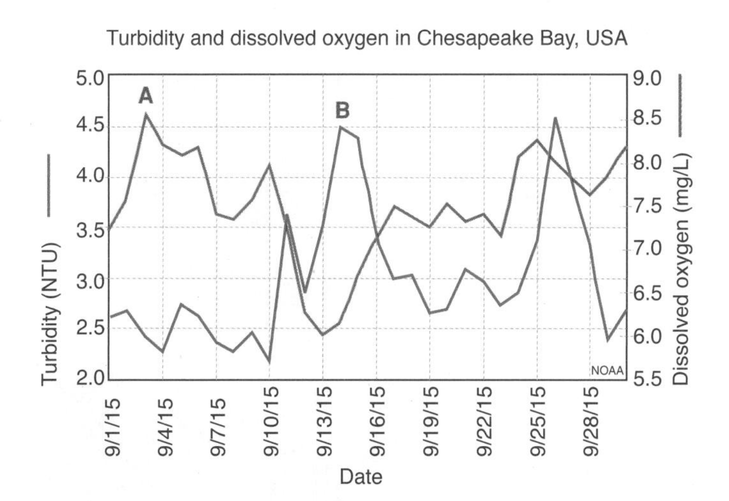

The effect of turbidity on foraging success

Many aquatic animals rely on sight to find and obtain food. An aquatic predator needs to be able to see to capture their prey, or a herbivorous organism needs to be able to see to find plants to eat. Visual predators can take much longer to find prey in turbid waters, reducing their foraging efficiency. The graph below shows the success of a fish species (*Gymnogeophagus terrapurpura*) hunting for amphipods in clear water and turbid water.

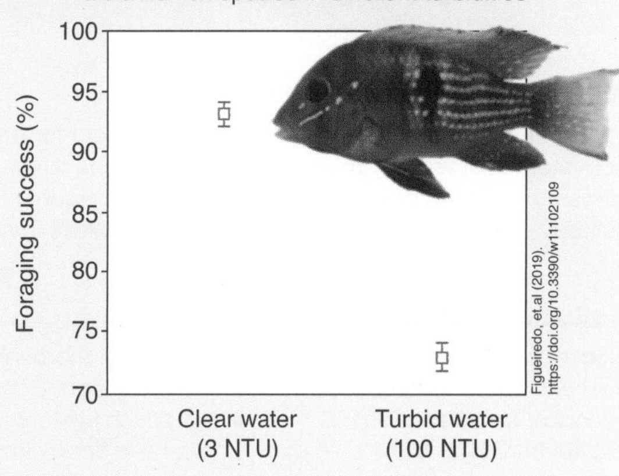

1. Study the graph of turbidity and dissolved oxygen (above left). Explain the relationship between turbidity and dissolved oxygen at points A and B:

2. (a) Study the graph of foraging success (above right) and describe the results:

   (b) Explain the likely reason for these results:

ISBN: 978-1-98-856632-0

134 Mercury in the Environment

Key Question: How does mercury enter the environment and why is it dangerous?

The heavy metal mercury (Hg) exists in several forms, some of which are extremely toxic and dangerous at very low levels. Mercury occurs naturally in the Earth's crust and is released into the environment during volcanic eruptions. Human activities (e.g. industrial activity and mining) have doubled the amount of atmospheric mercury in the last 150 years. Mercury emissions are widely dispersed in the atmosphere before being deposited back on the Earth's surface. Mercury converts through several forms as it cycles through the environment. The most toxic form is methylmercury.

The mercury cycle

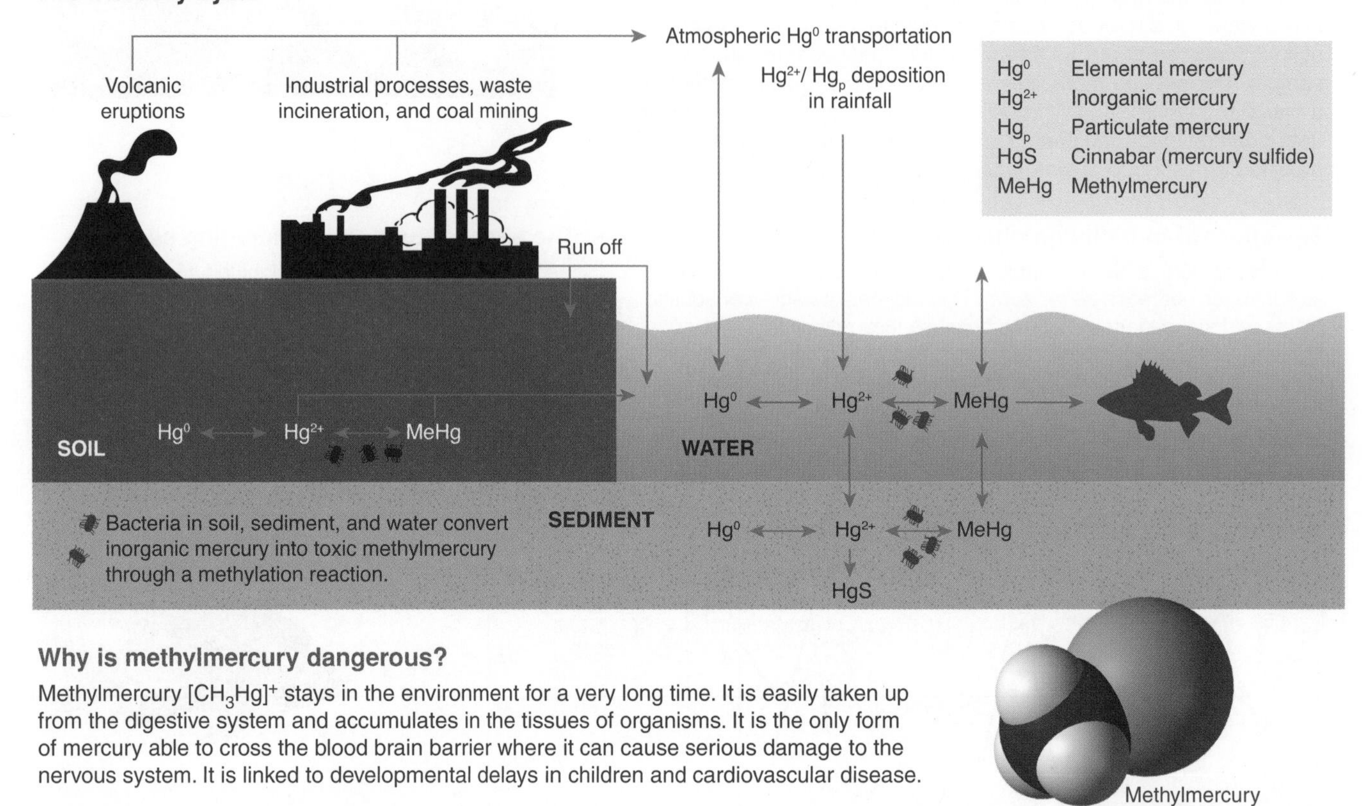

Why is methylmercury dangerous?

Methylmercury $[CH_3Hg]^+$ stays in the environment for a very long time. It is easily taken up from the digestive system and accumulates in the tissues of organisms. It is the only form of mercury able to cross the blood brain barrier where it can cause serious damage to the nervous system. It is linked to developmental delays in children and cardiovascular disease.

Methylmercury

Reducing mercury in the environment

Human activity releases around 2320 tonnes of mercury every year. Combustion of coal and oil is the largest source (810 tonnes/year). Some mercury is present from historical activities, such as gold mining, which left large amounts of mercury in the environment. Many gold mining sites have been cleaned up, but some continue to leach mercury into the wider environment. The US EPA regulates the level of mercury being released and therefore people's exposure. This includes regulating emissions from municipal waste combustors, coal- and oil-fired power plants, and incineration of medical waste.

Dental amalgam is used to fill dental cavities because it is inexpensive, strong, and long-lasting compared to non-mercury alternatives. It is generally considered to be safe for use because elemental mercury is used, and is not easily absorbed into the bloodstream. However, there are some concerns that the mercury vapor is released (when the filling is replaced or removed or from chewing food) could be harmful. Dental amalgam is still widely used because the positives outweigh potential problems and the long term effects of alternative materials are not yet known.

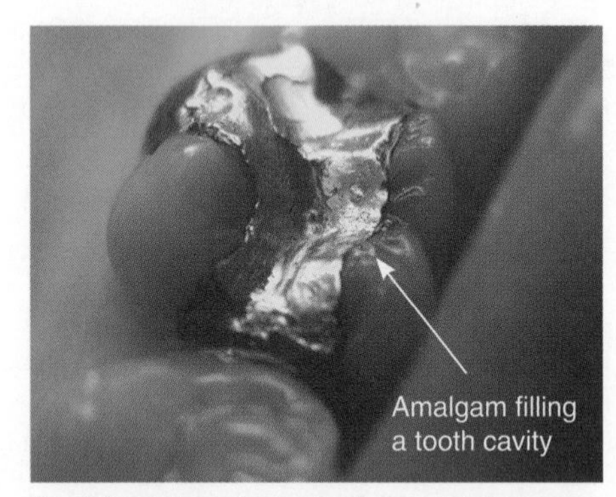

Dental amalgam is a mix of elemental mercury and a powdered alloy of silver, tin, and zinc.

1. The most toxic form of mercury is methylmercury. Explain how it is formed and why it is so dangerous: ______________

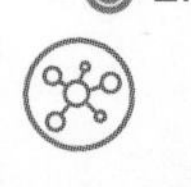

2. Debate! Dental amalgam is safe and should continue to be used by dentists. After reading the information on this page and the article on **BIOZONE's Resource Hub** pair up with someone and debate your points. Consider if the material provides a balanced, unbiased view point. At the end of the debate take a class vote to see if your classmates think dental amalgam is safe and should be continued to be used.

ISBN: 978-1-98-856632-0

135 Endocrine Disruptors

Key Question: What are endocrine disruptors and how do they affect health and wildlife?

The endocrine system produces chemicals called hormones that regulate and coordinate a wide range of functions needed to maintain life. Reproduction, growth and development, and metabolism are all controlled by hormones. Endocrine disruptors are chemicals that interfere with the normal function of an animal's endocrine system. They may mimic hormones or interfere with the endocrine system and disrupt normal processes. Endocrine disrupting chemicals (EDCs) are found in many commonly used products. Some break down very slowly, so their effects can be long lasting.

Sources of endocrine disruptors

Food products	Industry	Personal & home care products	Medical care
Agricultural chemicals	Water contaminants	Personal care products	Medical products, e.g. gels and pharmaceuticals
Phytoestrogens	Fire-fighting foams	Flame retardants	
Food additives	Air pollutants	Cleaning supplies	Medical equipment e.g. blood bags, syringes, catheters
Packaging materials	Industrial chemicals and by-products	Solvents and coatings	

The main way endocrine disruptors enter our body is by consuming food or drinking water containing them. EDCs may also be transferred to a fetus during pregnancy or an infant during breast-feeding

EDCs are all around us. Dust within our homes contains many endocrine disruptors, as do cleaning products, fragrances, and personal hygiene products. Inhalation or uptake through the skin contributes to our daily exposure.

The effects of endocrine disruptors

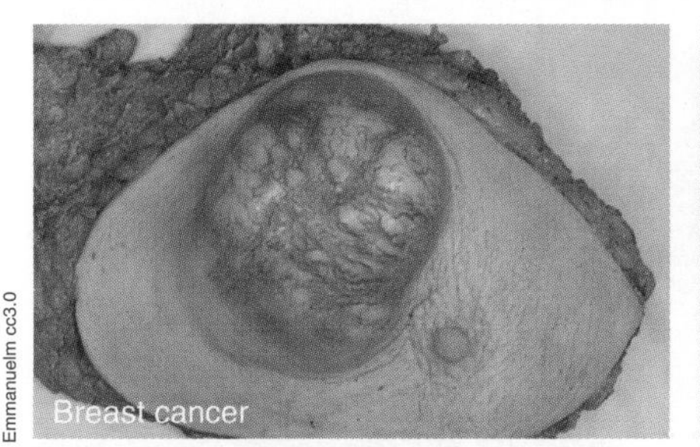

Breast cancer

Emmanuelm cc3.0

The World Health Organization have reported an increase in disorders linked to EDC exposure. These include learning difficulties, asthma, cardiovascular disease, cancers, Alzheimer's, and Parkinson's disease. Exposure to EDCs during development or early childhood can result in permanent consequences and increase an individual's likelihood of developing related diseases later in life.

Some EDCs cause sex ratio imbalances (an unusually greater proportion of one sex than the other). This has been seen in fish populations near pulp and paper mills. Exposure to EDCs at critical development times has been shown to cause disruption to the development of ovaries, testes, or genitalia in humans. EDCs are also linked to birth defects, declining fertility, and lower numbers of males born.

EDCs can be more harmful during key life stages, such as during periods of rapid growth and development. Laboratory studies have shown that fetuses and children do not have fully functioning enzymes to remove BPA, an EDC found in many plastic bottles. Their elevated BPA levels can cause metabolic dysfunction resulting in obesity or impaired insulin function (possibly causing type 2 diabetes).

1. Describe the nature and effects of endocrine disrupting chemicals: ______________________

____

____

____

2. Predict the effects on a species' survival if EDCs continue to cause sex imbalances over a long period of time:

____

____

____

3. BPA stands for bisphenol A. It has been used in the manufacture of some types of plastics and resins for many decades. Our exposure to BPA is widespread. Work in pairs to research BPA. Your research should address what consumer products BPA is commonly found in, what the potential risks of BPA are, and how you could take steps to limit BPA exposure. Summarize your findings on a shared document and discuss with another group or your class.

ISBN: 978-1-98-856632-0

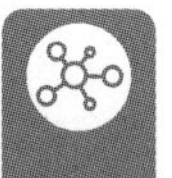

136 Human Impacts on Wetlands and Mangroves

Key Question: How do human activities affect the functioning of wetlands and mangroves?

Wetlands are areas of land where water is at or near the surface nearly all year round. Swamps, bogs, and marshes are all examples of wetlands. Mangrove habitat refers to coastal areas where mangrove trees grow. Both habitats are valuable and play important roles in stabilizing ecosystems and providing essential ecosystem services. Both can be easily damaged by human activities, and this can have wide ranging negative impacts on the ecosystem.

Wetlands

Wetlands provide a number of ecosystem services:

- A source of water to wildlife.
- Store water and recharge groundwater stores.
- Improve water quality by trapping sediment (filtration).
- Regulate water flows and control flooding by gradually releasing water.
- Provide habitat to many species (contribute to biodiversity).
- Contribute to food security by providing fertile habitat and resources for growing essential crops (e.g. rice).

Mangroves

Important roles of mangrove ecosystems include:

- Protect shorelines from being damaged by wind, waves and floods.
- Reduce and prevent erosion along coastlines by stabilizing sediments (the sediment becomes trapped in the dense mangrove root system).
- Improve water quality by trapping and filtering sediment.
- Contribute to biodiversity by acting as a nursery for many species (including commercially important species).
- Provides habitat to endangered or threatened species.

What are the threats to wetlands and mangroves?

Despite the importance of wetlands and mangroves, human activity is causing their decline. If this continues we can expect to see reduced biodiversity, increased erosion, poorer water quality, and less protection from the effects of severe weather events (e.g. floods and storm surge). Human activities contributing to the decline of wetland and mangrove ecosystems include:

- **Land development**: Wetlands are drained and mangroves are cleared to make way for new land development projects or for farming.
- **Dam construction**: Building the dam and supporting infrastructure (e.g. access roads) damages the land. Once the dam is operational flooding of some areas and changes in water flow to other areas damages the way the natural ecosystem functions.
- **Aquaculture and overfishing**: Conversion of mangrove ecosystems for aquaculture has been extremely destructive, resulting in pollution and a loss of mangrove forests globally. Most wild fisheries within mangrove ecosystems are on small scale. However, they are often open access and require minimal investment in equipment, so unregulated takes are common.
- **Enrichment**: Fertilizers, pesticides and other pollutants can enter waterways and kill organisms in the wetlands and mangroves. Mangrove trees have special roots (pneumatophores) that allow them to exchange gases with the environment even when the tide is high. If these become covered in oil, the gas exchange no longer takes place.

The city of Recife, in Brazil, is built around mangroves

Portal da Copa/ME CC3.0 Brasil

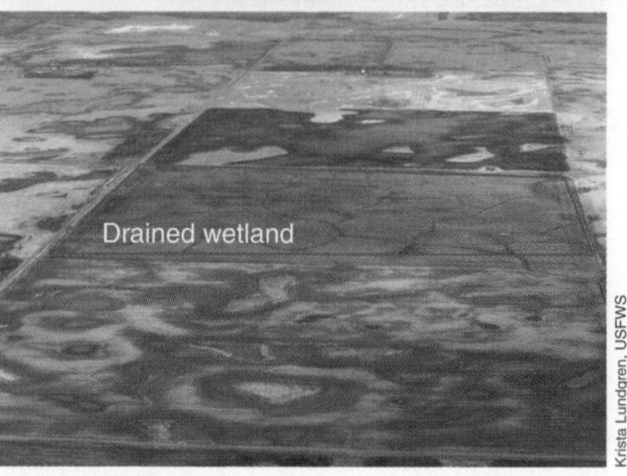
Drained wetland

Krista Lundgren, USFWS

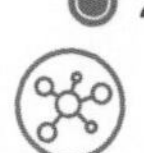

Legislation is in place to help conserve wetlands and mangroves. For example, the US is a signatory of the Ramsar Convention. This international treaty is about conservation and sustainable utilization of wetlands. In addition, farmers who conserve wetland are eligible for financial incentives under Swampbuster, a wetland conservation compliance program.

1. Look at the photo (above right) showing the effects of wetland drainage. Describe the differences you can see between the drained land (red box) and undrained land:

____

____

____

2. Go to **BIOZONE's Resource Hub** and open the link "*Loss of wetlands in the Southwestern United States*". Choose one of the states listed and describe the status of wetlands in that state. Then visit the EPA's site (also on the Resource Hub) to see what is being done to protect US wetlands. Summarize your findings in a shared document with your teacher.

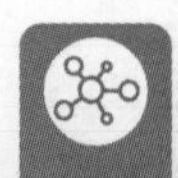
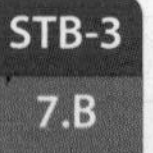

STB-3 7.B

ISBN: 978-1-98-856632-0

137 Eutrophication

Key Question: What contributes to eutrophication and what is the effect on water quality and the ecosystem?

The trophic status of a water body refers to the level of primary productivity it can sustain. Trophic status is measured using the **Trophic State Index** (TSI) and can be used as a measure of water quality (below). Several factors are taken into account when assessing water quality, including the level of phosphorus (P) and nitrogen (N) in a water body. Nutrients (P and N) are often limiting resources, so as their levels increase so does plant and algal growth, and therefore primary productivity. Excessive primary productivity can be harmful to the health of waterways.

Trophic status index

The TSI of a water body is rated on a scale from zero to 100. Using this scale, water bodies are classified as oligotrophic, mesotrophic, or eutrophic to hypereutrophic. Some factors relating to these classifications are described in the table below.

Classification status	Trophic State Index	Algal levels	Biological productivity	Water quality	Secchi depth (m)	Dissolved oxygen
Oligotrophic	0-40	Low	Low level of biological productivity	Good	>8 – 4	High
Mesotrophic	40-60	Moderate	Moderate level of biological productivity	Fair	>4 – 2	Moderate
Eutrophic to hypereutrophic	60-100	High	High level of biological productivity	Poor	2 – <0.25	Low

Eutrophication

- Eutrophication can occur naturally, but is usually the result of human activity. Discharge or runoff of nitrate or phosphate-containing detergents, fertilizers, or sewage into a waterway are the main causes of eutrophication. Phosphorus enrichment is particularly important in freshwater eutrophication.
- The high nutrient levels cause excessive algal growth (an algal bloom) such as the one shown far right. The algal bloom prevents sunlight penetrating far beneath the water's surface and aquatic plants (macrophytes) begin to die because they cannot photosynthesize. Oxygen levels begin to fall.
- Eventually the algae die and are decomposed along with dead plants by microbes. The decomposition process uses up oxygen and the oxygen levels become low (hypoxia).
- If dissolved oxygen levels become too low, life cannot be supported. Organisms will die if they cannot move out of the affected region.

Oligotrophic waterway

Hypereutrophic waterway

Alexandr Trubetskoy CC 3.0

1. Describe the causes and consequences of eutrophication: ______________________

2. Describe the differences between an oligotrophic waterway and an eutrophic waterway: ______________________

ISBN: 978-1-98-856632-0

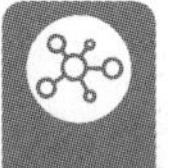

Cause and effects of eutrophication

Human activities, such as clearing land, building towns and cities, and applying fertilizers increase the rate of eutrophication. While eutrophication can occur quickly, it can be very slow to reverse. One reason for this is because the return of phosphorus to the water column from sediments is very slow in oxygenated waters, so phosphorus can stay in the environment for a long time. Eutrophication can have seasonal peaks related to annual fertilizer applications and seasonal deoxygenation of bottom waters (which increases phosphorus release). This means there are certain times of the year when eutrophication is worse.

Some of the potential effects of eutrophication include:

- Excessive growth of algae (and cyanobacteria) can lead to blooms. Some species produce toxins and these can harm organisms in the waterway and humans and other animals that come into contact with them.
- Esthetic value is decreased due to bad smell and poor appearance of the water.
- Low levels of dissolved oxygen force less tolerant species to move out of the affected area (or face death if they cannot). Dead fish are often observed at the site of an algal bloom (right).
- Waterways cannot be harvested for edible fish or shellfish.
- The water becomes cloudy and green/brown in color. Increased turbidity makes it harder for predatory fish to hunt, and for prey to avoid their predators.

The diagram below depicts the eutrophication process over time:

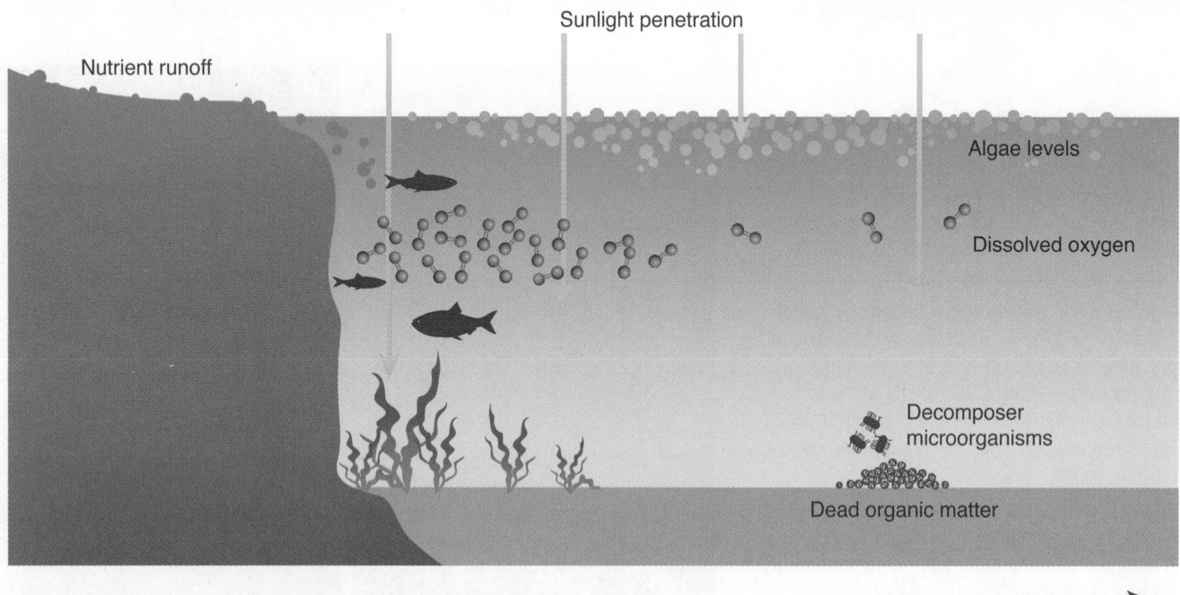

3. Use the diagram above to describe the process of eutrophication as it occurs over time. You should highlight the main changes and effects of these:

ISBN: 978-1-98-856632-0

138 Thermal Pollution

Key Question: What is thermal pollution and what effect does it have on aquatic ecosystems?

Thermal pollution occurs when human activity alters the temperature of a body of water outside its naturally occurring range. Thermal pollution can be a decrease or an increase in water temperature, but in this activity we will look at the effects of a temperature increase. The most common cause of a temperature increase is when a facility uses water to cool machinery or processes, and then returns the water back to the water body at a higher temperature. Discharge temperatures are closely monitored to ensure the thermal tolerance levels of local organisms are not exceeded. Ongoing thermal pollution can alter the structure and diversity of a community.

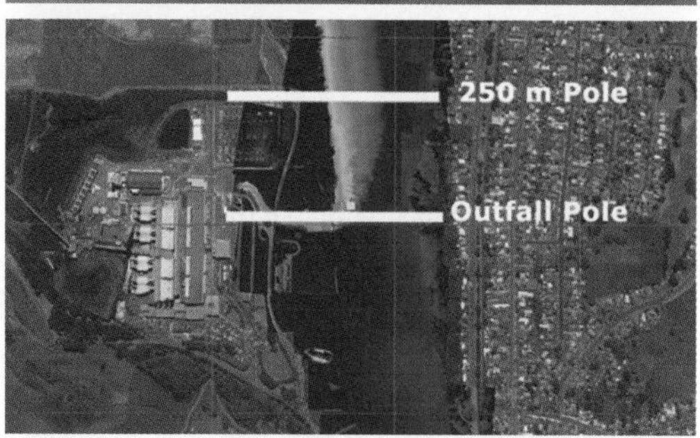

Sources of thermal pollution

Power plants are one of the most common sources of thermal pollution. Water is used as a coolant to dissipate the heat generated during electricity production. In the photo (top right) the water is removed from an adjacent river. During the cooling process, the water heats up, and is returned to the river at a higher temperature. The temperature is raised at the discharge point and for some distance downstream, creating a thermal plume. This is obvious in the thermal image (right). The outfall pole indicates where the water is discharged back into the river. Red = warmest water. Blue = coolest.

Thermal pollution can affect the survival, distribution, and biodiversity of organisms living in the affected area. Higher water temperatures can be problematic for several reasons:

- Organisms that can not tolerate a sudden change in temperature (or move away from it) may die of heat shock.
- Temperature affects oxygen solubility and availability (right). Recall that a dissolved oxygen level below 5 mg/L in intolerable for most species.
- Heat increases metabolic activity (i.e. enzyme activity rates). Oxygen is required at a faster rate to keep up with metabolic demands. This has two effects: oxygen consumption rates increase (see far right column of the table) and more food is consumed. As food consumption increases, fewer resources may be available to support the previous consumer biomass.
- Temperature changes outside an organism's thermal tolerance level cause physiological stress, movement away from the area, or death. These changes can alter community composition, so biodiversity is affected.

Temperature (°C)	**Oxygen solubility** (mg/L)	**Fish oxygen consumption** ($gO_2/g/hr$)
0	14.6	No data
5	12.8	No data
10	11.3	0.17
15	10.1	0.21
20	9.1	0.26
25	8.3	0.31
30	7.6	0.37

1. What is thermal pollution and what causes it?

___

___

___

2. (a) Use the data in the table (above right) to plot the effect of temperature on oxygen solubility (left axis) and fish oxygen consumption (right axis):

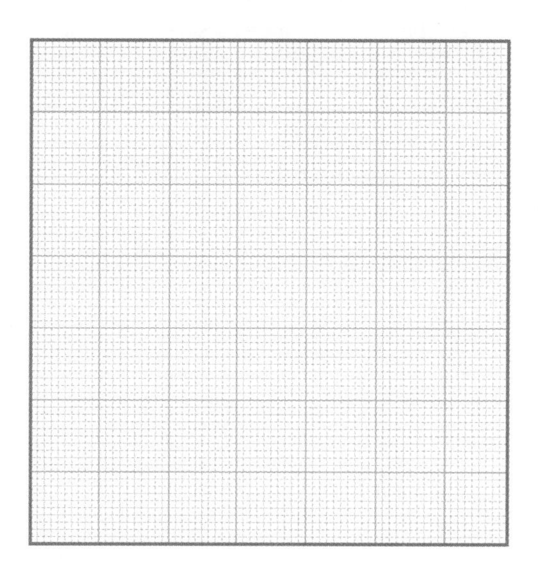

(b) Describe the relationship between temperature and the other two variables (one physical, one biological):

___

___

___

___

___

3. Explain how thermal pollution might alter the structure and composition of an aquatic community: ___

___

___

___

ISBN: 978-1-98-856632-0

32 ← STB-3 5.B STB-3 1.C

139 POPs, Bioaccumulation, and Biomagnification

Key Question: Why are persistent toxins so harmful?

Persistent toxins such as heavy metals (e.g. mercury) and organic pesticides and industrial chemicals (e.g. DDT) resist degradation and stay in the environment for a long time. These persistent toxins can be taken up by organisms in their food or absorbed from the surrounding environment and accumulate in their tissues. This is called bioaccumulation. Once within an organism, toxins can be passed through a food chain, becoming more concentrated at each trophic level. This is called biomagnification.

What's the problem with persistent organic pollutants (POPs)?

Persistent organic pollutants (POPs) are organic compounds that are highly resistant to being broken down through chemical, biological, or photolytic processes. DDT, for example, has a half life of 15-30 years in the soil (table right) and 150 years in water. The longer the half life of the toxin, the more likely it is to harm to the organism. POPs can be carried very large distances from their source by water and wind. Under certain conditions, POPs enter a gas phase and enter the atmosphere where they can be transported long distances. POPs are fat soluble and bioaccumulate within the fatty tissues of organisms. They are harmful to wildlife and humans (below). The most commonly occurring POPs are organochlorines, such as DDT, and polychlorinated biphenyls (PCBs), industrial chemicals that were once widely used in a range of products.

Year	Amount DDT remaining (kg)
0	100
15	50
30	25
45	12.5
60	6.25
75	3.13

Effect on top predators: Long range transport of POPs has seen them accumulate in the Arctic where polar bears are the top predator. The polar bear diet is rich in fats, so the potential to ingest contaminants is very high. Even though most POP production has stopped, the bears are exposed to legacy contamination and their immune system, bone density, metabolism and reproduction are adversely affected.

Eggshell thinning: A Swedish study in 2004 showed increasing levels of POPs (mainly DDT and PCBs) in peregrine falcon eggs cause the birds' eggshells to be thinner than normal. Thinner shells make the eggs more fragile. As a result, many break before they are fully incubated and the chick dies. Eggshell thinning has been linked to population declines in several bird species including the peregrine falcon and the bald eagle.

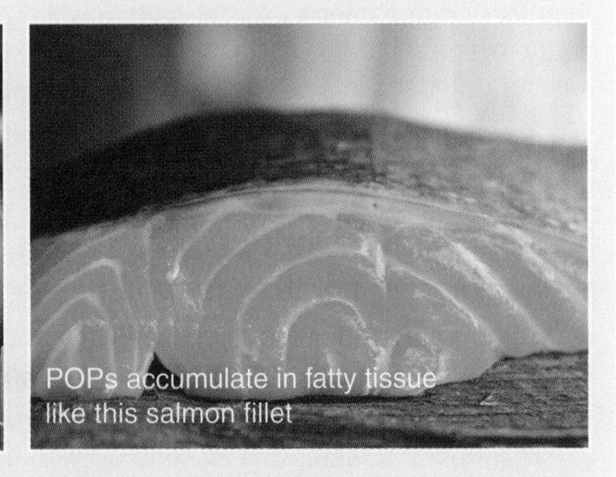

POPs accumulate in fatty tissue like this salmon fillet

Human health: Humans are exposed to POPs in food and from the air. POP exposure in humans has been linked to cancer, reproductive disorders, immune disorders, circulatory problems, birth defects, and endocrine disruption. The Stockholm Convention on POPs was established to protect human health and the environment through a number of pathways including reducing the use and production of POPs.

The biomagnification of a POP in a food chain

- DDT is a man-made (synthetic) insecticide and was first made in the 1940s. In the past it was widely used to control insect vectors carrying diseases such as malaria and typhus, and to control agricultural insect pests.
- However, it soon became obvious that DDT was harming non-target organisms too. For example, in the US, DDT sprayed onto agricultural crops washed into waterways and accumulated in the fatty tissues of fish. Bald eagles became poisoned when they ate the fish and their reproduction was affected. Their eggs had thin shells and broke during incubation.
- Agricultural use of DDT is banned in most countries and its use is restricted to controlling disease vectors (e.g. the mosquitoes that carry the malaria parasite).
- Biomagnification of POPs occurs within food chains (right). The DDT accumulates in the tissues of organisms. Higher order consumers may ingest toxic levels of a chemical because they eat a large number of lower order consumers. This bioaccumulation can prove fatal to apex predators, such as eagles and polar bears.

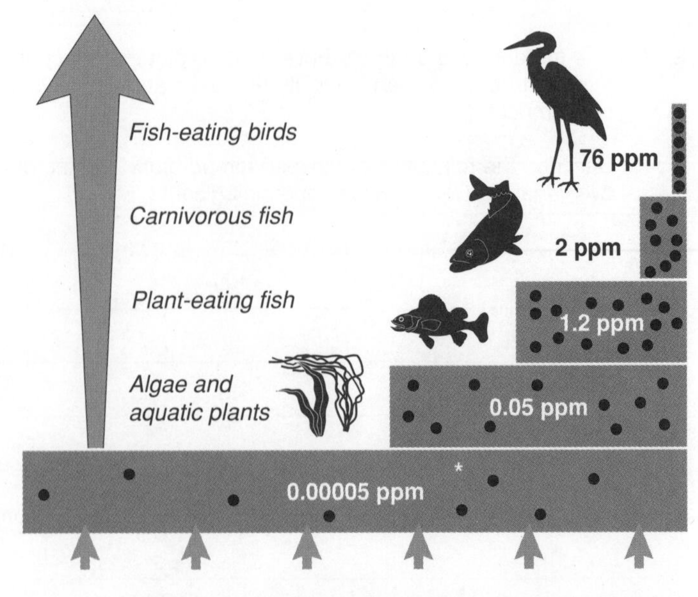

DDT enters the water as runoff from farmland sprayed with the insecticide. * ppm = parts per million

ISBN: 978-1-98-856632-0

Mercury in food chains

- Just as POPs accumulate in tissues and increase in concentration in food chains, so too do heavy metals such as mercury. During the Californian gold rush of the 1800s mercury was used to extract gold. Some mining sites still leach mercury into the Sacramento Delta and the San Francisco Bay, highlighting just how persistent mercury is.
- Recall that methylmercury is the most toxic form of mercury. Like POPs, methylmercury accumulates in the tissues of organisms. This occurs because it is taken in at a faster rate than it can be excreted (removed by metabolic processes) from the body.
- As methylmercury passes through successive trophic levels in a food chain it becomes more concentrated (biomagnification). When a predatory fish consumes smaller fish it acquires the mercury in all those smaller fish, which themselves have acquired mercury from the organisms they ate. In this way, mercury becomes more concentrated at higher trophic levels. This also applies to humans. Eating contaminated fish and shellfish is the most common source of methylmercury for humans.

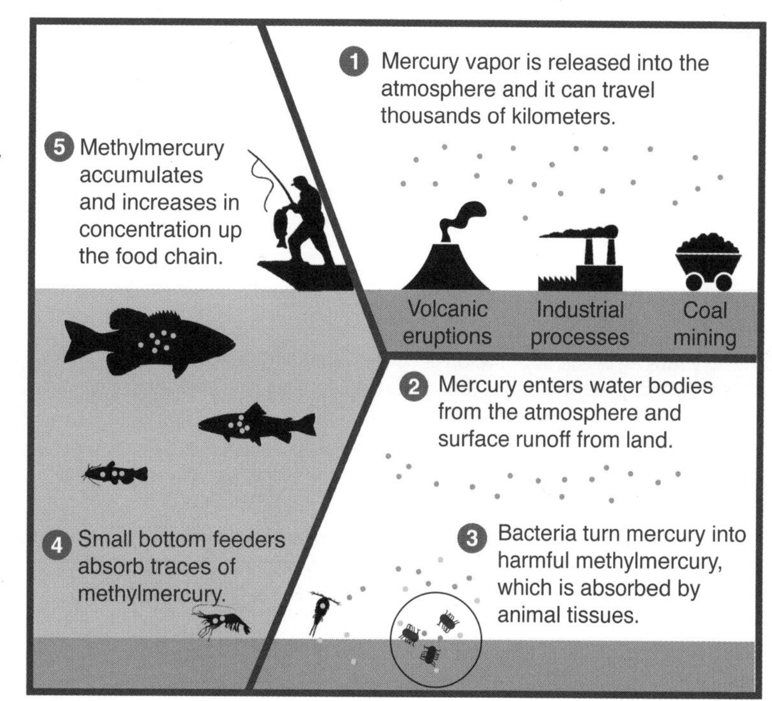

1. Explain the difference between biomagnification and bioaccumulation: ______

2. Explain why POPs are of particular concern for environmental health: ______

This table below right provides food chain information and mercury concentrations in the tissues of four organisms in a study of marine food chains in the Persian Gulf, a Mediterranean sea in Western Asia.

3. (a) Identify a testable scientific question that might apply to this study: ______

(b) Complete right hand column of the table by calculating the percentage increase in mercury between each of the consumers:

(c) Is this what you would expect? ______

(d) Explain: ______

Organism	Feeding habitat	Mercury concentration (μg/g)	Percentage increase per trophic level
Spinycheek grouper: benthic (bottom dwelling) fish	Eats mainly benthic invertebrates, detritus, and plants	0.82	–
Spottail needlefish: pelagic (open sea) fish	Eats mainly benthic fish, invertebrates, plants, and crustaceans	1.64	
Blue crab (estuarine and open water)	Fish predator, consumes mainly pelagic fish, but also detritus and plants	2.22	
Eurasian teal (sea bird)	Consumes mainly crab, fish, shrimp, and marine invertebrates	11.5	

ISBN: 978-1-98-856632-0

140 Solid Waste Disposal

Key Question: What is solid waste, how is it disposed of, and how does its disposal affect the environment?

Almost every activity we carry out generates waste. The Resource Conservation and Recovery Act (1976) is the principal federal law in the United States governing the disposal of solid waste. It ensures waste is safely disposed of so that people and the environment are not harmed. The EPA definition of solid waste includes not only wastes that are physically solid, but also liquid, semi-solid, or contained gaseous materials. For the purposes of this activity we will focus on municipal solid waste (MSW), i.e. the everyday waste generated in homes, schools, hospitals, and businesses.

What makes up our waste?

- The US EPA began collecting and reporting data about waste 30 years ago. The information is used to measure the success of materials management programs and provides information about what type of waste is produced.
- In 2017, 243 million tonnes of MSW was produced in the US. This is around 2 kg of waste per person every day. The diagram on the right shows the composition of the total MSW in 2017.
- One type of waste not specifically identified on the diagram is electronic waste (e-waste). This is the waste produced from discarded electronic devices (e.g. cell phones and computers).

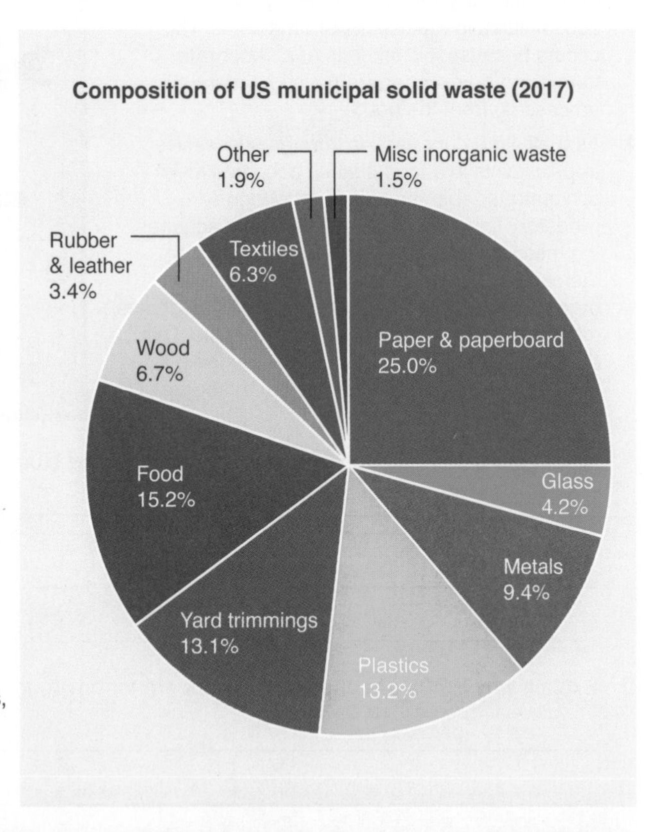

Landfills

Landfills are specially engineered areas where waste is dispose of. Landfills are the oldest and most common form of waste disposal and they are often used to get rid of MSW. It was once common for contaminants from landfill to escape (leach out) and contaminate ground water, or for the gases produced from waste decomposition to pollute the air. Modern landfills are designed to protect people and the environment by controlling emissions into water and air (opposite page). Regular monitoring helps to make sure no dangerous contaminants are escaping landfills.

Some waste is banned from MSW landfills because of the risk it poses to health and the environment. Banned waste includes paints, chemicals and cleaning solutions, motor oil, batteries, pesticides, and electronics. These wastes are treated differently under the Resource Conservation and Recovery Act (RCRA).

The South East New Territories Landfill (Hong Kong) covers 100 hectares (1 km^2). It now only accepts construction waste.

1. If one person generates 2 kg of waste a day, how much do they generate in a year? ______________________

2. (a) Of the MSW generated in 2017, 61 million tonnes was recycled and 24 million tonnes was composted. What percentage of the total MSW generated was either recycled or composted?

____

(b) A further 31 million tonnes of MSW was combusted for energy recovery. What percentage of MSW actually went to landfill in 2017?

____

ISBN: 978-1-98-856632-0

Municipal solid waste landfills

In the US, the RCRA regulates where and how landfills are built and operated. Sanitary municipal landfills are designed so that material from the landfill cannot contaminate the environment. Some features are described below.

Landfill gas conversion facility. Landfill gases can be utilized in energy recovery projects to make electricity, heat, or fuel. If the amount of gas is too low to use, **landfill vents** to allow the gas to escape.

Dumping into a designated area (**a cell**) improves land utilization. Trash is compacted so more can fit in. When a cell is full bulldozers cover it with soil to stop waste being blown away by the wind and to stop odors escaping.

The leachate is collected in perforated pipes (pipes with holes in them) where it is carried to **leachate collection tanks** for storage before it is treated to clean it up.

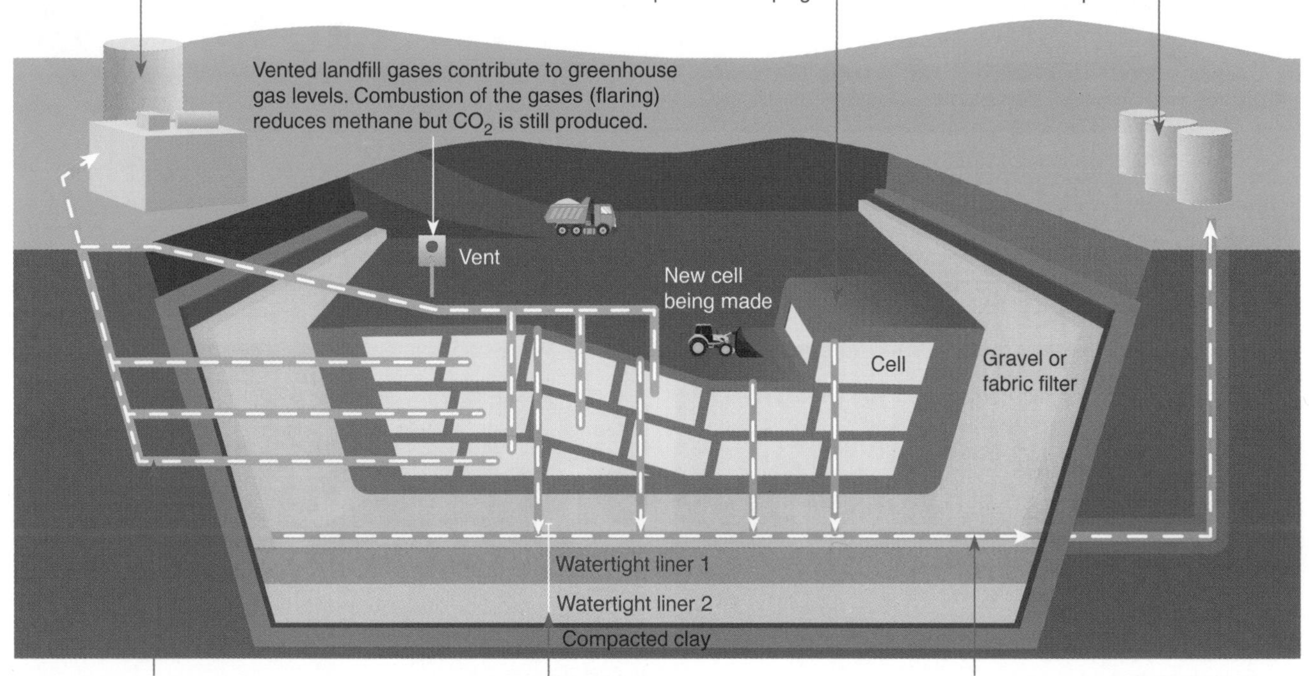

Anaerobic microbes decompose the waste and produced landfill gas (a roughly even mix of methane and carbon dioxide). **A system of pipes** removes the landfill gas to reduce the risk of explosion.

Layers of **compacted clay** and **watertight liners** prevent contaminated liquids from the landfill entering the surrounding land and groundwater systems.

Liquid produced in the landfill, as well as rain and snow, filters through the landfill and becomes contaminated by the landfill contents. The contaminated liquid (**leachate**) collects at the bottom of the landfill.

Rubbish is being dumped into a defined area called a cell. Once the cell is full it will be covered with soil. The protective landfill liner (arrowed) prevents leachate entering the ground water and drinking supply.

Landfill gas (a mixture of methane and carbon dioxide) is produced when anaerobic bacteria decompose organic waste. Both gases are greenhouse gases, and they contribute to global warming.

The landfill is capped (sealed) with clay or a plastic liner when it is full. At least 60 cm of compacted soil is deposited on top and vegetation (grasses or trees) is planted in the soil.

3. (a) Identify the main gases produced in landfills: ______________________

   (b) How are these gases managed? ______________________

   ____

   (c) Describe one benefit of the production of landfill gas: ______________________

   ____

   (d) Describe one disadvantage of the production of landfill gas: ______________________

   ____

ISBN: 978-1-98-856632-0

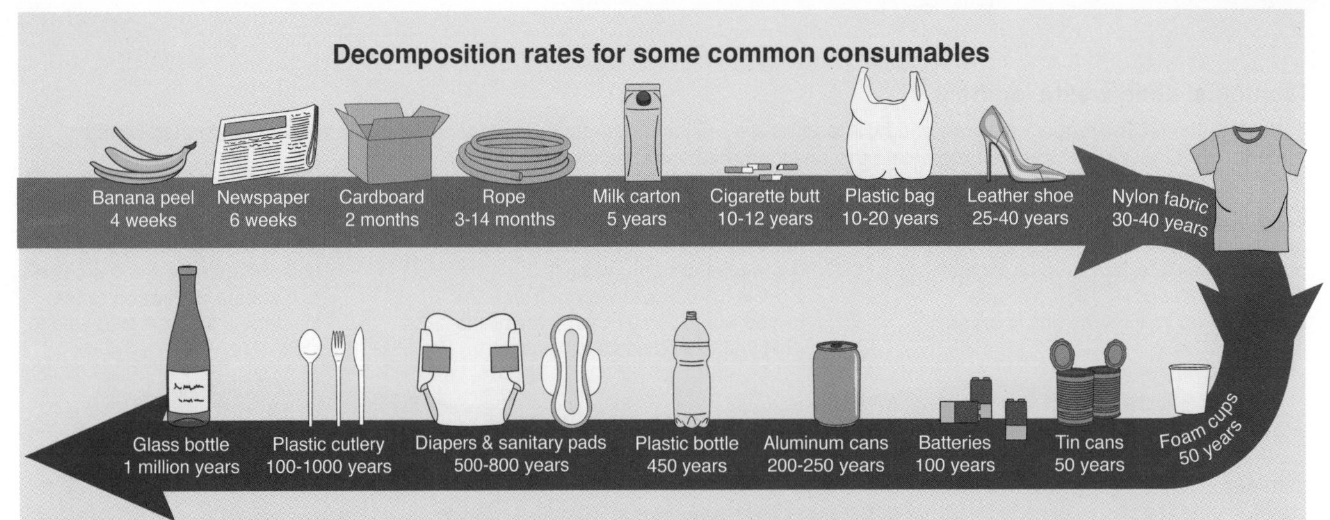

Rates of decomposition (breakdown) depend of several factors. Firstly, think back to the structure of a sanitary MSW landfill. The impermeable lining, compacted layers of trash, layers of soil, and capping mean the landfill doesn't have very much oxygen present. The lack of oxygen means anaerobic bacteria decompose the trash, and the rate can be very slow! Decomposition was faster in older landfills because they were uncovered and had plenty of oxygen present. Secondly, what waste is present? The diagram above shows decomposition times for commonly used household products. Some items take a very long time.

Waste incineration

As the population grows, so does the volume of waste produced. Finding suitable landfill sites will become harder, so reducing waste is important. Burning (incinerating) it is one way to reduce waste volumes. Waste is burned at very high temperatures in special facilities. One concern with this is that air pollutants (e.g. particulate matter) are produced, along with ash and flue gases. In regulated countries, incineration facilities must collect any particles in the flue gas before it is released into the atmosphere.

Illegal dumping

Some materials are illegally dumped because they cannot be disposed of in landfill and there is a cost for special disposal. A common example is tires. Water collects in them providing a breeding ground for mosquitoes. This is dangerous because some mosquitoes carry diseases that harm humans. Sometimes people dispose of their waste, including plastics, by dumping it in the ocean. The increase of plastic in oceans, and its effect on wildlife when animals eat it or become tangled in it, is concerning.

4. Why is it important that landfills are lined? ______________________________

5. Why was decomposition faster in older style landfills? ______________________________

6. How does incineration increase the lifespan of a landfill? ______________________________

7. How could tire piles cause harm to the local community? ______________________________

8. Why do you think it is becoming increasingly difficult to find suitable landfill sites? ______________________________

ISBN: 978-1-98-856632-0

141 Reducing Waste

Key Question: How can we reduce the amount of solid waste going to landfill? What are the environmental effects?

As the human population increases so does the amount of waste generated. We have seen in the previous activity that landfills are the most common way of dealing with MSW. Many landfills are filling up quickly, so finding ways to reduce their rate of filling is a priority. There are several ways to reduce how much trash goes into a landfill. These involve reducing waste production, reusing materials that would otherwise end up in landfill, and recycling materials when possible. Alternative ways to dispose of waste also help to reduce the volume of trash going to landfill.

Landfills in the US

In 1990, there were over 6000 landfills in the US. in 2020, there are now 1250. The number has dropped for several reasons. Landfills have closed because they have become full, it is harder to gain permission to open new landfills, and many new landfills are very large and can hold a lot of trash! Some states send their landfill to other states or even other countries if they don't have enough capacity themselves. For example, when the Staten Island landfill in New York City closed, trash was sent to Ohio, Pennsylvania, and West Virginia.

Waste generation in the US is increasing. In 1960, 80 million tonnes were generated. This increased to 243 million tonnes in 2017. So how long does the US have before its landfills become full? Estimates vary, but it could be within the next few decades. This means it very important that households, businesses, manufacturers, and policy makers do everything they can to reduce landfill waste. The best method is to reduce the amount of material made or used in the first place (right). For example, drinking from a reusable water bottle instead of buying single use water bottles every time you want water. Composting, reusing, and recycling are also good waste reduction methods.

Waste management hierarchy

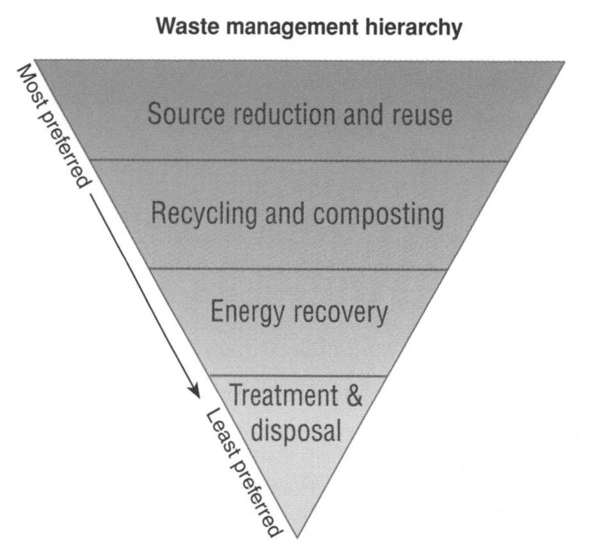

Reusing something is the simplest way to reduce waste. You can do this by buying used goods, borrowing items if it is something that you are not going to need very often, or buying reusable items instead of disposable ones. A common example is encouraging the use of reusable shopping bags. In England, customers are charged a few cents for single use bags. This has reduced their annual use from 7.6 billion to 1.5 billion.

Composting breaks down biodegradable waste like food scraps, yard waste, and paper. Composting is possible in almost every household, even those without a yard. Many homes have small worm farms or cultured composts for kitchen scraps. The nutrient rich final product can be used as fertilizer, returning nutrients back to the soil. However, composting can attract rodents or begin to smell if it is not done properly.

Recycling converts waste materials into new materials. It reduces the waste going to landfill and conserves the Earth's resources because there is no need to mine and process new materials. However, recycling comes at a cost. Building the plant, investing in specialist equipment, and running cost can be expensive. Material must be transported and cleaned before processing, and the recycling process itself can require a lot of energy.

1. (a) Briefly describe the difference between reusing and recycling: ______________________

____

____

(b) Explain why both strategies are helpful in reducing waste: ______________________

____

____

____

2. Identify two potential disadvantages of composting: ______________________

____

ISBN: 978-1-98-856632-0

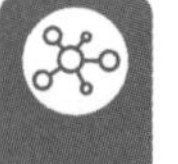

E-waste

- Electronic waste (e-waste) refers to electronic products that are no longer useful. Computer equipment, cell phones, TVs, lamps, and kitchen appliances are examples of e-waste. It is estimated 50 million tonnes of e-waste was generated globally in 2018.
- Up to 60 elements from the periodic table can be found in complex electronics and many are technically recoverable. However e-waste also contains hazardous materials like lead and mercury. E-waste represents 2% of solid waste streams but it can make up 70% of the hazardous waste that ends up in a landfill.
- Its hazardous nature means that e-waste should be treated at a specialist facility where the goods are safely dismantled, the components are extracted, and the remaining waste is properly disposed of. Dumping e-waste into landfill or improper processing can release dangerous contaminants into the environment.
- There are concerns about the future supply of new materials for electronics and electrical devices. Yet they are routinely discarded and very little e-waste (~20%) is recycled. Recycling metals is much more energy efficient and 13 times less costly than extraction from ore and produces fewer CO_2 emissions. It follows that making use of the secondary raw materials in electronic goods could help considerably towards a more sustainable future.

Smartphones contain many valuable materials such as gold, silver, copper, palladium, platinum, aluminum and copper. They also contain a number of rare Earth elements that are very difficult and expensive to mine. Smartphones only contain a small amount of these, but there are over 2 billion smart phones in use, so sometimes the concentration of these materials is higher in the phone than it is in the Earth. It is estimated Americans replace their phone every 12-18 months.

Energy cost of reusable cups vs disposable cups

The manufacture of reusable items, such as ceramic cups, uses a large amount of energy. Energy is also used in heating water and manufacturing detergent to wash them. Disposable styrofoam or paper cups require little energy to produce and none for cleaning because they are thrown away after they have been used. The table on shows how much energy is needed to produce a single cup. Five different materials are compared.

A ceramic cup is designed to be long lasting and can be used 3000 times. Styrofoam and paper cups are designed to be used only once before they are thrown away.

Cup type	Cup mass g/cup	Material specific energy MJ/kg	Energy per cup MJ/cup
Ceramic	292	48	14
Plastic	59	107	6.3
Glass	199	28	5.5
Paper	8.3	66	0.55
Foam	1.9	104	0.20

3. One million mobile phones contain 16 tonnes of copper, 350 kg of silver, 34 kg of gold, and 15 kg of palladium. Calculate the mass of these materials for the total estimated mobile phones currently in use (2 billion):

4. (a) Study the table above showing energy cost of making different types of cups. How many times more energy does it take to make a ceramic cup compared to a styrofoam cup?

(b) Use the information on the table and text to show mathematically why ceramic reusable cups are considered better environmental options even though they take more energy to make:

ISBN: 978-1-98-856632-0

Landfill mitigation

Mitigation means to reduce how harmful, unpleasant, or bad something is. Landfills have the potential to be unpleasant (smelly and unsightly) or dangerous if they are not properly managed. We have already seen that a correctly designed sanitary landfill reduces its environmental impact and that there several ways to reduce the amount of trash that ends up there (reduce, reuse, recycle). But there are other mitigation strategies too (below).

Mount Trashmore Park

Mount Trashmore Park (Virginia Beach, Virginia) covers almost 67 hectares on what was once a large landfill. The park contains two man-made 'mountains', two lakes, playgrounds, a skate park, recreational facilities, picnic areas, and multi-use paths. The main mountain, Mount Trashmore, is over 18 m tall and 243 meters long, and was created by compacting layers of solid waste and clean soil. Around 900,000 people visit it each year. Converting old landfill sites into recreational or green spaces is common around the world.

Combustion of landfill trash and gases

Z22 CC 4.0

The heat produced from incinerating trash can be used to generate electricity. According to the EPA, landfills are the third largest source of methane emissions in the US. The methane can be harvested (above) and used in several ways. It can be used on site in a combustion system to provide heat (e.g. a boiler), it can be sold as natural gas and sent off site, or it can be burned and used to turn a turbine to generate electricity. Utilizing methane also reduces the amount in the atmosphere contributing to global warming.

5. Landfills in America are filling up fast. Some estimates predict they will all be full in a few decades. Discuss why this is happening and what can be done to reduce their fill rate:

6. How can landfill trash and landfill gases be used to generate energy?

ISBN: 978-1-98-856632-0

142 Your Waste

Key Question: How much trash do you generate in a day?
We have seen that every day each American generates around 2 kg of trash. Some can be recycled but some can't or isn't, so it ends up in the landfill. Photographer Gregg Segal's "7 Days of Garbage" project captured trash generated by his family, friends, and neighbors over one week. Some of his photos are displayed below. Take a moment to look at the photos and think about the following questions. How does the amount of trash vary for each scenario? What sort of trash is generated, can it be recycled? In this activity you will investigate how much trash you generate in one day. How much your trash is recyclable? How much goes into landfill?

All photos used with permission: Gregg Segal (https://www.greggsegal.com/)

ISBN: 978-1-98-856632-0

INVESTIGATION 8.2: Recording your trash

See appendix for equipment list.

In this investigation you will collect or record all of the trash you generate in a single day. Try to choose a day that represents a typical day in your week so that it provides a fair representation of your daily trash generation.
Record any trash you collect. Your trash may include: food packaging, left over food waste (e.g. food scraps from meal preparation, apple cores, unfinished meals or snacks that are not being kept for leftovers), take-out containers, straws, single use utensils, single use drink containers, magazines, newspapers or paper advertising material, any packaging where you were the last person to use the item (e.g. milk or juice carton, bread bag, toilet roll, toothpaste tube), ticket stubs (e.g. movies, bus, or subway tickets), till receipts, packaging or bags from purchased items.

1. Collect or record of all the trash you generate during the day. You can do this in several ways:
   - Place all of your trash in spill proof bags as you go throughout your daily activities.
   - Use your phone to take photos of all the trash you generate during the day.
   - Write down every item of trash you generate during the day.
2. Now separate your trash into the categories listed in the table below. Record the numbers of items you have collected for each category. Note: food scraps from a single meal count as one item.

	Food waste	Paper	Plastic	Glass	Aluminum cans	Tin cans	Other	Total
Item count								
Percentage								

3. Work out the percentage of trash in each category. Record it in the table above.
4. Graph the percentage composition data in the grid provided.
5. Roughly estimate what percentage of your trash is recyclable:

   ____

6. Now reflect on your findings. Were you surprised about how much trash you generated? What did you learn about the types of trash you generated? How much of your recyclable trash would you actually recycle (this includes composting food scraps) and how much of your recyclable trash would you put in landfill bins?

   ____

7. Is there anything you would do differently now you have analyzed you trash generation? ______________________

ISBN: 978-1-98-856632-0

143 Environmental Remediation

Key Question: How can we remove pollutants or contaminants from an area so that it is safe again?

Land is often redeveloped for other purposes. For example the conversion of abandoned industrial sites into housing, or an old landfill into a green space. However, sometimes the land is contaminated from previous activities and the contaminants must be removed to make the area safe. The process of cleaning up contaminated land is called environmental remediation. The method of remediation used depends on the extent and type of contamination present. For example, polluted top soil can be removed and treated off-site, or plants and bacteria may be introduced to the site to absorb and break down the contaminants. Monitoring is also required to make sure that no further leaching of contaminants occurs.

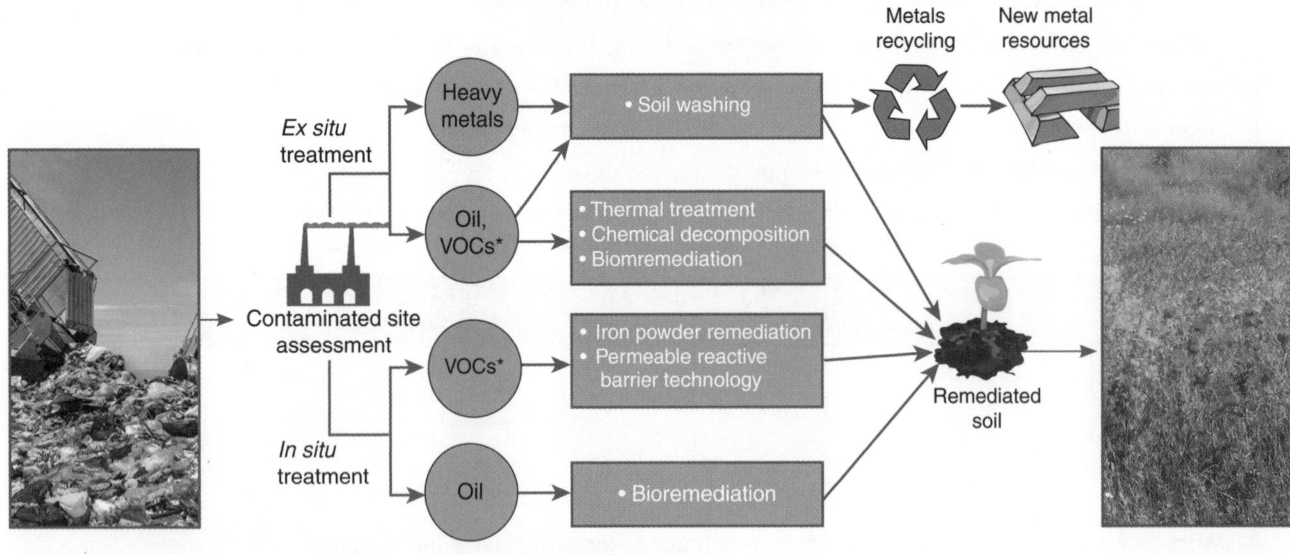

*VOCs: Volatile Organic Compounds

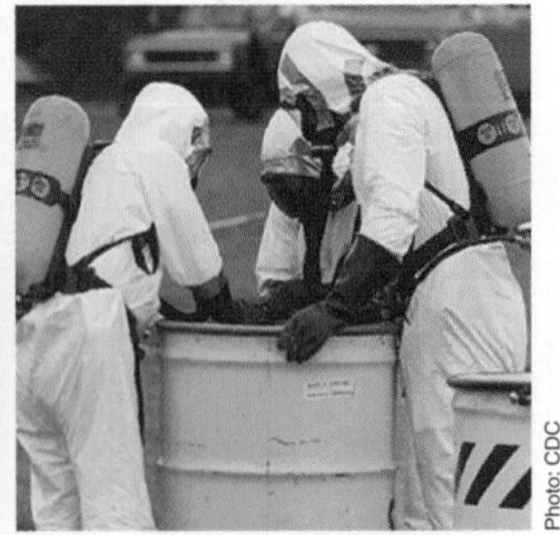

Photo: CDC

Photo: Nick Carson

The US Superfund Law is formally known as the Comprehensive Environmental Response, Compensation and Liability Act (CERCLA). It was enacted in 1980 to investigate and clean up sites contaminated with hazardous substances. Sites managed under this act are called Superfund sites. They are highly toxic abandoned sites that the EPA has identified for extensive remediation. The most highly contaminated sites are listed on the National Priorities List (NPL). There are approximately 1600 sites listed on the NPL and over 40,000 Superfund sites in total.

The EPA offers a number of grants for environmental assessment, clean-up, and job training activities related to contaminated sites. The level of environmental remediation achieved depends on the extent and nature of the contamination. Even after many years of remediation, some sites can never be made safe enough for humans to occupy. CERCLA allows the EPA to force the responsible parties to perform clean-ups or reimburse the government for EPA-led cleanups. When no responsible party can be identified, CERCLA authorizes the EPA to clean up sites itself.

1. What is the purpose of environmental remediation? ___

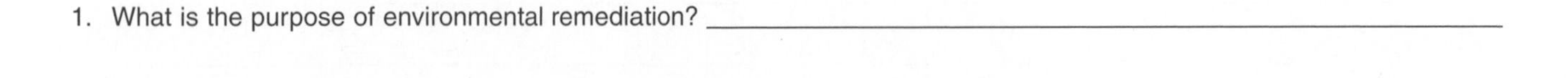

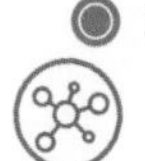

2. One minute essay! Use the link on **BIOZONE's Resource Hub** to navigate to the map showing all of the NPL Superfund sites. Choose a Superfund site in your state. Write a one minute essay (as bullet points) to cover the following points:
• The cause of the contamination • The methods being used to clean up the site • The potential success of the clean-up
• The implications of the outcome to the local community. Record your findings on a separate piece of paper or share in an electronic document with your class.

ISBN: 978-1-98-856632-0

144 Sewage Treatment

Key Question: How are sewage treatment plants designed to be most effective?

Sewage is wastewater that has been used by households or industry (e.g. toilet waste). Sewage contains organic waste, debris, and contaminants that must be removed before the water can be returned to the environment. Failure to treat sewage properly can lead to pollution of waterways and spread of disease. Sewage treatment occurs at specially built plants and usually consists of three steps; primary, secondary and tertiary treatment. Primary treatment involves removing solid debris in a pre-settling basin. Secondary treatment uses biological activity to remove contaminants from the liquid waste. Tertiary treatment usually involves filtration and often chemical or UV treatment to kill any remaining microbes.

Sewage treatment process

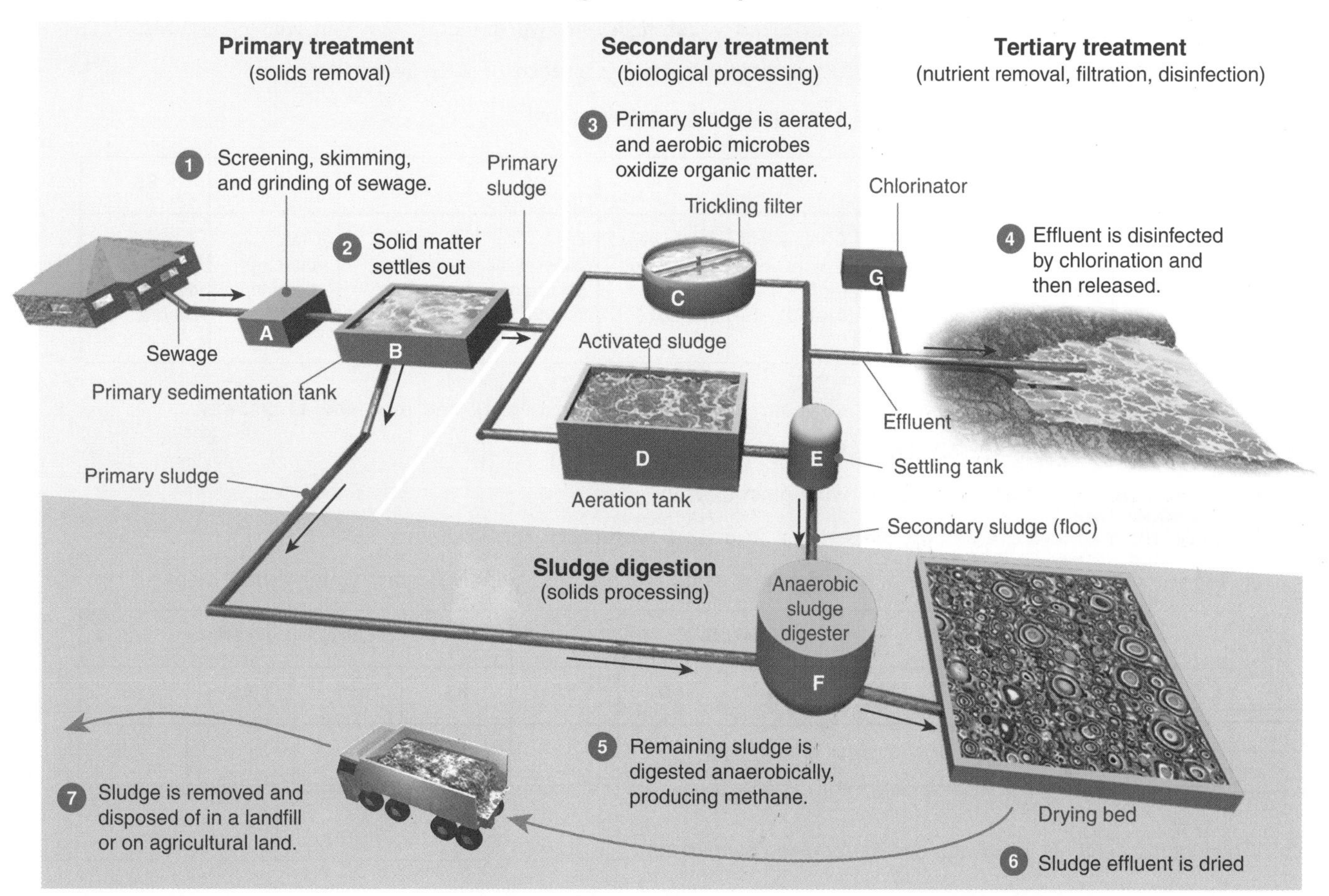

Primary treatment

Mechanical processes (screens, grates and skimming) are used to remove large objects from the sewage. This is followed by a settling out process where solid matter settles out in tanks.

Secondary treatment

Aerobic bacteria are used to break down dissolved organic matter into carbon dioxide and sludge. This process is aerated to increase the reaction rates.

NOTE: Anaerobic microbes can be used later to digest the sludge more. They function in the absence of oxygen.

Tertiary treatment

The effluent passes through filters to remove any fine particles still in solution. It also is disinfected to kill any remaining harmful microbes. In the past this involved the addition of chlorine, but ozone or UV light may be used instead of (or in addition to) chlorine.

1. Using the information provided in the diagram and text above, classify each of the processes indicated A-G as either mechanical, biological, or chemical.

A: ______________________ D: ______________________ G: ______________________

B: ______________________ E: ______________________

C: ______________________ F: ______________________

2. Work in pairs or small groups to research the sewage treatment process in your town or city, identifying the specific techniques and problems of wastewater management in your area. Your research should include:
the volume of sewage processed, the degree of purification, the treatment processes used, the point of discharge.

Record your answers either on a separate piece of paper or as an electronic document.

ISBN: 978-1-98-856632-0

131

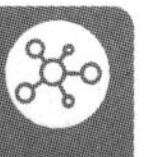

Modeling microbial activity in sewage treatment

An important step in treating sewage or wastewater is removing dissolved nutrients. These are usually removed by microbes. This can be done aerobically in aeration tanks, or anaerobically in tanks that exclude oxygen.

The following experiment can be used to model microbiological activity in the wastewater treatment process. *Saccharomyces* yeast represents the microbes involved. This yeast uses fermentation when sugars are not limiting. Fermentation is an anaerobic process (it does not require oxygen). In this model, glucose represents the dissolved nutrients.

INVESTIGATION 8.3: The role of microbes in sewage treatment

See appendix for equipment list.

Work in pairs or groups for this investigation.

1. Rehydrate the yeast by adding 14 g of dried yeast to 40 mL warm water. Mix and wait 5 minutes.
2. Add 500 mL of glucose solution (100 g/L concentration) into each of 8 large beakers.
3. Label and prepare the beakers as specified in the table below:

Beaker	2A	4A	6A	8A	2S	4S	6S	8S
Treatment	2 mL yeast + aeration (not sealed)	4 mL yeast + aeration (not sealed)	6 mL yeast + aeration (not sealed)	8 mL yeast + aeration (not sealed)	2 mL yeast + no aeration, sealed	4 mL yeast no aeration, sealed	6 mL yeast no aeration, sealed	8 mL yeast no aeration, sealed

4. Add the correct volume of activated yeast mixture into each beaker and mix well to disperse.
5. Aerate beakers 2A, 4A, 6A, and 8A using a fish tank aerator.
6. Cover beakers 2S, 4S, 6S, and 8S with plastic wrap.
7. Once the beakers are set up, place them in a 32°C waterbath for 48 hours.
8. Measure the level of glucose after 48 hours using glucose test paper. Record your results below.

	Aerated				Sealed, no aeration			
Beaker	2A	4A	6A	8A	2S	4S	6S	8S
Final glucose conc. (g/L)								

3. Which of the contents in sewage can be removed by microbes? ______________________

4. (a) Which treatment was most effective at removing glucose (dissolved nutrient)? ______________________

   (b) Which letter(s) in the diagram on the previous page represents this step in sewage treatment? ______________________

   (c) How could the most effective result above be replicated in a treatment plant? Explain your reasoning: ______________________

5. The students decided to repeat the experiment using *Brettanomyces* yeast, which preferentially respires aerobically. Predict the outcome of the experiment and suggest which part of the sewage treatment process this may represent.

ISBN: 978-1-98-856632-0

145 Measuring Toxicity

Key Question: How is toxicity measured?

Toxicity is the degree to which a chemical substance can cause harm to an organism. The toxicity of all chemicals (including pollutants) can be measured. This establishes the level at which the chemical stops being safe and begins to cause harm. Each chemical has its own toxicity. Some are toxic in very low concentrations whereas others need to be present in very high concentrations to be harmful. Toxicity also varies among individuals of the same species (e.g. due to sex, weight, or age) and between species. Toxicity can be measured a number of ways, e.g. median lethal dose (LD_{50}) and dose response curves.

LD_{50}

- The LD_{50} (Lethal Dose 50%) test determines how much of a specific substance is required to kill 50% of a test population.
- The lower the figure, the more toxic the substance.
- The species tested, their relative health, and the mode of administration (oral, intravenous, or surface) all influence the final LD_{50} value.
- LD_{50} is calculated over a specific test period, so it is an acute (short term) measure. It does not provide information about chronic (low level, long term) exposure to a substance.

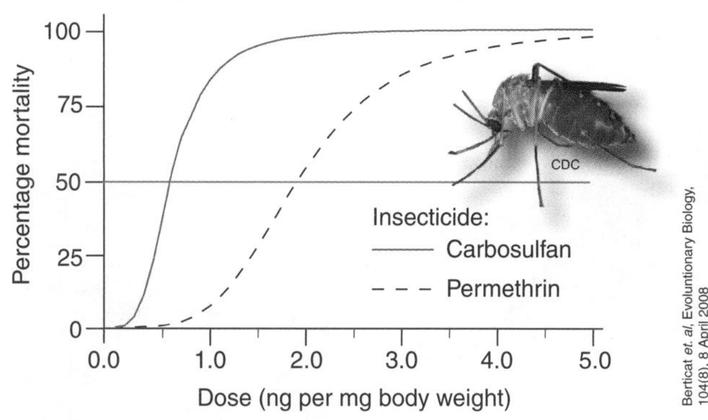

The southern house mosquito (*Culex quinquefasciatus*) can carry the West Nile virus (WNV), which is the leading cause of mosquito-borne disease in the US. Insecticides are used to kill the mosquitoes and help control the spread of WNV. LD_{50} testing of insecticides is routinely carried out to calculate the effectiveness of current and new insecticides against this species (graph above).

Dose response curves

- A dose-response curve shows the relationship between the dose of a substance (e.g. toxin or drug) administered and its effect on a population.
- The shape and slope of the dose-response curve provide information about the effect or toxicity of substances at specific doses. This includes:
  - The threshold response (TR). This is the lowest dose where an effect is observed.
  - The concentration of a drug that gives the half-maximal response is the half maximal effective concentration (EC_{50}). It is used to measure the potency of the substance being tested.
- Dose-response curves for different substances, including TR and EC_{50} can be compared (below).

Dose-response curves for two hypothetical chemcials

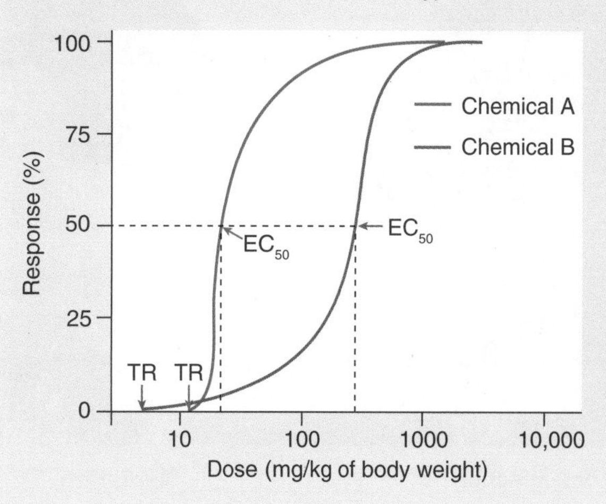

1. (a) State the LD_{50} for the insecticide carbosulfan against *C. quinquefasciatus*: ______

   (b) State the LD_{50} for the insecticide permethrin against *C. quinquefasciatus*: ______

   (c) Which insecticide is the most effective? Explain why: ______

2. Study the dose response curves above for chemicals A and B. How would you describe the difference between the two?

ISBN: 978-1-98-856632-0

146 Health Effects of Pollution

Key Question: How can pollution harm human health?

The effects of pollution on health depends on concentration and type of pollutant and extent of exposure. People living in cities usually have a greater exposure to pollutants than those in rural areas, although people in intensively farmed areas can be exposed to high levels of toxins from fertilizers and pesticides. It can be difficult to avoid some pollutants, such as carbon monoxide from traffic, but others (e.g. cigarette smoke) are more easily avoided. Sometimes the cause of ill health can be hard to identify because humans are exposed to different pollutants daily.

Air pollution

- Air pollutants, such as lead, severely affect nerve function.
- CO reduces the blood's ability to carry oxygen and results in headaches, and impaired thinking and slower reflexes.
- SO_2, NO_x and high levels of tropospheric ozone (O_3) harm respiratory function.

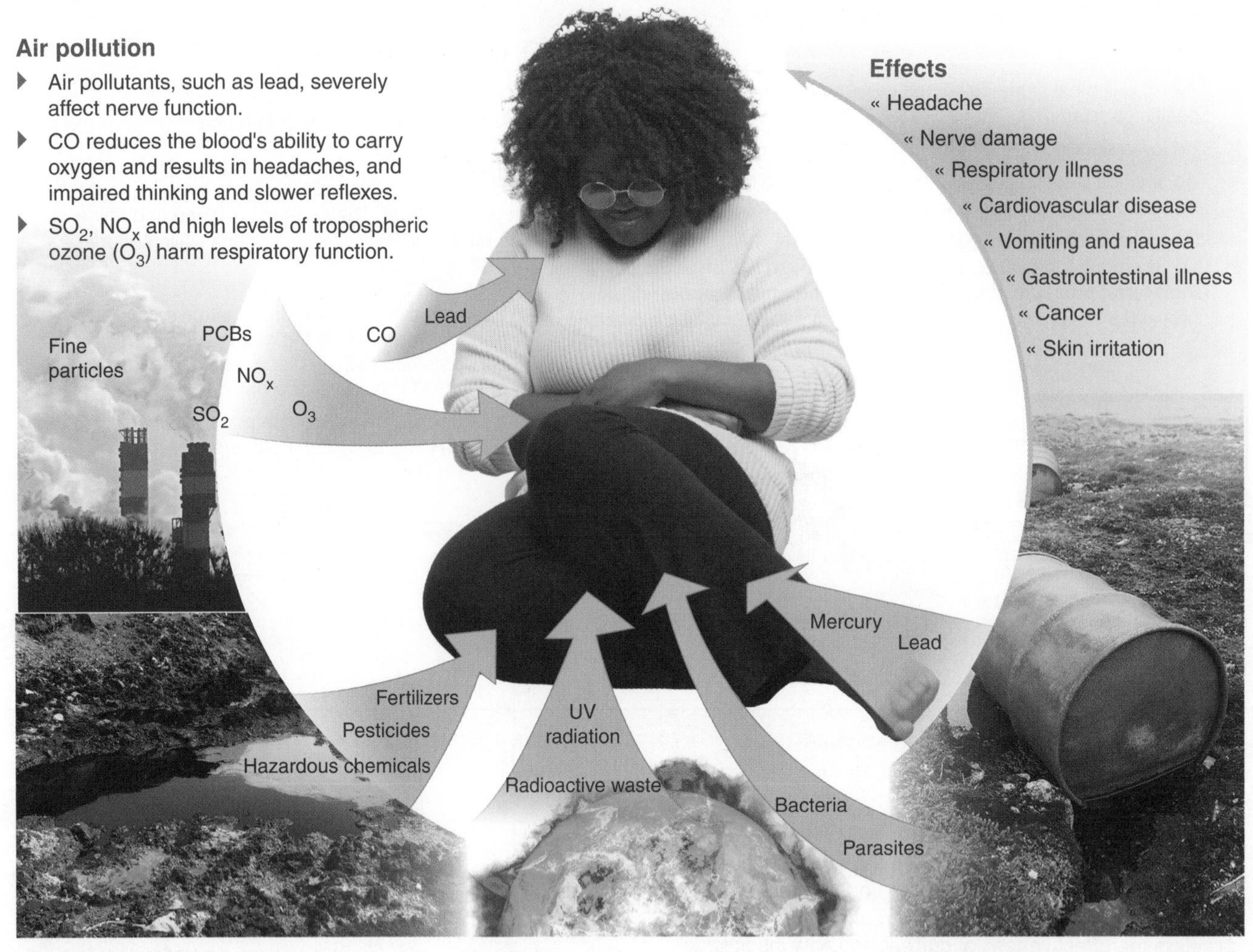

Soil contamination

- Pesticides based on organophosphates are extremely toxic to humans and other mammals.
- Fertilizers can cause acute methemoglobinemia (a life-threatening blood disorder), cancer, and respiratory illness.

Radiation

- UV radiation from sunlight and UV lamps causes melanoma skin cancer. If left untreated, it can spread and become life threatening.
- Radioactive waste can cause genetic defects in fetuses and cancer in adults and children.

Water pollution

- Heavy metals (e.g. mercury and lead) cause nerve damage.
- Untreated sewage may contain pathogenic microbes (cholera, giardia), which cause serious, or even fatal, gastrointestinal illnesses such as dysentery.

1. Why can it be difficult to identify the precise cause of an illness? ______________________

____

____

2. Carry out your own research to determine the main source of asbestos in the US and outline its link to mesothelioma. Describe measures used to diagnose mesothelioma and explain why several measures are applied:

____

____

____

____

____

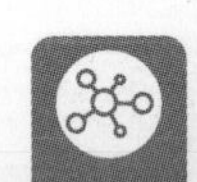

ISBN: 978-1-98-856632-0

147 Environment and Disease

Key Question: What are pathogens and what factors influence their spread in the human population?

We encounter microbes (viruses, bacteria, or fungi) in our life every day. Most are harmless, but some are pathogens, meaning they cause disease. The characteristics of pathogens vary widely. Some cause relatively harmless diseases like the common cold, while others cause serious illness or death (e.g. measles and Ebola). Some pathogens have a very low infection rate, whereas others spread through the population very easily and infect a large number of people. Geographical conditions and socio-economic factors influence the spread and prevalence of pathogens. Vaccinations help to reduce the likelihood of some infections, but there are no vaccinations for others because the pathogens change (mutate) very quickly, making vaccines ineffective. Rapidly mutating pathogens can be dangerous because the changes may allow them to exploit new hosts or new conditions, or may provide protection from our immune system or medical treatments like antibiotics.

Pathogens are all around us

People often assume pathogens are only found where there are sick people, such as hospitals and medical centres, or in dirty or unhygienic places, such as busy restrooms and dirty kitchens. However, pathogens can occur almost anywhere, even in places that seem clean and sanitary to the naked eye. The photo below shows an upmarket grocery store. The store looks clean and tidy and the food looks to be of good quality. However, there are many places we could come into contact with pathogens while shopping.

High touch surfaces such as door handles, grocery carts, shopping baskets, and payment pads at the checkout, have the potential to accumulate large numbers of pathogens because many people touch them. It is a good idea to wash your hands or use sanitizer after coming into contact with these surfaces.

This man has a cold. If he coughs or sneezes without covering or containing the droplets, the cold virus will spread several meters: over the food, the cart, and into the aisle where it could be inhaled by other shoppers. Many dangerous pathogens, such as measles and Covid-19, are spread this way.

Many foods, including fresh produce or meat, may be contaminated during harvesting or processing. If contaminated food is not washed, prepared, or cooked properly before it is eaten, people can become sick.

Air conditioning units can contain pathogens. As the air is pumped out of the air conditioning unit, pathogens can be distributed throughout the store. If the pathogens are inhaled they may cause illness.

If this woman has not washed her hands after going to the bathroom she may be spreading fecal matter (and pathogens) on the produce she touches. She may contaminate food she does not buy, and others could become infected.

The person who used this cart earlier had an uncovered cut on their hand. If they have a blood or skin infection it could be deposited on the handle of the cart and transferred to the next shopper. If an airborne pathogen settles on the handle this could also be transferred if the next shopper touches the handle and then their face or mouth.

Types of pathogens

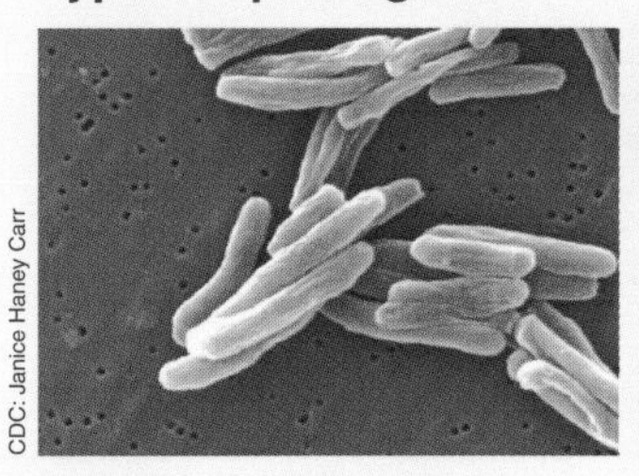

CDC: Janice Haney Carr

Bacterial pathogens

Pathogenic bacteria can be transmitted through food, water, air, or by direct contact. They cause a wide range of diseases. Many are treated with antibiotics.

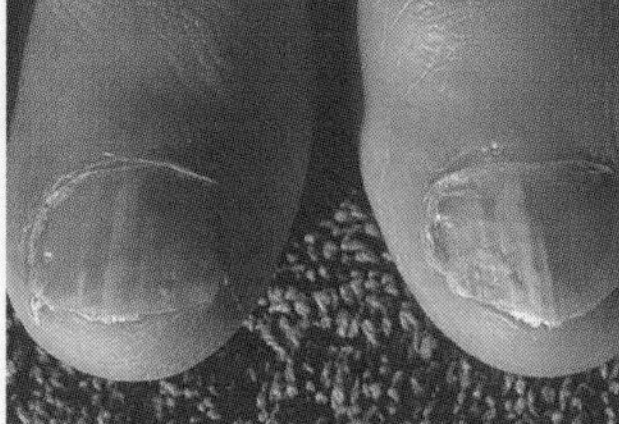

Fungal pathogens

Pathogenic fungi spread by spores and the infections they cause are generally chronic (long-lasting) infections because fungi grow relatively slowly.

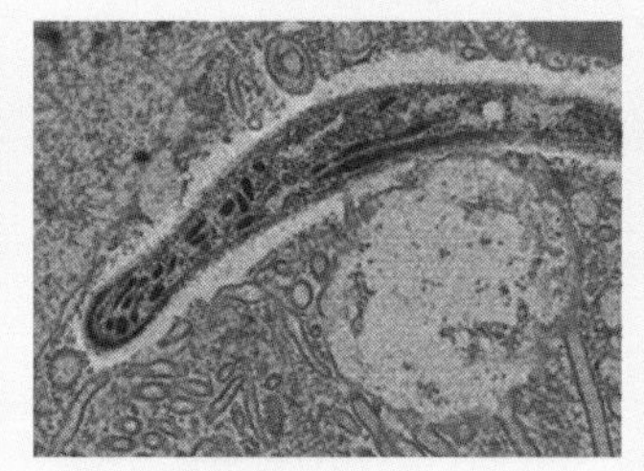

Protistan pathogens

Protistans are eukaryotes. Pathogenic protists have very complex life cycles, often involving a number of different hosts and several life stages.

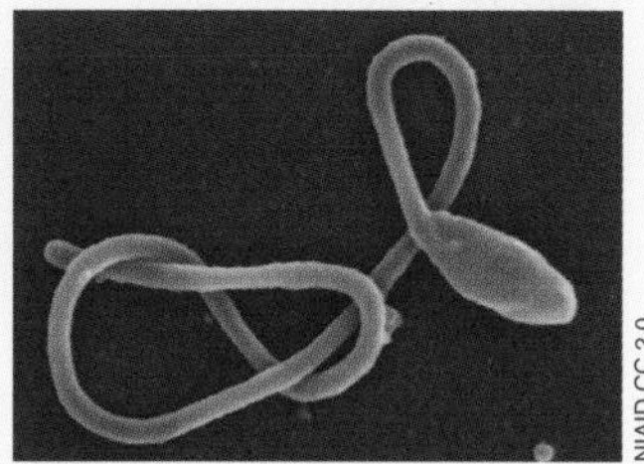

NIAID CC 2.0

Viral pathogens

A virus is a highly infectious pathogen that infects living cells and uses the cell's metabolic machinery to replicate. They cause many diseases.

1. What is a pathogen? ______________________________

____

____

ISBN: 978-1-98-856632-0

Socioeconomic factors and disease

Socioeconomic factors (low income, poor education, poor infrastructure, and lack of facilities) can increase the rate of disease. This is why many infectious diseases persist in developing countries (which often lack resources) but have often been eliminated where the standard of living is higher. It is estimated 1.7 million people die each year from drinking unsafe water or poor sanitation.

Untreated water source in Tanzania

Outdoor toilet in Bangladesh

SuSanA Secretariat cc 2.0

Clean drinking water

In many countries there is no access to safe drinking water. Millions of people drink and prepare their food using water from unprotected or contaminated water sources. Diarrhea caused by drinking contaminated water kills 800,000 people each year. Dangerous diseases such as cholera, hepatitis A, and polio are picked up by drinking unsafe water. Parasites can also be present and cause diseases.

Sanitation

Most developed countries have good sanitation enabling them to safely treat and dispose of human waste. However, some developing countries have inadequate sanitation and the risk of becoming sick from contact with human waste is high. The WHO estimates 400,000 people each year die as a result of poor sanitation. Most deaths are from untreated diarrhea, but deaths due to cholera, dysentery, hepatitis A, or typhoid are common.

Climate change and malaria

All pathogens require specific conditions for optimal growth, survival, and spread. Some pathogens require another organism, called a vector, to spread the pathogen. An example of this is the transmission of the disease malaria. Malaria is caused by a protozoan pathogen called *Plasmodium,* and it is transferred to people when they are bitten by an *Anopheles* mosquito infected with the pathogen. Malaria is currently limited to the warm, wet tropical regions around the equator where the *Anopheles* mosquito can quickly reproduce (map below). However, with global temperatures predicted to increase as a result of global warming, *Anopheles* may expand its range into areas that are currently malaria-free. Other insect-borne diseases could also expand their range as global temperatures rise. This would place new health and economic burdens on countries that are already poorly equipped to deal with disease.

Anopheles gambiae, a principal vector for the malarial parasite

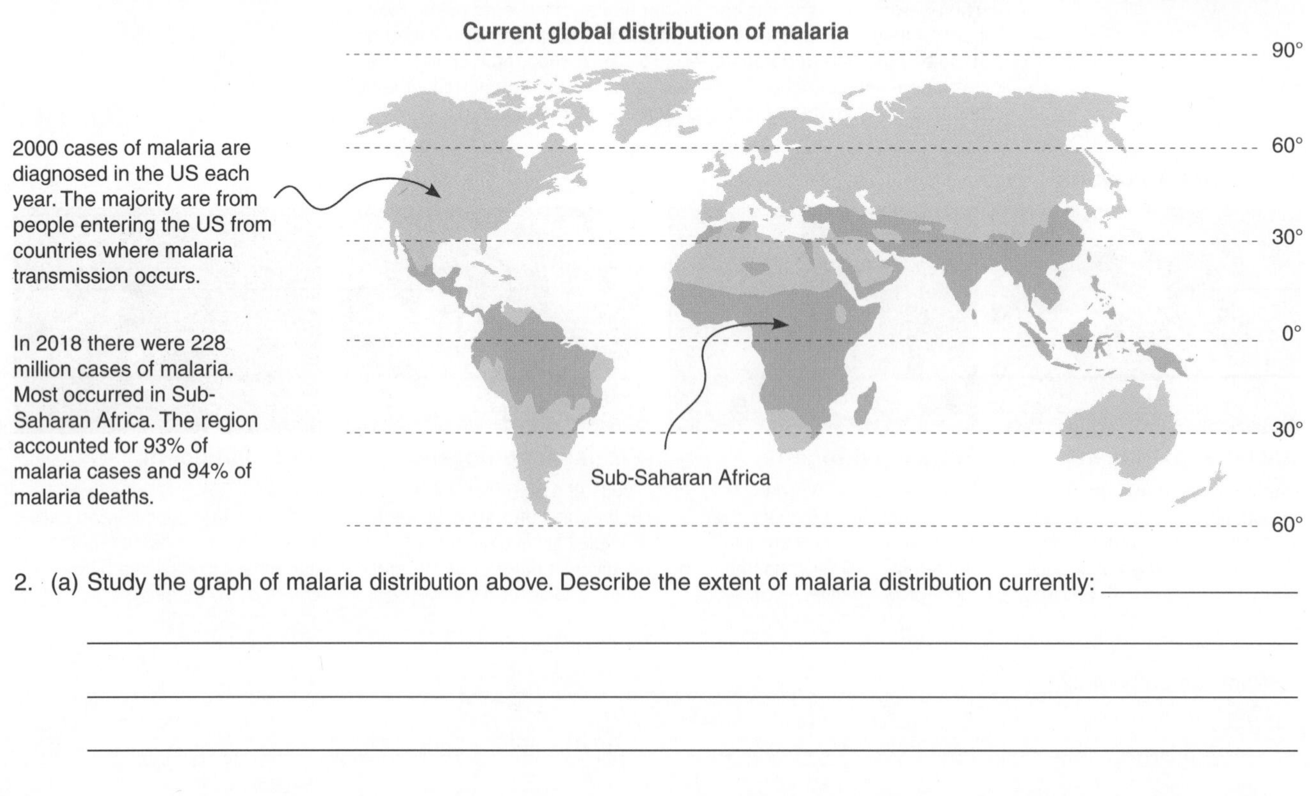

2. (a) Study the graph of malaria distribution above. Describe the extent of malaria distribution currently: ________________

ISBN: 978-1-98-856632-0

Climate change and Lyme disease in North America

- Lyme disease is the most common tick-borne disease in the US. Up to 300,000 people are infected each year.
- Blacklegged ticks infected with the bacterium *Borrelia burgdorferi* bite humans and pass on the bacterium causing Lyme disease. If left untreated Lyme disease can be very serious, affecting joints, the heart, and the nervous system.
- Temperature, precipitation, and humidity are important factors regulating the survival of the blacklegged tick and so also the spread of Lyme disease. Models predict that suitable habitat for the tick may expand up to 218% by 2080 due to climate change.

Effect of global warming on the predicted distribution of the blacklegged tick

KEY
Constant suitability
Expanded suitability
Constant unsuitability
Expanded unsuitability

2020
2050
2080

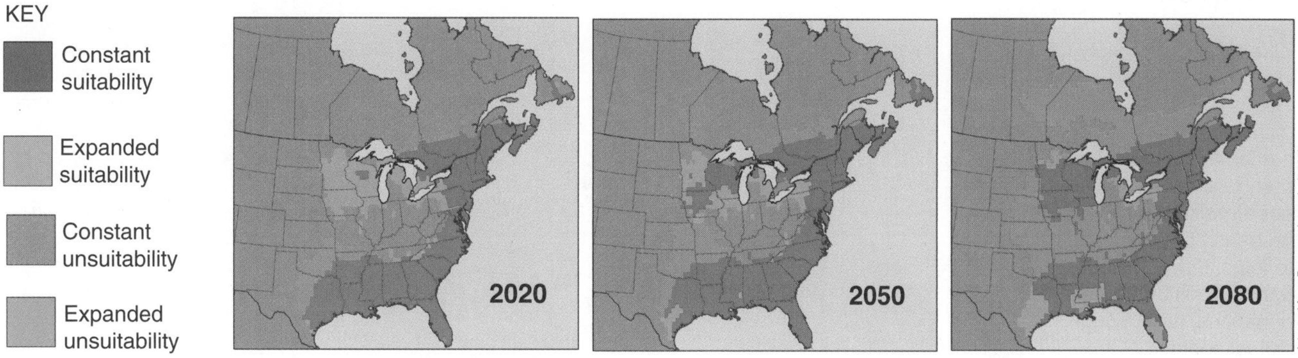

Adapted from Brownstein et al., (2005). doi: 10.1007/s10393-004-0139-x

(b) Why are scientists concerned about the potential effect of global warming on malaria distribution? ________________

3. Study the diagrams showing the predicted effects of global warming on blacklegged tick distribution in North America.

(a) Describe what happens to its suitable range over time: ________________

(b) Predict how this could affect the cases of Lyme disease in North America: ________________

4. Explain why infectious disease rates are often higher in developing countries compared to developed countries: ________________

ISBN: 978-1-98-856632-0

148 Global Disease Threats

Key Question: What diseases affect humans globally?

The presence of infectious disease never goes away. Some diseases are very difficult to eradicate and are always present, and some diseases are new (emerging). Diseases that are always present at low levels in a population or region are known as endemic diseases. Occasionally there may be a sudden increase in the prevalence of a particular disease. On a local level this is known as an outbreak. When an infectious disease spreads rapidly through a nation and affects large numbers of people it is called an epidemic. On rare occasions a new kind of disease will appear and spread to other countries. The rapid spread of a disease throughout the world is a pandemic. Examples of pandemic diseases include HIV/AIDS, influenza, Zika virus, and Covid-19.

Viral diseases

Zika virus is primarily transmitted to people when they are bitten by an infected *Aedes* mosquito. Symptoms are usually mild but infection during pregnancy carries a high risk of miscarriage, pregnancy complications, and fetal abnormalities. Zika virus can also be transmitted from the mother to fetus, through blood transfusions and organ donations, and through sexual contact.

West Nile virus mainly cycles between infected birds and the mosquitoes that feed off the bird's blood. People become infected and develop West Nile fever when they are bitten by an infected mosquito. Only 20% of people show symptoms. These are usually very mild but in some cases the symptoms can cause serious complications.

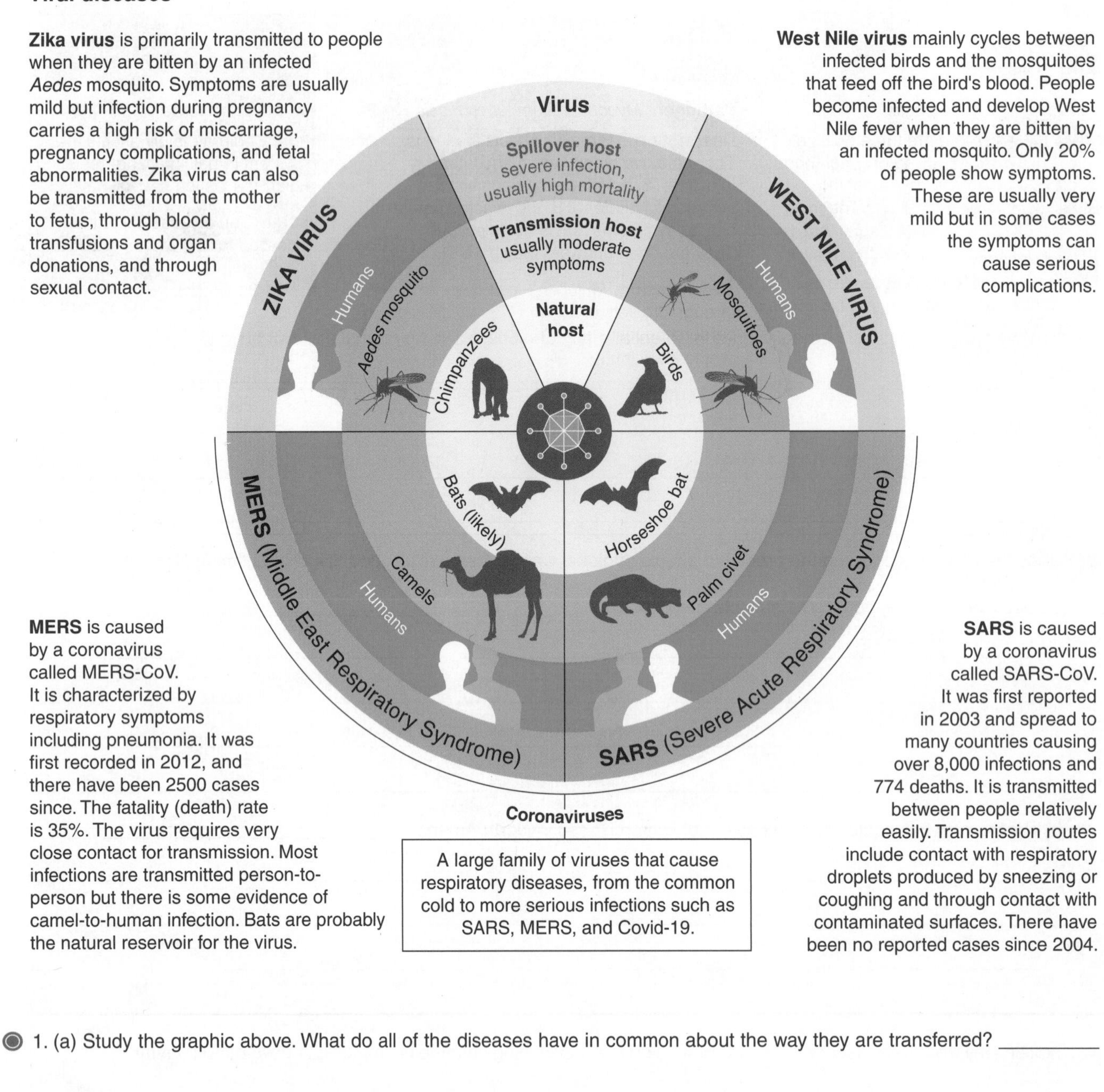

A large family of viruses that cause respiratory diseases, from the common cold to more serious infections such as SARS, MERS, and Covid-19.

MERS is caused by a coronavirus called MERS-CoV. It is characterized by respiratory symptoms including pneumonia. It was first recorded in 2012, and there have been 2500 cases since. The fatality (death) rate is 35%. The virus requires very close contact for transmission. Most infections are transmitted person-to-person but there is some evidence of camel-to-human infection. Bats are probably the natural reservoir for the virus.

SARS is caused by a coronavirus called SARS-CoV. It was first reported in 2003 and spread to many countries causing over 8,000 infections and 774 deaths. It is transmitted between people relatively easily. Transmission routes include contact with respiratory droplets produced by sneezing or coughing and through contact with contaminated surfaces. There have been no reported cases since 2004.

1. (a) Study the graphic above. What do all of the diseases have in common about the way they are transferred? ______

(b) Suggest why this might make viral diseases difficult to control: ______

ISBN: 978-1-98-856632-0

Bacterial diseases

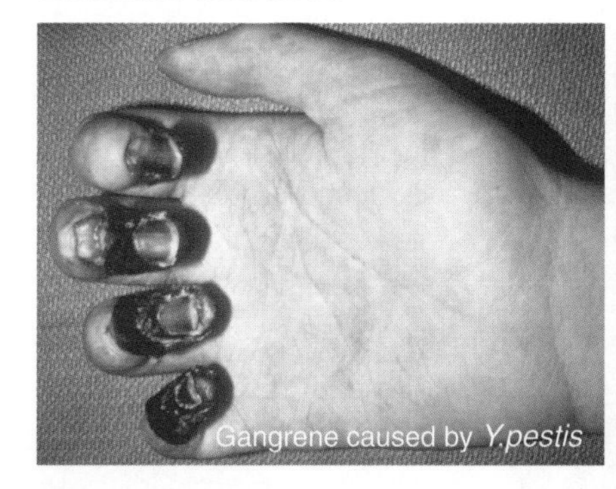
Gangrene caused by *Y.pestis*

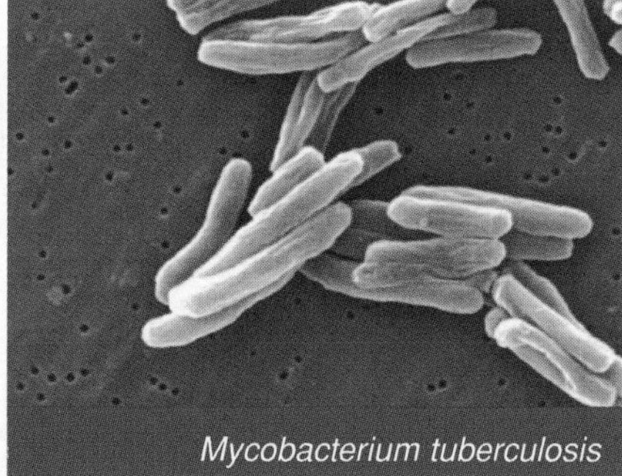
Mycobacterium tuberculosis

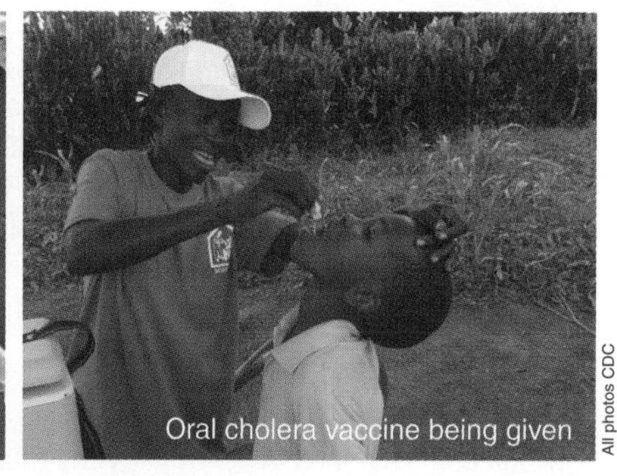
Oral cholera vaccine being given

All photos CDC

Disease: Plague

Pathogen: *Yersinia pestis*

Description: There are three types of plague; bubonic (swelling of lymph nodes), septicemic (skin and tissue death), and pneumonic (respiratory). The most common form is bubonic plague, but pneumonic is the most serious.

Transmission: *Y.pestis* is carried by rodents and other small mammals. Fleas feeding off their blood become infected and bubonic and septicemic plague are transmitted to humans by the bites of infected fleas. Transmission can also occur via contact with the tissues or fluid of an infected animal. Pneumonic plague is spread by inhaling respiratory droplets from an infected animal or human.

Prevention/treatment: No vaccine. Avoid flea bites and contact with dead animals. Early antibiotic treatment is effective.

Disease: Tuberculosis (TB)

Pathogen: *Mycobacterium tuberculosis*

Description: TB mainly affects the lungs. There are two types, active and latent. In active TB, an infected person shows symptoms. In latent TB, the infected person has no symptoms and is not infectious. They are often unaware they have TB.

Transmission: *M. tuberculosis* is spread through droplets in the air when an infected person coughs, sneezes, or spits and the droplets are inhaled.

Prevention/treatment: Avoid crowded living conditions where the bacteria can spread easily. Smoking and alcohol use increase TB risk. Antibiotic treatment is effective but compliance with treatment is often low because of the duration of treatment. A vaccine is available where TB is common, but it is not always effective.

Disease: Cholera

Pathogen: *Vibrio cholerae*

Description: Cholera mainly affects the digestive system (small intestine) resulting in severe diarrhea lasting several days.

Transmission: The disease is contracted through ingesting food or water contaminated with human feces containing the *V.cholerae* bacterium.

Prevention/treatment: Improved sanitation to stop *V.cholerae* transmission is the most important and effective prevention strategy. An oral vaccine is available and is often used in high risk areas (e.g. where a natural disaster has resulted in a contaminated water supply). Oral rehydration solutions (ORS) are used to treat dehydration caused by diarrhea. Severe cases also need IV fluids. Antibiotics are ineffective.

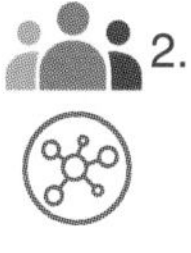

2. In groups of three, carry out some research of your own to learn more about plague, TB, and cholera. Your research should include where most cases occur, how many cases occur each year, the number of deaths caused by each, their estimated fatality rates, and whether the disease is present in the US or not. Use the links to the WHO and CDC (Centers for Disease Control and Prevention) on **Biozone's Resource Hub** to help you. Summarize your findings below:

ISBN: 978-1-98-856632-0

149 The Covid-19 Pandemic

Key Question: What do we know about Covid-19 and how has it affected the environment?

In December 2019, a new strain of coronavirus was detected in Wuhan, China. The new virus was named Severe Acute Respiratory Syndrome Coronavirus 2 (SARS-CoV-2). Infection with the virus causes a disease called Covid-19. The WHO declared a pandemic in March 2020 as the virus spread around the world and a pandemic status was still in place at the time of writing this book. The Covid-19 pandemic has disrupted the world travel and global economies. Millions of people have been infected and hundreds of thousands have died. Enormous stress has been placed on health systems, and the harsh financial impacts will be felt for years because millions of people have lost their jobs.

What is Covid-19?

- Covid-19 is the disease caused when someone is infected with the SARS-CoV-2 virus (right).
- The virus affects the respiratory system.
- 80% of infected people recover without hospital care.
- 20% of infected people develop severe breathing problems and may require high level hospital care. The elderly and people with underlying medical problems are most at risk of becoming very sick.
- The virus is spread through the environment in small droplets from the nose and mouth (e.g. when a person speaks, sneezes, or coughs). People become infected when they breathe these droplets in, or when they touch a surface contaminated with the virus.
- There is currently no vaccine, but attempts to develop one are underway.

A representation of the SARS-CoV-2 virus

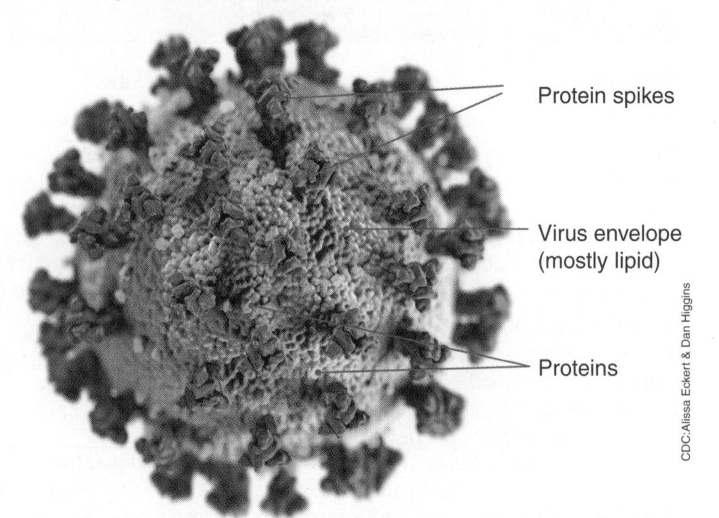

CDC:Alissa Eckert & Dan Higgins

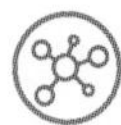

Spread of coronavirus

Reports of viral pneumonia (a lung infection) in Wuhan, China were reported on the 31st December 2019. Early in January 2020, a new coronavirus was identified as the cause of the infections. The new virus, SARS-CoV-2, is thought to have arisen in bats, passing to humans through another, as yet unknown, animal. SARS and MERS probably transferred to humans this way also.

Despite strict restrictions, including travel bans, being placed on the residents of Wuhan and the surrounding region, the virus began to spread through China. On the 13th January 2020 the first case outside of China was recorded in Thailand. Within 10 days the virus had spread to a number of countries, including the US, as infected travelers flew around the world. The situation is changing daily and the best way to find the most recent information is to visit the WHO Covid-19 Interactive Dashboard or the Johns Hopkins University of Medicine Covid-19 Dashboard. Find the details for both sites on **BIOZONE's Resource Hub**.

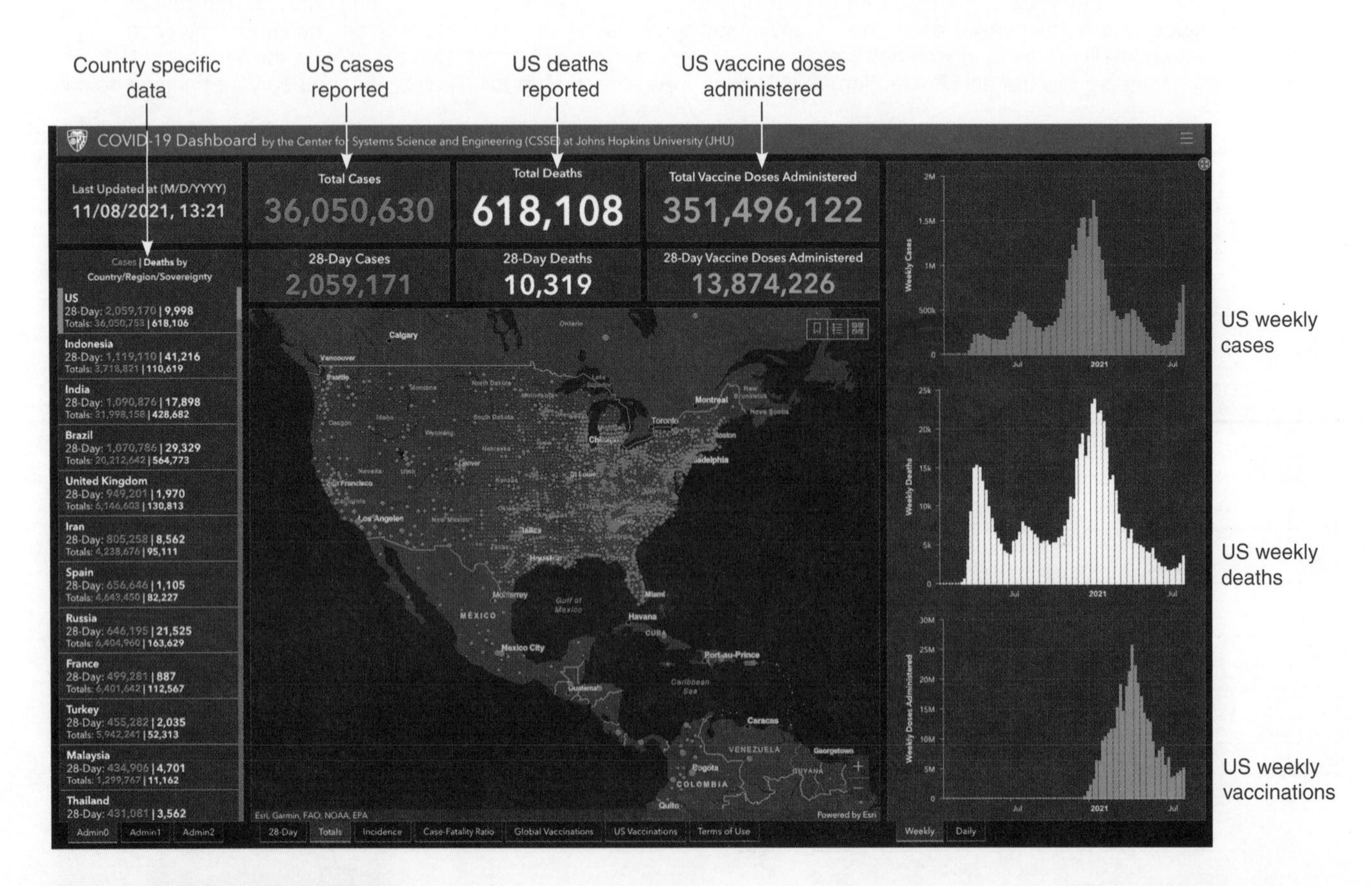

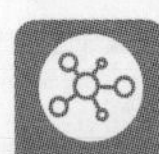

ISBN: 978-1-98-856632-0

Different countries, different outcomes

Some countries have been very successful in slowing or containing the spread of the virus, while in other countries the virus has spread widely causing high numbers of infections and deaths. The graph (right) shows the number of confirmed cases (July, 2020) for three countries; China, New Zealand, and the US. The way their governments, health departments, and populations responded to the disease has been important in the pattern of Covid-19 spread.

The diagram below shows the number of confirmed cases of Covid-19 by country as of 20 July 2020. The darker shades of blue indicate higher numbers of confirmed cases. Real time updates can be found on the WHO Covid-19 Dashboard.

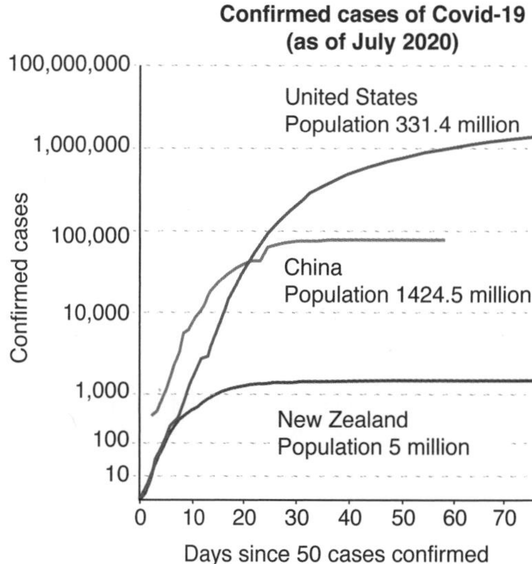

Confirmed cases of Covid-19 by country (as of 20 July 2020)

Data source: WHO https://covid19.who.int/

Modeling the spread of disease

Epidemiologists are people who study the spread of disease. They look at where disease originates, how it spreads, and who it infects. This information can help to evaluate control measures and determine who is most at risk. It also allows resources (equipment, medicines, and healthcare workers) to be distributed effectively.

Epidemiology relies heavily on mathematics, because mathematical models help to predict how a disease will behave in a population.

Week	S	I	R
0	7,000,000	2	0
1	6,999,986	15	1
2	6,999,881	113	8
3	6,999,090	847	65
4	6,993,162	6352	488
5	6,948,741	47,597	3664
6	6,618,002	354,538	27,462
7	4,271,669	2,523,602	204,731
8	0	5,533,470	1,466,532
9	0	2,766,735	4,233,267
10	0	1,383,368	5,616,634
11	0	691,684	6,308,318
12	0	345,842	6,654,160
13	0	172,921	6,827,081
14	0	86,460	6,913,542

A predictive mathematical model called SIR can be used to show the transmission of infectious diseases. In this model there are three compartments; **S** (the number of **s**usceptible individuals), **I** (the number of **i**nfected individuals), and **R** the number removed (those who have been **r**emoved through recovery or death). Equations behind the calculations for each compartment are used to show the relationships and change over time between the three compartments.

The data in the table below left is a theoretical example. It assumes a closed system (e.g. a single state with no travel), no prior immunity (everyone is susceptible), no vaccine, and no physical distancing or other precautionary measures in place. Visit **BIOZONE's Resource hub** if you want to find out more about the mathematics used to show the relationships.

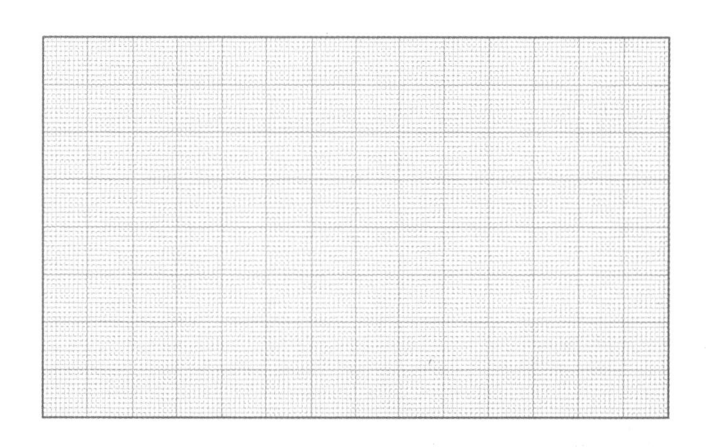

ISBN: 978-1-98-856632-0

Other ways to track a pandemic

Traditional disease surveillance relies on obtaining data through formal reporting systems. The data is very good, but collating and analyzing it takes time. Researchers are exploring faster, less formal ways to identify and track a pandemic.

Social media tags and internet search terms may help detect and map the spread of disease. In a disease outbreak, certain words (e.g. fever or cough) begin to trend on social media. People also do online searches for symptoms before visiting their doctor. Analyzing the frequency and location of key terms could provide an early alert system. This type of analysis is not conclusive, but companies and health agencies are exploring it as a tool for early detection tool of disease outbreaks.

Environmental testing can detect viruses in a population. Infected people shed SARS-CoV-2 in their feces and into the sewage system. Analyzing wastewater for the virus' genetic material could detect outbreaks quickly, perhaps even before the community begin to show symptoms. By sampling different parts of the sewage network an outbreak could be pinpointed to a particular geographical area. This practice is being used in several countries to detect Covid-19. Several UK universities have reliable detection methods and are now looking at how to quantify the amount of virus in wastewater.

1. Study the graph on the previous page showing the number of confirmed Covid-19 cases in the US, China, and New Zealand. Determine how well each country has limited the spread of Covid-19 infections:

2. (a) Plot the tabulated SIR data on the previous page on the grid provided. Plot all three data sets on one axis with a key:

   (b) Describe the relationship between the three compartments (S,I,and R) over time:

   (c) Do you think the SIR data is a good way to model Covid-19 spread through a population? Explain your reasoning:

ISBN: 978-1-98-856632-0

150 Environmental Effects of Covid-19

Key Question: How has Covid-19 affected the environment?
Many countries went into some level of lockdown as it became evident strong measures were needed to reduce the spread of the new coronavirus. For many countries this meant banning travel, and closing public facilities, schools, and physical places of business. Industrial activity, energy demand, and the number of vehicles on roads fell dramatically. Scientists have been monitoring the effect of these changes.

Italy was one of the first European countries to report Covid-19 cases. Italy went into a national lockdown in March 2020 in an attempt to reduce its spread. Within weeks a reduction in air pollution over Italy was observed. The images on the right show nitrogen dioxide concentrations over Italy in March 2019 (left) and during the lockdown in March 2020 (right). The main source of nitrogen dioxide from human activities is the combustion of fossil fuels (coal, gas and oil) especially fuel used in cars.

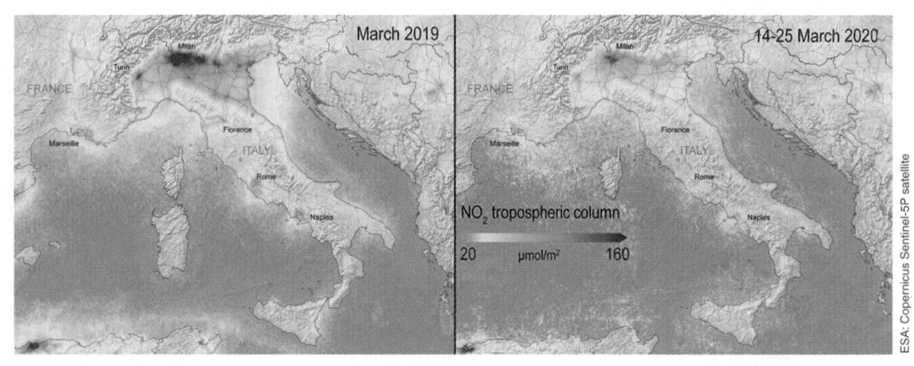

How has Covid-19 affected daily global CO_2 emissions?

The lockdown reduced the demand for energy and also reduced global carbon dioxide emissions (below). So, what does this mean for the environment? Many countries have signed the Kyoto Protocol, an international treaty designed to lower greenhouse gas emissions and help reduce the effects of global warming. Carbon dioxide is a greenhouse gas, so the reduced CO_2 emissions observed over lockdown are helpful in reducing the effects of global warming. However, for the Kyoto Protocol to succeed, the reduction in emissions must be sustained over a long period. Most researchers predict that maintaining the low emission levels seen between January and May 2020 will be very difficult once the world returns to a pre-pandemic level of activity.

Daily global CO_2 emissions (1970-2020)

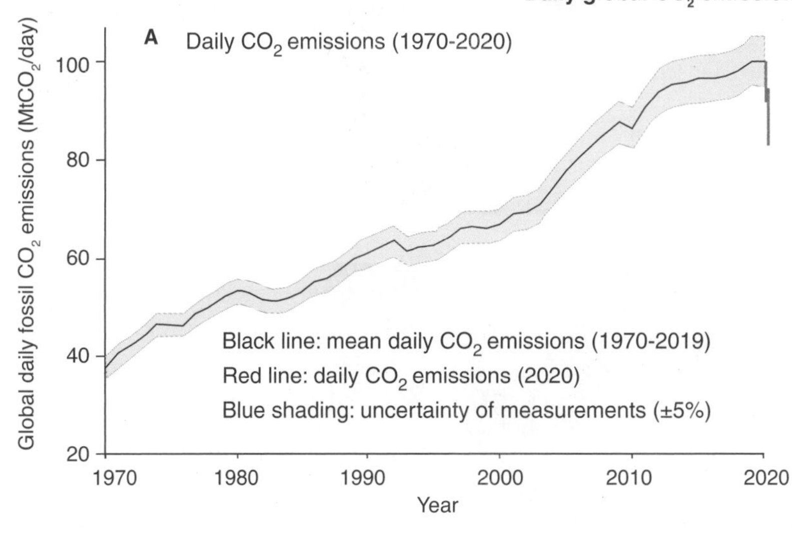

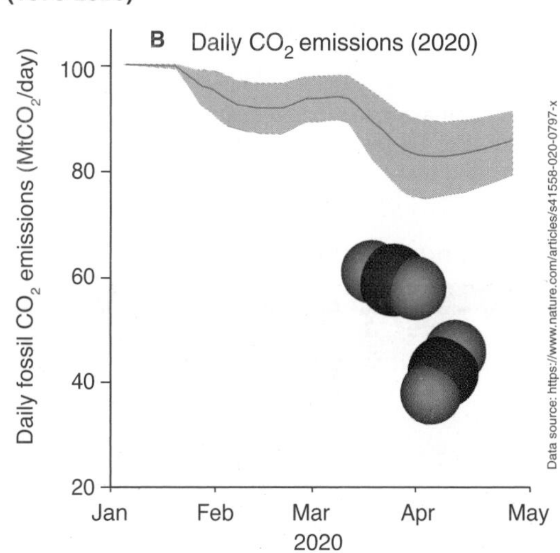

1. Describe some of the environmental benefits observed during the Covid-19 lockdown: ____________________

2. Suggest why scientists do not think the reduction in emissions will be sustainable after the lockdowns are lifted:

ISBN: 978-1-98-856632-0

151 Future Viral Threats

Key Question: What viral threats may arise in the future? Viruses mutate (alter their genetic material). The changes may be minor (antigenic drift), but major antigenic shifts sometimes occur (below), producing a novel virus to which humans have no immunity. For example, the Spanish flu killed 50 million people between 1918-1919. Scientists estimate there are 1.6 million undiscovered viruses in animals and half could jump from animals to humans (these viruses are called zoonoses) causing new diseases. Often the viruses aren't discovered until people become ill, so finding new viruses before they cause harm gives researchers a head start in finding out how to protect human populations.

Antigenic drift

Incremental mutations cause small changes in the virus over time. Updated vaccines can protect against these changes.

Population has some immunity. *Example: Seasonal influenza*

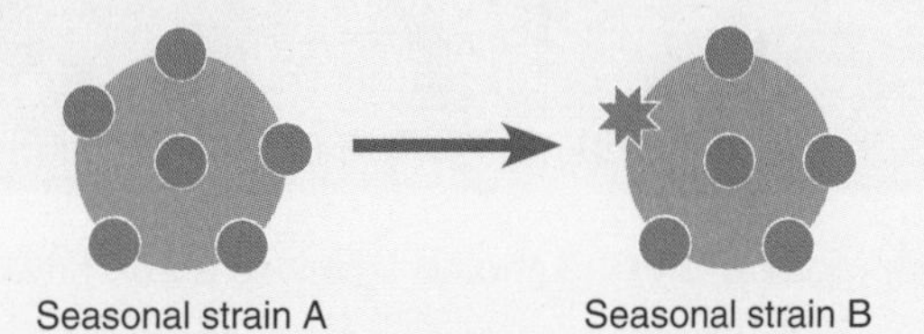

Antigenic shift

Major, rapid change caused when two viral strains (or different viruses) combine to form a new subtype.

No immunity in humans. *Example: 2009 swine flu pandemic*

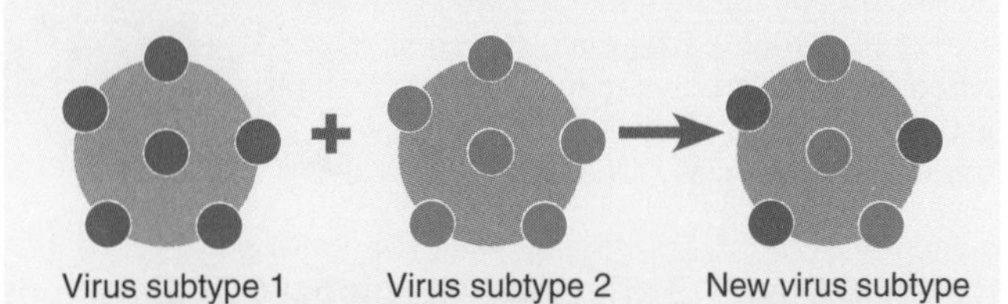

The hunt for new viruses

PREDICT, a USAID collaborative program, takes a proactive approach where researchers go into the field looking for new animal viruses.

Bats are often a viral reservoir. The viruses causing SARS, MERS, and probably Covid-19, all originated in bats, so testing bats is logical when looking for new viruses. Blood samples are taken from bats (right) and analyzed for viral genetic material. If the genetic material matches an entry in the database, the presence of a known virus can be confirmed. If there is no match in the database it means a new virus has been found.

The database can also be used to diagnose patients and identify outbreaks. By testing a patient's blood it may be possible to identify the virus and develop a management plan. The detection of an unknown virus in a person's blood signals a new disease has emerged in humans.

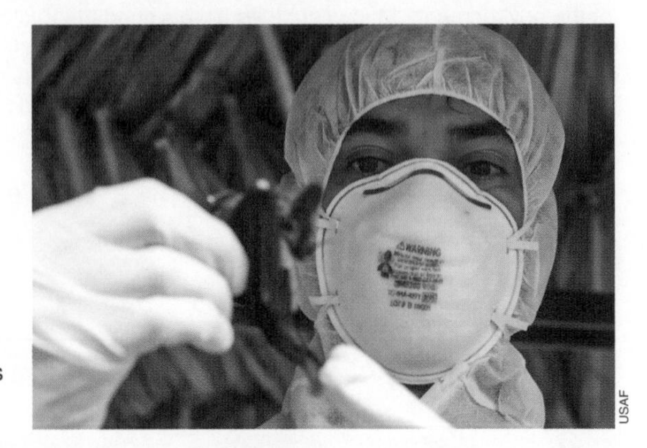
USAF

Emerging viral threats

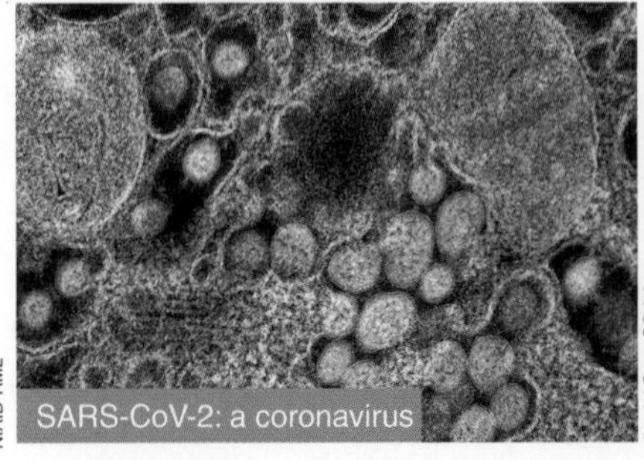
NIAID-RML

SARS-CoV-2: a coronavirus

Daniel Case CC 3.0

Traditional wet market

Humane Society of the United States CC3.0

Coronavirus can jump from pigs to humans

Coronaviruses continue to pose a high threat to humans. There are several reasons for this:

- They are widely found in bats and adapt to a variety of intermediate animal hosts such as birds, pigs, rodents, camels, and cows.
- Past experience has shown coronaviruses move from animal host to humans. Several disease outbreaks have been linked to traditional wet markets where numerous live animal species are sold, increasing the chances of viral infection to humans.
- Once in humans they spread easily between people through coughing and sneezing. However, coronaviruses are not the only type of viruses scientists are concerned about. Four other viral groups, picornaviruses, pneumoviruses, paramyxoviruses, and orthomyxoviruses, all have the potential to mutate into deadly strains.

1. Explain why coronaviruses are a threat to human health: ______________________

____

____

____

____

____

ISBN: 978-1-98-856632-0

152 Personal Progress Check

Answer the multiple choice questions that follow by circling the correct answer. Don't forget to read the question carefully!

1. Which statement about non-point source pollution is true:
   - (a) It is easy to identify the source
   - (b) It can be difficult to locate the source
   - (c) It originates from a single source
   - (d) Controlling non-point source pollution is easy

Questions 2 and 3 relate to the diagram below. It shows the concentration of an organic pollutant in an aquatic ecosystem released at the blue line.

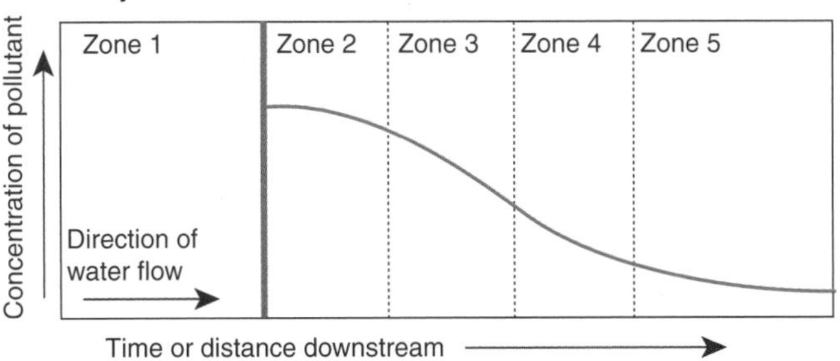

2. The highest number of organisms would mostly likely be found in:
   - (a) Zone 1
   - (b) Zone 5
   - (c) Zone 2
   - (d) Zones 3 and 4

3. An abiotic factor likely to be affected by the introduction of the organic pollutant is:
   - (a) Water temperature
   - (b) Dissolved oxygen
   - (c) pH
   - (d) Salinity

4. The Clean Water Act (CWA) is a federal law primarily regulating:
   - (a) The supply of drinking water.
   - (b) The discharge of pollutants into water.
   - (c) The disposal of plastic into the oceans.
   - (d) The bottling of water from natural springs.

5. Which of the following occurred as a result of the *Deepwater Horizon* oil spill in 2010?

   I A large economic loss to fisheries and tourism
   II Vast numbers of marine organisms died
   III The oil was cleaned up quickly

   - (a) I only
   - (b) II only
   - (c) I and II
   - (d) All three are correct

6. Which of the following oil spill clean-up methods is considered to be the most hazardous for the environment?
   - (a) Using chemical dispersants to break down the oil
   - (b) Using microbes to break down the oil
   - (c) Using floating booms to contain the oil
   - (d) Using skimmers to collect the oil

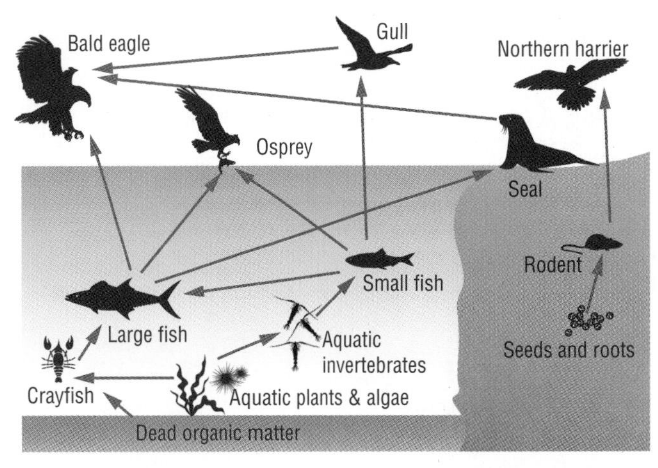

7. The organisms in the aquatic food web above have been exposed to a DDT breakdown product, which has entered the sea via land runoff. Their susceptibility to DDT's toxic effects from most to least susceptible is:
   - (a) Large fish → small fish → aquatic invertebrates → aquatic plants
   - (b) Bald eagle → seal → osprey → Northern harrier
   - (c) Bald eagle → large fish → crayfish → small fish
   - (d) Gull → osprey → large fish → crayfish

8. The most dangerous form of mercury to humans is:
   - (a) Elemental mercury
   - (b) Inorganic mercury
   - (c) Particulate mercury
   - (d) Methylmercury

9. A marine dead zone is:
   - (a) The area of deep water where there is no light
   - (b) A hypoxic region lacking marine life
   - (c) An area where migratory fish have disappeared
   - (d) A seasonal period of toxic algal blooms

10. Plastic litter in the ocean:
    - (a) Collects in ocean regions called gyres
    - (b) Breaks down slowly in sunlight
    - (c) Can be mistaken for food by marine organisms
    - (d) All of the above

11. Suspended sediment in water contributes to:
    - (a) An increase in pH
    - (b) An increase in dissolved oxygen
    - (c) An increase in turbidity
    - (d) All of the above

12. What is the purpose of a leachate collection system in a modern sanitary landfill?
    - (a) Prevents the landfill becoming too waterlogged
    - (b) Extract methane gas from the landfill
    - (c) Collect and remove contaminated water for treatment
    - (d) Provide a source of income from the landfill

ISBN: 978-1-98-856632-0

13. Which of the following components is not found in a wastewater treatment plant:
    (a) A series of screens and grates to filter material
    (b) Tanks containing microbes to decompose organic material
    (c) A bottom liner of plastic or clay to prevent groundwater contamination
    (d) A disinfection step using chemicals or UV light to kill any harmful bacteria

14. Which element is consumed during decomposition in an aquatic environment, potentially leading to hypoxia?
    (a) Carbon
    (b) Nitrogen
    (c) Phosphorus
    (d) Oxygen

15. Which of the following laws is dedicated to cleaning up contaminated sites:
    (a) Resource Conservation and Recovery Act
    (b) Comprehensive Environmental Response, Compensation, and Liability Act
    (c) Kyoto Protocol
    (d) Montreal Protocol

16. The name given to cleaning up sites contaminated with hazardous substances is:
    (a) Remediation
    (b) Bioremediation
    (c) Decontamination
    (d) Sterilization

17. An acute measure of the toxicity of a substance is given by:
    (a) The threshold response
    (b) The LD_{50}
    (c) The EC_{50}
    (d) The 50% survival rate

18. Chemicals that mimic hormones can act as:
    (a) Carcinogens
    (b) Endocrine disruptors
    (c) Pollutants
    (d) All of the above

19. Eutrophication can result in:
    (a) Improved water quality
    (b) Lower turbidity
    (c) Algal blooms
    (d) Lower pest fish biomass

20. Discharge of cooling water from power stations:
    (a) Rarely affects organisms as it is not a pollutant
    (b) Can change community composition and diversity
    (c) Is only a problem with coal-fired power stations
    (d) Increases oxygen levels in the discharge zone

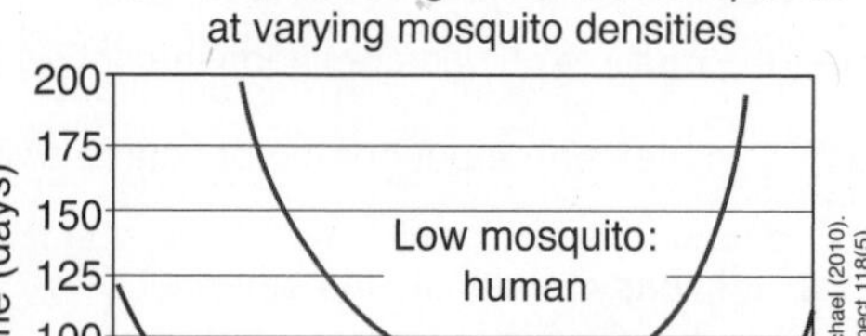
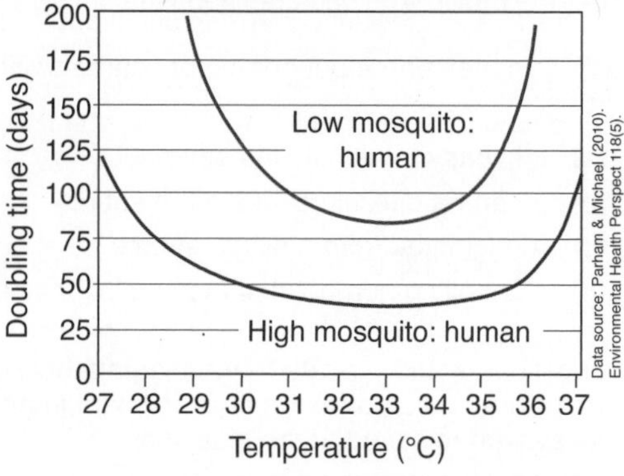

Questions 21 and 22 refer to the plot above which shows the estimated doubling time of the malaria parasite over a range of temperatures for different mosquito densities.

21. The graph indicates that:
    (a) Parasite growth rate is greatest between ~31-36°C when mosquito density is high.
    (b) Parasite growth rate is greatest between ~31-36°C when mosquito density is low.
    (c) Mosquito density has no effect on parasite population doubling time.
    (d) Infection rates are higher between 27 and 30°C.

22. The situation that poses the greatest malaria risk to humans is:
    (a) Low mosquito: human ratio and <30°C.
    (b) Low mosquito: human ratio and >36°C.
    (c) High mosquito: human ratio and 30-36°C.
    (d) High mosquito: human ratio and <30°C,

23. Infectious diseases are caused by:
    (a) Being poor
    (b) Pathogenic organisms
    (c) Bacteria
    (d) International travel

24. Vaccination is a public health strategy to:
    (a) Protect against the spread of infectious diseases
    (b) Reduce disease transmission
    (c) Increase herd immunity
    (d) All of the above

25. Mosquitoes are vectors in the transmission of:
    (a) Zika virus, Covid-19, malaria
    (b) Malaria, Zika virus, West Nile virus
    (c) Covid-19, tuberculosis, MERS
    (d) Covid-19, MERS, SARS

26. Droplet transmission is important in the transmission of:
    (a) SARS, Covid-19, MERS
    (b) SARS, Covid-19, tuberculosis
    (c) Covid-19, tuberculosis, cholera
    (d) SARS, tuberculosis, cholera

ISBN: 978-1-98-856632-0

Solving the problem of e-waste

Every year, humans generate millions of tonnes of electronic waste and the volume is on an increasing trajectory (below). Very little is recycled. Globally, the average is 20%. The remaining 80% is undocumented, dumped, traded, or recycled under inferior conditions. The metals are technically difficult to extract. For example, total recovery rates for cobalt are only 30%, despite technology existing that could recycle 95%. In 2015, the extraction of raw materials accounted for 7% of the world's energy consumption. By 2060, the overall consumption of material in electronic goods is projected to double (graph below).

E-waste economics

Copper: Value in US$/kg; Market price; E-waste; 2011, 2013, 2015

Gold: Value in US$/kg (x1000); Market price; E-waste; Year: 2011, 2013, 2015

resource-recycling.com

Projected e-waste trends

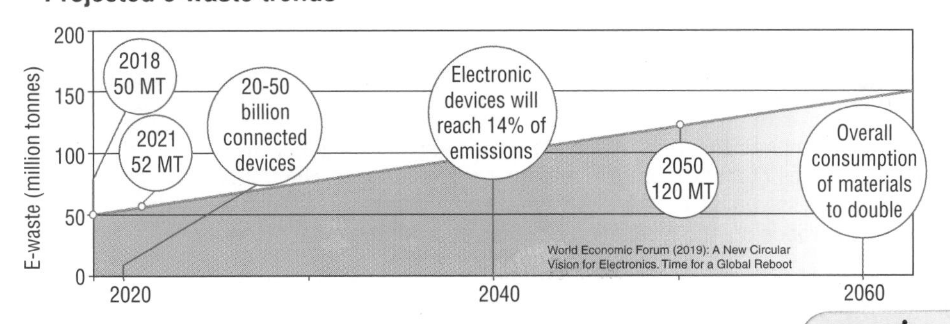

E-WASTE	Examples	Volume in 2017 (million tonnes)	Percentage
Small equipment	Vacuum cleaners, coffee makers	16.8	
Large equipment	Washers, dryers	9.1	
Temperature exchange equipment	Air-conditioning units	7.6	
Screens	Televisions, monitors	6.6	
Small IT	Cell phones, laptops	3.9	
Lamps	Light bulbs	0.7	

29% ABS-PC
16% Ceramics
15% Copper & compounds
10% Silicon plastics
10% Other metals
8% Other plastics
9% Epoxy
3% Iron

E-WASTE CHALLENGE
Recovering material
Consumer relationships with electronics (trends)
Lack of recycling
Pollution
Export of e-waste: highest generating countries export to the lowest

27. (a) Analyze the problem of e-waste using the information above and in activity 141:

(b) Calculate the total volume of e-waste produced in 2017:

(c) Complete the percentage column in the table above for each category of e-waste.

(d) Using the plot of projected e-waste trends above:

i) Calculate the projected rate of increase in e-waste between 2018 and 2050:

ii) Calculate the volume of e-waste in 2060 (in MT) assuming the projected rate of increase stays the same:

(e) The graphs of e-waste economics show the change in value of copper and gold when mined vs recovered from e-waste. For each element, calculate the change in value (effectively this is cost) between 2010 and 2015:

i) Copper:

ii) Gold

(f) How do these 2015 e-waste values compare with market values at the same time:

(g) Use your analysis of the problem and the calculations you have made to propose possible solutions to e-waste challenges. Write your free response on a separate sheet and attach it to this page.

ISBN: 978-1-98-856632-0

Learning Objectives

9. Global Change

Developing understanding

Content: This concluding unit invites you to evaluate the global impact of local and regional human activities and provides an opportunity for you to examine the interrelationships among the natural world. In this unit, you will come to understand how human activities affect the diversity and functioning of the natural world and how we can mitigate that impact with practical and feasible solutions.

Skills: This final unit emphasizes skills in describing and explaining global changes in the environment, the causes of these changes, and their consequences. Here, there is opportunity for you to apply the skills you have developed in earlier chapters. You will use an evidence based approach to proposing and evaluating solutions to environmental problems.

9.1 Stratospheric ozone depletion .... activity 153

☐ 1. Explain the importance of stratospheric ozone to life on Earth. Describe the natural and anthropogenic causes of stratospheric ozone depletion and explain its consequences.

9.2 Reducing ozone depletion .... activity 153

☐ 2. Describe how the depletion of ozone can be reduced by replacing ozone depleting chemicals with substitutes that do not deplete the ozone layer. Describe some of the challenges associated with these substitutions.

9.3 The greenhouse effect .... activity 154

☐ 3. Explain the greenhouse effect and its importance to life on Earth. Identify the principal greenhouse gases and explain why water vapor,although it is a greenhouse gas does not contribute significantly to global climate change.

☐ 4. Identify the sources of various greenhouse gases and compare their global warming potential (GWP). Include reference to CO_2, CFCs, nitrous oxide, and methane (CH_4).

9.4 Increases in greenhouse gases... activities 154,156

☐ 5. Explain the link between increases in atmospheric greenhouse gas concentrations and global climate change. Describe the threats to human health and the environment from global climate changes including rising sea levels, spread of disease, and population changes.

9.5 Global climate change .... activities 155 - 159

☐ 6. Interpret data to describe how the Earth's climate has changed throughout geological time. Identify periods associated with major shifts in global temperatures.

☐ 7. Describe some of the consequences of climate change, including rise in average global temperatures, melting permafrost and sea ice, rising sea levels, and human displacement. Describe how sea level changes can affect coastal and marine communities.

☐ 8. Recall how winds generated by atmospheric circulation help to transport heat around the Earth. Describe the predicted effects of climate change on these circulation patterns, including on Hadley circulation, the jet stream, and the ITCZ.

☐ 9. Describe how oceanic currents (the ocean conveyor belt) transport heat throughout the world. Describe how climate change is predicted to affect patterns of ocean circulation and what the consequences of these changes might be.

☐ 10. Describe the effects of predicted changes in temperature and precipitation on soils and agriculture. Interpret data linking increases in temperature to changes in crop yields and shifts in the distribution of important food crops.

☐ 11. Interpret data to describe the current and predicted effects of climate change in the Earth's polar regions. Explain the role of ice-albedo and positive (reinforcing) feedback in accelerating rates of ice loss and permafrost thaw in Arctic regions. Explain the consequences of loss of snow and ice in polar regions on the species that live there.

9.6 Ocean warming .... activity 159

☐ 12. Describe the causes and consequences of ocean warming. Include reference to oxygen depletion, loss of habitat, and effects on species biology, including coral bleaching.

9.7 Ocean acidification................. activities 160 - 161

☐ 13. Explain what is meant by ocean acidification and represent these changes as chemical equations. Describe the causes of ocean acidification and its effects on marine organisms.

9.8 Invasive species .... activity 162

☐ 14. Describe the typical characteristics of invasive species and explain their effects on native species and the ecosystems into which they are introduced. Describe and evaluate strategies to control invasive species.

9.9 Endangered species .... activities 163 - 165, 170

☐ 15. Describe the factors that contribute to species becoming endangered (at high risk of extinction). Why are different species not equally at risk from the same threats?

☐ 16. Describe the responses of different species to disruptions such as habitat loss, introduction of non-native species, and hunting pressure. Species unable to adapt in response to new selection pressures in their environment, including competition from introduced species, are at risk of extinction.

☐ 17. Explain strategies to protect species from threats to their populations. These strategies include legislative protection and criminalizing poaching, habitat protection, anti-poaching technologies, and translocation of threatened populations. Interpret data to evaluate the success of these strategies.

9.10 Human impacts on biodiversity activities 166 - 170

☐ 18. Describe the main factors leading to a decline in biodiversity (HIPPCO). Explain the causes habitat loss, including global climate change, and discuss its consequences. Explain the significance of scale in habitat loss with reference to specific examples, e.g. recent widespread wildfires.

☐ 19. Explain how the domestication of plants and animals can lead to a loss of biodiversity and the consequences of this.

☐ 20. Explain how humans can reduce the impact of habitat fragmentation, e.g. through the use of habitat corridors, sustainable land use practices, and habitat restoration.

153 Stratospheric Ozone Depletion

Key Question: What is the importance of stratospheric ozone and why is it being depleted?

Recall that Earth's atmosphere is divided into layers. The stratosphere begins at an altitude of about 10 km. Within this layer, mostly at around an altitude of 20 km, ozone (O_3) becomes abundant. Incoming UV radiation from the Sun strikes O_3 molecules and splits them into an oxygen molecule (O_2) and a free oxygen atom (O). The free O atom then combines with an O_2 molecule to reform O_3. This process absorbs 99% of the UV radiation from the Sun and is extremely important for life on Earth. UV (especially UV-B) radiation is very dangerous. Exposure can cause damage ranging from sunburn (mild exposure) to cancer (repeated exposures) and cataracts. In 1984, scientists discovered the ozone layer above Antarctica was thinning. The cause was traced to chemicals called chlorofluorocarbons (CFCs) commonly used in refrigeration. These were eventually banned. Decades on the ozone layer is beginning to show signs of repairing itself.

The ozone hole

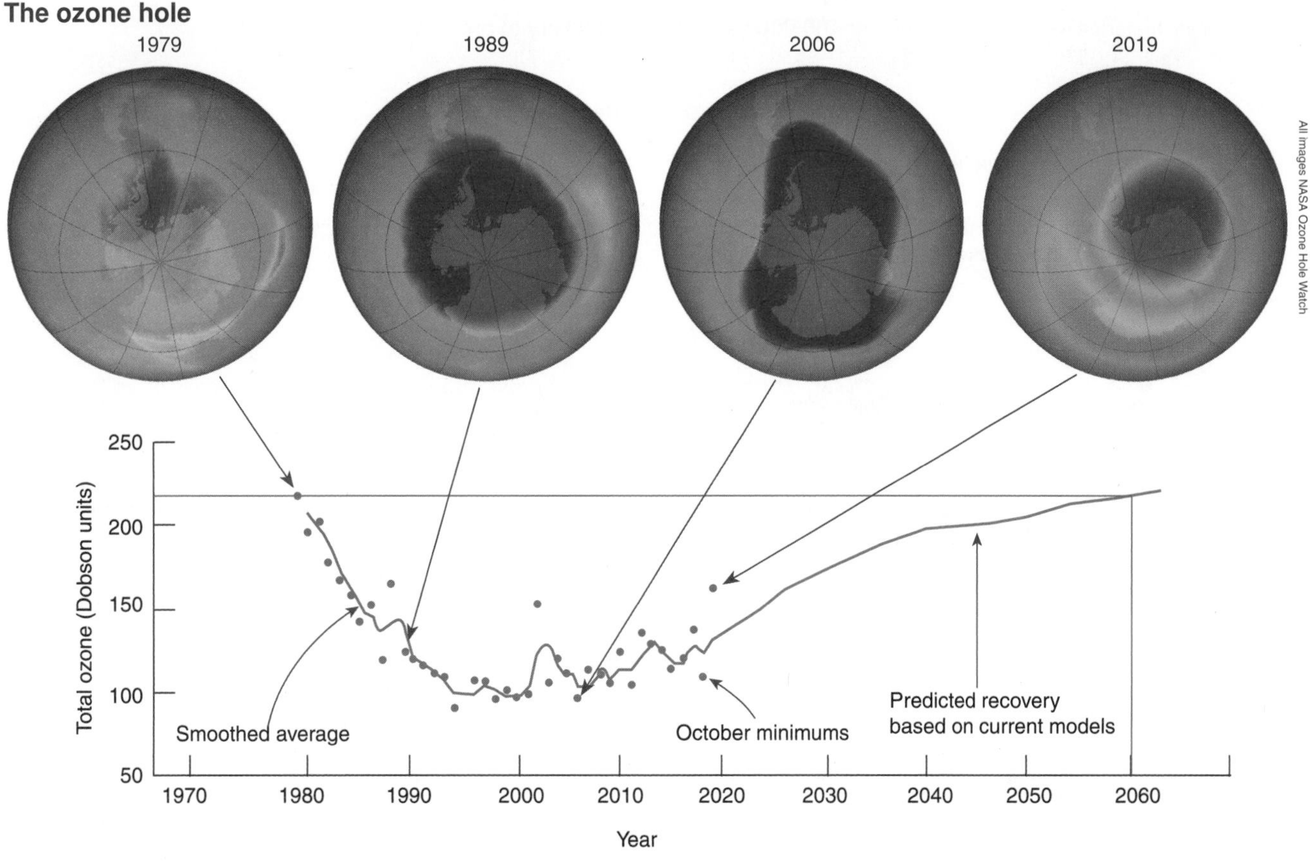

- The ozone layer surrounds the entire planet. Under certain conditions this layer is thinned in certain places. This thinning is most well known for its annual occurrence over Antarctica, however it also thins over the Arctic, although more rarely. In 2020, the Arctic experienced its largest ozone hole at nearly three times the size of Greenland, which lasted for over a month.
- Mapping of the ozone layer first began in 1979 and the hole over Antarctica was discovered shortly afterwards.

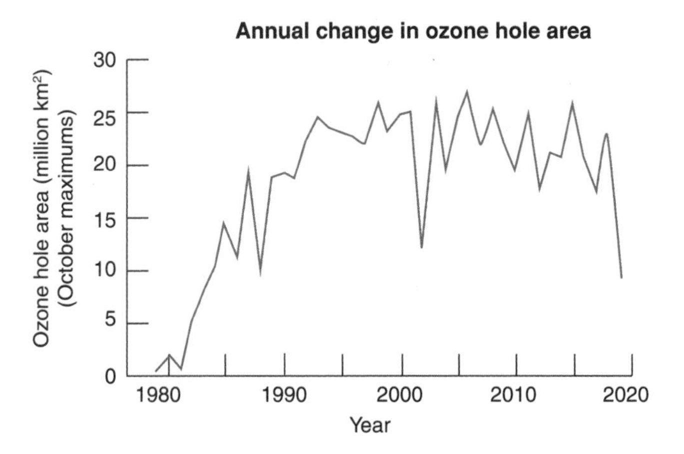

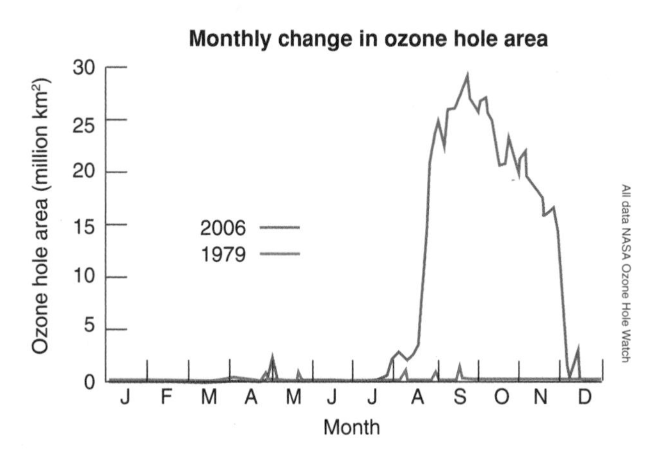

1. In which month(s) does the ozone hole over Antarctica appear? ____________________

2. What is the trend in the ozone hole maximums since 1979? ____________________

____

3. In which year will the ozone layer hole return to 1979 levels? ____________________

ISBN: 978-1-98-856632-0

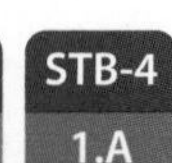
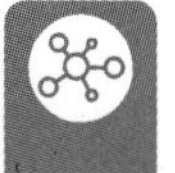

What causes the ozone hole?

- The primary cause for ozone depletion was the increased use of chemicals such as chlorofluorocarbons (CFCs) in the 1960s and 1970s. These were used as refrigerants in air conditioners and refrigerators, and propellants in aerosols. They have low toxicity, flammability, and reactivity, so were a considerable advancement on earlier refrigerants such ammonia, which are toxic.
- It was only after their widespread use that it was found that CFCs became unstable at high altitudes where they could be exposed to UV radiation from the Sun. There they react with ozone, breaking it down into oxygen.

- In 1987, the **Montreal protocol** was agreed internationally. It banned the production of ozone-depleting CFCs. Despite this international agreement, there continues to be a considerable black market for CFCs. A study in 2018 found somewhere in east Asia was producing 13,000 tonnes of CFCs annually. CFCs are just one group of ozone depleting chemicals. Others including halons, methyl bromide, methyl chloroform and carbon tetrachloride.
- Free chlorine in the stratosphere peaked around 1999 and is projected to decline for more than a century. Ozone loss is projected to diminish gradually but will take another 100-200 years for full recovery to pre-1950 levels.

Mechanism of ozone destruction

Catalytic destruction of ozone

O_3 Ozone — **Chlorine reacts with ozone** → O_2 Oxygen molecule

Cl-O˙ Chlorine oxide molecule — **Chlorine oxide reacts with ozone** (O_3 Ozone) → 2 oxygen molecules (O_2, O_2)

Cl Free chlorine

- CFCs are swept by winds to high altitudes. There UV light causes them to lose chlorine atoms. These react in two ways:
- $Cl + O_3 \rightarrow ClO$. $ClO + NO_2 \rightarrow ClONO_2$ (does not react with ozone)
- $Cl + CH_4 \rightarrow HCl$ (does not react with ozone)
- $ClONO_2$ and HCl form reservoirs in the stratosphere. In the Antarctic, winter winds form the polar vortex, which concentrates and isolates these reservoirs. The stratosphere can become cold enough to form **polar stratospheric clouds**. Crystals of ice form within these clouds.
- The reservoirs of HCl and $ClONO_2$ react together on the surface of these ice crystals forming HNO_3 (nitric acid) and a Cl_2 molecule (chlorine gas). This process removes NO_2 from the atmosphere, limiting its ability to remove free chlorine.
- In the Antarctic spring, the ice crystals melt, releasing the Cl_2. This is split by sunlight into two free chlorine atoms which are now free to enter the catalytic cycle on the left.

4. Describe some of the damaging effects of excessive amounts of ultraviolet radiation on living organisms:

5. (a) Describe how CFCs in the atmosphere deplete stratospheric ozone:

(b) Write the chemical equations showing how a single Cl atom in the catalytic cycle reacts to deplete ozone:

(c) Describe how this affects the amount of UV radiation reaching the surface:

(d) Why does the ozone hole occur during the spring at the South Pole?

ISBN: 978-1-98-856632-0

Replacing CFCs

- CFCs were developed in the 1920s and were in widespread use by the 1970s. However the dramatic evidence of their effect on the ozone layer shown in the late 1970s was enough for countries to act collectively to ban their use.
- Since then, other chemicals to replace CFCs have been developed. However these have their own sets of problems, the most notable being that most of them are very potent greenhouse gases.

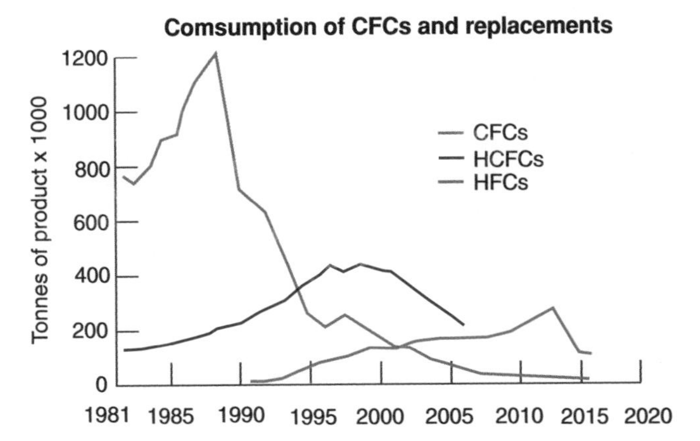

Consumption of CFCs has decreased since 1987. HCFCs were developed which have a lesser effect on the ozone layer but are greenhouse gases. HFCs have no effect on the ozone layer but are again potent greenhouse gases. A new replacement, HFOs, appear to have no effect on the ozone layer and are only weak greenhouse gases.

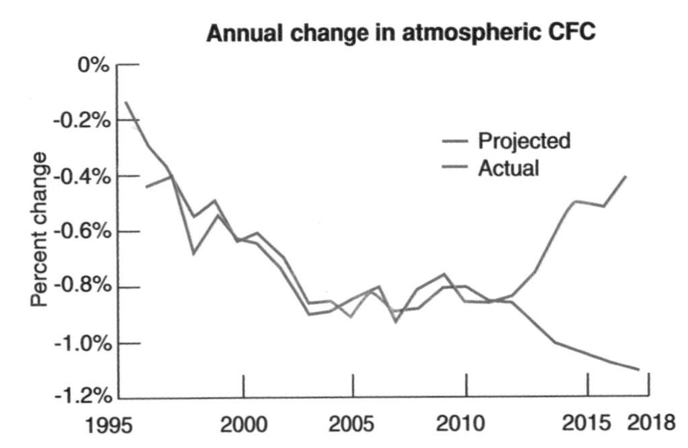

Until the early 2010s, reduction in CFC use was proceeding as expected. However, a decrease in the rate of reduction has been observed and this has been traced to the manufacture of CFC-11 (trichlorofluoromethane) in China for use in polyurethane insulation manufacture. International agreements meant the manufacture of CFC-11 should have ended in 2010.

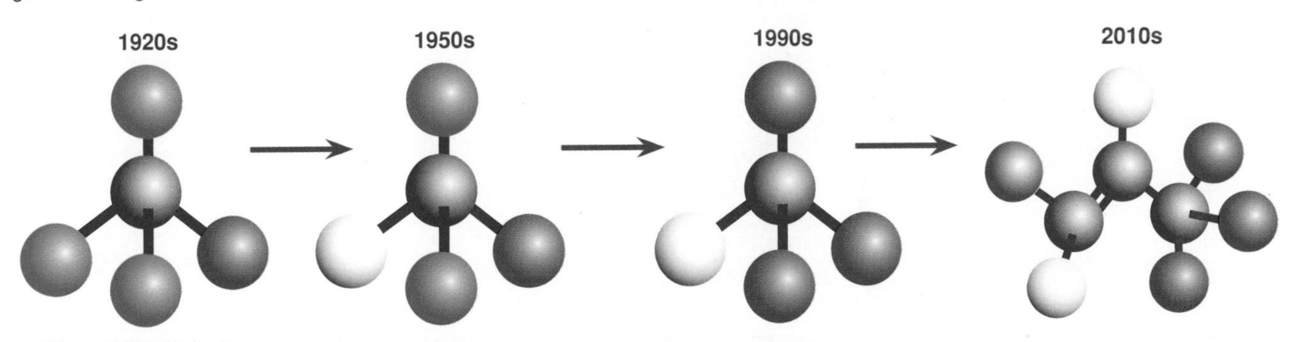

CFC: Chlorofluorocarbon
High ozone depletion
High greenhouse potential

HCFC: Hydrochlorofluorocarbon
Low ozone depletion
High greenhouse potential

HFC: Hydrofluorocarbon
Zero ozone depletion
High greenhouse potential

HFO: Hydrofluoroolefin
Zero ozone depletion
Very low greenhouse potential

6. Describe the trend in CFC consumption and its replacements since 1981: ______________________

7. What caused the decrease in the reduction of CFCs in the 2010s? Why do you think this happened?

8. Describe the development of CFCs and its replacements: ______________________

ISBN: 978-1-98-856632-0

154 The Greenhouse Effect

Key Question: What is the greenhouse effect and what influences it?

The Earth's atmosphere comprises a mix of gases including nitrogen, oxygen, and water vapor. Small quantities of carbon dioxide (CO_2), methane, and a number of other trace gases are also present. The term 'greenhouse effect' describes the natural process by which heat is retained within the atmosphere by these greenhouse gases. They act as a thermal blanket around the Earth, letting in sunlight, but trapping the heat that would normally radiate back into space. The greenhouse effect results in the Earth having a mean surface temperature of about 15°C, 33°C warmer than it would have without an atmosphere. About 75% of the natural greenhouse effect is due to water vapor. The next most significant agent is CO_2. Fluctuations in the Earth's surface temperature as a result of climate shifts are normal, and the current period of warming climate is partly explained by the recovery after the most recent glacial that finished 12,000 years ago. However since the mid 20th century, the Earth's surface temperature has been increasing. This phenomenon is called global warming and the majority of researchers attribute it to the increase in atmospheric levels of CO_2 and other greenhouse gases emitted into the atmosphere as a result of human activity (i.e. it is anthropogenic).

The greenhouse effect

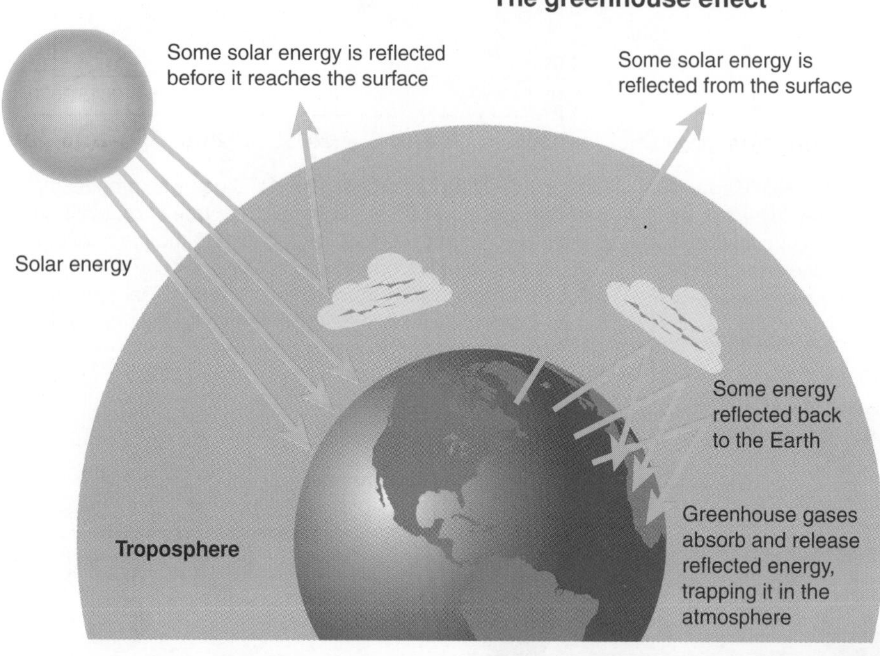

Water and the greenhouse effect

Water vapor plays an important part in keeping the planet's temperature stable. However it does not directly influence the Earth's temperature, rather it is influenced by the temperature. An increase in temperature causes more water to evaporate and this can enhance the warming effect of other greenhouse gases. Water constantly cycles from the atmosphere and back and so its effect is short lived unlike other greenhouse gases which can remain in the atmosphere for many years.

Sources of greenhouse gases

Carbon dioxide
- Exhaust from cars
- Combustion of coal, wood, oil
- Burning rainforests

Methane
- Plant debris and growing vegetation
- Belching and flatus of cattle

Chlorofluorocarbons (CFCs)
- Leaking coolant from refrigerators
- Leaking coolant from air conditioners

Nitrous oxide
- Car exhaust

Tropospheric ozone*
- Triggered by car exhaust (smog)

*Tropospheric ozone is found in the lower atmosphere (not to be confused with ozone in the stratosphere)

Greenhouse gas	Tropospheric conc.		GWP¶	Atmospheric lifetime (years)§	Increased radiative forcing (W/m^2)
	Pre-industrial 1750	Present day (2020)			
Carbon dioxide	280 ppm	411 ppm	1	120	1.94
Methane	700 ppb	1834 ppb	25	12	0.5
Nitrous oxide	270 ppb	328 ppb	310	120	0.2
CFCs	0 ppt	232 ppt	4000+	50-100	0.060
HFCs	0 ppt	84 ppt	1430	14	0.0134
Tropospheric ozone	25 ppb	34 ppb	17	Hours	0.4
Sulfur hexafluoride	0 ppt	8.6 ppt	23,500	3200	0.0049

ppm = parts per million; ppb = parts per billion, ppt = part per trillion; ¶ GWP: Global warming potential. Figures contrast the radiative effect of different greenhouse gases relative to CO_2 over 100 years, e.g. over 100 years, methane is 25 times more potent as a greenhouse gas than CO_2 § How long the gas persists in the atmosphere.

Controlling greenhouse gases

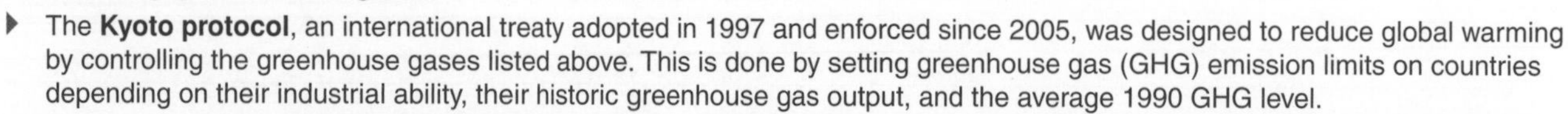

- The **Kyoto protocol**, an international treaty adopted in 1997 and enforced since 2005, was designed to reduce global warming by controlling the greenhouse gases listed above. This is done by setting greenhouse gas (GHG) emission limits on countries depending on their industrial ability, their historic greenhouse gas output, and the average 1990 GHG level.
- The protocol has had limited success. Although it is acknowledged that without the protocol GHG emissions would probably have risen, the global reductions seen are largely due to the collapse of the Soviet Union and its industrial sector in 1991, before the protocol was even signed. Reductions in GHG emissions since 1997 have been limited.

ISBN: 978-1-98-856632-0

Changes in atmospheric CO_2

- Around the world are a network of observatories that are constantly measuring the concentration of CO_2 in the atmosphere. Below are the measurements from Mauna Loa, Hawaii. These match readings from around the world. Note that the concentration rises and falls on an annual basis.

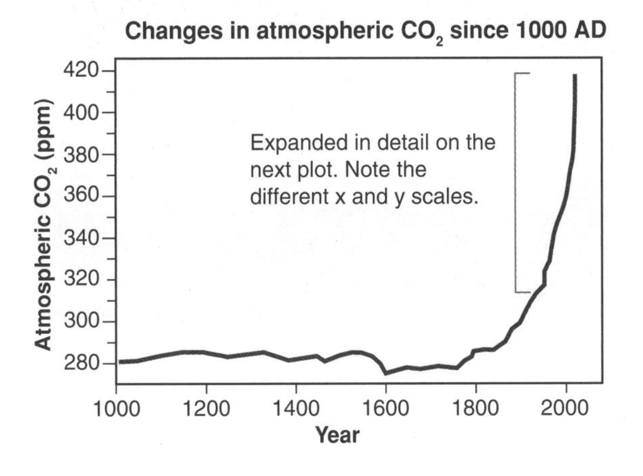

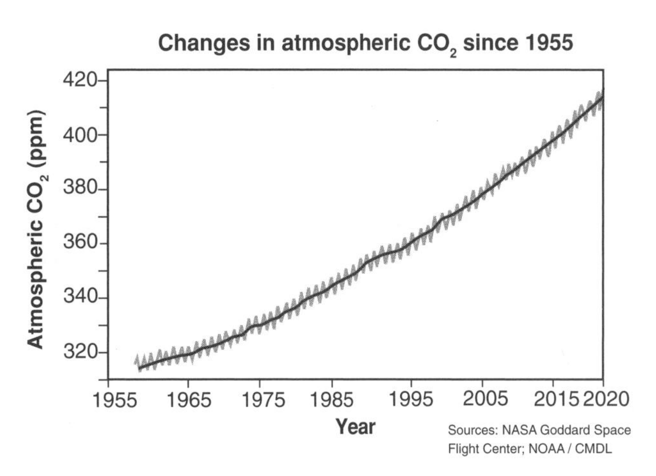

Changes in global near surface temperature

- One of the consequences of adding greenhouse gases to the atmosphere is that they cause the Earth's surface temperature to rise. Measurements from around the globe show a steady increase in near surface temperatures over the last half a century.

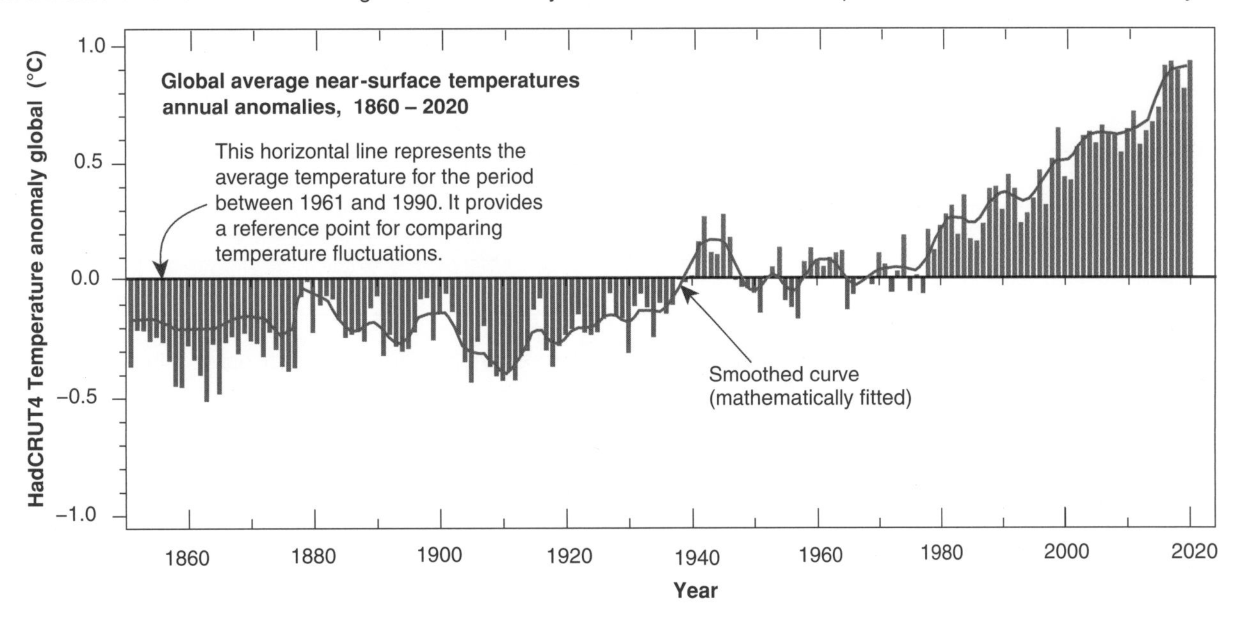

1. Of the greenhouse gases listed on the previous page:

   (a) Which is producing the largest radiative forcing (most amount of warming)? ______________________

   (b) Which has largest global warming potential? ______________________

   (c) Which has the greatest presence in the atmosphere? ______________________

2. Calculate the increase (as a %) in the 'greenhouse gases' between the pre-industrial era and the 2020 measurements (use the data from the table, see previous page). **HINT**: The calculation for carbon dioxide is: (411 - 280) ÷ 280 x 100 =

   (a) Carbon dioxide: ______________ (b) Methane: ______________ (c) Nitrous oxide: ______________

3. Explain the greenhouse effect and its importance for Earth: ______________________

4. How does an enhanced greenhouse effect affect the Earth? ______________________

ISBN: 978-1-98-856632-0

Mapping greenhouse gases with the International Space Station

The Orbiting Carbon Observatory-3 (OCO-3) was launched on 4 May 2019 and installed in the International Space Station (ISS). It is an additional carbon observatory that will supplement OCO-2, an independent satellite, launched in 2014. OCO-3 was assembled out of the spare parts from OCO-2, and installed in an empty science module aboard the ISS that is awaiting a prebooked experiment. As such OCO-3 will map CO_2 for just 3 years.

However its mission is important because the timing of the ISS orbit allows it to see the same part of the globe at different times of the day. OCO-2 can only see a part of the globe at the same time every day. The two sets of measurements should provide high precision data for changes in atmospheric CO_2.

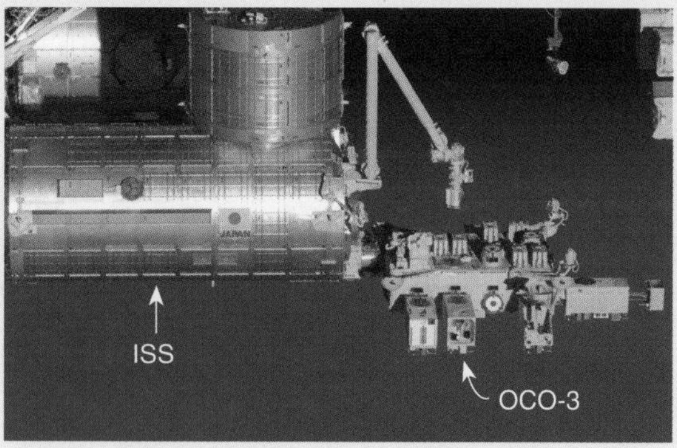

NASA

5. What is the role of water in the greenhouse effect? ______________________________

6. Compare the changes in concentrations of CO_2 (and other greenhouse gases) and the changes in near surface temperatures. Explain any relationships you see:

7. Think carefully about the annual environmental processes that occur on the Earth. What processes might explain the annual rise and fall in CO_2 concentrations?

8. What is the purpose of the OCO-3 and why is its placement on the ISS important? ______________________________

9. Why is the location of Mauna Loa ideal for measuring CO_2 in the atmosphere? (If you're not sure of the location, search on Google maps, Google Earth, or similar):

ISBN: 978-1-98-856632-0

155 Earth's Long Term Climate

Key Question: How has the Earth's climate changed over its history?

The Earth's climate has varied considerably when viewed over the long term. There have been frequent ice ages consisting of glacials and interglacials. At times ice has covered virtually the entire planet, while at other times there has been almost no ice at all. These changes in climate are related to many different variables including changes in the orbit and tilt of the Earth, and the evolution of life, especially plants and photosynthesis. Carbon dioxide and other greenhouse gases also play a part in these changes, helping to either trigger changes or enhance an effect already underway. Studies of gas trapped in ice cores taken from the polar ice caps have helped reveal these climatic changes.

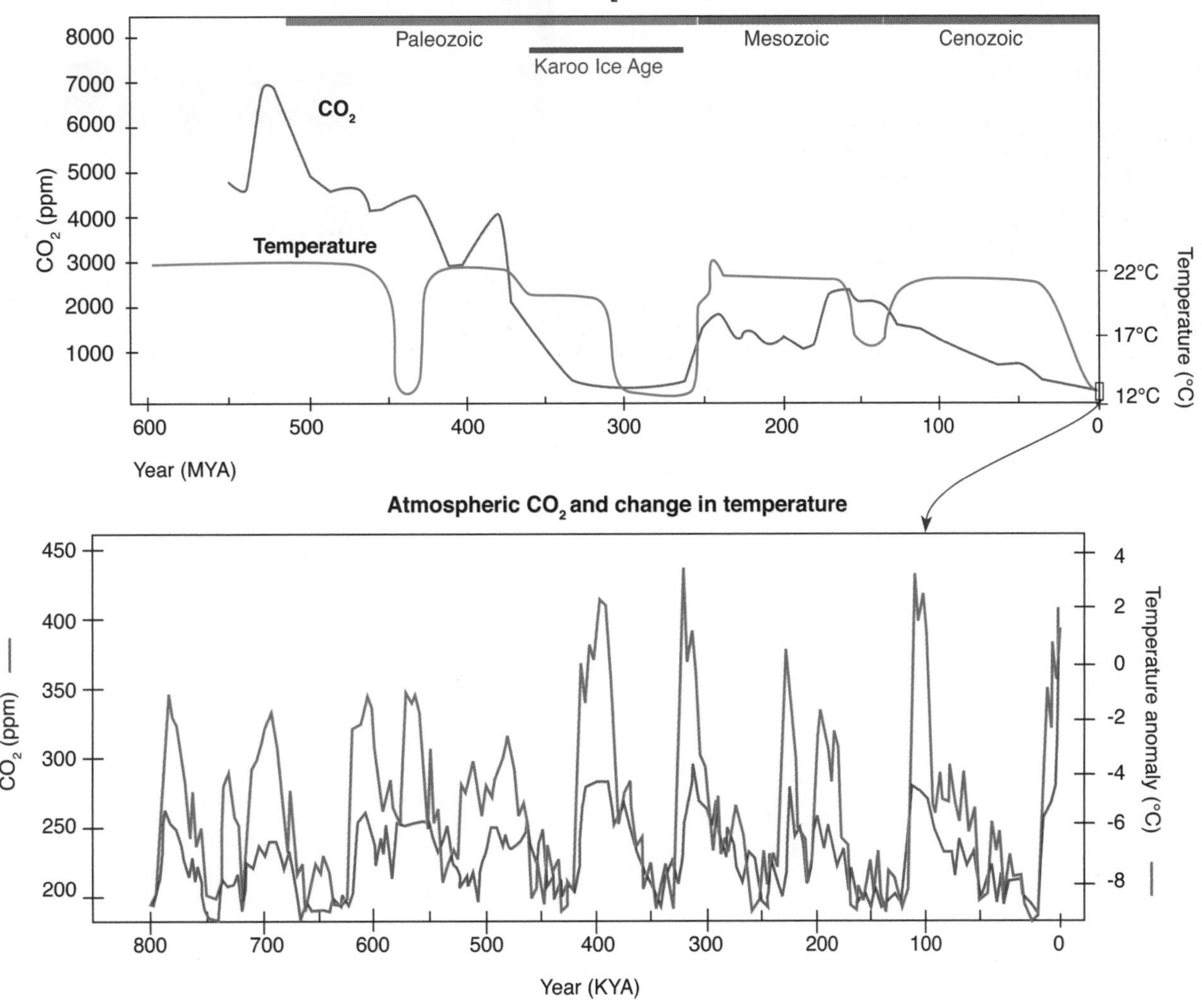

1. Approximately when was the last time CO_2 levels equaled those of the present?

2. What evidence is there that CO_2 levels affect global surface temperature?

3. Has the global surface temperature over the last 800,000 years been on average above or below the present's surface temperature?

4. Has the global surface temperature over the last 600 million years been on average above or below the present's surface temperature?

5. Why would the evolution of plants and photosynthesis affect the climate on Earth?

ISBN: 978-1-98-856632-0

156 What is Climate Change?

Key Question: What does the term climate change mean?

The terms greenhouse effect, global warming, and climate change are a common part of many conversations at present. They are sometimes used interchangeably but each has its own particular meaning. While the greenhouse effect refers to the warming effect of the Earth's atmosphere and global warming to the steady measured increase in the Earth's surface temperature, climate change refers to the long term climatic effects of those. It is important to separate climate from weather. Climate is widespread and long term, over many years or decades. Weather is local and short term. For example, an increase in the number and intensity of hurricanes may indicate climate change, whereas one single strong hurricane over a certain area may be an isolated event.

Potential effects of climate change

- The potential effects of climate change are wide ranging. Rises in sea level, glacial melt and loss of ice sheets, and an increase in storm intensity are just some.

Sea levels are expected to rise by 30-50 cm by the year 2100. This is the result of the thermal expansion of ocean water and melting of glaciers and ice shelves. Many of North America's largest cities are near the coast. The predicted rises in sea levels could result in inundation (flooding) of these cities and entry of salt water into agricultural lands.

Tropical marine ecosystems could suffer more energetic wave surges as sea levels rise. Barrier reefs protect large parts of tropical coastlines from ocean waves. This provides areas of low wave energy where sea grasses and corals can grow, providing habitat for marine animals. Sea level rise could allow waves to surge into these habitats.

Global warming may cause regional changes in **weather patterns**, affecting the intensity and frequency of storms. High intensity hurricanes now occur more frequently, driven by higher ocean surface temperatures. The devastating effects of disasters, such as hurricane Katrina, illustrate the vulnerability of low lying cities to sea level rises.

Finding climate change in the data

- The data below shows the number and intensity of hurricanes in the Atlantic. Analyzing patterns in this kind of data can help us understand changes in climate.

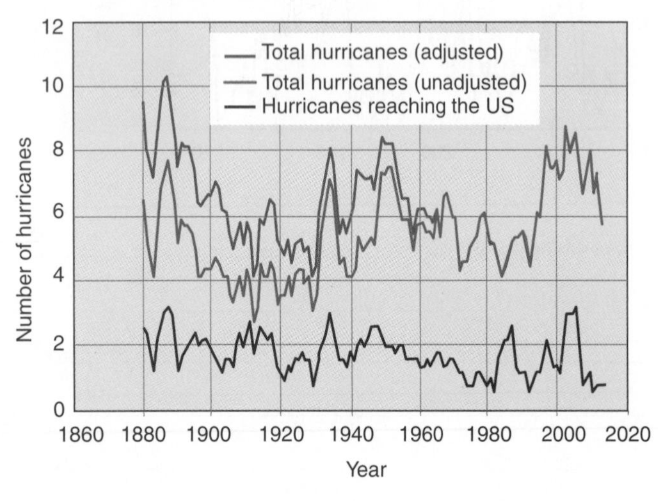

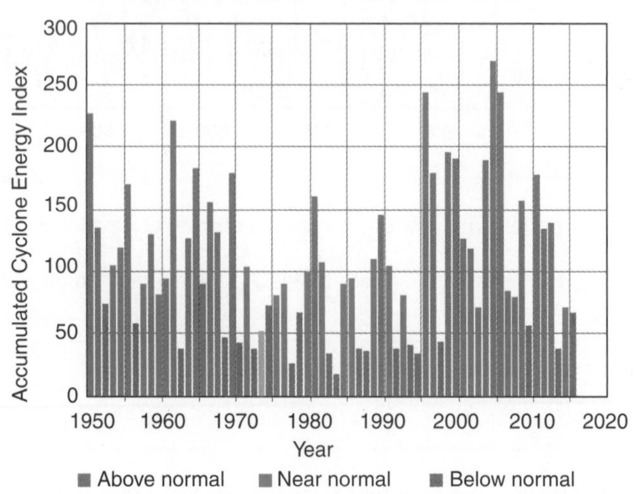

1. What are the consequences of global temperature rise on low lying land?

ISBN: 978-1-98-856632-0

Visualizing a warming world

- It can be difficult to see the trends in the complex patterns of hurricanes and other events. Probably the simplest or most obvious aspect of climate change measured is the change in the surface temperature of the Earth over time. This has been measured in meteorological stations around the globe.
- The diagrams below visualize the annual temperatures of various regions. The color scale is ± 2.6 standard deviations from the annual average temperature for each area (thus the same colors in different visualizations may be different temperatures). Red are above average years, blue are below average years. Explore for yourself at *showyourstripes.info*

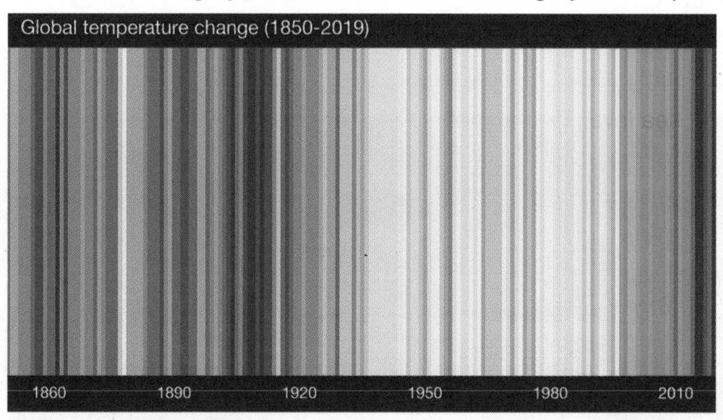

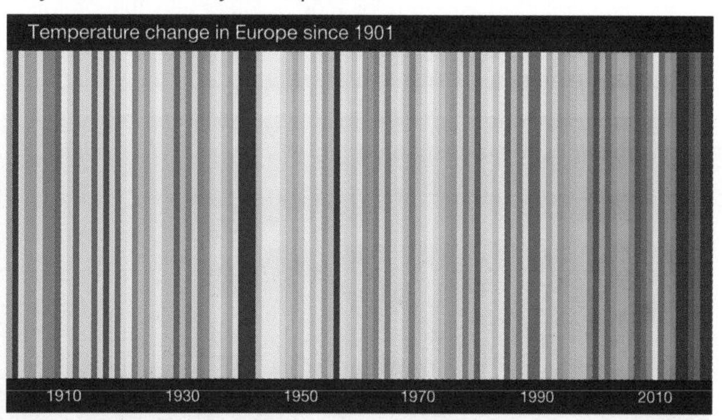

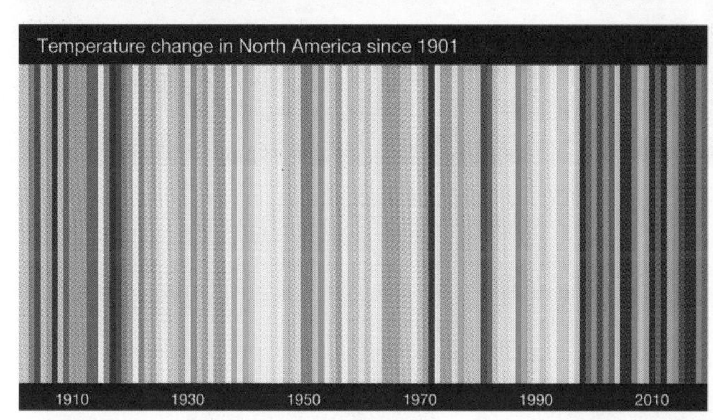

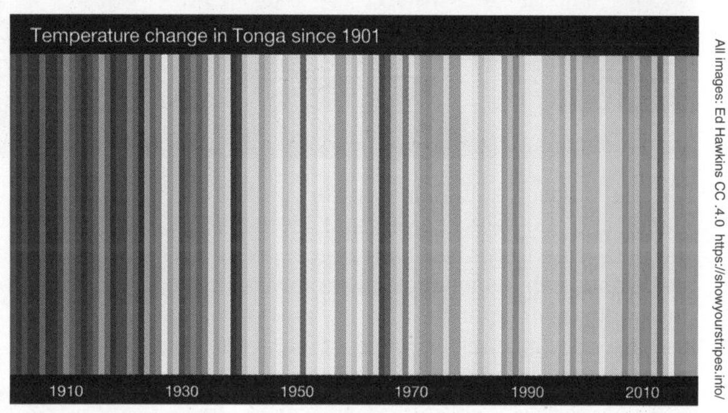

2. Study the graph on the previous page of the number of hurricanes forming in the North Atlantic. Why do you think the number of adjusted hurricanes differs from the unadjusted number? Hint: Note how the curves converge more recently.

3. Is there a trend in the number of hurricanes reaching the US? Explain your answer:

4. Study the plot of cyclone energy.

   (a) How many cyclones were above normal for the period 1950-1983:

   (b) How many cyclones were above normal for the period 1984-2015:

   (c) Has there been a change in the cyclone energy between the two periods?

5. (a) What do all the temperature visualizations above have in common?

   (b) Why is the inclusion of Tonga in this set of visualizations important? Check the location of Tonga on a physical or digital map if you need a clue:

ISBN: 978-1-98-856632-0

Climate change and threats to human populations

- Climate change will affect human populations in numerous ways including sea level rise and an expansion in the range of disease vectors, such as the mosquitoes that can carry malaria.

Climate change and the fate of island nations

- Even under the most conservative projections of climate change, rising sea levels will place many coastal and low lying regions of the world at risk of inundation. Many of these at-risk island nations are located in the Pacific and Indian Oceans and, for many populations, permanent relocation is the only viable option for the future.
- Mean sea level rose by about 15 cm during the 20th century and a further rise of up to 58 cm is projected before 2090. A rise in global mean sea level of 1 m would inundate many island groups and coastal communities.

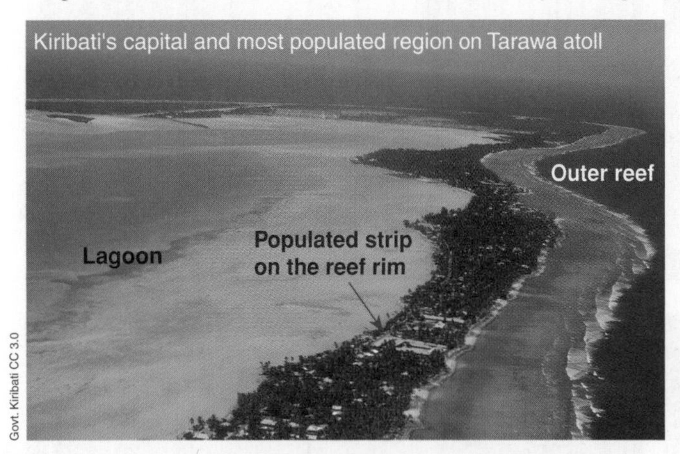

The island nation of Kiribati is made up of 33 atolls and reef islands and one raised coral island. More than 33% of its 100,000+ inhabitants live in an area of 16 km^2. Although atolls and reef islands can respond to sea level by increasing in surface area (through greater coral growth), there is no increase in height, so they are still vulnerable to inundation and salt water intrusion.

Some 2800 km south of Kiribati, the tiny island nation of Tuvalu (maximum elevation 4.6 m) is also under threat from climate change, being vulnerable to tropical cyclones, storm surges, and king tide events. A sea level rise of 20-40 cm will make Tuvalu unhabitable for its population of around 11,000 and already its leaders are making plans for evacuation, probably to nearby Fiji.

An Australian study in 2004 found the centre of distribution for the AdhS gene in *Drosophila*, which helps survival in hot and dry conditions, had shifted 400 kilometers south in the last 20 years. This could affect the production of fruits vulnerable to fruit fly damage.

Disease vectors (e.g. mosquitoes above) (and therefore disease) could spread or become more prominent as global temperatures rise. In 1997-1998, Kenya experienced an increase in malaria and Rift Valley fever due to a short term increase in temperature produced by El Niño conditions.

Coastal areas may become uninhabitable and subtropical areas may experience rises in tropical disease. These changes could drive changes in human migration. These migrations could affect international relations as island and coastal peoples move to higher land.

6. (a) Explain why the people of low lying island nations are at high risk of forced migration: ______________________

   ____

   (b) Coral atolls can be relatively resilient to sea level rise by increasing in surface area. Why is this unlikely to help the people of island nations threatened by sea level rise and increased air and sea surface temperatures?

   ____

   ____

7. How might disease vectors (and therefore disease) be affected by climate change and how might this affect populations?

   ____

   ____

   ____

   ____

ISBN: 978-1-98-856632-0

157 Projections For Climate Change

Key Question: What might be some of the larger scale effects of climate change?

The Earth is such a complex system and we have such incomplete records of most of its individual subsystems that making predictions about how they all interact is difficult. One of the more unpredictable aspects of climate change is whether or not there will be a "tipping point" in which there will be a sudden (and possibly irreversible) change in climate or whether the climate will incrementally change to a new regime. Systems vulnerable to tipping point scenarios include ocean circulation and global wind patterns, including the jet stream and Hadley cells. Predictions range from these suddenly stalling to their strength increasing. More data is needed to satisfactorily model these systems and predictions.

Modeling climate change

- The accuracy of climate models has improved steadily over the last 30 years as we have gathered more information on the Earth's climate systems and computing power has improved. Using these models, scientists have been better able to predict various aspects of climate change. The models below show how the resolution of climate change models has improved over the years and the various systems included in the models.

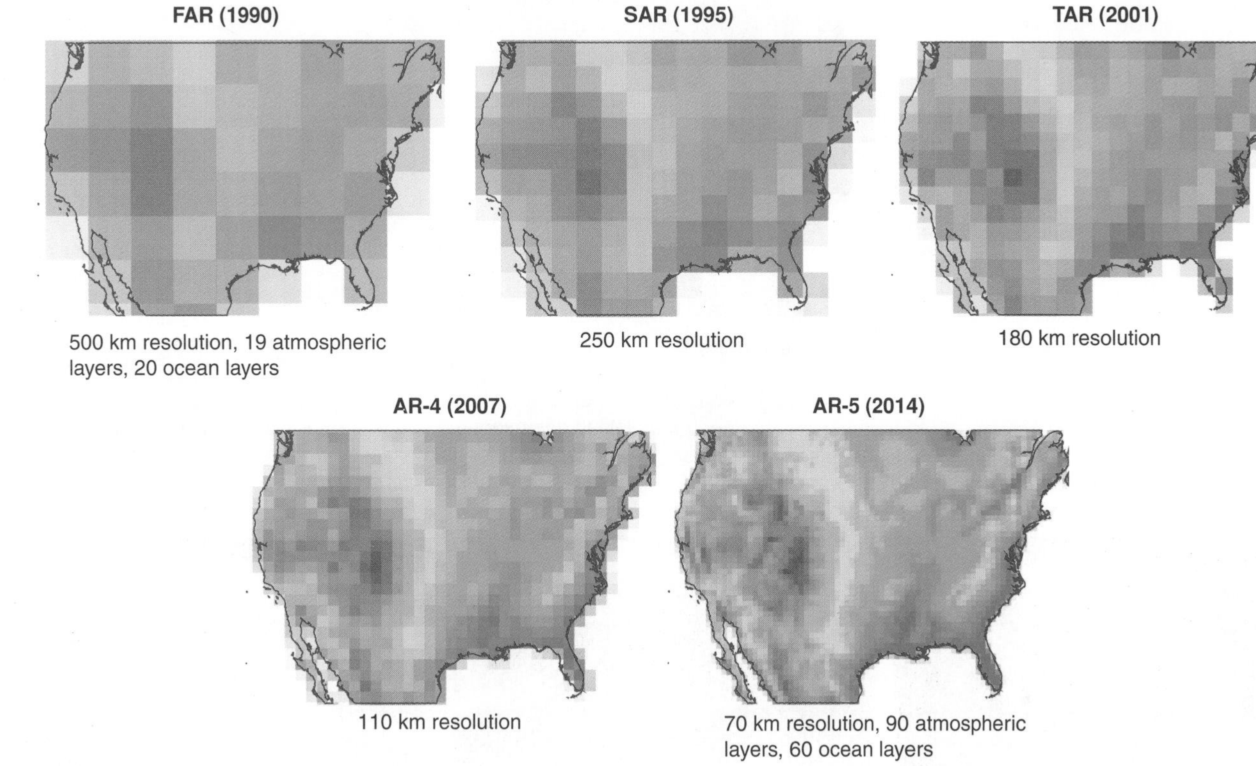

FAR (1990): 500 km resolution, 19 atmospheric layers, 20 ocean layers

SAR (1995): 250 km resolution

TAR (2001): 180 km resolution

AR-4 (2007): 110 km resolution

AR-5 (2014): 70 km resolution, 90 atmospheric layers, 60 ocean layers

- The original models used in the first IPCC assessment report incorporated the effects of sea ice, oceans, land, and the atmosphere. The resolution of the models was low, meaning any predictions were wide ranging.
- Assessment Report 5 (2014) also incorporated the effect or aerosols, the carbon cycle, vegetation, atmospheric chemistry, and land ice. The resolution was very high, so predictions from the models could be narrowed to particular regions.
- The improvements in predictive power have only been achieved because of the massive increase in computing power. To increase the resolution by a factor of two requires about ten times the computing power.

1. Explain the importance of using climate models: ______________________________

____

____

____

____

2. How has the resolution of climate models changed over time, and why is this important? ______________________________

____

____

____

____

ISBN: 978-1-98-856632-0

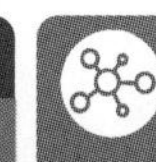

Ocean circulation

- The deep-water ocean currents (the thermohaline circulation) is driven by the cooling and sinking of water masses in polar and subpolar regions. Cold water circulates through the Atlantic, penetrating the Indian and Pacific oceans, before returning as warm upper ocean currents to the South Atlantic. Deep water currents move slowly and, once a body of water sinks, it may spend hundreds of years away from the surface.
- Greater than normal melting of ice at the poles is releasing vast amounts of freshwater to the oceans. Freshwater is less dense than seawater and this could slow the sinking of ocean waters at the poles and so alter patterns of global ocean circulation.

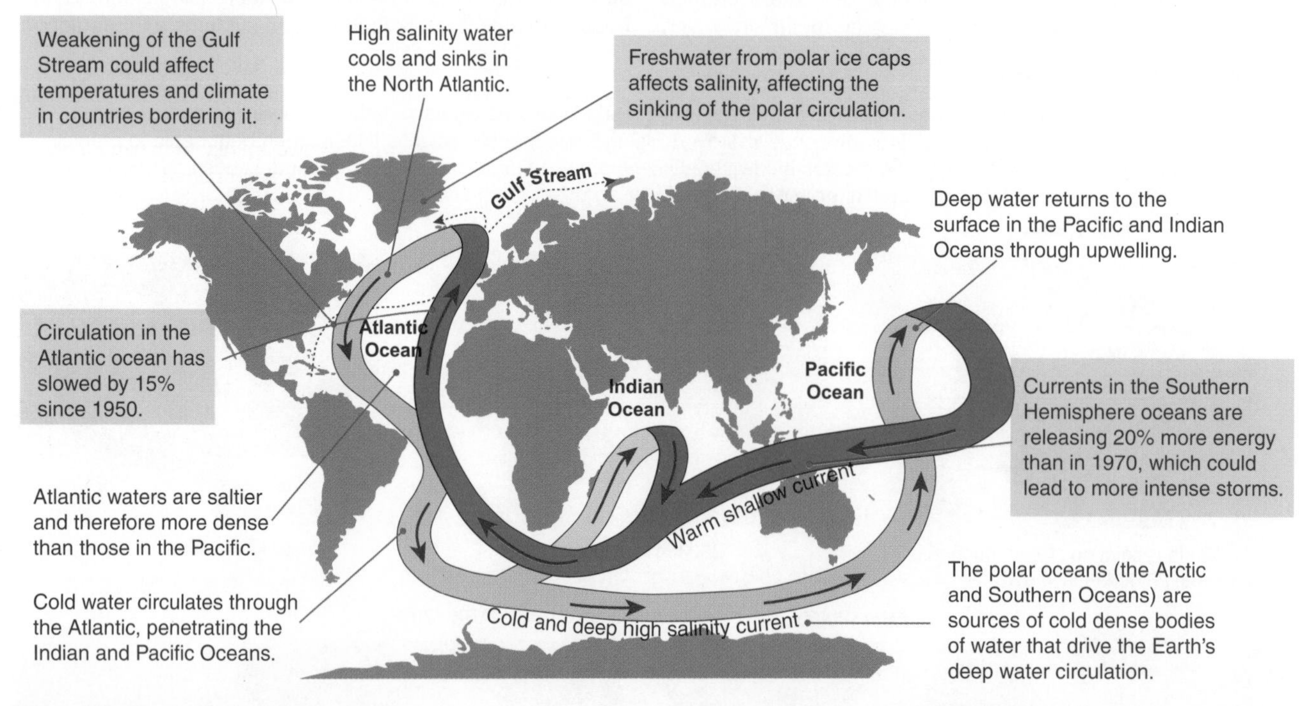

Atmospheric circulation

The Hadley cells (north and south) cover the area from the equator to the subtropics/desert boundary. Measurements of the Hadley cells show they are expanding their subtropic/desert edges. This could lead to deserts expanding. There is also evidence that the cell may be weakening as atmospheric temperature rises.

The intertropical convergence zone (ITCZ) is a planetary-scale band of heavy precipitation close to the equator. The ITCZ shapes climate in the tropics and has narrowed in recent decades. Climate models predict further narrowing as climate warms. These changes will alter patterns of precipitation and could result in sub-tropical droughts and equatorial floods.

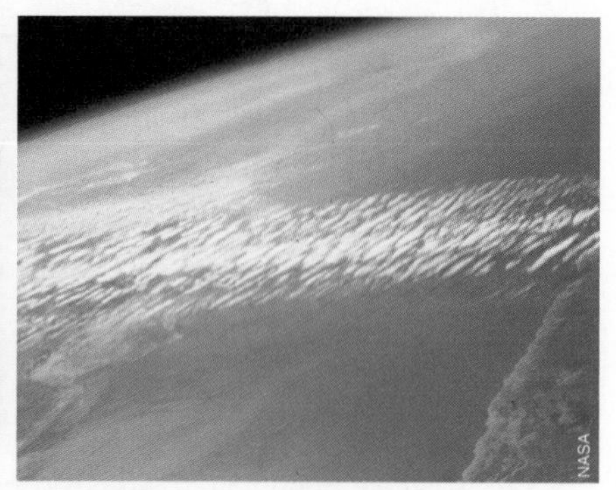

Rising global temperatures may be affecting global jet streams. The jet stream circles the edges of the poles. Warming in the poles disrupts this edge and so where the jet stream flows. Models show disruption of the jet streams could lock weather events into place, stalling them over regions. In storm events, this could lead to severe flooding.

3. Explain how changes in thermohaline circulation could influence global climate: ______________________________

____

____

____

____

4. How could changes in atmospheric circulation affect weather patterns? ______________________________

____

____

ISBN: 978-1-98-856632-0

Agriculture

- The impacts of climate change on agriculture and horticulture in North America will vary because of the size and range of its geography. In some regions, temperature changes will increase the growing season for existing crops, or enable a wider variety of crops to be grown. Changes in temperature or precipitation patterns may benefit some crops, but have negative effects on others. Increasing atmospheric CO_2 levels will enhance the growth of some crops (e.g. wheat, rice, and soybeans). Soils may become drier or wetter depending on location.

Effects of increases in temperature on crop yields

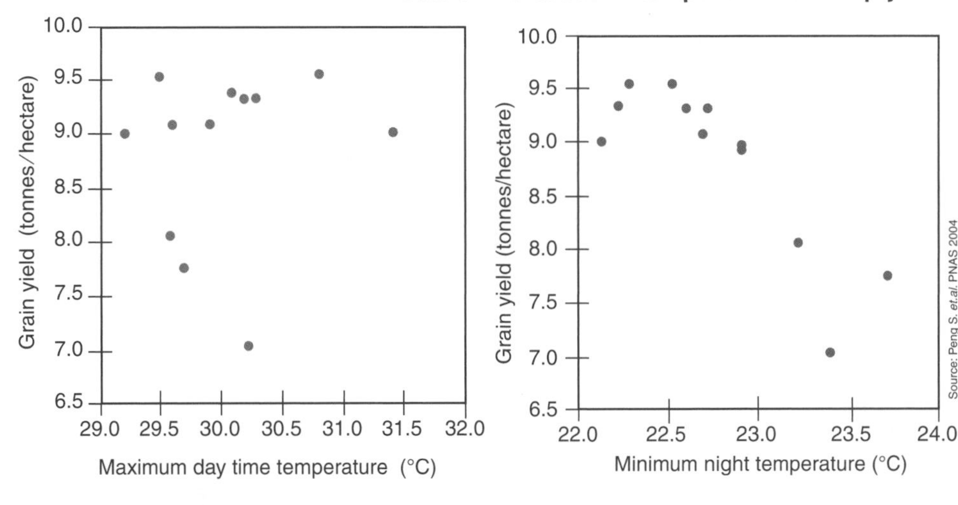

Studies on the grain production of rice have shown that maximum daytime temperatures have little effect on crop yield. However, higher minimum night time temperatures lower crop yield by as much as 5% for every 0.5°C increase in temperature.

Possible effects of climate change on soil

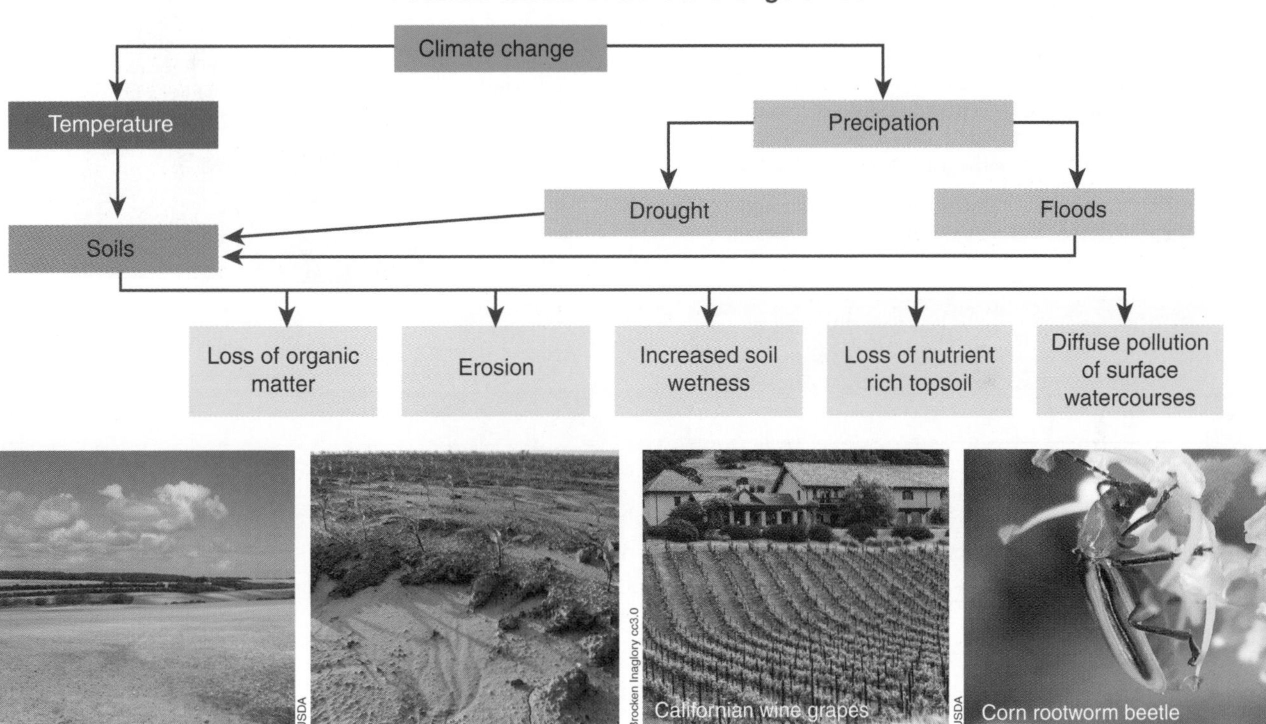

Drier conditions could see soils (especially peat soils) dry out. Carbon stored in them could quickly be lost.

Wetter conditions could make soils difficult to work and wash valuable nutrients from them. Soil erosion could also increase.

Crops grown near to their climate threshold may suffer reduced yields, quality, or both. Weeds may expand in range.

Milder winters and longer growing seasons may see the distribution of agricultural pest species spread.

5. Why will global warming benefit some agricultural crops, while disadvantaging others? ______________________

____

____

6. Use the schematic diagram above to explain how climate change could affect soils and agriculture: ______________________

____

____

____

ISBN: 978-1-98-856632-0

158 Climate Change and Polar Regions

Key Question: How will climate change affect polar habitats? The surface temperature of the Earth is in part regulated by the amount of ice on its surface, which reflects a large amount of heat into space. However, the area and thickness of the polar sea-ice is rapidly decreasing. From 1980 to 2008 the Arctic summer sea-ice minimum almost halved, decreasing by more than 3 million square kilometers. The 2012 summer saw the greatest reduction in sea-ice since the beginning of satellite recordings. This melting of sea-ice can trigger a cycle where less heat is reflected into space during summer, warming seawater and reducing the area and thickness of ice forming in the winter. At the current rate of reduction, it is estimated that there may be no summer sea-ice left in the Arctic by 2050.

Modeling the effect of albedo on ice sheet melting

- The investigation below provides a model for you to explore and understand the importance of heat absorbance and reflectivity (albedo) to ice sheet melting.

INVESTIGATION 9.1: Albedo and ice cube melting

See appendix for equipment list.

1. Work in pairs or groups of three. Collect two 500 mL Florence or Erlenmeyer flasks. Paint one of the flasks black and wrap the second flask in aluminum foil.
2. Weigh out six ice cubes (~60-90 g). Record the mass of the ice in the table below. Weigh out a second lot of ice cubes, it must have the same mass as the first.
3. Add 200 mL of 20°C water and the weighed ice cubes to each flask.
4. Seal the flasks and insert a thermometer into each. Record the temperature (time zero) on the table.
5. Place the flasks in a sunny spot and record the temperature every 2 minutes for 10 minutes. If it is not a sunny day, use a 60 W tungsten lamp placed 15 cm from the flasks as the heat source.
6. After 10 minutes remove the ice cubes and reweigh them. Record the values on the table below.

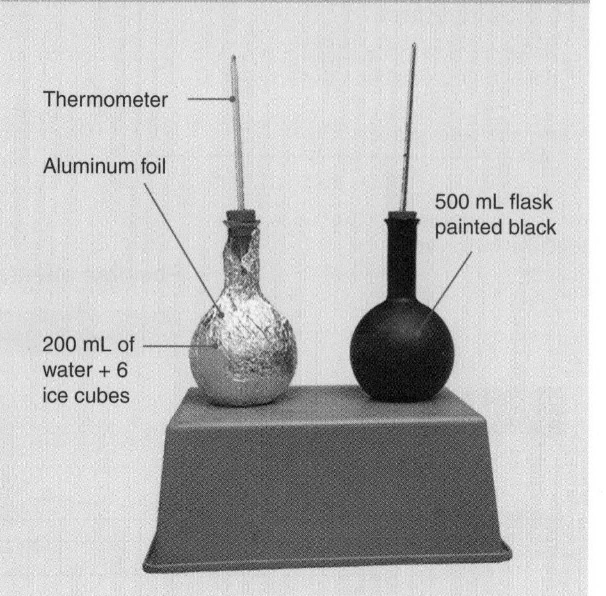

Time (minutes)	Temperature - black flask (°C)	Temperature - foil coated flask (°C)
0		
2		
4		
6		
8		
10		
Initial mass of ice (g)		
Final mass of ice (g)		

1. Write a suitable aim for this investigation: ______________________________

____

2. Plot the temperature changes on the grid (above):

3. Which flask has the greatest albedo? ______________________________

4. Calculate the change in mass of the ice cubes for both the black and foil covered flasks: ______________________________

____

ISBN: 978-1-98-856632-0

5. Why is it important to start with the same total mass of ice in each flask? ______________________________

6. What would you change if you wanted to show the effect of more or less sea ice on albedo? ______________________________

7. Write a conclusion for the investigation: ______________________________

The albedo effect

- The thickness of ice is important in determining its albedo (reflectivity).

A model where sea ice is retained

Arctic sea-ice summer minimum (white area)
1980: 7.8 million km^2

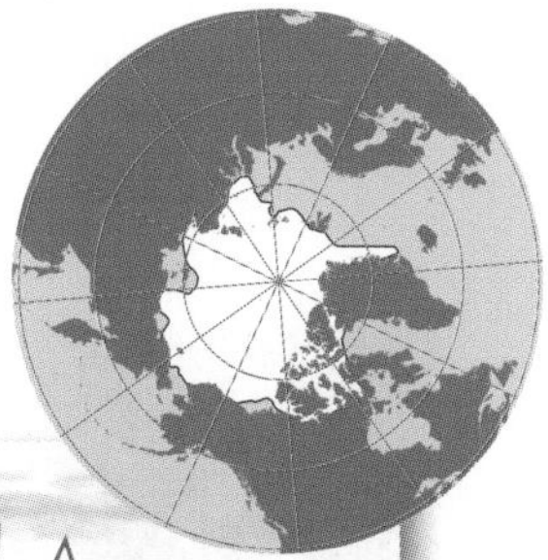

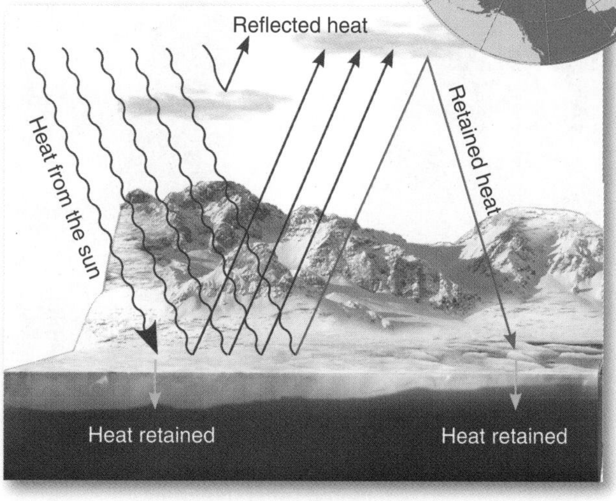

A model where sea ice is decreasing

Arctic sea-ice summer minimum (white area)
2012: 3.41 million km^2

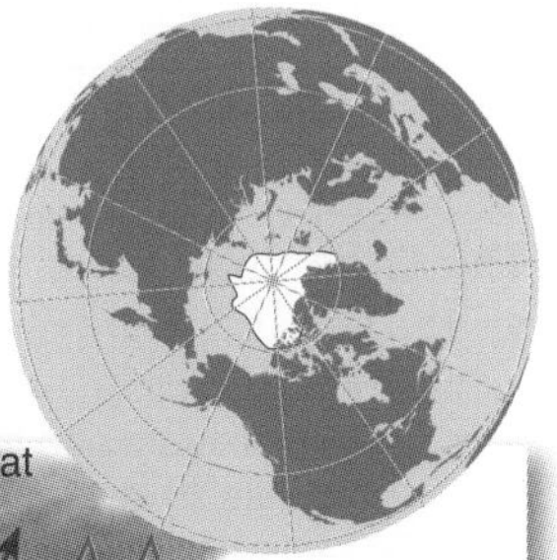

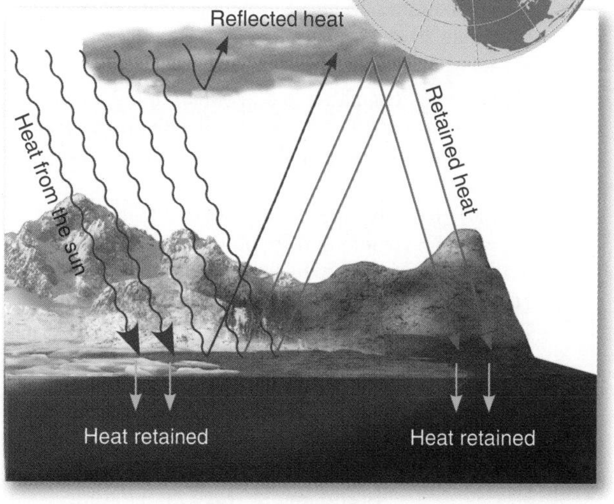

The high **albedo** (reflectivity) of sea-ice helps to maintain its presence. Thin sea-ice has a lower albedo than thick sea-ice. More heat is reflected when sea-ice is thick and covers a greater area. This helps to reduce the sea's temperature.

As sea-ice retreats, more non-reflective surface is exposed. Heat is absorbed instead of reflected, warming the air and water and causing sea-ice to form later in the fall than usual. Thinner and less reflective ice forms, continuing the cycle.

8. Using the sea ice models above, calculate the difference in summer sea-ice area between 1980 and 2012: ______________________________

9. Explain how low sea-ice albedo and volume affects the next year's sea-ice cover: ______________________________

10. Forest fires often produce soot and ash that can spread over vast areas. Ash from wildfires in Australia in 2019 reached glaciers in New Zealand, more than 2000 km away. The fires have been blamed for adding to the rate of retreat of New Zealand glaciers. Explain how this happens: ______________________________

ISBN: 978-1-98-856632-0

Average monthly Arctic sea ice extent (May 1979 - 2018)

Extent (millions of square kilometers): 15.0, 14.5, 14.0, 13.5, 13.0, 12.5, 12.0, 11.5, 11.0

Year: 1980, 1988, 1996, 2004, 2012, 2018

Data source: National Snow and Ice Data Center

Arctic air temperature* changes

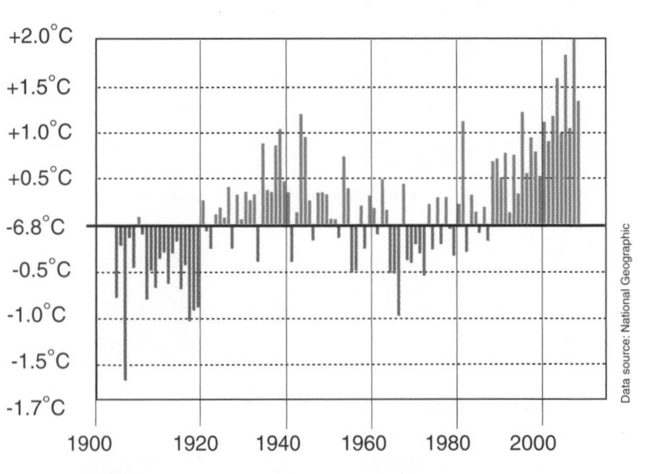

*Figure shows deviation from the average annual surface air temperature over land. Average calculated on the years 1961-2000.

The Greenland ice sheet

- The Greenland ice sheet is the second largest in the world after the Antarctic ice sheet. It covers around 100,000 square kilometers and has a mean thickness of over 2000 meters. In some areas the ice sheet is more than 3000 meters thick.
- The ice sheet is estimated to contain around 2.8 million cubic kilometers of ice. If it were to all melt and be added to the world's oceans the global sea level would rise by over 7 meters.
- Greenland plays an important role in the polar climate because of the volume and shape of its ice sheet. Large high-altitude plateaus on the ice sheet alter storm tracks and create cold down-slope winds close to the ice surface.
- As a result there is great interest in and research into the effect of a warming globe on the Greenland ice sheet. Studies show it is melting at an increasing rate.

Greenland surface melt extent

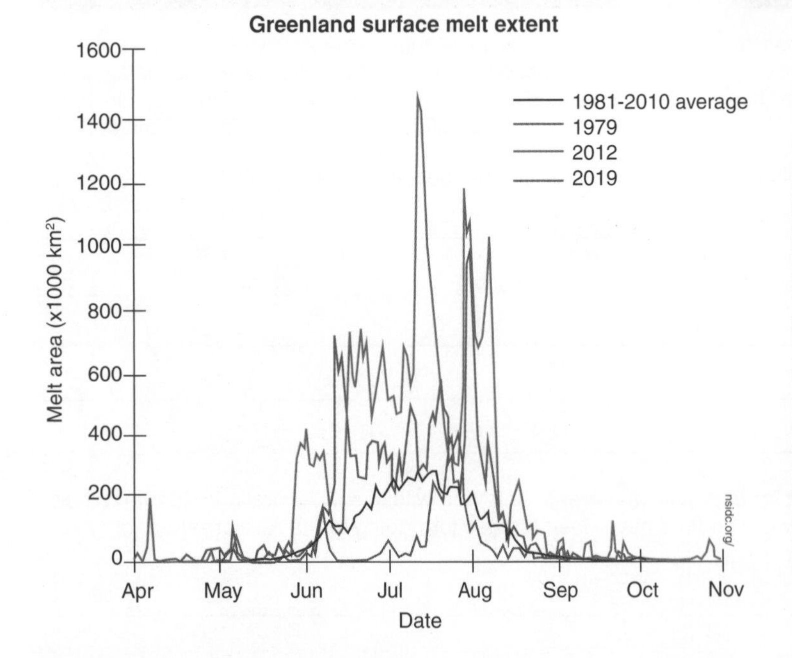

Melting of the Greenland ice sheet occurs during the Arctic summer. Since 1979 the area of ice melting and the length of time melting occurs has increased. 2012 saw the greatest amount of melting on the ice sheet.

Changing reflectiveness

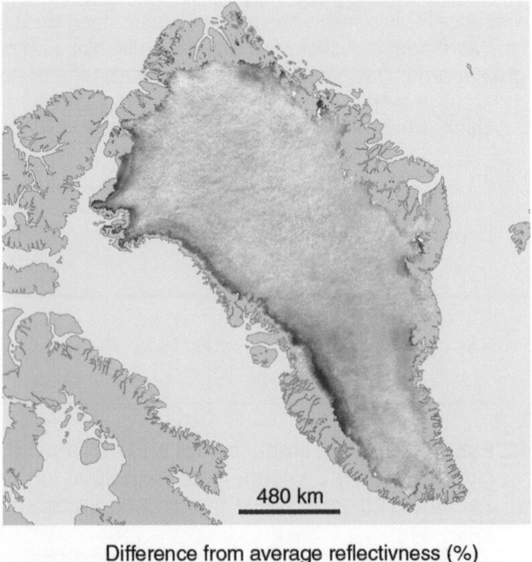

The map above shows the difference in sunlight reflected during the 2011 summer vs the average reflection. In some areas there is a 20% decrease in the amount of light being reflected.

ISBN: 978-1-98-856632-0

The rising Arctic temperatures are affecting the polar habitat and the organisms living there

Melting permafrost

- Permafrost is ground that remains continuously frozen for two years or more at a time. It can be located on land or under the sea (as part of the seabed) and underlies nearly 25% of the Northern Hemisphere.
- Climate change is beginning to have an effect on permafrost, with areas beginning to melt as Arctic temperatures rise.
- This causes a number of problems. One is the increase, extension, or exacerbation of the thermokarst (irregular hummocky landscape).
- During the Arctic summer, areas of ice across the tundra melt, forming thaw lakes. With increasing Arctic temperatures, these landscapes have expanded, causing parts of the Arctic, including areas of boreal forest, to permanently collapse. Thaw has also caused hillsides to collapse as the underlying permafrost loses structure and gives way.
- Another problem is the potential release of methane (both trapped methane and methane produced by decomposition of the thawed organic matter) and carbon dioxide (from increase bacterial respiration and decomposition).
- These releases can result in positive feedback and lead to increased warming. Positive (reinforcing) feedback loops on Earth tend to drive large scale changes to environments and the climate. The current increase in CO_2 in the atmosphere is driving many positive feedback loops. The diagram (below right) shows the effect of methane release from permafrost. Recall that methane is a potent greenhouse gas.
- Several positive feedback loops acting at the same time can potentially cause large, potentially destabilizing changes to the climate. Although these are balanced to some extent by counterbalancing negative feedbacks, it is possible there will eventually be a "tipping point" at which a runaway climate change event will occur.
- Various studies in the Arctic region show the temperature of the permafrost is indeed increasing, in some areas by 2-3°C since 1980.

Permafrost thaw

Thermokarst landscape caused by melting permafrost, Hudson Bay, Canada

Methane bubbles under frozen lake

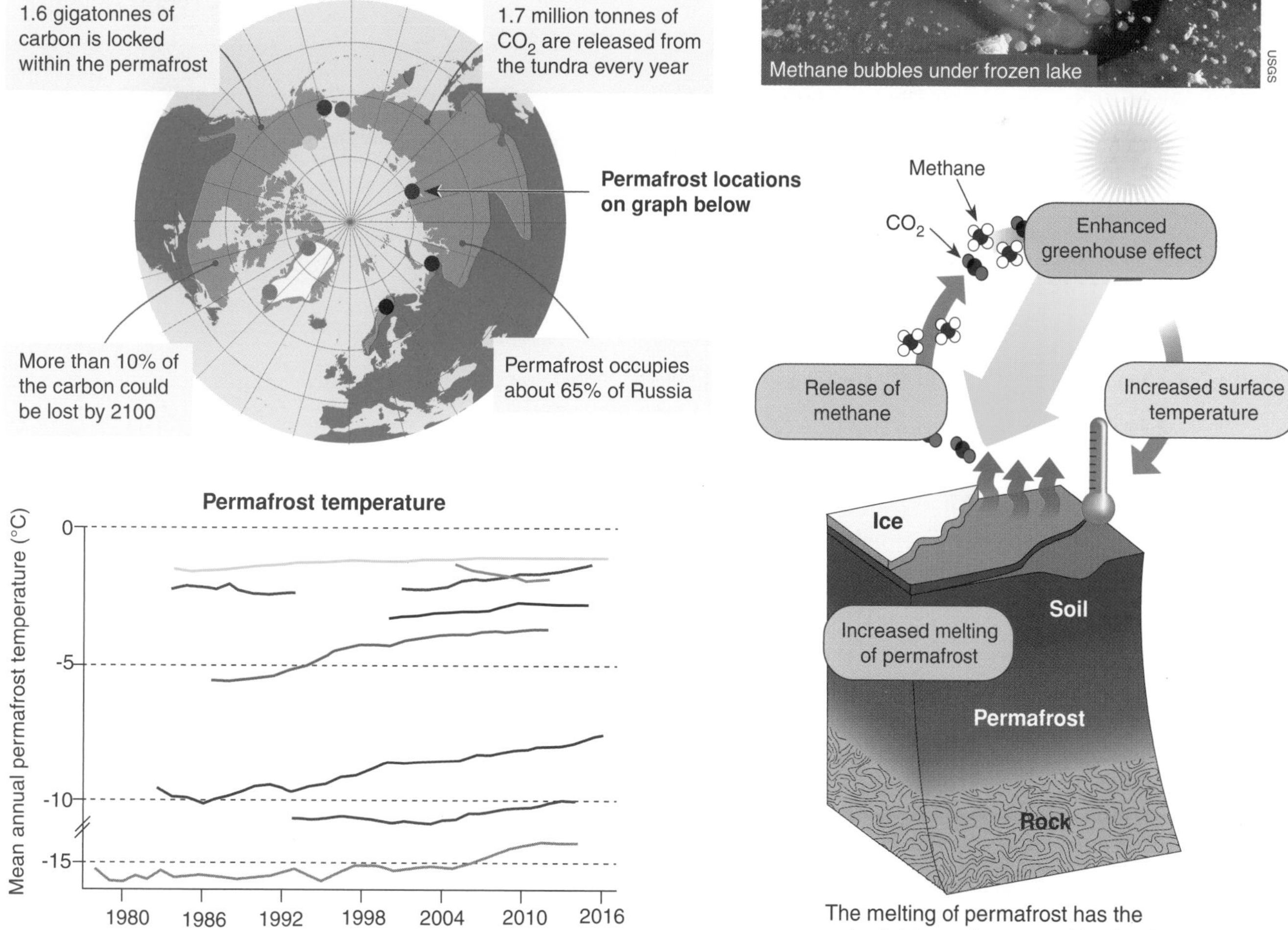

The melting of permafrost has the potential to produce a positive feedback loop, producing even more heating.

ISBN: 978-1-98-856632-0

Polar bears

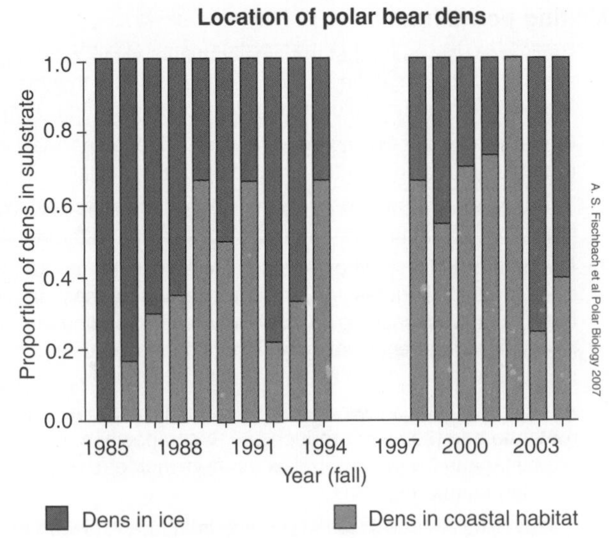

- Polar bears mainly hunt seals, which surface at breathing holes in the ice. The reduced sea ice levels have changed the distribution patterns of seals and many polar bears have been forced to swim long distances to hunt.
- Between 1979 and 1991, 87% of bears observed were on sea ice during summer. However in the period between 1992 to 2004, this declined to just 33%.
- In addition, the thinner sea ice cannot hold the weight of an adult bear, and they are forced to the mainland before they have built up their winter fat stores. The loss of condition is affecting reproductive rates, and juvenile survival rates are lower as a result.
- Pregnant females must also swim for longer distances to reach their dens, and so lose more condition in the process. A 2007 study (above right) shows a decrease in the number of bears denning in pack ice over a 20 year period.

11. (a) Describe what has happened to the extent of Arctic sea ice since 1980: ______________________

____

(b) Describe what has happened to Arctic air temperature since the early 1900s: ______________________

____

(c) Based on the data on page 322, do you think that the change in Arctic air temperature is affecting the extent of the Arctic sea ice? Justify your answer:

____

____

____

12. How is the thawing of permafrost extending the thermokarst landscape of the Arctic? ______________________

____

____

13. How might the melting of the permafrost accelerate global warming? ______________________

____

____

14. Discuss the impact of the reduction of the Arctic ice sheet on polar bear populations: ______________________

____

____

____

____

____

ISBN: 978-1-98-856632-0

Antarctica

- Because the majority of the world's population live in the Northern Hemisphere and because Antarctica is isolated at the South Pole, the effect of climate change on Antarctica is often overlooked. However there has been a large amount of recent research into changes in the Antarctic ice sheet and it has produced very worrying results.
- The Antarctic ice sheet covers 98% of the continent at about 14 million square kilometers. It contains 26.5 million cubic kilometers of ice, enough to raise sea levels by 58 meters if it were to all melt.
- Recent studies of the ice sheet show rapid melting in some areas. Large ice shelves have already disintegrated (e.g. the Larsen ice shelf between 1995 and 2017).
- Scientists have now focused their attention on the Thwaites Glacier. The glacier drains part of the West Antarctic ice sheet and is about 192,000 square kilometers. It is important because of the topography of the land and seabed underneath the glacier. Unlike in Eastern Antarctica, the ice in Western Antarctica is anchored on land that is far below sea level. The seabed beneath Thwaites Glacier angles downwards and so gets deeper. As the ice retreats, warm water flowing beneath the glacier increases the melting effect. Adding to this is the fact that as the glacier melts it moves faster towards the sea, draining ice off the glacier into the sea at an ever increasing rate.
- It has been estimated that since 1980 Thwaites Glacier has lost around 600 billion tonnes of ice.

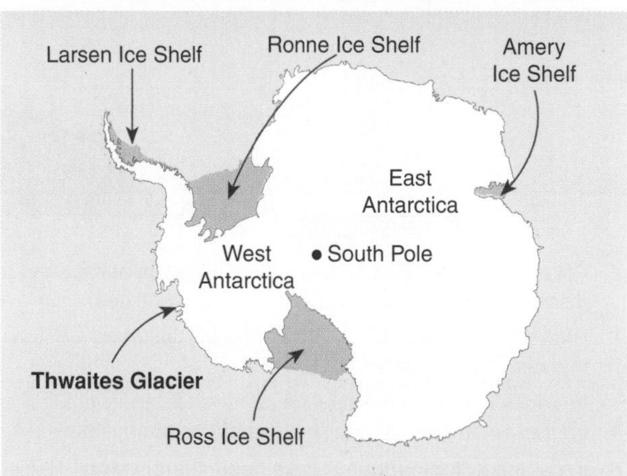

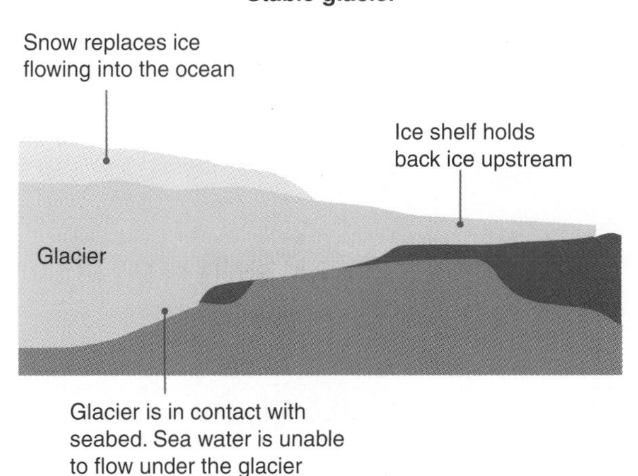

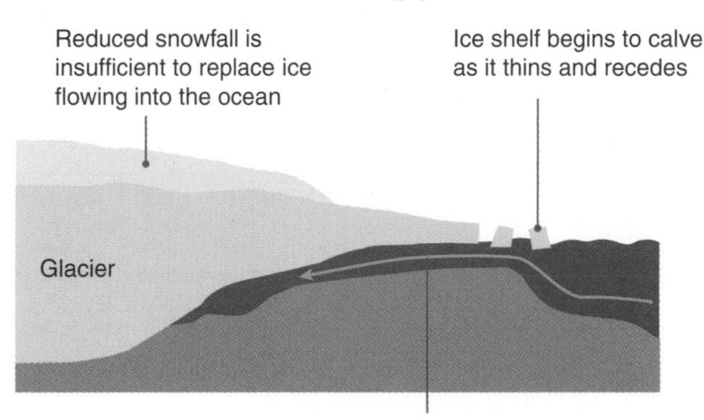

15. Describe the effect of a warming climate on the Greenland ice sheet: ______________________

16. How could the melting of permafrost enhance climate feedback loops? ______________________

17. Why is the Thwaites Glacier receiving increased scientific attention? ______________________

ISBN: 978-1-98-856632-0

159 Ocean Warming

Key Question: How is global warming affecting the oceans? The rise in the global atmospheric temperature must ultimately affect the oceans. Measurements show that the average ocean temperature is rising, although more slowly than atmospheric temperatures. Also the temperature of the Southern Ocean is rising faster than elsewhere. The rise in temperature is of concern for two primary reasons. The first is that rising temperatures will affect marine communities adapted to live at certain temperatures. The second is that above 4°C, water volume increases as temperature rises. This could have serious effects on sea levels and coastal communities, adding to sea level rise from melting ice caps.

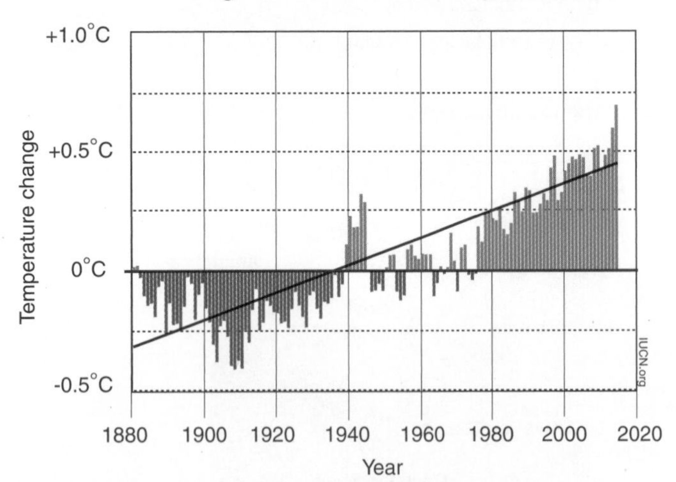

Average ocean temperatures have risen sharply since 1970. Water absorbs a large amount of energy for every degree Celsius it rises (4.2 joules per milliliter or gram). Thus even a small rise in sea temperature equates to the absorption of an enormous amount of energy when considering the entire oceans.

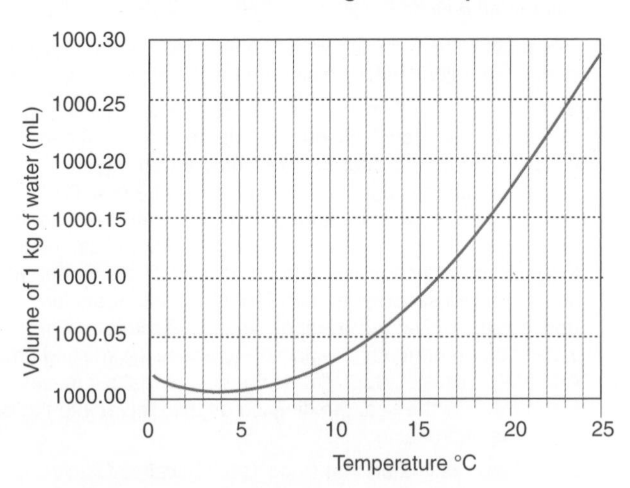

Water at 0°C is less dense than water at 4°C. That is why icebergs float. Above 4°C, water begins to expand. A rise of 2°C above 4°C produces a small expansion per kg of water, but with trillions of tonnes of water in the ocean the increase in volume would be enormous.

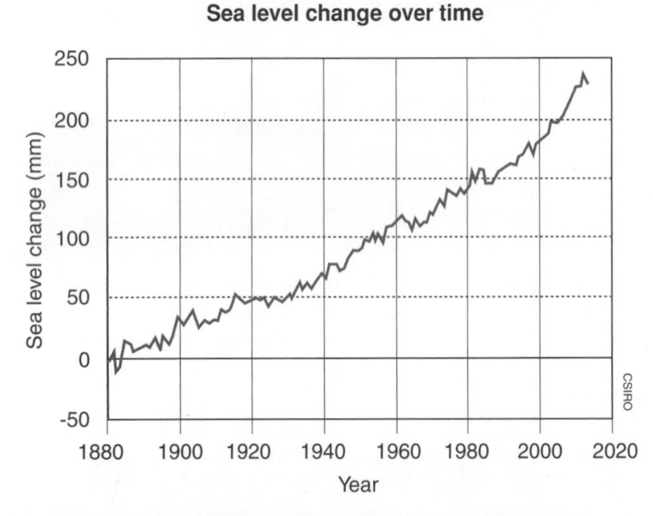

Tidal measurements show that the average sea level has steadily risen since at least the 1880s. Part of this is a gain in water volume from melting ice caps and glaciers, but a large part is the thermal expansion of the water in the oceans themselves.

Habitat effects

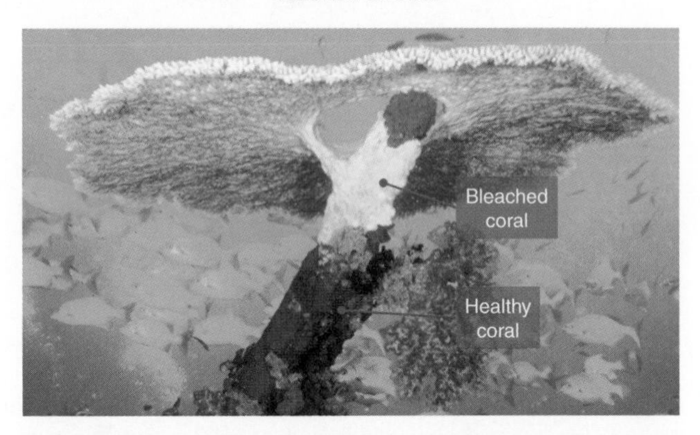

An increase in sea temperatures could mean the death of coral reefs. Healthy coral reefs depend on the symbiotic relationship between a coral polyp that builds the reef and photosynthetic protistans called zooxanthellae. Zooxanthellae live within the polyp tissues and provides it with most of its energy. A 1-2°C temperature increase is enough to disrupt the photosynthetic enzymes. The zooxanthellae either die, or are expelled from the coral due to stress. The result is coral bleaching.

1. What is the general trend in ocean temperature since 1880? ___

2. What is the general trend in sea level since 1880? ___

3. How does water volume change with temperature? ___

ISBN: 978-1-98-856632-0

Ocean warming affects oxygen saturation

- Warm water holds less oxygen than cold water. Thus as the oceans warm, oxygen saturation decreases. Indeed measurements show oxygen saturation of the oceans has declined by about 2% since the middle of the 20th century and it is expected to fall by about 3-4% by 2100.
- This could cause shifts in species distribution, expanding algal blooms, and reductions in fisheries resources (with implications to human sustainability).
- Much of the ocean's oxygen is concentrated in the upper 1000 meters. This is the area of highest biodiversity. A reduction in oxygen will therefore affect marine biodiversity.
- Warm water increases the oxygen demand of organisms. As a result organisms in warmer oceans are increasingly likely to suffer from a lack of oxygen (hypoxia). Eutrophication due to runoff from the land will add to this problem.
- Additionally, warming the upper layer of the ocean increases stratification (layering) and reduces mixing of the upper and lower layers. Thus deep ocean waters will become even more oxygen depleted.

Global warming and nutrient input on ocean oxygen

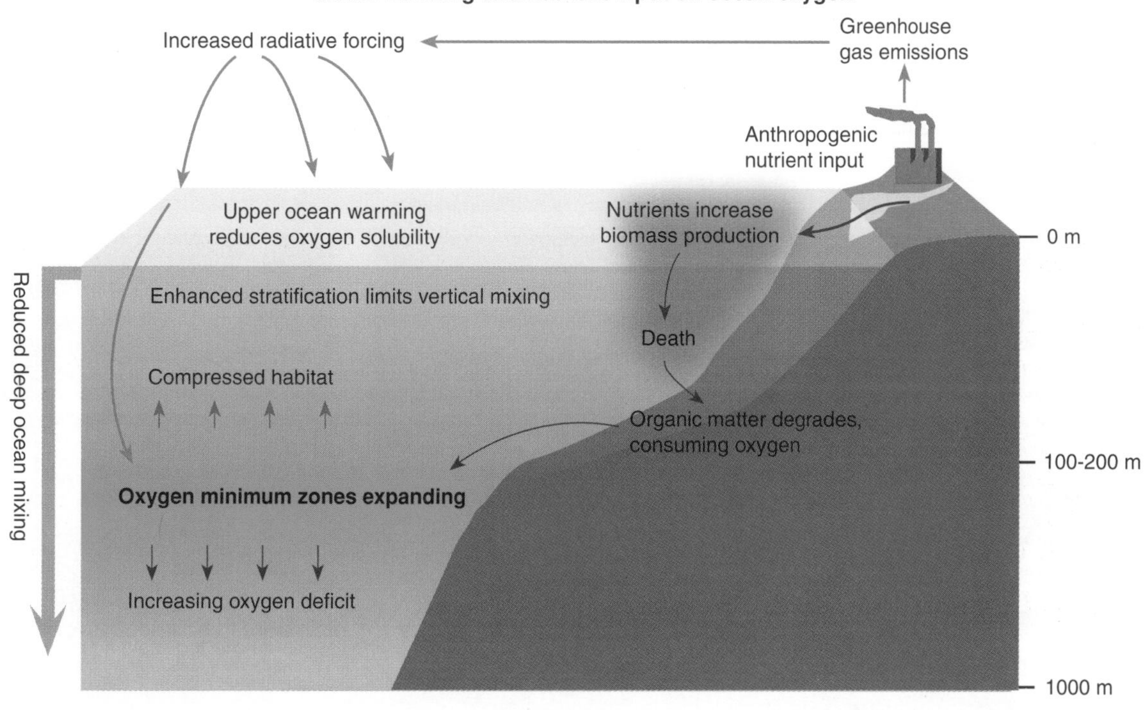

4. (a) The oceans contain about 1.35 billion cubic kilometers of water (1.35 x 10^{21} L). Assuming an average ocean temperature of 17°C (ocean temperature varies considerably depending on depth and latitude) calculate the gain in volume if ocean temperature increased by 1°C (1000 cm^3 = 1 L):

   (b) Since the oceans can only expand upwards (because they are, of course, in a confined space) what would be the effect of this expansion?

5. How does a warming sea temperature affect marine life?

6. Explain the effect of ocean temperature on oxygen and how this will affect marine habitats:

ISBN: 978-1-98-856632-0

160 Ocean Acidification

Key Question: What is ocean acidification?

The oceans act as a carbon sink, absorbing much of the CO_2 produced from burning fossil fuels. When CO_2 reacts with water it forms carbonic acid, which produces hydrogen ions, which decreases the pH of the oceans. This could have major effects on marine life, especially shell-making organisms. Ocean acidification is a relative term, referring to the oceans becoming less basic as the pH decreases.

Carbon dioxide and pH

- Recall that in the carbon cycle the oceans are a large reservoir of carbon because carbon dioxide from the atmosphere dissolves into them. This is evident in the plot right, which shows how the ocean constantly exchanges carbon dioxide with the atmosphere.
- The effect of carbon dioxide on water can be seen by bubbling it through water containing a pH indicator. Bromothymol blue is an indicator that is blue in basic (alkaline) solutions, blue/green in neutral water and yellow/green in acidic solutions. Adding carbon dioxide to water containing bromothymol blue causes the solution to turn yellow/green as the carbon dioxide dissolves into the water (below).

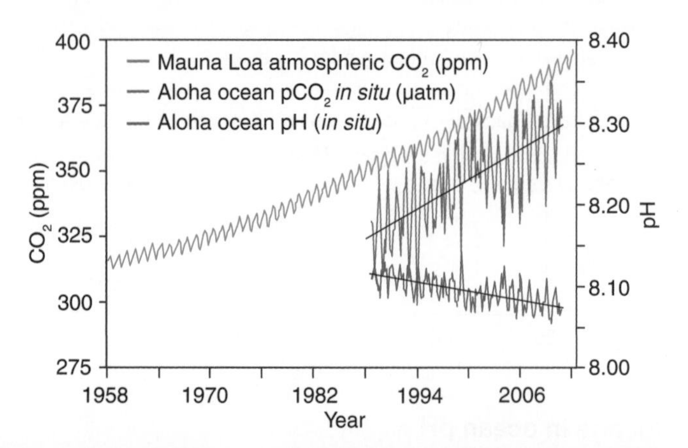

Bromothymol blue in basic solution

Adding CO_2 to bromothymol blue

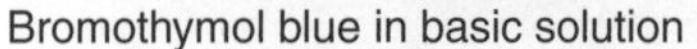

Bromothymol blue in acidic solution

The chemistry of ocean acidification

- Increases in atmospheric CO_2 levels cause more CO_2 to dissolve into ocean waters. This reacts with water to form carbonic acid and lowers the pH of the water. The carbonic acid dissociates into HCO_3^- and H^+ ions. Carbonate ions (CO_3^{2-}) from the ocean waters react with the extra H^+ ions to form more HCO_3^- ions. This process lowers the CO_3^{2-} ions available to shell-making organisms, leading to thinner and deformed shells.

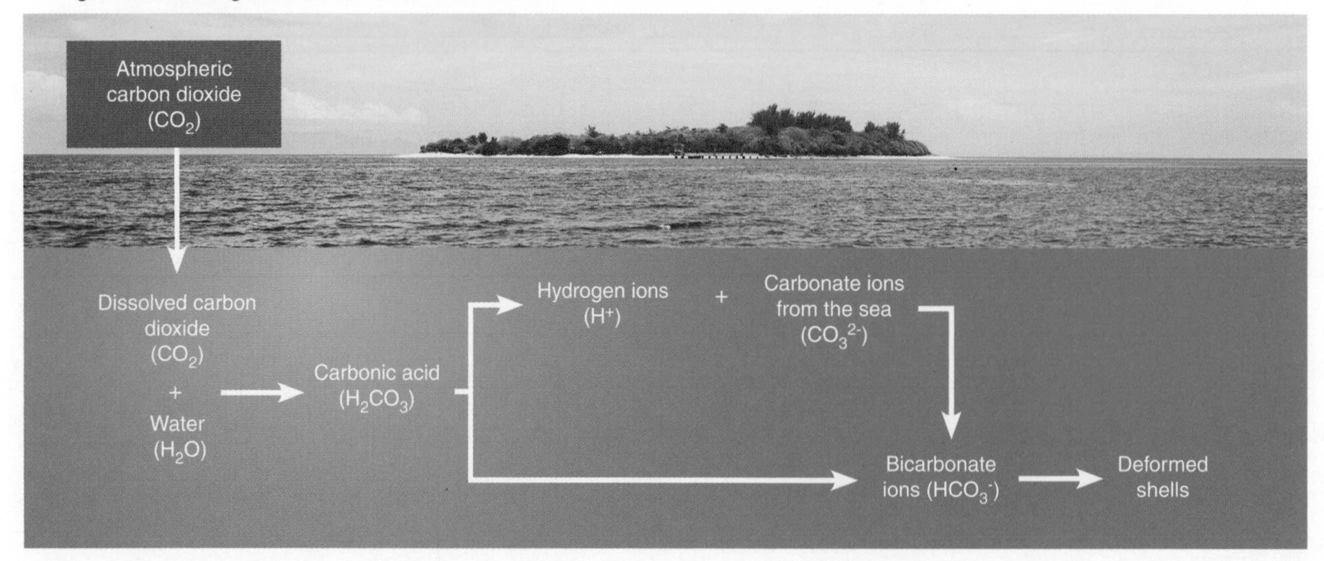

1. What does the term "ocean acidification" mean? ______________________________

____

____

ISBN: 978-1-98-856632-0

Ocean pH

▸ The pH of the oceans has fluctuated throughout geologic history but has always remained at around pH 8.2.

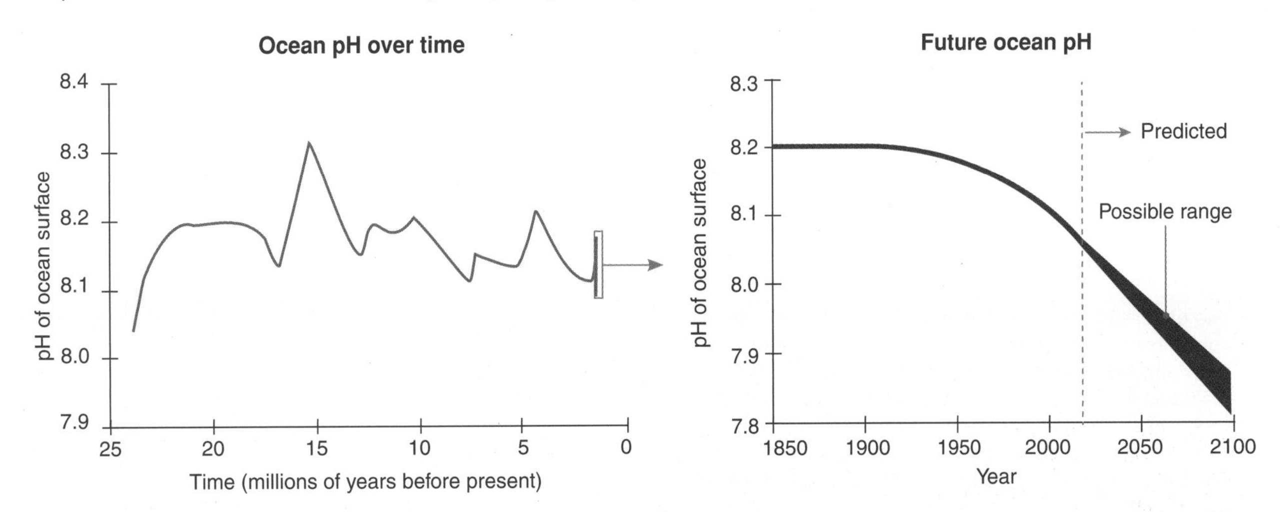

Change in ocean pH

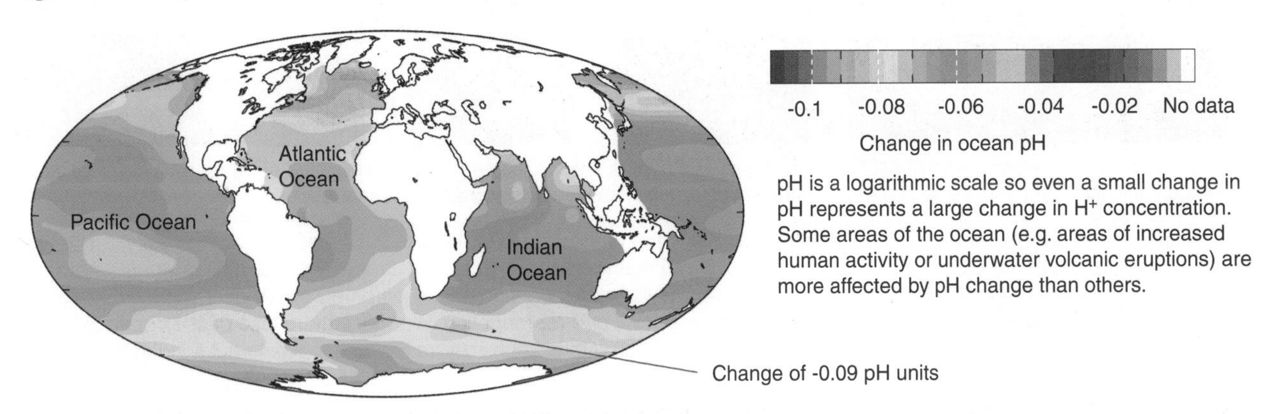

2. (a) Does bubbling carbon dioxide through water cause the water to become acidic or basic?

____

(b) Does this increase or decrease the pH? ______________________________

3. (a) What do you notice about the peaks and dips in ocean and atmospheric CO_2 in the graph on the previous page?

____

____

(b) What does this pattern indicate? ______________________________

(c) What is the trend over time in the CO_2 concentration in both reservoirs? ______________________________

____

4. Is the ocean acidic or basic? ______________________________

5. Why is the ocean pH dropping so rapidly? ______________________________

____

____

____

6. Which parts of the oceans have experienced the greatest change in pH? ______________________________

____

____

ISBN: 978-1-98-856632-0

161 The Effects of Ocean Acidification

Key Question: How does decreasing pH affect marine life?

Shell-building marine organisms build their shells from calcium carbonate ($CaCO_3$). The calcium carbonate occurs as two minerals calcite and **aragonite**, which have the same molecular formula but different crystal structures. Aragonite is stronger than calcite but more soluble. In solution, aragonite forms an equilibrium with its ions Ca^{2+} and CO_3^{2-}. If CO_3^{2-} is removed from the solution (by adding H^+ ions to form HCO_3^-(bicarbonate)) then the aragonite splits into more Ca^{2+} and CO_3^{2-} ions. This has the effect of dissolving or removing aragonite from its crystal form. Decreasing the pH (by increasing H^+) therefore has the effect of reducing available CO_3^{2-} and making it more difficult for marine organisms to build aragonite shells. Decreasing pH also has an effect on the behavior of marine organisms. Reasons why are not yet fully understood and it is an area of ongoing research.

- What evidence is there that high levels of dissolved CO_2 negatively affect marine life? Direct evidence can be obtained by comparing sites where CO_2 seeps naturally from volcanic vents to sites where it does not. Consider the images below:

Reef with carbon dioxide seep: sparse beds of algae. Such sites include Ili Ili Bua Bua, Normanby Island, Papua New Guinea.

Reef with no carbon dioxide seep. A high diversity of corals and other marine life is present.

- The increase in carbon dioxide not only favors the dissolution of aragonite from shells but it also affects the ability of shell-making organisms to obtain the CO_3^{2-} ions they need to build and maintain their shells. This causes them to expend more energy on shell building than they would in less carbonated waters. This energy expenditure is ultimately costly because less energy is available to carry out other biological functions, such as growth and reproduction. Warmer waters also cause corals to expel the zooxanthellae in their tissues causing it to whiten or 'bleach'. Corals can survive bleaching events but it indicates stress and results in reduced survival.

Brocken Inaglory CC 3.0

Experiments have shown that larval brittle stars die in less than a week in seawater with higher than normal CO_2. Adults (above) show a loss of muscle mass.

Ocean acidification has been linked to coral bleaching and the reduction in the growth of corals. Rising temperatures may make this even worse.

Ocean acidification (resulting in the reduction of carbonate ions) weakens the shells of mollusks (shellfish). Investigations show fertilization is also affected.

1. How does increased dissolved CO_2 affect shell building marine organisms? Explain the chemistry involved:

ISBN: 978-1-98-856632-0

Ocean acidification and mollusks

- Pteropods ('wing-foot') are mollusks specialized for life in the open ocean. They are called sea butterflies because of the wing-like structures that help them swim in the oceans. These have evolved from their sea-snail foot.
- Shelled pteropod species have calcium carbonate shells that are around 5-10 mm in diameter. The species *Limacina helicina* (right) is an Arctic species and is an important part of the ocean food web.
- Because these small mollusks have calcium carbonate shells and live in parts of the ocean saturated with aragonite, they are likely to be indicators of the wider effects of ocean acidification. For this reason they are closely studied (along with their close relatives in the Southern Ocean around Antarctica).
- The effect of ocean acidification on *Limacina helicina* shell deposition was studied under CO_2 levels equal to 350 ppm (pH 8.09) and 760 ppm (pH 7.78) (as predicted in 2100 CE). Specimens were grown with $^{45}CaCl_2$. ^{45}Ca is radioactive with a half life of 163 days. The rate of $CaCO_3$ shell deposition was estimated from the radioactivity in each shell after incubation with ^{45}Ca.
- The table below shows the conditions of the study:

Conditions	pH	pCO² (ppm)	Temperature
Normal pH (as per 1990 average)	8.09	350	5
Low pH (predicted 2100)	7.78	765	5
Fjord where collected	8.12	320	2.2

- The graph shows the effect on $CaCO_3$ shell deposition:

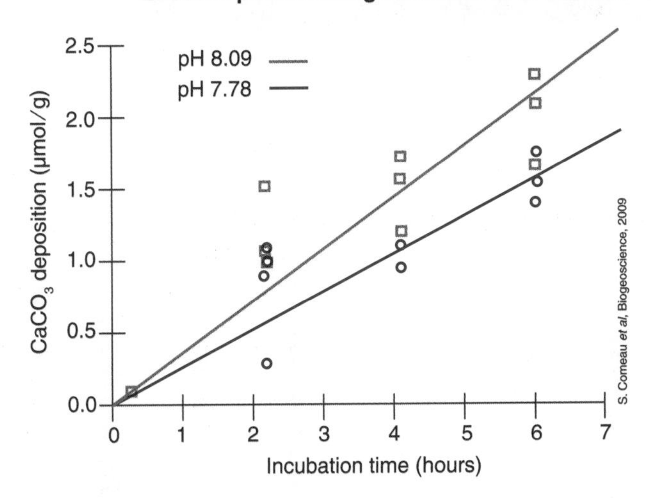

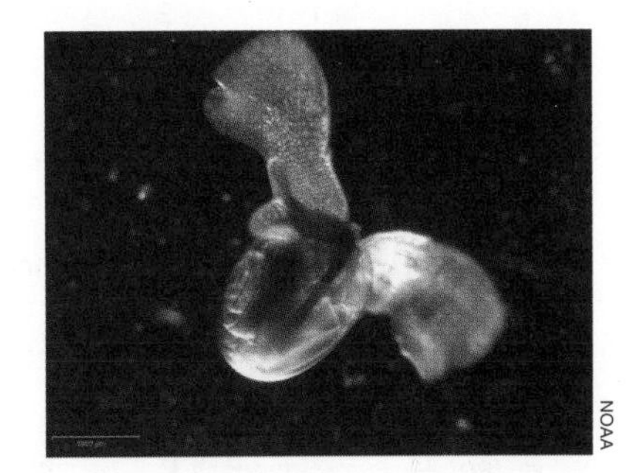

2. (a) How was the rate of shell deposition in *Limacina helicina* estimated? ______

(b) What was the effect of decreasing pH on the $CaCO_3$ shell deposition in *Limacina helicina*? ______

(c) How would this affect the possible survival of *Limacina helicina*? ______

(d) Why is *Limacina helicina* a good indicator species of the effects of increased CO_2 absorption in the oceans? ______

ISBN: 978-1-98-856632-0

Ocean acidification and fish

- A lower ocean pH does not only affect animals that build shells. New studies on fish show that increased CO_2 can affect their behavior and ultimately their chances of survival.
- A study of the behavior of clownfish (*Amphiprion percula)* (right) was carried out by raising larval clownfish in seawater at ambient CO_2(390 ppm), 550 ppm, 700 ppm and 850 ppm CO_2.
- At each CO_2 concentration, the larval fish were given a choice of water streams. One contained the chemical cue of a natural predator and the other did not. The results are shown in the graph below. For each set of trials, there was also an untreated control, where both water streams lacked the predator cue (purple bars).

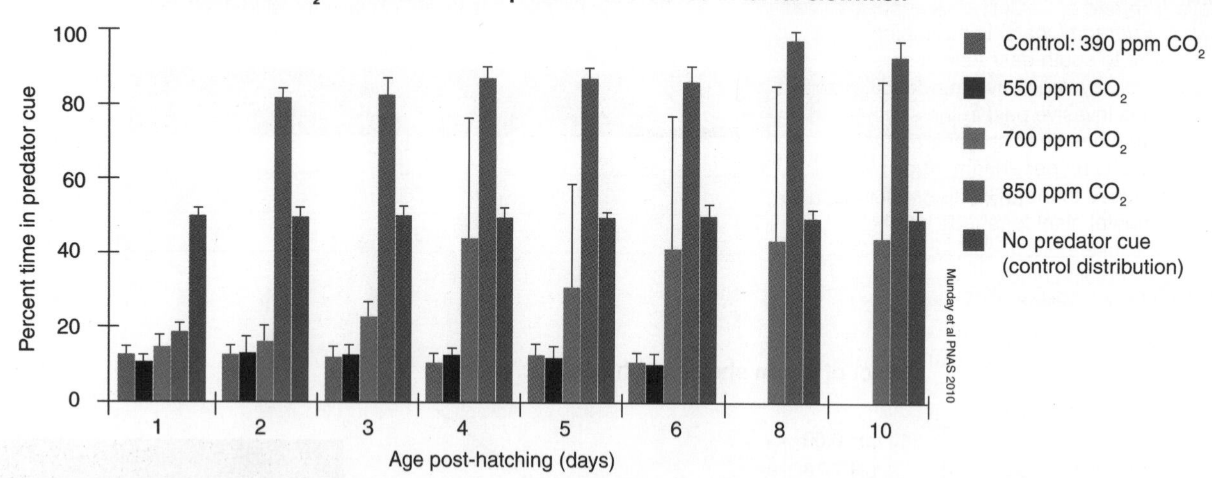

- The clown fish were tested for predator avoidance again at the settlement stage (transformation to a juvenile). These were compared to wild caught damselfish (*Pomacentrus wardi*) that were also treated with the same levels of CO_2. The graphs below shows their behavior at different levels of CO_2.

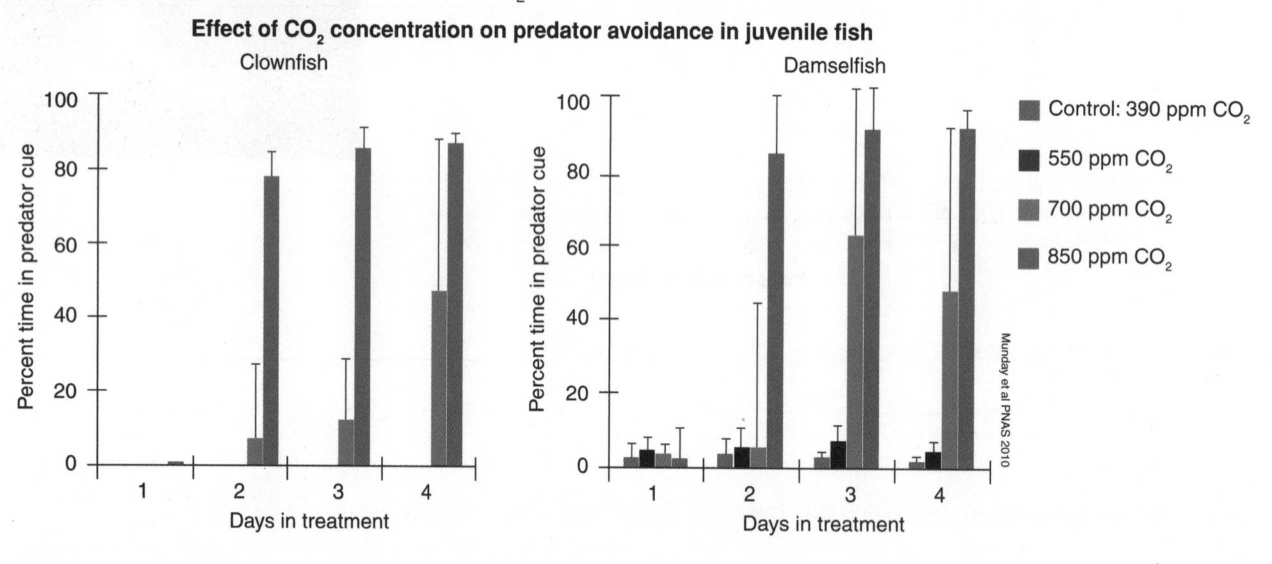

3. (a) Describe the effect of increasing CO_2 on the behavior of larval clownfish: __________

   (b) What was the purpose of the no predator test? __________

4. Describe the effect of increasing CO_2 on the behavior of juvenile clownfish and damselfish. Was there any difference in behavioral response between the two fish species?

ISBN: 978-1-98-856632-0

162 Invasive Species

Key Question: Why are invasive species such a problem and how can they be dealt with?

Introduced (or alien) species are those that have evolved at one place in the world and have been transported by humans, either intentionally or inadvertently, to another region. Some of these introductions are beneficial, e.g. introduced agricultural plants and animals. **Invasive species** are those alien species that have a detrimental effect on the ecosystems into which they have been imported. There are hundreds of these species with varying degrees of undesirability to humans and the environment they have invaded. Humans have deliberately introduced many of these species into new environments whereas others have been accidentally imported with cargo shipments or in the ballast of ships. Some have been deliberately introduced to control another pest species and have themselves become a problem. Some of the most destructive of all alien species are fast growing plants, e.g. mile-a-minute weed (a perennial vine from Central and South America), velvet tree (a South American tree invading Hawaii and Tahiti), and *Caulerpa* seaweed, the aquarium strain now found in the Mediterranean. Below are two invasive species now causing real problems in the United States.

Kudzu

- Kudzu (*Pueraria lobata*) is a climbing vine native to south-east Asia. It spreads aggressively by vegetative reproduction and is a serious invasive pest in the southern US, where it has been spreading at a rate of 61,000 ha per annum. Kudzu was first introduced to the US in the 1800s as an ornamental plant for shade porches, and was subsequently widely distributed as a high-protein cattle fodder and as a cover plant to prevent soil erosion. It grew virtually unchecked in the climate of the Southeastern US and was finally listed as a weed in 1970, more than a decade after it was removed from a list of suggested cover plants. Today, kudzu is estimated to cover 3 million ha of land in the southeastern US.

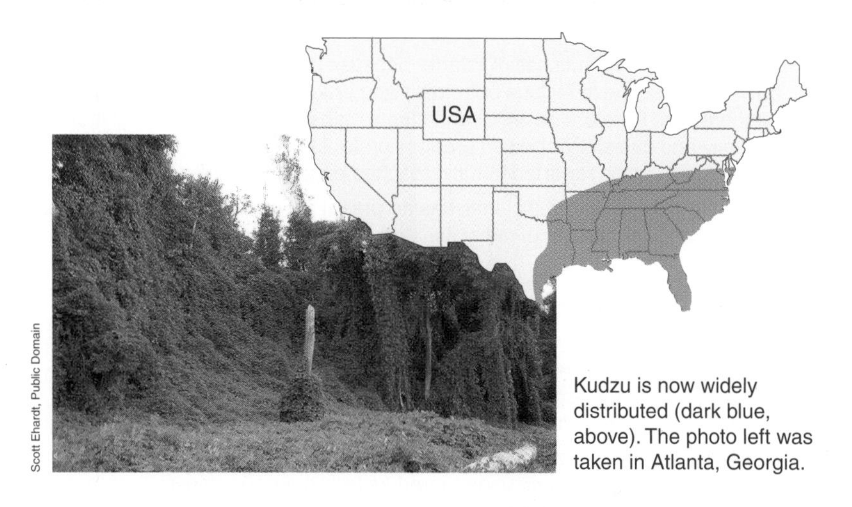

Kudzu is now widely distributed (dark blue, above). The photo left was taken in Atlanta, Georgia.

Red imported fire ant

- Red fire ants (*Solenopsis invicta*) were accidentally introduced into the United States from South America in the 1920s and have spread north each year from their foothold in the Southeast. Red fire ants are now resident in 14 US states where they displace populations of native insects and ground-nesting wildlife. They also damage crops and are very aggressive, inflicting a nasty sting. The USDA estimates damage and control costs for red fire ants at more than $6 billion a year. Red fire ants lack natural control agents in North America and thrive in disturbed habitats such as agricultural lands, where they feed on cereal crops and build large mounded nests.
- Red fire ants have been spreading progressively northwards into the US (darker blue on map) from South America (red). They have also been accidently introduced to many other countries where they are causing similar problems as those in North America.

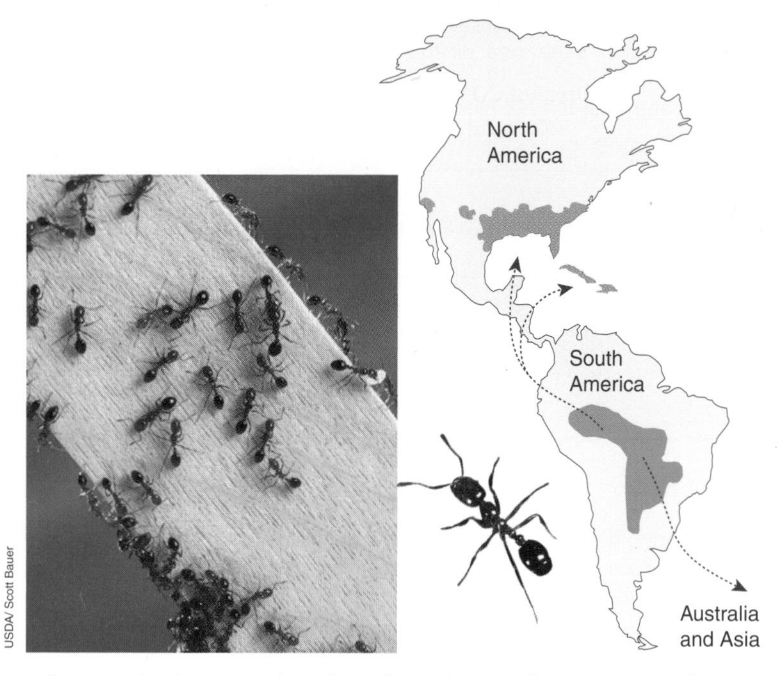

1. What factors seem to play a part in whether an alien species becomes invasive when introduced to a new area?

____

2. Why is it important to try to keep potentially invasive species out of ecosystems where they don't belong? _______________

ISBN: 978-1-98-856632-0

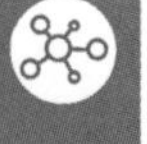

What makes an invasive species?

- Many native species live in what can be called "balance with their ecosystem". Their population never gets too high because they normally have predators, parasites, or pathogens that reduce or keep the population in check, or they run out of food or space.
- Slow breeding species are unlikely to become invasive because of the time it takes for their population to increase, meaning they can be controlled by culling. Animals with specific habitats or diets are also unlikely to become invasive.
- Invasive species therefore tend to be *r*-selected species and generalists. Being in a new environment they have few predators or pathogens and so their population can increase rapidly. An example of this is the New Zealand mud snail (*Potamopyrgus antipodarum*).
- The NZ mud snail is a freshwater snail that lives in streams and lakes. It is endemic to New Zealand and is only about 12 mm long and 5 mm high.
- Despite being so small and from a country 2000 km away from the nearest larger landmass, the NZ mud snail has been accidently introduced to at least a dozen countries including in Europe and North America. Outside of New Zealand it is considered one of the worst invasive freshwater species.
- The snail is such a successful invader because it tolerates a wide range of environments. These include both fresh and brackish water, disturbed environments, temperatures from 0°C to 34°C, and long lengths of time out of water. It breeds both sexually and asexually and can produce up to 230 young per year. In Lake Zurich, Switzerland, it was reported to have reached population densities of 800,000 per m^2.
- Outside of New Zealand the snail has no predators, parasites, or pathogens. It survives passage through the gut of many fish and birds, and can float, allowing for rapid spread.

NZ mud snail

Dan Gustafson USFWS CC 2.0

NZ mud snail in the United States

- The NZ mud snail was first detected in the US in 1987 in Snake River in Idaho. It has since spread throughout the United States. It is thought the snail arrived in ship ballast or possibly via live game fish or contaminated wading gear.
- Densities have reached up to 500,000 per m^2 in some rivers. Native snail species have become endangered as they are out-competed. This affects species further up the food chain as their natural food source is reduced.

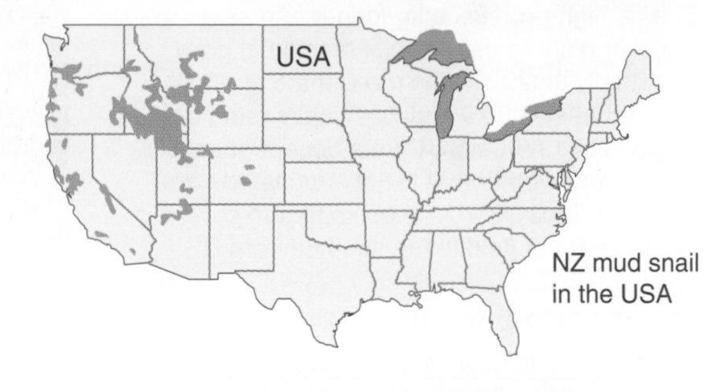

NZ mud snail in the USA

3. What features of the NZ mud snail make it such an invasive species? ______________________

4. How does it affect the ecosystem it invades? ______________________

5. Considering the snail's life cycle, how might the spread of the snail be stopped? Would it be possible to eradicate it from the United States?

6. Investigate an invasive species in your region. When did it arrive? What area does it cover? What effects is it having on the environment? Are there any plans in place for its removal?

ISBN: 978-1-98-856632-0

163 Endangered Species

Key Question: Why do species become endangered?

Species under threat of severe population loss or extinction are classified as either **endangered** or **threatened**. An endangered species is one with so few individuals that it is at high risk of local extinction, while a threatened (or vulnerable) species is likely to become endangered in the near future. While extinctions are a natural phenomenon, the rapid increase in the rates of species extinction in recent decades is of major concern. It is estimated that every day up to 200 species become extinct as a result of human activity. Even if a species is preserved from extinction, remaining populations may be too small to be genetically viable. Human population growth, rising non-sustainable resource use, poverty, and lack of environmental accountability are the underlying causes of premature extinction of organisms. The biggest direct causes are habitat loss, fragmentation, or degradation and the accidental or deliberate introduction of non-native species into ecosystems.

Causes of species declines

NASA

Habitat destruction

Natural habitat can be lost through clearance for agriculture, logging (above), urban development and land reclamation, or vegetation destruction by introduced pest plants and animals. Habitats may become too small or isolated to support viable populations.

Pollution

Toxic substances released by humans into the environment, e.g. from industry, cause harm directly or accumulate in food chains. Estuaries, wetlands, river systems and coastal ecosystems near urban areas are particularly vulnerable to the effects of pollutants.

Introduced exotic species

Introduced predators (e.g. rats, mustelids, pigs, and cats) prey on endangered birds and invertebrates. Introduced grazing and browsing animals (e.g. deer, pigs) damage sensitive plants. Invasive pest plants, such as kudzu and purple loosestrife, may out-compete native species.

Trophy hunting

Black rhino

Infrared technology

WWF-US James Morgan

Hunting and collecting

Decline can be caused by hunting or collecting specimens where rate or scale are poorly controlled. Some species are hunted because they interfere with human use of an area. Illegal trade threatens the population viability of some species.

Poaching and the rise in technological protection of reserve areas

Black rhinoceros were once plentiful throughout much of Africa but now only remnant populations remain. In 2019, there were 5500 in the wild. Despite armed patrols by park rangers and risk of prosecution, poachers still target rhinos for their horn, which is sold for traditional Asian remedies. Increasingly, technology such as infrared tracking, is being used to monitor the perimeters of reserves and provide early warning of poaching activity. In trials, this technology has been highly successful in reducing rhino losses.

1. Identify the factors that might contribute to the extinction of an animal species: ______________________

____

____

2. Go to **BIOZONE's Resource Hub** and watch the videos on new wildlife protection strategies through Connected Conservation and WWF thermal imaging. Describe the evidence for the value of technology-based solutions to poaching as part of wider strategies to protect endangered species:

____

____

____

____

ISBN: 978-1-98-856632-0

Competition and endangered populations

- Competition can play a big role in whether or not a species becomes extinct. Interspecific competition is important when native species are out-competed by invasive species and lose habitat or food resources. Intraspecific competition can play a role when declining populations compete for mates, limiting genetic diversity and leading to inbreeding.
- Competition within populations is normally beneficial to the species as a whole, leading to increased population fitness over time. Individuals with adaptations most suited to the prevailing environment will be better able to compete for resources and will have higher rates of survival and reproduction (higher fitness) compared to those that are less well adapted. When the gene pool is large, the population becomes better adapted over time.
- However in small populations with restricted ranges, intraspecific competition can reduce genetic diversity by causing only some to breed and so removing some genes from an already limited gene pool. This is especially so when males compete for females. In these cases, too many of the next generation can be related and inbreeding depression (reduced fitness as a result of inbreeding) is a likely (and adverse) outcome.

Kakapō with chick

Kakapo are one of the world's most endangered parrots, with only around 200 individuals left. Because this population was built up from just 50 kakapo there is little genetic diversity in the population. One of the most important parts of the kakapo conservation program is to maintain genetic diversity. However kakapo males display to females and females mate with their most preferred male (a lek system). This has the effect that some males do not mate and just a few individuals sire the majority of offspring, thus reducing genetic diversity. This reduces the kakapo's ability to adapt to changing environmental conditions and increases the likelihood of inbreeding.

Gray squirrel

Interspecific competition can drive organisms to extinction if one species cannot compete with another that uses the same resources. Eurasian red squirrels (*Sciurus vulgaris*) are native to the UK, while gray squirrels (*S. carolinensis*) were introduced to the UK from the United States. Reds have declined drastically in recent years and, although the reasons for this are complex, an important contributor is competition with gray squirrels for food. Gray squirrels are larger and able to monopolize food resources in areas where the two are found together. This reduces the food available for the red squirrels. In many areas of the UK, the decline of red squirrels is mirrored by the spread of grays.

3. (a) How can intraspecific competition push an endangered species towards extinction? __________

   (b) How can interspecific competition push an endangered species towards extinction? __________

4. Investigate an endangered species native to your state or country. Why is it endangered? What protections for it have been put in place (if any) and are there any programs in place to help its recovery?

ISBN: 978-1-98-856632-0

164 Adaptation, Migration, or Extinction

Key Question: Must species become extinct when their environment changes? Or can they adapt or move elsewhere? Most species have what is termed phenotypic plasticity. This means they are able to change their behavior, physiology, or morphology as their environment changes (within limits). This includes aspects such as learning a new behavior or changing breeding strategies (from sexual to asexual). If this plasticity is extensive enough, individuals can keep up with environmental changes (e.g. rising temperatures). However phenotypic plasticity is not adaptation. It involves changes to the phenotype (behavior, morphology, etc) without a change in genotype (the genetic material or DNA). It may allow species to track environmental changes or reduce selection pressures and give them time to adapt genetically. This is only if the environmental change or selection pressure is within the range of each generation's plasticity. If not, species will not be able to keep up with the changes or adapt to selection pressures and will be a high risk of extinction.

North American red squirrels

- North American red squirrels (*Tamiasciurus hudsonicus*) in Canada have adapted to a 2°C increase in spring temperature by breeding earlier in the year. Records were kept of cohorts of female squirrels to determine the day of the year they gave birth. Over a period of ten years, the squirrel breeding time shifted to be earlier in the year (by 18 days). The change was linked to an increase in the abundance of spruce cones, an important food source for the red squirrels.
- This change in breeding times shows that breeding time is not heavily influenced by genetics. Its plasticity means that the squirrel has a good ability to survive climate changes (at least in terms of maintaining its ability to breed).

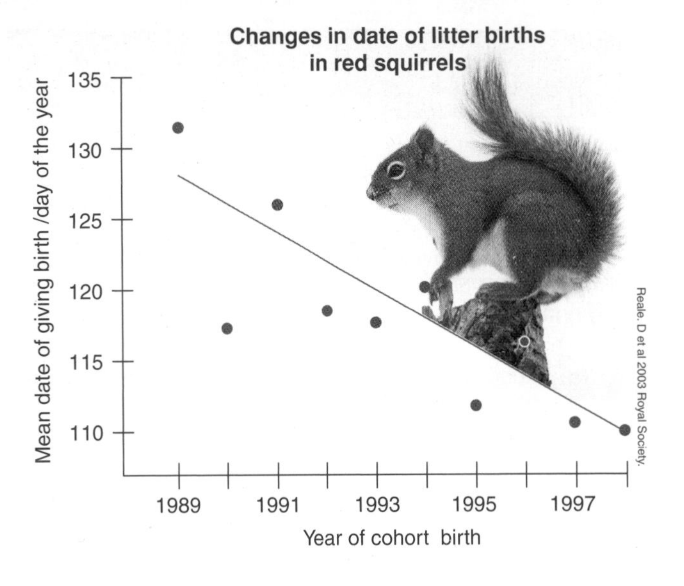

Polar bears

- Some organisms have limited phenotypic plasticity and will be unable to respond immediately to shifts in climate. For these organisms, relocation may be their only chance for survival. For species with an already limited range there may be nowhere to go. As food supplies dwindle, they may be faced with extinction.
- Polar bears are specialized hunters. They prefer hunting on sea ice. However, recent losses in sea ice during the summer has reduced their hunting range. Polar bears have a limited capacity to change hunting behavior. Some are able to scavenge the remains of whales (left from human hunters) but this is not a substitute for hunting, because it is too scarce and unpredictable.
- Data from measurements of polar bears shows they are not able to change their physiology or behavior to keep pace with their changing environment. The body mass index of measured bears is dropping every year, indicating decreased feeding. Also body condition is dependent on the date of ice break up. Early ice break up (due to higher spring temperatures and thinner ice) means a shorter hunting period and so reduced feeding and reduced body condition.
- The success of polar bear reproduction is linked to feeding and body condition, so as their hunting grounds reduce, they become at greater and greater risk of extinction.

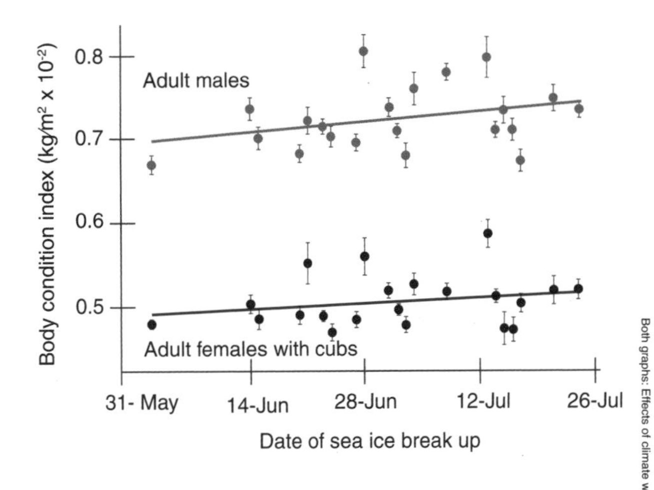

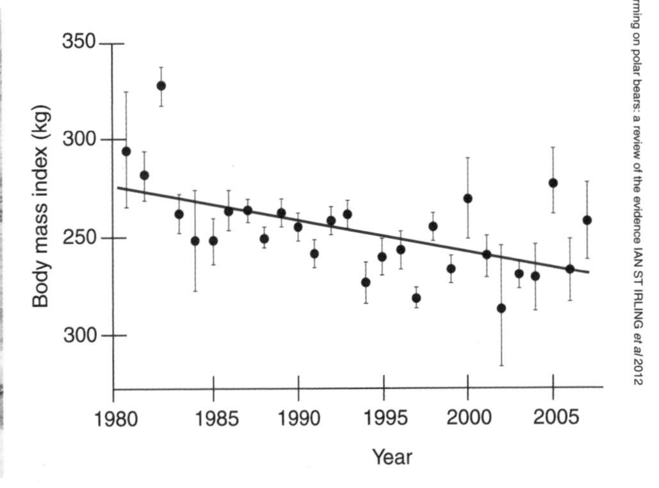

Both graphs: Effects of climate warming on polar bears: a review of the evidence IAN STIRLING *et al* 2012

ISBN: 978-1-98-856632-0

Migration may help organisms survive climate change

- While the range of some species such as the polar bears will reduce due to a warming climate, other species will find their range either expands or shifts. There are already numerous examples of species moving into new areas that were previously unsuitable. These species are less likely to feel the impacts of climate change and their risk of extinction is significantly reduced (at least in the short to medium term) providing their food resources are still available.

Jacek Lesniowski CC 3.0

Atlantic mackerel (above) have moved up to 250 km north since 1968. Their move appears to be linked to a warming of the waters along the continental shelf of North America. Whether this is directly linked to climate change or to a cyclic event is not fully understood.

A warming Arctic has had widespread effects on the tundra. Shrubbery that once grew close to the ground and very slowly now grows more rapidly and much taller. This has attracted animals such as moose, thus expanding their range north. Snowshoe hares have also moved north.

Photo: Xavierschmit at lb.wikipedia

Studies of non-migratory butterflies in the UK have shown 63% have ranges that have shifted northwards between 35 and 240 km since record keeping began. In Europe, the purple emperor butterfly (*Apatura iris*), pictured above, moved about 200 km northwards over just 5 years.

1. (a) Explain the difference between phenotypic plasticity and adaptation through evolution: ______

   (b) How can phenotypic plasticity help a species adapt to environmental change?: ______

2. Explain why some organisms are more likely to become extinct as a result of climate change than others:

3. (a) Why are many Northern Hemisphere temperate species expanding their range northwards?

   (b) How might this help them survive (or even thrive because of) climate change? ______

ISBN: 978-1-98-856632-0

165 Conservation Legislation

Key Question: How can legislation help conservation efforts?

Trade in various species has been part of human culture for millennia, from animal skins in prehistoric camps, to growing roses for florists today. However when a species is endangered, its continued trade can affect its survival. In many cases, the rarer a species is, the more valuable it becomes and so it is hunted even more, e.g. rhinoceros for their horns and elephants for their tusks. Countries have enacted legislation to control this trade. Countries also pass laws that help the conservation of species that are not traded. These laws may protect land where an endangered species is found or give various government departments powers and responsibilities designed to protect and manage species and land and enhance conservation efforts.

CITES

- One of the most well known international treaties designed to control trade on endangered species is the Convention on International Trade in Endangered Species of Wild Fauna and Flora (CITES). CITES is a voluntarily adopted framework around which signature parties can base their own national laws. Since it was finally agreed in 1973, around 37,000 species have been registered under CITES.
- CITES controls trade in species, whether or not they are traded as live specimens. Its aim is to ensure that international trade in specimens of wild animals and plants does not threaten their survival. It includes everything from dried specimens (e.g. dried plants) to fur coats and powders.

USFWS

Elephant ivory, seized by the US Fish and Wildlife Service, ready to be crushed (2013).

CITES and wildlife trade

- CITES lists species under appendixes. Appendix I is reserved for species that are in imminent danger of extinction. These species can't be traded commercially. Appendix II species are those that could face extinction if traded freely. They require permits for export trade. Appendix listings are based on data and whether or not the species can be sustainably traded.
- Many of CITES achievements are based on legislation, such as voting to move certain species into Appendix I. However this only works if all countries enforce the changes.

Problems

- One of the main problems with adding species to appendixes is that there is often not enough data to accurately know a species' sustainability and often the data is inconsistent. For example, in 2010, China registered 130 ivory carvings, 40 elephant feet, 219 kg of tusks, and no trophies imported from Zimbabwe. However Zimbabwe's export data shows 2512 ivory carvings, 8 feet, 4 trophies and 41 tusks for the same period.
- Like most international treaties, CITES power comes from those countries that enforce its rules. However enforcement varies from country to country, and many fail to return data on seizures and trade (or pay dues associated with being part of CITES).
- It is estimated the international volume of trade in wildlife registered under CITES is less than a tenth of the trade in wildlife not registered.

Dan Bennett CC 2.0

Illegal trade in pangolins

Endangered Species Act

- The purpose of the Endangered Species Act (1973) (ESA) is to protect and recover endangered or threatened wildlife in the United States and the ecosystems they depend upon. The ESA serves as the legislation under which CITES can function in the United States. The Fish and Wildlife Service and the Marine Fisheries Service administer the ESA.
- Under the ESA, species can be listed as threatened (likely to become endangered) or endangered (in danger of extinction). There are around 1500 species listed as endangered or threatened in the United States.
- Species may be listed under the act based on their biological status and threats to their environment. Ultimately the goal of the ESA is to recover a species to the point they no longer need to be listed.

In 1978 critical habitat was designated to help whooping crane recovery. Intensive habitat management and captive breeding have helped to save it from extinction.

The American crocodile was listed as endangered in 1975 (only 200 were left). By 1983 the population reached 1000. In 2005 it was down listed to threatened.

Gray wolves were listed as endangered as early as 1967. After recovering from near extinction they were delisted in 2008 and are now again subject to heavy hunting.

ISBN: 978-1-98-856632-0

The need for conservation legislation and its enforcement

- Producing legislation is of no use unless it is enforced at all levels of government and has public buy in. Without either, enacted laws of any kind inevitably fail. The illegal wildlife trade is a prime example. Another example is the side effects of illegal harvesting, such as by-catch or illegal logging.
- The vaquita (*Phocoena sinus*) is a species of porpoise endemic to the Gulf of California. It is on the brink of extinction with fewer than 20 (and possibly fewer than 10) known individuals. Its numbers have declined rapidly since it was first described in the 1980s despite various conservation laws passed by the Mexican government.

NOAA

Year	Vaquita population
1997	567
2008	245
2015	59
2016	30
2018	19

- The fish totoaba (*Totoaba macdonaldi*) is intensively fished in the Gulf of California, even though it is very rare and listed under CITES Appendix I. It is caught for its swim bladder, which is highly prized in Chinese cuisine. Fishing uses gillnets in which the vaquita can become entangled in and so drown.
- Totoaba fishing has been banned, and gillnets are banned from at least half the vaquita's range. Sonar is being used to locate ghost nets left by illegal totoaba fishermen.
- Despite this the vaquita population has continued to decline.

1. What is the purpose of CITES? ______________________

2. How can intergovernmental treaties like CITES help save endangered species? ______________________

3. (a) What is the purpose of the Endangered Species Act? ______________________

   (b) Which government services administer the ESA? ______________________

4. Explain why some species are still heavily poached and traded illegally despite international treaties like CITES:

5. (a) Why has the population of vaquita declined so rapidly? ______________________

   (b) Using the information above and any extra information you wish to research, provide a potential solution to the decline in the vaquita's population:

ISBN: 978-1-98-856632-0

166 Habitat Fragmentation

Key Question: How does habitat fragmentation affect populations?

There is no question that the world's biodiversity is under threat. The many factors that are causing the global decline in biodiversity and increasing number of species extinctions can be summarized as HIPPCO (**H**abitat destruction, **I**nvasive species, (human) **P**opulation growth, **P**ollution, **C**limate change, and **O**ver exploitation). Habitat destruction is a major part of HIPPCO. Vast areas of land (and sea) are exploited for their resources and land is needed to grow food, often with no concern as to the damage on the environment. When a large area of habitat is fragmented, either naturally or by human actions, species populations are divided and may not be able to reach each other. If an isolated population is too small to breed effectively (or becomes inbred) and gene flow between fragmented areas ceases, then that population isolate may die out (a local extinction or extirpation). If this occurs throughout the fragmented habitats then the species may also die out.

Habitat fragmentation and biodiversity

- Habitat fragmentation is the process by which large habitats become divided up into smaller ones, usually with areas of completely changed (and often uncrossable) land between them. This can happen naturally (e.g. lava flows dividing areas of forest) but more often it occurs as a result of human activities (e.g. building roads or removing large parts of forests).
- Habitat fragmentation can be a driver of evolution, creating greater biodiversity by separating species' populations. This has occurred many times on the islands of Hawaii for example. However this is usually a response of smaller organisms, such as insects.
- Usually habitat fragmentation causes a loss of biodiversity, especially in larger animals that are territorial or require large areas of land to find food. Habitat fragmentation reduces population sizes and can reduce gene flow because individuals are unable to move easily between habitat fragments. This can lead to inbreeding because access to mates is limited. Fragmentation also affects plants. Invasive plant species are more able to invade fragments due to more open edges, which often provide disturbed land where they can easily become established.
- The degree of fragmentation of a species' habitat is a significant predictor of the likelihood of a species going extinct. The IUCN (International Union for Conservation of Nature) lists species from least concern to critically endangered. When the species in these categories are matched against the degree of their habitat's fragmentation a clear pattern emerges (right).

Forest fragmentation, Brazil

NASA

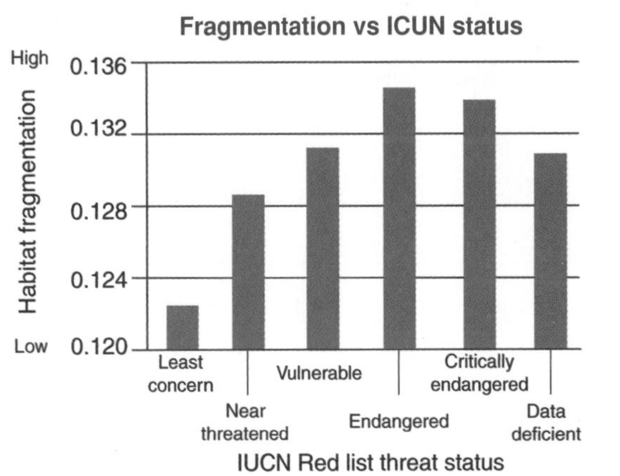

Quantification of habitat fragmentation reveals extinction risk in terrestrial mammals Kevin R. Crooksa 2017

Habitat fragmentation affects all levels of the ecosystem

- Research into habitat fragmentation has become very important because of the continuing large scale destruction of global habitats. Many large areas of tropical forest are being removed for oil palm plantations, livestock farming, and lumber, leaving many smaller areas of forest. These frequently aren't large enough to sustain even one large mammal (especially predators).
- Studies have shown that fragmentation affects all trophic levels, from producers (plants) to all levels of consumers.
- The study below was carried out in central Argentina, where 94% of forest land has been cleared. Three trophic levels are shown, with parasitoids being level 2 consumers (feeding on leaf miners).
- The higher the species richness the greater the number of species found in the study area.

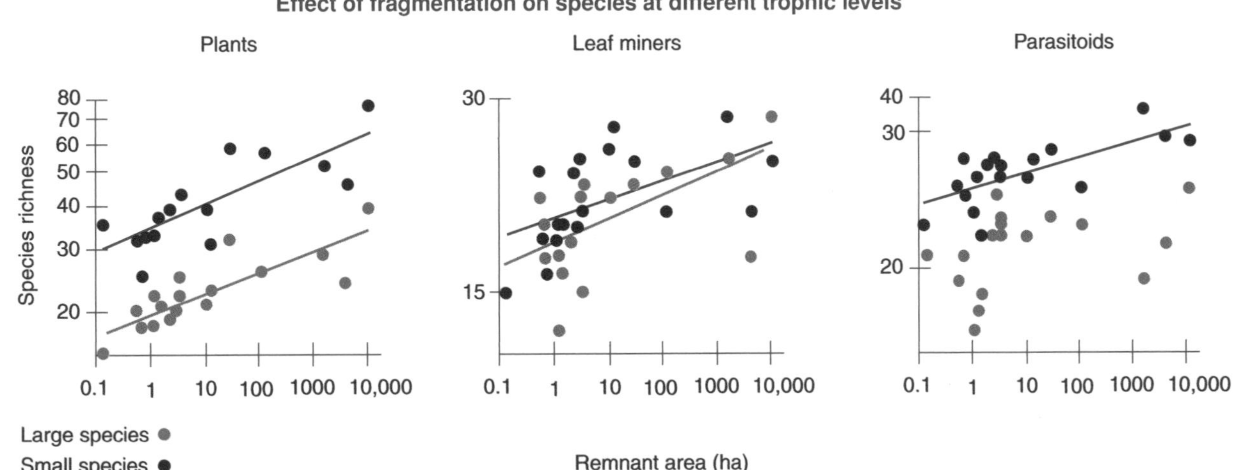

Q Habitat Fragmentation and Species Loss across Three Interacting Trophic Levels Luciano Cagnolo Conservation Biology 2009

ISBN: 978-1-98-856632-0

Habitat fragmentation in Madagascar

- Madagascar has three main forest types, dry, humid, and spiny (diagram far right) and is known as a biodiversity "hotspot". Over 90% of its wildlife is endemic.
- Madagascar's forests and wildlife are increasingly threatened by encroaching human activity. Many of its forests are being slowly destroyed by activities such as slash and burn farming. This has led to an increasing amount of forest fragmentation with large areas of forest becoming increasingly scarce.

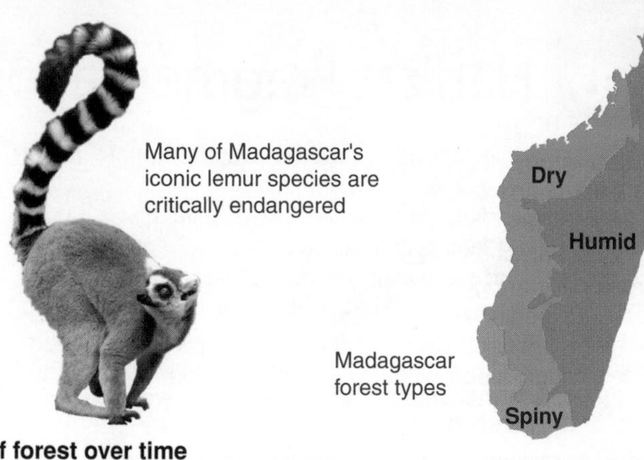

Many of Madagascar's iconic lemur species are critically endangered

Madagascar forest types

Area of forest over time

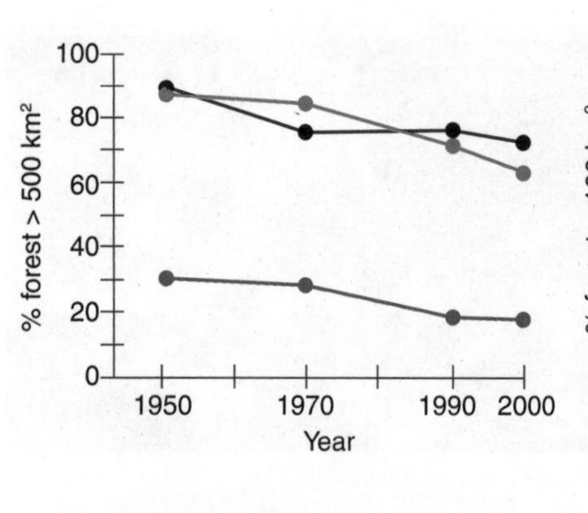

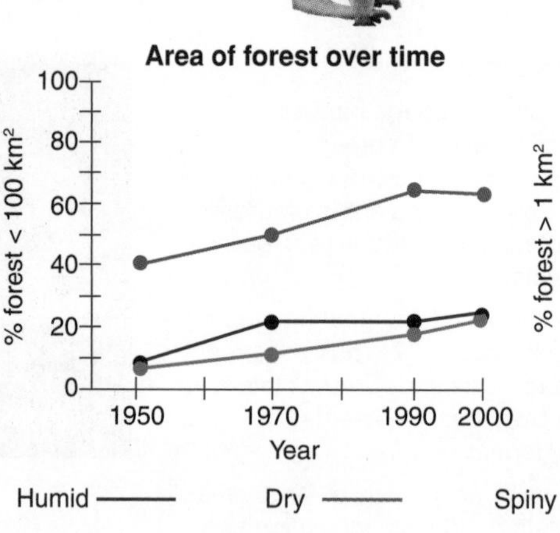

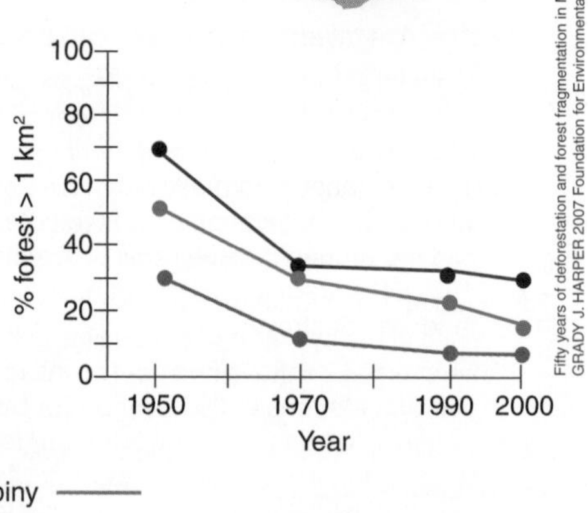

Humid —— Dry —— Spiny ——

Fifty years of deforestation and forest fragmentation in Madagascar GRADY J. HARPER 2007 Foundation for Environmental Conservation

1. (a) What is habitat fragmentation? ______

   (b) Describe some of the causes of habitat fragmentation: ______

2. Describe three ways in which habitat fragmentation can reduce biodiversity:

   (a) ______

   (b) ______

   (c) ______

3. A study found a species habitat was moderately fragmented. What is its probable IUCN threat status?

   ______

4. Study the graphs at the bottom of the previous page and describe the relationship between habitat fragmentation and species richness:

   ______

5. Interpret the data above to describe how habitat fragmentation has affected forest size in Madagascar: ______

6. Why would loss of Madagascar's forests be particularly significant for global biodiversity? ______

ISBN: 978-1-98-856632-0

167 Wildfires

Key Question: What is the effect of global wildfires?

The decade 2010 to 2020 saw an unprecedented increase in the number, area, and intensity of forest and bush fires around the world. Forest fires has always been part of nature, with fire seasons occurring every year. However the last decade has seen fires begin earlier in the season and become larger and more frequent. Some of these fires are deliberately lit, either through arson or farm fires that get out of control. In some cases, the fires are set to clear debris after land has been logged, and so are not the direct cause of deforestation. Some arise naturally from lightning strikes. However, since the world is warming, the results of these lightning strikes are far more severe, especially after droughts, which themselves are becoming more frequent. Recent years have seen fires in the Alaskan and Siberian tundra which threaten to affect permafrost and fundamentally change the Arctic landscape.

Australian bush fires

- The Australian bush fire season 2019-2020 (also known as the Black Summer) was a period of unusually intense bush fires throughout Australia.
- The fire season normally begins around August, but began earlier in 2019. Major fires peaked around January 2020. An estimated 186,000 square kilometers of bush and scrub land was destroyed.
- Australia is particularly prone to intense bush fires but the fires of 2019-2020 came after a prolonged drought and higher than normal temperatures. Bush and forest that would normally withstand or be a barrier to large fires were particularly dry and so burned.

Smoke from Australian bush fires as seen from the ISS

- Australian bush fires often occur near populated regions and present a particular hazard to those living nearby. Fire fronts can move extremely quickly, fanned by high winds, trapping residents and fire fighters. Because of this, the fire fighting effort is extremely intensive, with many hundreds of people, fire trucks, helicopters, and planes employed to control the fires.
- Most of the fires in Australia are caused by lightning, and so are not linked to deforestation by farmers or logging.
- The fires have had a particularly devastating effect on Australian wildlife. Experts estimate more than a billion mammals, birds, and reptiles were killed in the 2019-2020 season. Deaths from starvation and thirst added to the large number of animal deaths from the fires. Kangaroo island, an important habitat for a number of native and endangered species was severely affected, with more than a third of the island burned.
- In December 2019, NASA estimated the fires had emitted over 300 million tonnes of carbon dioxide. The damage from the fires not only releases the carbon dioxide, but affect the forest's ability to absorb it.

Gospers Mountain fire NSW

Kangaroo Island fire (SA)

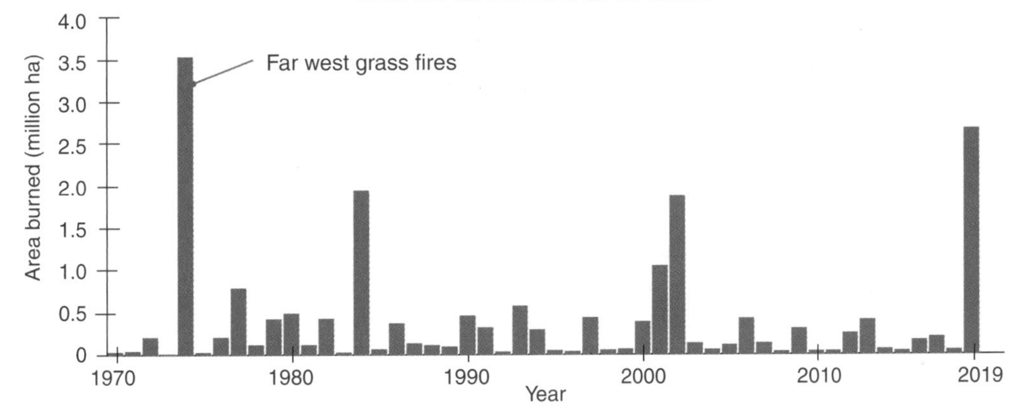

ISBN: 978-1-98-856632-0

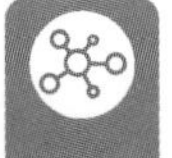

Arctic tundra

- The Arctic region is warming at twice the rate of the rest of the world. This heating is melting permafrost and then drying out the tundra, making it extremely susceptible to fire.
- Because of the freezing temperatures there is little decay of plant material on the tundra. Thus a large amount of organic material builds up over the centuries. This has helped to store vast quantities of carbon.
- Now that the Arctic is warming, that carbon is under threat of decaying and burning, both of which release carbon dioxide. And the more warming there is, the more carbon dioxide (and trapped methane) could be released and so there is more warming.
- Tundra in Alaska, Canada, Greenland, and Eastern Siberia has been affected. In 2019, more than 3 million hectares of tundra was affected by fire. The fires can be typical large surface fires, but they can also form slow smoldering fires. These smoldering fires can persist through cold and wet conditions. Because they burn longer, these fires can actually transfer heat deeper into the soil and permafrost, melting and burning it.
- Tundra fires in 2019 released at least 100 million tonnes of CO_2.

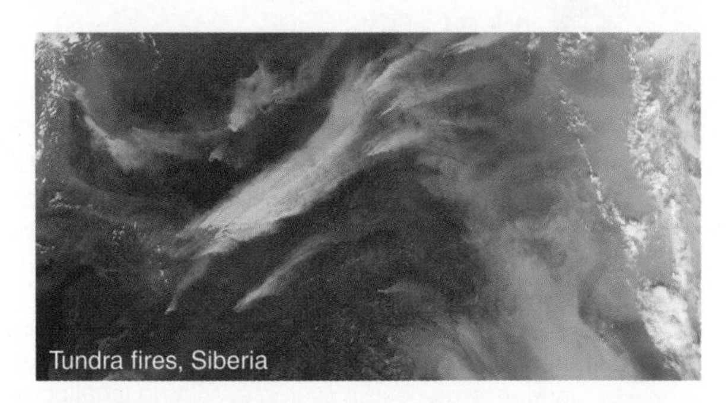
Tundra fires, Siberia

California wildfires

- Like Australia, California's hot dry environment is particularly prone to wildfires. Since the start of the century these wildfires have been becoming more intense. Fourteen of the largest 20 wildfires in California have occurred since 2007, and there are 78 more annual fire days now than 50 years ago.
- A number of factors influence the frequency and severity of fires (how often and how much land is burned). These include moisture level, the amount of undergrowth, tree density, and the types of trees present. Climate variability (especially moisture levels) is the main driver of forest fires. When fires become more frequent and more intense, the forest may be less able to regenerate (grow again with a similar makeup). There are several reasons for this:
  - Trees do not have time to regenerate or grow between fires, they reestablish more slowly, or fail to reestablish at all.
  - Fast growing shrubs and grasses establish more quickly than tree seedlings, which then cannot compete for resources (e.g. sunlight and space). Fewer tree species will establish, and the make-up of the area will change.
  - Seed stock is reduced, so fewer seedlings grow after a fire.

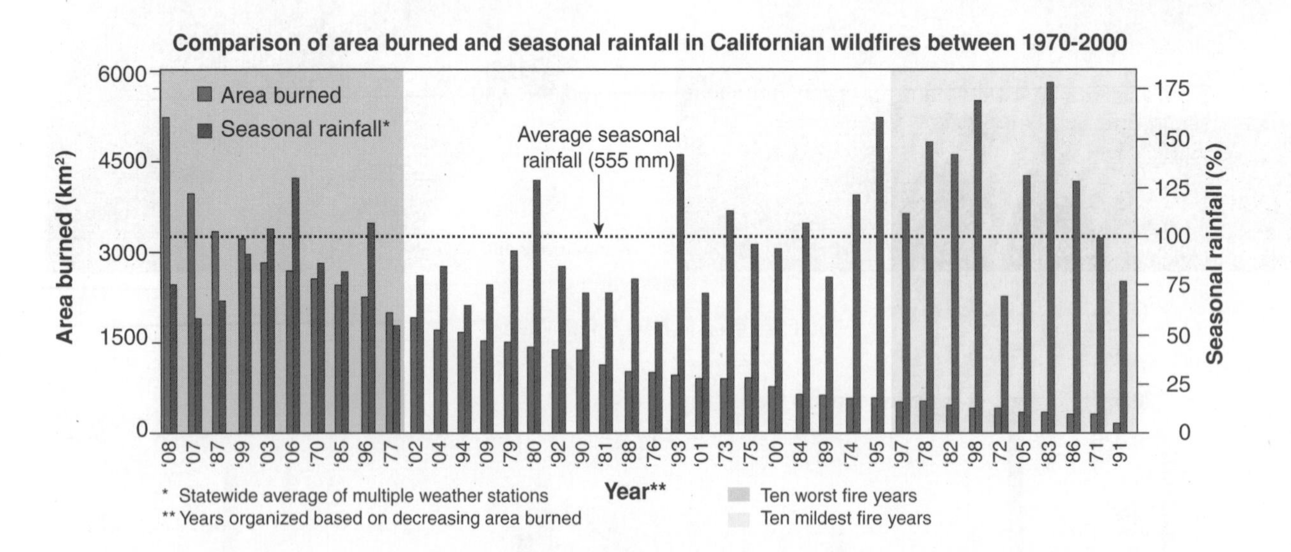

Adapted from Rogers, P (01 June, 2010). Do wet winters mean bad summer fire season in California? Not usually according to History. Bay Area News
Original data from Cal fire, U.S. Forest Service and NOAA data

1. Study the graph above. What is the relationship between rainfall in California and the area burned? ______________________

ISBN: 978-1-98-856632-0

Amazon forest fires

- 2019 saw a large spike in the number of fires in the Amazon. These became a concern because the Amazon is the largest terrestrial carbon sink, absorbing about a quarter of all the carbon taken up by forests each year. The 2019 spike in fires threatened to release huge amounts of carbon dioxide back into the atmosphere and damage future uptake ability.
- Up to 60 million hectares of the Brazilian Amazon are considered public areas. This means they have no defined legal purpose. They are not declared as conservation areas or indigenous territories for example. With no legal purpose, people simply clear the land by logging. Once the logs are removed, the debris is burned and the land occupied, normally as cattle ranches. Thus the fires in Brazil are normally directly linked to deforestation or logging.

Fires in the Amazon, 2019, can be clearly seen by the cameras on the International Space Station. Around 43,000 square kilometers of forest was burned in 2019.

The MODIS instrument onboard the Terra satellite can detect hot spots caused by fires. The red patches on the image show fires from August 15 to August 22, 2019.

2. What was the immediate cause of the Black Summer fires in Australia? ______________________

____

3. Why are the wildfires in Australia and California more immediate problems and receive more intense fire suppression than those in Brazil and the Arctic?

____

____

4. Describe two ways in which large fires can contribute to climate change: ______________________

____

____

5. Why might the fires in the Arctic be much worse for climate change than they might first appear (or compared to the usual forest fires)?

____

____

____

6. How did the 2019 fires in the Brazilian Amazon compare to other years? ______________________

____

ISBN: 978-1-98-856632-0

168 Climate Change and Habitat Loss

Key Question: How will climate change affect various habitats?

Rising atmospheric temperatures are predicted to cause numerous changes in habitats around the world. Higher temperatures will cause sea level rises which will affect coastal habitats. Less snow in mountains and higher melt rates will reduce alpine environments and may affect rivers due to lower volumes of melt water.

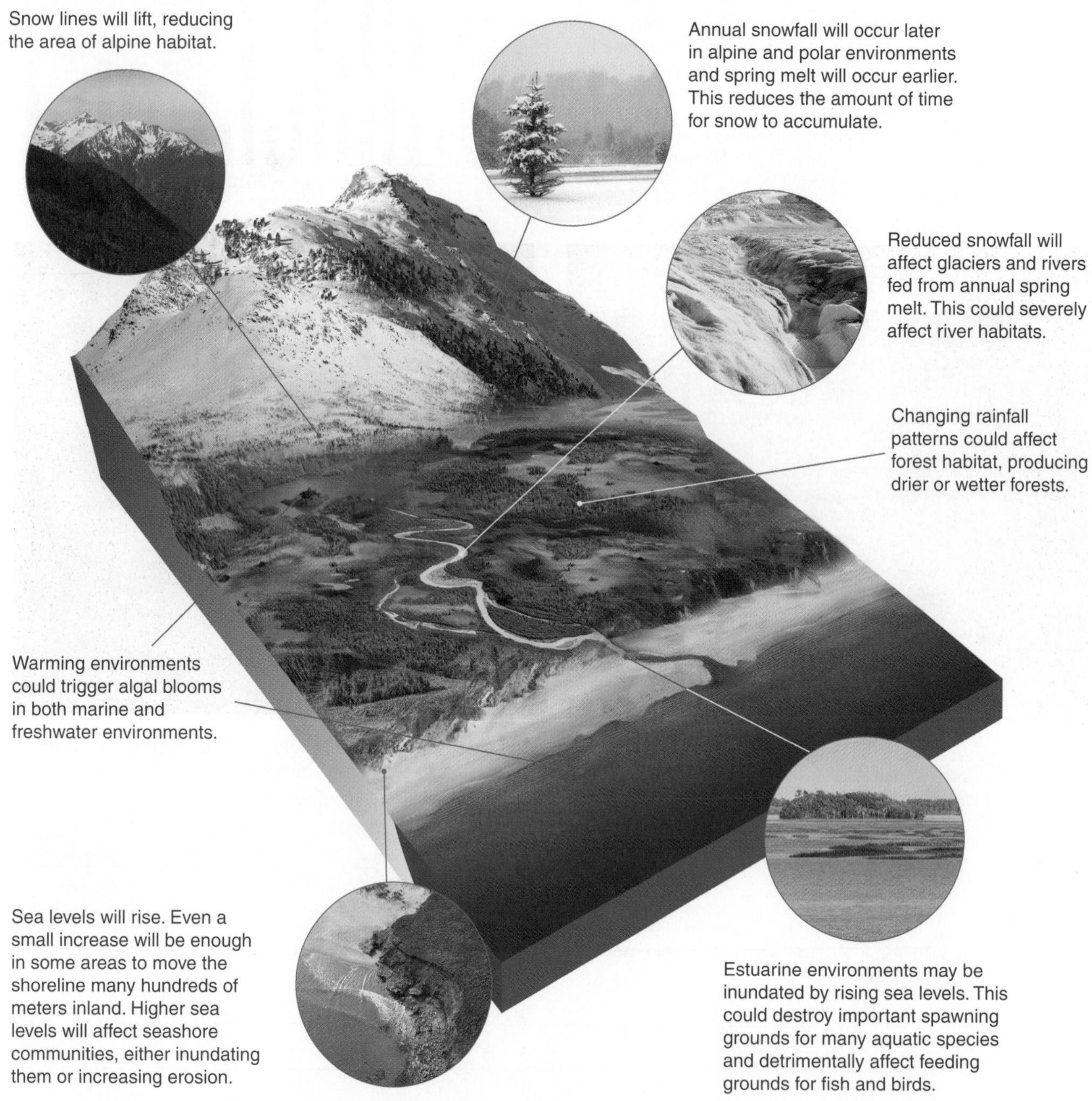

1. Using the diagram above, describe how each of the following climate change indicators could cause a loss of habitat:

   (a) Increasing atmospheric temperature: ______________________

   ____

   (b) Sea level rise: ______________________

   ____

   ____

   (c) Changes in precipitation (rainfall, snowfall) : ______________________

   ____

   ____

ISBN: 978-1-98-856632-0

169 The Effect of Domestication of Biodiversity

Key Question: How can domestication of species affect biodiversity?

Domestication of plants and animals began thousands of years ago, sometimes deliberately, sometimes not. Only certain species of animal or plant are suitable for domestication and, of those, only the most domesticable individuals are allowed or able to breed. This immediately limits the genetic diversity of the population being domesticated. Once domesticated, the species has tended to be spread about the globe as humans moved about. The species numbers have also increased, often displacing other species. For example, various breeds of domestic cattle and sheep now dominate grazing land and vast areas of cropland are covered with just a few species of crops. This reduces the biodiversity of the local ecosystem.

Domestication reduces genetic diversity

- The process of domestication actively takes the most suitable individuals of each successive generation and breeds them together to produce more desirable offspring. Over time this produces docile animals or crop plants that produce large fruit. It also has the effect of reducing genetic variation in the domestic population.
- A recent study of the New Zealand rock lily (*Arthropodium cirratum*) (right) has shown how quickly this loss of genetic variation can occur. Domestication of most commonly farmed species began hundreds to thousands of years ago making their time lines difficult to study. However New Zealand was only populated about 800 years ago. Soon after, the first Maori began cultivating the endemic rock lily. Studies show that around the country there are at least 29 genetic lineages of the rock lily. However these studies also show just two lineages were domesticated. In fact, cultivated lilies found in the South Island were shown to have been transported from the northern part of the North Island, hundreds of kilometers away.

Mike Dickison CC 4.0

Domestication can increase genetic diversity

- Although domestication can (and often does) reduce genetic diversity there are instances in which diversity appears to increase due to domestication. Even until very recently it was thought that the genetic diversity of domesticated honey bees was very low. It was even suggested that this lack of genetic diversity was a contributing factor to the recent loss of many colonies (e.g from colony collapse disorder).
- However new research shows that honey bee diversity may actually increase due to domestication. This appears to be because of transportation and interbreeding of honey bee lineages around the world. A 2014 study showed Africanized honey bees had the same genetic diversity as African subspecies despite originating from just 47 queens. Similarly, in Australia, a closed honey bee breeding program found the genetic diversity to have remained undiminished even after 25 years of breeding. Managed honey bee populations in America have been shown to have higher genetic diversity than European bees.

Domestication can reduce ecosystem biodiversity

- Probably the biggest effect of domestication on biodiversity has been on the wider ecosystem. Domestication of plants and animals requires land (for farming and cultivation). This has been obtained by clearing forests or grasslands and replacing them with monocultures of genetically very similar plants or animals. Vast parts of the North American prairies are now used to grow just a few types of crops or grasses. Less than 1% of the original prairie tall grass cover is left.
- Similarly, the once immense herds of bison and pronghorn that roamed central North America have been replaced by various breeds of domesticated cattle or sheep.

1. Why might domestication reduce genetic diversity? ______________________________

2. How does domestication affect the biodiversity of an ecosystem? ______________________________

3. Why has the honey bee been able to maintain its genetic diversity? ______________________________

4. Why are some advantages and disadvantages of domestication? ______________________________

ISBN: 978-1-98-856632-0

170 Reducing the Impact of Biodiversity Loss

Key Question: How can we reduce the global loss of biodiversity?

One of the biggest concerns facing conservationists today is the rapidly accelerating rate at which species are being lost. Various strategies are available to protect at-risk species and help the recovery of those that are threatened. Ecological protection and restoration are important tools in maintaining biodiversity. Restoration is often a long term process and usually involves collaborative work between institutions with scientific experts and the local communities involved. Captive breeding programs and intensive management in the wild have in many cases saved endangered populations from the brink of extinction. However, for many of these species, active management may be needed for many years or decades.

Reducing habitat fragmentation

- Recall that habitat fragmentation plays an important role in species extinction. Fragments of habitat left over after land disturbance are often too small to support large animals on their own. However it is possible to join smaller fragments together using **green corridors**.
- These are strips of land connecting areas of habitat and can include windbreaks, hedgerows, riparian zones along waterways, or simply narrow bands of vegetation connecting habitats. Organisms, especially larger animals, can use these corridors to travel between reserves, allowing wider foraging and maintaining gene flow.

Green corridors joining two ares of forest

Pinhook Swamp corridor, Florida, USA

- The Okefenokee National Wildlife Refuge, straddles the border of Florida and Georgia. It spans 162,000 ha and is the largest wildlife refuge in the eastern United States.
- Sixteen kilometers to the south is the Osceola National Forest. This is an area of wetlands, swamps, and pine forests that spans 65,000 ha.
- The larger Okefenokee swampland preserve is home to a number of endangered species including the red-cockaded woodpecker and gopher tortoises. The smaller Osceola swamp forest is not large enough to support many larger species including the red-cockaded woodpecker and the black bear.
- However between these two refuges is the Pinhook Swamp, which covers 24,000 ha. The swamp is privately owned, but has been bought by conservation groups and the government patch-by-patch so that now about a third is publicly owned.
- Together these three sections of swamp forest cover a continuous areas of over 250,000 ha. The continuous habitat allows populations from the Okefenokee refuge to further south and so establish territories and maintain gene flow.
- The Okefenokee-Pinhook-Osceola system has potential to act as the center of a much larger conservation area as it is linked by smaller green corridors along the Suwannee and Santa Fe rivers.

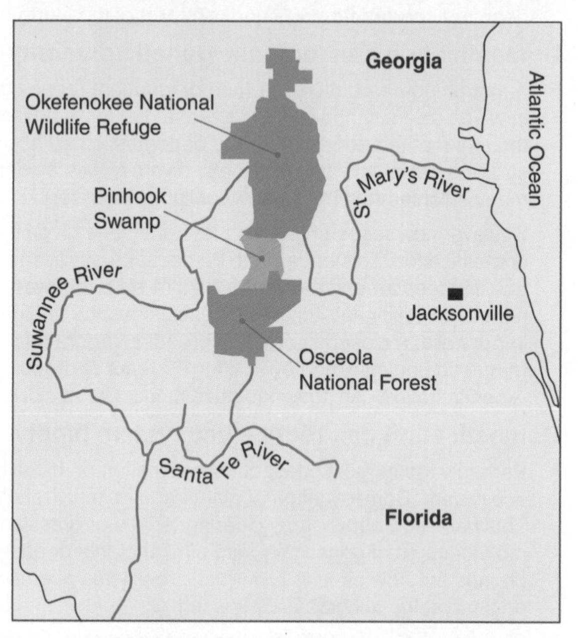

Okefenokee National Wildlife Refuge
USFWS

Red cockaded woodpecker
USDA

Osceola National Forest
Geoff Gallice CC 2.0

Alligator
USFWS

ISBN: 978-1-98-856632-0

Habitat restoration

- Habitat restoration is an important part of conservation efforts. Habitat must be suitable for plants and especially animals if populations are to flourish. Restoring habitat may involve replanting the original flora (below left), controlling, removing, or excluding introduced pests and predators (below center and right), and removing waste.

Replanting the original plants is important in stabilizing cleared land and making the habitat more suitable for native animals already living there or for reintroductions.

AnnieDick CC 4.0

Removing or reducing animal pests is an important but difficult part of habitat restoration. Automatic traps (above) can remove many pests between servicing.

MIET

Mainland islands are important ecological sites that are surrounded with predator proof fences. They are used to rebuild native populations of animals and plants.

Habitat size

- Restoring a habitat is only useful if it is large enough to sustain the organisms in it. Different animals have different area requirements and these need to be carefully considered before reintroducing a species to an area of suitable habitat.
- The minimum area requirement (MAR) (in km^2) can be calculated from the Individual Area Requirement (IAR)and the minimum viable population (MVP) (the smallest population required to maintain the species).
- The MAR for mammals can be calculated as: **MAR = MVP x IAR**.

Species	MVP estimate	IAR (km^2)
Bighorn sheep	224	0.29
Gray wolf	411	7.8
Chimpanzee	29	0.56
Tiger	973	27.7
Brown bear	172	3.2

Jana Verboom *et al* WOt paper 33 2014

1. Describe how a green corridor can help species conservation and reduce biodiversity loss:

2. What is the importance of Pinhook Swamp in the Okefenokee-Pinhook-Osceola system?

3. Describe the importance of habitat restoration to conserving species and reducing the loss of biodiversity:

4. (a) What is the MAR for bighorn sheep?

   (b) What is the MAR for brown bears?

5. Given that the MAR is very large for some species and many habitat fragments are very small, how is it possible for these species to remain viable?

6. Explain why MAR is more important in enclosed or fenced habitats than in open or unfenced habitats:

ISBN: 978-1-98-856632-0

171 Personal Progress Check

Answer the multiple choice questions that follow by circling the correct answer. Don't forget to read the question carefully!

1. Which of the following is most likely to reduce stratospheric ozone?
   (a) Clearcutting 200 ha of primary forest
   (b) Increasing production and emissions of trichlorofluoromethane
   (c) Increasing combustion of fossil fuels
   (d) Reducing the production and emissions of sulfur hexafluoride

The graph below shows the area of the ozone hole over Antarctica. Use it to answer questions 2 and 3:

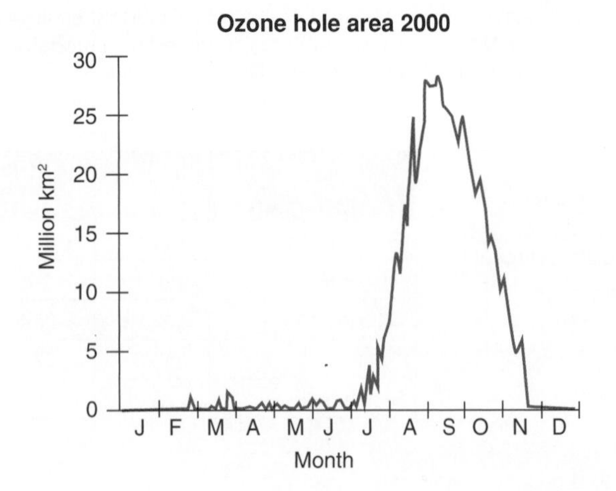

2. In which month does the ozone hole reach its maximum area?
   (a) June
   (b) August
   (c) September
   (d) October

3. In which season does the ozone hole reach its maximum area?
   (a) Summer
   (b) Fall
   (c) Winter
   (d) Spring

4. Which of the following molecules has the lowest ozone depletion potential:
   (a) CFC
   (b) HFO
   (c) HCFC
   (d) HFC

5. The Kyoto Protocol is an international treaty designed and agreed to:
   (a) Reduce the production of ozone depleting molecules
   (b) Control global wildlife trade
   (c) Protect endangered animals by controlling land use
   (d) Reduce global warming by controlling the production of greenhouse gases

6. Which of the following molecules has the greatest global warming potential?
   (a) Carbon dioxide
   (b) Sulfur hexafluoride
   (c) Nitrous oxide
   (d) Methane

The graph below shows the monthly atmospheric CO_2 concentration at the Mauna Loa Observatory in Hawaii. Use it to answer questions 7 to 9:

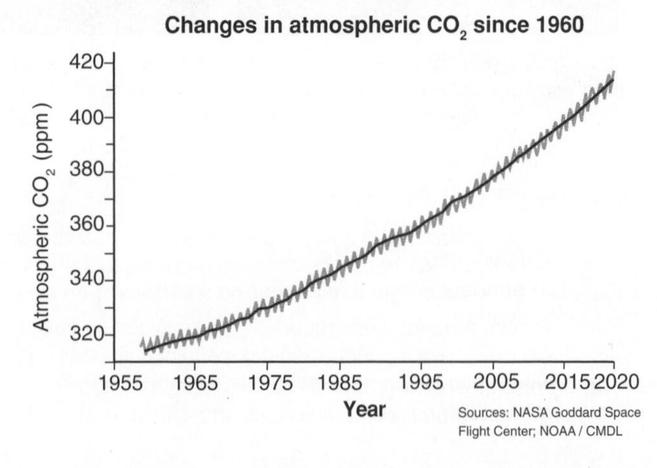

7. The increased atmospheric CO_2, in parts per million (ppm) between 1960 and present day is:
   (a) 100 ppm
   (b) 70 ppm
   (c) 50 ppm
   (d) 25 ppm

8. Which of the following best explains the periodic fluctuations in the curve?
   (a) Daily variation in sunlight levels
   (b) Daily variation atmospheric temperature
   (c) Seasonal variation in photosynthesis
   (d) Seasonal variation in atmospheric temperature

9. Which of the following is the likely cause of the trend in the graph?
   (a) Increased consumption of fossil fuels
   (b) Increased levels of solar activity
   (c) A constant annual increase in atmospheric temperature
   (d) An increase in evaporation from the oceans

10. Greenhouse gases are produced from:
    (a) Combustion of fossil fuels
    (b) The high temperature reaction of oxygen and nitrogen in internal combustion engines
    (c) Belching and flatus of cattle
    (d) All of the above

11. Rising atmospheric carbon dioxide is likely to cause:
    (a) A rise is sea level
    (b) A reduction of the ice caps
    (c) A rise in global atmospheric temperature
    (d) All of the above

ISBN: 978-1-98-856632-0

12. In models of global warming, the most important contributor to sea level rise is:
    (a) Thermal expansion of water in the oceans
    (b) Melting of the polar ice caps
    (c) Increased rain
    (d) Decreased snow

13. Which of the following processes results is a positive feedback loop that continues to affect the environment?
    (a) Volcanic activity
    (b) Increased summer melting of the polar sea ice
    (c) Increased cloud cover over the oceans
    (d) A decrease in solar activity

14. Climate change is:
    (a) The warming effect of the gases in Earth's atmosphere
    (b) The steady increase in atmospheric temperature
    (c) The long term effects of a warming atmosphere on the global and regional climate
    (d) The annual change in climate and weather conditions

The graph below shows the pH of the oceans around Hawaii. Use it to answer question 15 and 16:

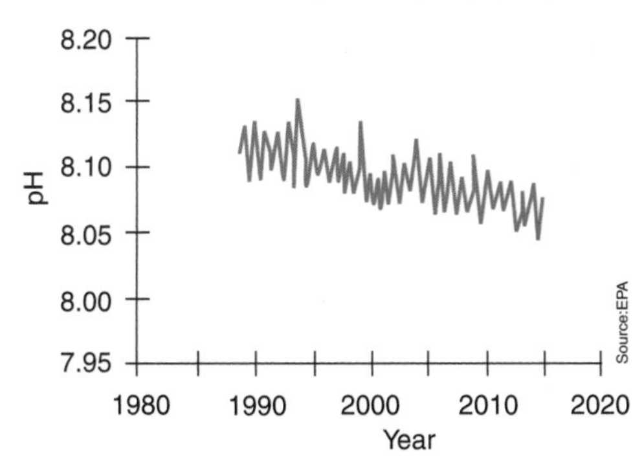

15. The lower pH of the oceans means:
    (a) The oceans are becoming less acidic
    (b) The oceans are becoming more basic
    (c) There is a decrease in the hydrogen ion concentration in the oceans
    (d) There is a increase in the hydrogen ion concentration in the oceans

16. The decreasing pH is caused by:
    (a) More CO_2 dissolving into the oceans
    (b) Less CO_2 dissolving into the oceans
    (c) Dilution of ocean water due to melting ice caps
    (d) Increased runoff of nutrients from farmland

17. CITES stands for:
    (a) Convention on International Trade in Endangered Species of Wild Flora and Fauna
    (b) Convention for International Tariffs on Endangered Species of Wild Flora and Fauna
    (c) Convention for International Trade and Enforcement Strategies
    (d) Conservation of Internationally Traded Endangered Species

18. Which of the following laws or treaties is designed to protect and recover endangered wildlife in the United States?
    (a) The Montreal protocol
    (b) Comprehensive Environmental Response, Compensation, and Liability Act
    (c) The Delaney Clause
    (d) The Endangered Species Act

The graph below shows the amount of ice melting in Greenland. Use it to answer questions 19 and 20

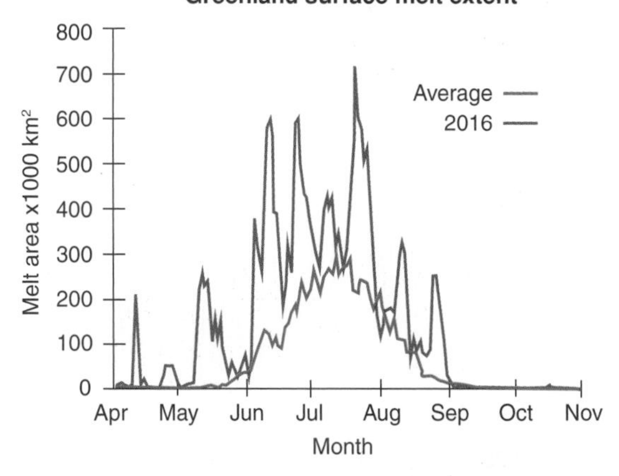

19. The surface melt extent in Greenland for 2016:
    (a) Was below average
    (b) Was above average
    (c) Was within the typical range for melting
    (d) Occurred mostly in winter

20. The maximum extent of the melt reached approximately:
    (a) 200,000 km^2
    (b) 400,000 km^2
    (c) 700,000 km^2
    (d) 1,000,000 km^2

21. Invasive species tend to be:
    (a) Slow breeding K-selected species
    (b) Generally only plants, especially weeds
    (c) Fast breeding *r*-selected species
    (d) Small and difficult to find

22. Habitat fragmentation:
    (a) Doesn't affect plants because they don't move around anyway
    (b) Is only caused by human activities
    (c) Is when habitat is lost by logging and forest fires
    (d) Occurs when large tracts of forest are divided up by impassable boundaries

23. A threatened species is one that is:
    (a) In danger of becoming extinct
    (b) In danger of losing important habitat
    (c) Likely to become endangered in the near future
    (d) Being over-hunted

ISBN: 978-1-98-856632-0

24. Figures 1 and 2 below show the dissolved CO_2 concentration and the pH of the sea near Bermuda in the North Atlantic. Figure 3 shows the effect of increasing ocean pH on the survival of juvenile red king crabs (*Paralithodes camtschaticus*).

Figure 1: CO_2 near Bermuda

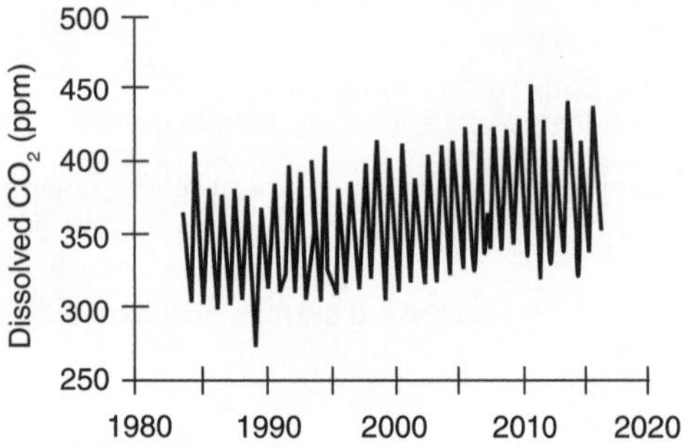

Figure 2: pH near Bermuda

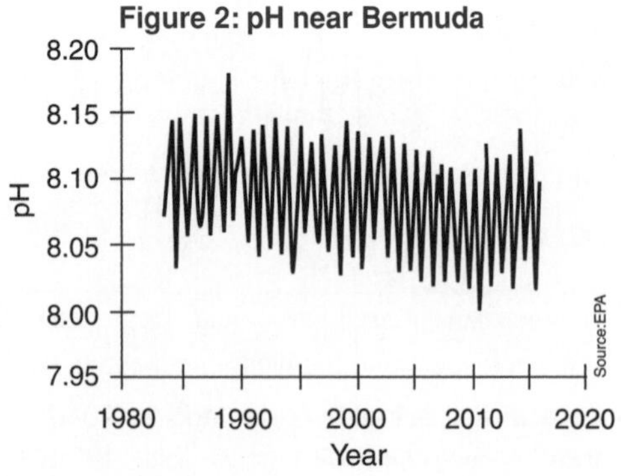

Source:EPA

Figure 3: Effect of pH on juvenile red king crabs

Long et al. PLOS ONE, 2013

NOAA

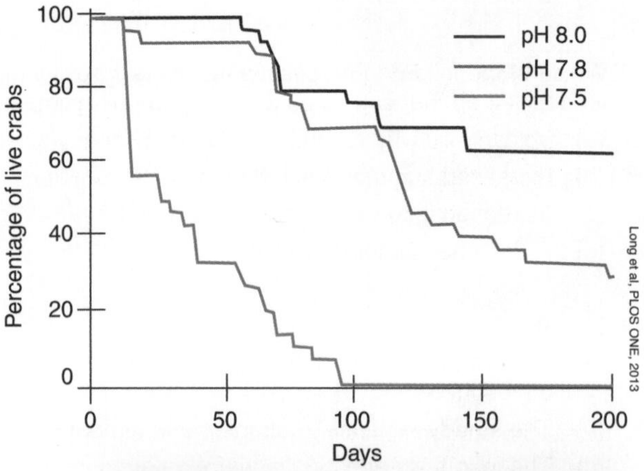

Red king crab

(a) What is the effect of decreasing pH on juvenile red king crabs? ____________________

(b) What is the cause of the decreasing ocean pH? Give the details of the chemistry involved: ____________________

(c) How does the decreasing ocean pH affect shell building organisms? Why is decreasing ocean pH a problem?

(d) What can be done to stop or reduce the decrease in ocean pH (at least in the long term)? ____________________

ISBN: 978-1-98-856632-0

10. Science Practices for Environmental Science

Developing understanding

Science practices: Science practices describe the things you should be able to do while you are covering the content of this environmental science course. They represent the practices that underlie the study of any science and are categorized into skills. See the table on page vii-ix at the front of this book for a list of skills and practices.

Skills: This supporting unit provides a background reference for the skills you will use throughout this course of study. You will apply these skills as you complete the activities in this book. These skills form the basis of the tasks on the APES exam.

1 Concept explanation .... activity 172

- ☐ A. To describe environmental concepts and processes you will need to identify relevant features of a concept or process.
- ☐ B. To explain environmental concepts or processes you will need to provide explanatory detail relating to the concept or process, rather than just describing its components.
- ☐ C. To explain environmental concepts or processes in applied contexts you must relate your explanations to real world situations, e.g. explaining how birth and death rates change during demographic transition.

2 Visual representations .... activity 173

- ☐ A. Describing the features of an environmental concept, process, or model represented visually might involve describing the features of a diagram or a plot.
- ☐ B. Explaining relationships between characteristics of concepts/ processes represented visually might involve comparing or predicting patterns or trends or explaining a visual model.
- ☐ C. Explaining how a visual representation relates to broader issues might involve drawing a conclusion based on concepts or processes in the model or representation.

3 Text analysis .... activity 174

- ☐ A. To identify an author's claim you must be able to identify and state the main point the author is making in the text.
- ☐ B. Describing the author's perspective and assumptions involves being able to recognize the point of view of the author and what assumptions that point of view involves.
- ☐ C. Describing the author's reasoning requires you to describe the evidence supporting the author's claim.
- ☐ D. Evaluating the credibility of a source involves recognizing bias and evaluating scientific accuracy (how true it is).
- ☐ E. Evaluating the validity of conclusions requires that you recognize and describe the limitations of an investigation.

4 Scientific experiments .... activity 175

- ☐ A. Identifying a testable hypothesis means asking, refining, and evaluating questions about natural phenomena.
- ☐ B. To identify methods, designs, or measures you need to identify variables, and identify and evaluate controls.
- ☐ C. To describe a method, design, or measure you need to describe the variables and the method of data collection.
- ☐ D. To make observations or collect data from laboratory setups you will need to collect first-hand data from observations.
- ☐ E. Explaining modifications to experimental procedures involves evaluating and refining your research to obtain valid data.

5 Data analysis .... activity 176

- ☐ A. Describing patterns or trends in data involves visualizing patterns over the time of the data.
- ☐ B. To describe relationships in data you need to describe *how* the dependent variable changes in response to the independent variable.
- ☐ C. To explain patterns and trends in data to draw conclusions you must be able to explain *why* the dependent variable changes in response to the independent variable.
- ☐ D. To interpret data in relation to a hypothesis you must explain *why* the dependent variable responded the way it did to the independent variable.
- ☐ E. To explain what the data illustrates about environmental issues you need to be able to make and then justify a prediction based on data, or justify a given prediction.

6 Mathematical routines .... activity 177

- ☐ A. To determine an approach for solving a problem you need to be able to explain the best way to calculate a quantity.
- ☐ B. Applying mathematical relationships to solve problems involves calculating values, with working shown.
- ☐ C. Calculating an accurate numerical answer with appropriate units involves awareness of significant figures and units.

7 Environmental solutions .... activity 178

- ☐ A. To describe environmental problems you need to recognize and then describe a problem.
- ☐ B. To describe potential responses to environmental problems you need to first recognize the causative factors in the problem and their relative contributions to the problem.
- ☐ C. Describing advantages, disadvantages, or unintended consequences of potential solutions to environmental problems recognizes that no solution is without risk or cost. Solutions must be feasible and realistic.
- ☐ D. Using data and evidence to support a potential solution may involve evaluating data to compare the viability of different possible solutions or proposing a solution based on data gathered over a period of time.
- ☐ E. Making a claim that proposes a solution to an environmental problem in an applied context must involve a real world application such as sustainable agriculture or urban mining (extraction of metals from e-waste).
- ☐ F. To justify a proposed solution you must explain its advantages and weigh them against the benefits and drawbacks of alternative solutions.

172 Concept Explanation

Key Question: When and how should systems be described or explained using text?

Putting data or a diagram into words adds information that may not be obvious in the data. Explanations can be added to descriptions of data and so better explain the concept being shown. Sometimes data or diagrams can be complex or show multiple concepts. It is important to be able to describe and explain these and how they relate to each other.

Describing a concept may include:

- Describing characteristics and attributes using defining terms, e.g. describing a process as a positive or negative feedback loop.
- Classifying or grouping concepts or parts of concepts, e.g. identifying trophic levels.
- Describing components, e.g. describing the parts involved in carbon cycling.
- Describing how a process occurs, e.g. giving a simple description of an ecological process.
- Describing structure and function, e.g. describing the structure of energy pyramids and the function of each component.
- Describing trends and patterns, e.g. describing patterns in graphs or data tables.

Explaining a concept may include:

- Explaining each of the points in the description table on the left.
- Explaining these points in applied contexts. This might include:
  - Explaining the effect of domestication on biodiversity.
  - Explaining the relationship between photosynthesis and carbon cycling.
  - Explaining competition or cooperation between and within species.
  - Explaining how birth rates change as countries become more developed or industrialized.

- The data below shows the temperature and daylight hours of four cities located in the Americas.

High and (low) temperatures (°C)

City	Jan	Feb	Mar	Apr	May	Jun	Jul	Aug	Sep	Oct	Nov	Dec
New York	4 (-3)	6 (-2)	11 (2)	18 (7)	22 (12)	27 (18)	29 (20)	29 (20)	25 (16)	18 (10)	13 (6)	7 (0)
Miami	23 (17)	24 (18)	25 (19)	26 (21)	28 (23)	30 (25)	31 (26)	31 (26)	30 (25)	28 (24)	26 (21)	24 (19)
Quito	19 (9)	19 (10)	19 (9)	19 (10)	19 (9)	19 (9)	19 (8)	20 (9)	20 (9)	20 (9)	19 (9)	19 (9)
Rio Gallegos	20 (8)	20 (7)	17 (5)	13 (3)	9 (0)	5 (-2)	5 (-2)	8 (-1)	12 (1)	15 (3)	17 (5)	19 (7)

Average monthly daylight hours

City	Jan	Feb	Mar	Apr	May	Jun	Jul	Aug	Sep	Oct	Nov	Dec
New York	9.5	10.5	12	13	14.5	15	15	14	12.5	11	10	9.5
Miami	10.5	11.5	12	12.5	13.5	13.5	13.5	13	12.5	11.5	11	10.5
Quito	12	12	12	12	12	12	12	12	12	12	12	12
Rio Gallegos	16	14.5	12.5	10.5	9	8	8.5	9.5	11.5	13.5	15.5	16.5

1. The four cities above are Miami (USA), New York (USA), Quito (Ecuador), and Rio Gallegos (southern Argentina).

(a) Describe two trends in the daylight hours shown in the table above:

i. ______________________________

ii. ______________________________

(b) Explain the relationship between daylight hours and the position of the city in the Americas:

____

(c) Explain the relationship between a city's temperature and its position in the Americas:

____

ISBN: 978-1-98-856632-0

173 Visual Representations

Key Question: How are diagrams and models useful for explaining scientific concepts?

Diagrams and models are important ways of visually representing scientific concepts and ideas. They help explore and explain concepts and can be used to some the complexity of relationships within a system.

Describing visual representations may include:

- Describing the characteristics and attributes of the representation, e.g. how are various parts related or connected?
- Describing patterns or trends, e.g. describing trends in graphs or diagrams.

Explaining visual representations may include:

- Comparing patterns or trends, e.g. how does the monthly temperature in city A compare to the monthly temperature in city B?
- Explaining the concept being represented visually, e.g. explaining what the flow diagram is showing.
- Predicting patterns based on the representation/model.
- Drawing conclusions based on the information being represented visually.

▸ Scientific concepts and data can be represented or modeled in many different ways. The way the data is represented depends on the concept being expressed Some examples of visual representations are shown here:

A: Physical model of a water molecule

B: Nitrogen inputs and outputs

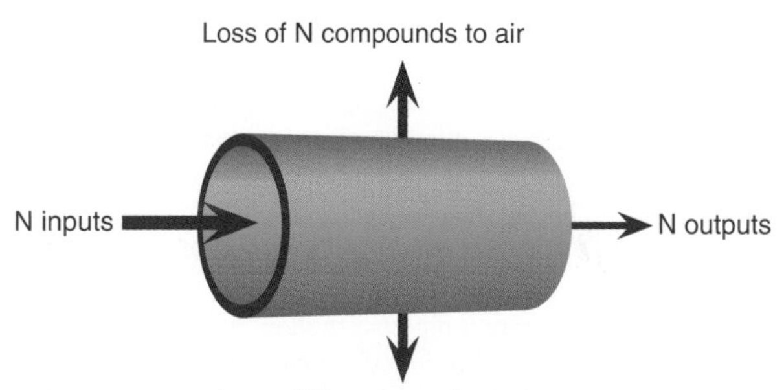

Nitrogen balance = Nitrogen input – Nitrogen output + N lost

C: Mathematical model of population growth

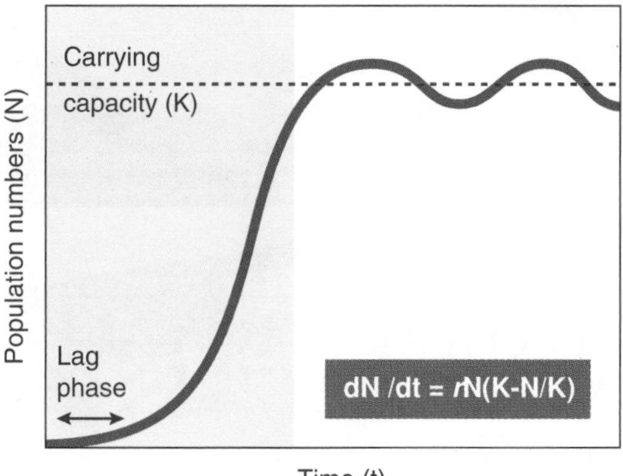

D: Diagram of nutrient cycling in an ecosystem

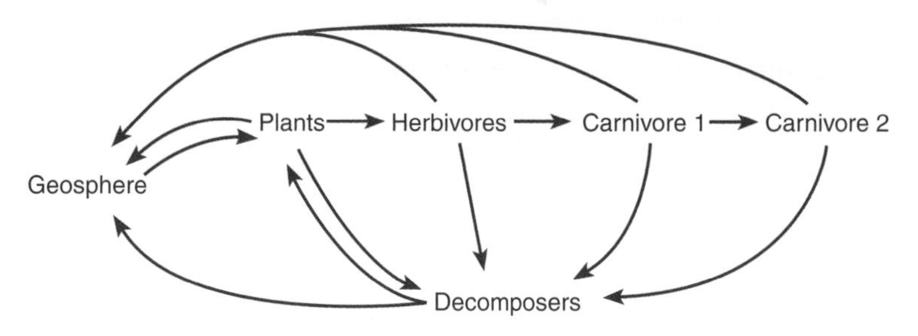

1. For each of the models A - D describe what each is showing:

   A: ______________________

   B: ______________________

   C: ______________________

   D: ______________________

2. (a) Use the diagram D above to explain nutrient movements in an ecosystem: ______________________

   ____

   ____

   (b) Use the diagram C above to predict the effect of reducing the carrying capacity by half: ______________________

   ____

   ____

ISBN: 978-1-98-856632-0

174 Text Analysis

Key Question: Why is carefully analyzing text and written documents so important?

The amount of written information available on any particular topic has increased exponentially since the internet became readily available. Choose any environmental topic and there will be hundreds if not thousands of websites on it. Some will be factual, others will be opinionated, some will be just inaccurate, and a few will be intentionally misleading. Data and information should be checked to make sure it comes from a reputable source. It is also important to make sure the information has not been used out of context or been "cherry picked" for data to put forward biased ideas.

Text analysis may include:

- Describing the article:
  - Stating the main points in article.
  - Describing the author's perspectives and assumptions.
  - Identifying any claims made by the author and any evidence presented to justify them.
- Evaluating the article:
  - Identifying and describing any bias in the article. How might this have affected the article's accuracy?
  - Describing the limitations of an investigative article.
  - Describing the article's conclusions.

What can be trusted?

- Environmental science covers many contentious and emotive topics. Many new ideas about the environment clash with traditional views or threaten livelihoods and economies. As a result people may have certain views they feel invested in. This leads to people putting forth information to support their view, lobbying to a certain extent.
- When reading environmental information, especially on the internet, it is important that you take note of where the information comes from and whether it makes sense in a wider context. This will help you identify biased or flawed information.
- Note the site from which you obtained information. Is it reputable or just someone's blog with their own unverifiable ideas? Be cautious with video clips (e.g. YouTube). Again, these often present an unsubstantiated personal view. Check the comments as they may identify errors (if any) in the video.

Evaluating environmental information

- In order to form an opinion about the information presented, you must critically evaluate the information. Points to consider include:
- Validity of the information.
  - The currency of the information. Is it up to date?
  - Is the information peer reviewed? Has it been accepted by the scientific community?
- Does the information present an unbiased view?
  - Is information presented in a fair, unbiased way? Is it based on fact and not emotion?
  - Is the information presented clouded by the attitudes, beliefs, or values of the person, group, or organization supplying the information?
- Journals are peer-reviewed. That is, the information is checked by experts in the topic area. This greatly improves the reliability of the information. However, journals are often very technical and require a high level of in-area expertise to understand.
- Newspaper articles are a good starting point as a source of generally reliable information, but beware of the newspaper's particular leaning. Tabloids often sensationalize stories, while some newspapers may have left or right political leanings, which can skew the focus of a story.
- Online sites that are specific for a topic need to be carefully scrutinised for validity. Stay away from conspiracy sites as these often sensationalize stories and misreport the science. Government sites often have the most current and reliable data based on information from skilled advisers.

- Periodicals or technical magazines, e.g. National Geographic, Scientific American, or Popular Mechanics, are useful sources of reliable information. As they are written for the general public they make understanding the technical information much easier.

ISBN: 978-1-98-856632-0

Read the article below and answer the questions:

Glacial stream insect may tolerate warmer waters

Scott Hotaling *et al*, Mountain stoneflies may tolerate warming streams: evidence from organismal physiology and gene expression. Global Change Biology, 2020; DOI: 10.1111/gcb.15294. Text below based on an article in Science Daily.

Stoneflies may be able to tolerate warmer water temperatures and may even be stressed in their cold water environment. This goes against most current theory which states that rising temperatures will be disastrous for glacial stream insects and ecology. However lead author Scott Hotaling says that still may be so for mountain stoneflies.

"These species are still in peril," says Hotaling. "They live in these extreme environments for a reason, but we don't fully understand why. Threats from warming and loss of glaciers are likely more complicated, and potentially, it is not about physical factors. It might be about ecological factors."

Hotaling and his colleagues tested the thermal tolerance of several species of mountain stoneflies found in the Rocky Mountains, at least one of which was listed under the Endangered Species Act due to rapid loss of its glacial habitat. The researchers collected larval specimens of the stoneflies from streams in Glacier and Grand Teton National Parks. Some of the larvae were then subjected to increasingly warmer water temperatures over short time periods, imitating what might happen to a stream on a hot summer day.

All of the species could tolerate waters of at least 20°C, well above the maximum 10°C of their natural habitat.

Hotaling and his team found that the stoneflies that experienced warmer temperatures expressed "heat shock proteins" within the cells. These proteins are named because they were first discovered in relation to exposure to high temperatures. It has since been found that heat shock proteins are also related to other stressful events, including exposure to cold.

The study found that the heat shock proteins were also present in the stoneflies kept in water at 3°C, similar to the temperature of their glacial habitat. This indicated the stoneflies might be stressed in their natural home.

The study raises many questions, such as why the insects aren't found naturally in warmer waters. Co-author Alisha Shah says: "It is possible that these mountain stoneflies are just bad competitors, and they are pushed up to these higher elevations by stronger competitors that prefer somewhat warmer temperatures."

The researchers are now investigating how stoneflies respond to living in warmer water for longer periods (as might happen with global warming). So far, the stonefly nymphs appear to develop faster. Shah said it was hard to tell yet if that was good or bad since faster development might mean the stoneflies produce more deformities or fewer eggs. Hotaling and Shah are investigating these variables in a race to better understand the cold communities that live downstream of glaciers before they disappear.

"We're stuck between having so little knowledge about the ecology and physiology of what lives on or downstream of glaciers and having so little time," Hotaling says. "These are some of the most rapidly changing places on the planet, so we have little time left have to understand them."

1. State the main purpose of the article: ______________________________

2. What does the author claim about the stonefly's ability to withstand climate change? ______________________________

3. What evidence is there for these claims? ______________________________

4. Are there any limitations in the investigation? ______________________________

5. What are the study's conclusions? ______________________________

6. Are there any assumptions made? If so, what are they? ______________________________

ISBN: 978-1-98-856632-0

175 Scientific Experiments

Key Question: What methods should be used to carry out, write, and analyze scientific investigations?

Articles in scientific journals are written in a standardized way. They usually open with an abstract, which summarizes the reasons for carrying out the investigation, the results and conclusions. They include methods, so others can reproduce or modify the method in their own experiments, and the results. They finish with the conclusions, often written as part of a discussion. You should be able to understand this format and extract important data from it.

Describing aspects of scientific investigations may include:

- Identifying the purpose or aim of the investigation, or the hypothesis being tested.
- Identifying and describing the method, including the dependent and independent variables.
- Identifying the control (if present) and justifying any factors that need to controlled.
- Being able to draw data from the method and results, including photographs and diagrams (e.g. graphs).
- Identifying and describing how a method could be modified or refined to obtain more accurate data.

Carrying out a scientific investigation may include:

- Identifying the aim and writing a hypothesis.
- Deciding which variable will be changed (the independent variable) and which will be measured (the dependent variable) and how this will done.
- Writing the method of data collection so that it can be followed and repeated by someone else.
- Recording data in a systematic way.
- Drawing conclusions from the data.
- Writing a concluding discussion identifying what the results mean and any limitations in the investigation.

Start with an observation, ask a question, then write a hypothesis

- Investigations normally start from observations, either from a previous investigation or from observing natural phenomena. An observation could be: there are more exhaust fumes during rush hour, summers appear to be getting warmer, or its harder to catch fish from the jetty now than a decade ago.
- These observations may or may not be true, but they allow us to ask questions: Is air pollution greater during rush hour? Are the summers getting hotter? Are the local fish populations getting smaller? We can turn the questions into statements than can be tested to be true of not, that is, the statement (hypothesis) can be accepted or rejected.
- For example: There are higher levels or particulate matter in the air during rush hour than during other times of the day. This statement can be tested by measuring amounts of particulate matter at different times of the day. If particulate matter is higher during rush hour then the statement can be accepted. If not, it can be rejected.

Identifying variables

- A **variable** is any characteristic or property able to take any one of a range of values. Investigations often look at the effect of changing one variable on another. It is important to identify all variables in an investigation: independent, dependent, and controlled, although there may be nuisance factors of which you are unaware. In a fair test, only one variable is changed by the investigator.

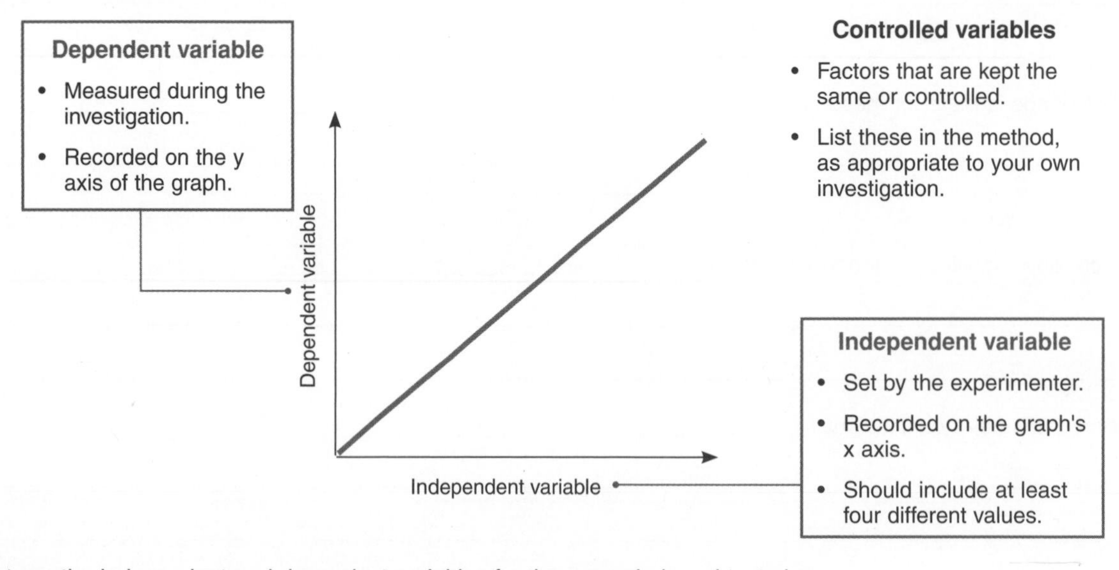

1. What are the independent and dependent variables for the example in red text above:

   (a) Dependent: ______________________________

   (b) Independent: ______________________________

ISBN: 978-1-98-856632-0

Experimental controls

- A **control** refers to a standard or reference treatment or group in an experiment.
- It is the same as the experimental (test) group, except that it lacks the one variable being manipulated by the experimenter.
- Controls are used to demonstrate that the response in the test group is due a specific variable (e.g. temperature).
- The control undergoes the same preparation, experimental conditions, observations, measurements, and analysis as the test group. This helps to ensure that responses observed in the treatment groups can be reliably interpreted.
- Data gathering investigations, such as the one for particulate matter already mentioned, sometimes have the control built into the investigation. By measuring particulate levels at set time intervals throughout the day the experimental group (rush hour) and the control (non-rush hours) can be compared.

Gathering data

- Investigations should be carried out multiple times in order to make sure the data collected is consistent.
- Multiple trials and measurements for the same variable allow statistics (e.g. the mean) to be calculated.
- The more trials and data gathered, the more confident you can be of the final results, providing there is no systematic bias in your methodology.

How do I analyze my data?

- Check your data to see that it makes sense. Do the results seem logical? Are there any outliers? If so, you must decide whether to include them in your analysis.
- Raw data may need to be transformed to see trends and patterns. These transformations may be quite simple (e.g. percentages, rates, ratios). Other transformations are used to normalize the data so that it can undergo further analysis (e.g. log transformations when working with large numbers).
- Descriptive statistics (e.g. mean and standard deviation) provide a way to summarize your data, and provide results that can easily be presented and compared across groups. Summary statistics are also useful in identifying trends and patterns in the data.
- Sometimes an appropriate statistical analysis is required to test the significance of results. However, with simple experiments, if the design is sound, the results are often clearly shown in a plot of the data.

Presenting your data

Tables and graphs provide a way to organize and visualize data in a way that helps to identify trends. Each has a different purpose. Tables provide an accurate record of numerical values and allow you to organize your data so that relationships and trends are apparent. Columns can be inserted for calculations such as rates. Graphs provide a visual representation of trends in the data in a minimum of space and are an excellent choice for displaying results in a poster or report. Histograms, line graphs, and scatter graphs are common ways to display data graphically. The graph and table below display the same data.

Level of particulate matter from 05:00 to 12:00 hours	
Time (hr)	ppm particulate matter
05:00	70
06:00	71
07:00	80
08:00	100
09:00	150
10:00	100
11:00	80
12:00	85

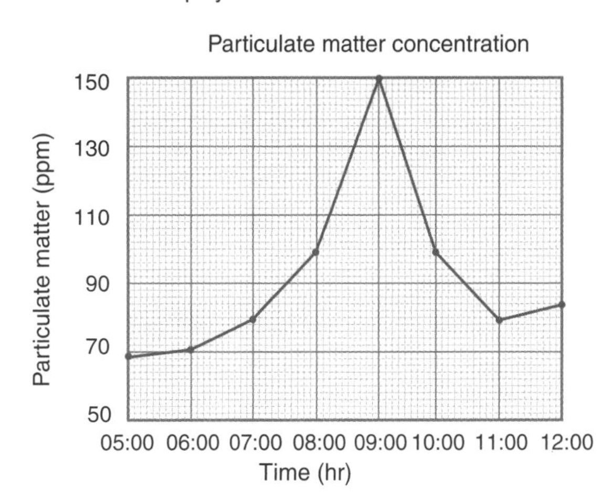

Conclusions and discussion

Your conclusions summarize how your results support (or don't support) the hypothesis. Your may include a discussion of what the results mean and what caused them. Usually this discussion is within the context of what is already known and published. Any limitations of the investigation should be included. In scientific journals the discussion is often one of the longest sections. It may discuss the significance of the results in a wider context and so is probably the most important part of the report.

2. What do the results above show? What might cause them and why are they significant? ______________________

____

____

____

ISBN: 978-1-98-856632-0

176 Data Analysis

Key Question: How can we analyze data?
Once data has been collected its is important to be able to analyze or interpret it in order to make sense of it. Graphs are an excellent way to summarize trends in data or relationships between different variables. It is important to be able to be construct and interpret different kinds of graph. Common graphs include scatter plots and line graphs (for continuous data), and bar charts (for categorical data).

Interpreting data may include:
- Describing patterns or trends (e.g. does a variable rise or fall over time).
- Describing how the dependent variable changes in response to changes in the independent variable.
- Explaining why the dependent variable changes in response to changes in the independent variable.
- Making predictions based on trends in the data and justifying the prediction.
- Justifying the predictions of others based on the data presented.

Types of data

Quantitative (interval or ratio)
Characteristics for which measurements or counts can be made, e.g. height, weight, number.
Summary measures: mean, median, standard deviation

- **Discontinuous (discrete)**
  e.g. Number of children in a family (3, 0, 4)
- **Continuous**
  e.g. Height of children in a family (1.5 m, 0.8 m)

Qualitative (nominal)
Non-numerical and descriptive, e.g. sex, color, viability (dead/alive), presence or absence of a specific feature.
Summary measures: frequencies and proportions

e.g. Sex of children in a family (male, female)

Ranked (ordinal)
Data are ranked in order, although the intervals between the orders may not be equal, e.g. abundance (abundant, common, rare).
Summary measures: frequencies and proportions

e.g. Birth order in a family (1, 2, 3)

Discontinuous or discrete data:
The unit of measurement cannot be split up (e.g. you cannot have half a child).

Continuous data:
The unit of measurement can be a part number (e.g. 5.25 kg).

Presenting data in tables

- Tables provide a way to systematically record and condense a large amount of information. They provide an accurate record of numerical data and allow you to organize your data in a way that allows you to identify relationships and trends. This can help to decide the best way to graph the data if graphing is required.
- Table titles and row and column headings must be clear and accurate so the reader knows exactly what the table is about. Calculations such as rates and summary statistics (such as mean or standard deviation) may be included on a table.
- Summary statistics make it easier to identify trends and compare different treatments. Rates are useful in making multiple data sets comparable, e.g. if recordings were made over different time periods.

Table 1: Population, land area, and calculated population density in four US states.

State	Population	Land area (km^2)	Population density (people/km)
Alabama	4,871,547	135,754	35.9
Florida	20,636,975	170,307	121.2
Montana	1,032,949	380,847	2.7
Texas	27,469,114	695,662	39.5

1. For each of the photographic examples A-C below use the flow chart top to classify the data.

A: Flower color

B: Eggs per nest

C: Tree trunk diameter

A: ______________________

B: ______________________

C: ______________________

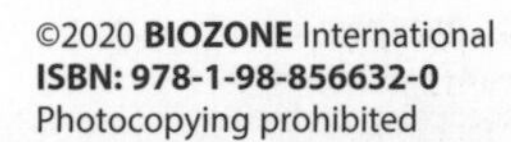

ISBN: 978-1-98-856632-0

Presenting data in graphs

- Graphs are a good way to show trends, patterns, and relationships visually without taking up too much space. Complex data sets tend to be presented as a graph rather than as a table, although the raw data can sometimes be tabulated as an appendix.
- Presenting graphs properly requires attention to a few basic details, including correct orientation and labeling of the axes, accurate plotting of points, and a descriptive, accurate title.
- Before representing data graphically, it is important to identify the kind of data you have. Common graphs include scatter plots and line graphs (for continuous data), and bar charts (for categorical data). For continuous data with calculated means, points can be connected. On scatter plots, a line of best fit is often drawn.

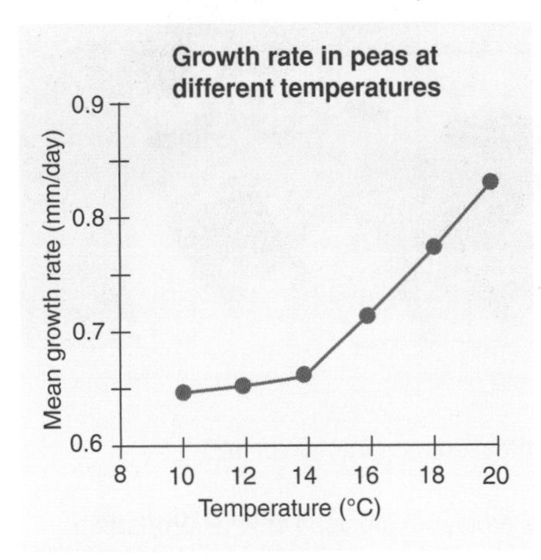

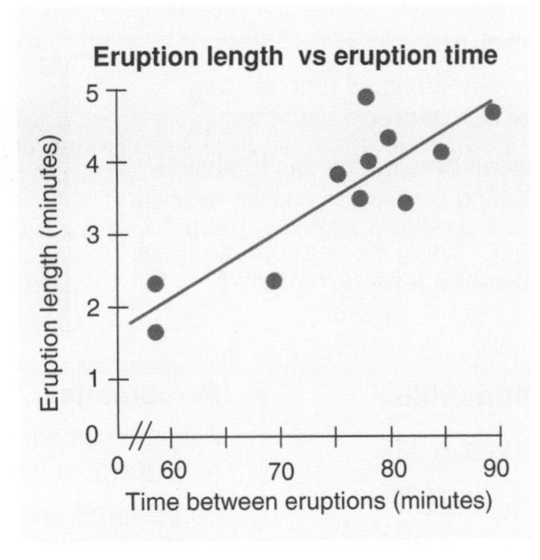

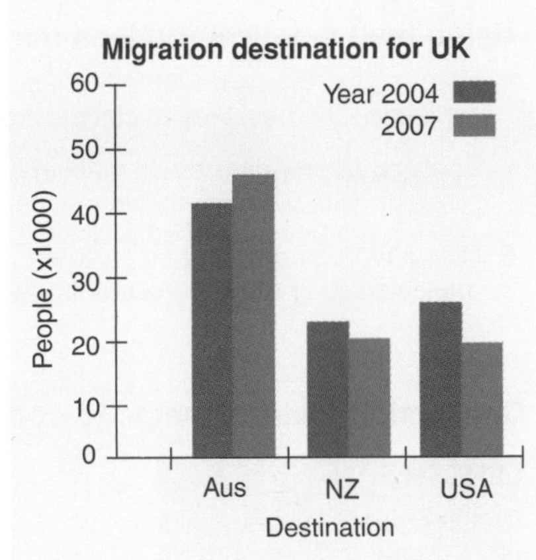

Guidelines for line graphs

- Line graphs are used when one variable (the independent variable) affects another, the dependent variable.
- The data must be continuous for both variables. The independent variable is the experimental treatment. The dependent variable is the response.
- The relationship between two variables can be represented as a continuum and the plotted data points are connected directly (point to point).

Guidelines for scatter graphs

- A scatter graph is a common way to display continuous data where there is a relationship between two interdependent variables.
- There is no independent (manipulated) variable, but the variables are often correlated, i.e. they vary together in a predictable way.
- The points on the graph are not connected, but a line of best fit is often drawn through the points to show the relationship between the variables

Guidelines for bar/column graphs

- Bar and column graphs are appropriate for data that are non-numerical and discrete (categorical) for one variable. There are no dependent or independent variables.
- Data is discontinuous so bars do not touch (continuous data can be shown on a histogram where bars do touch).
- Multiple sets of data can be displayed side by side for comparison (e.g. males and females in the same age group).

2. Explain the choice of graph types for the three data sets above: ______________________

____

____

____

3. The data below shows the percentage of pollen in sediments from a region in northeastern United States, laid down over 15,000 years. By graphing the percentages of pollen types beside each other and matching the pollen type to known trees and landscapes we can develop a picture of what the land looked like at any particular time in the last 15,000 years.

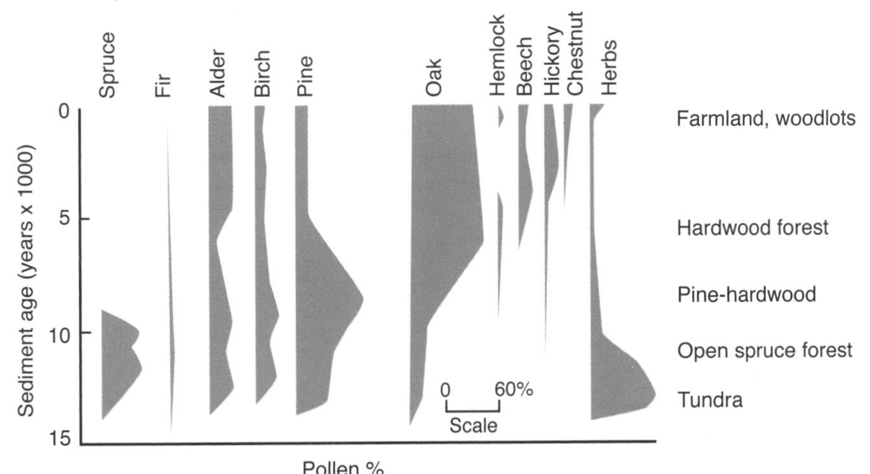

Dartmouth Electron Microscope Facility (Public Domain)

(a) What was the most common tree type(s) 10,000 years ago? ______________________

(b) What was the predominant forest type 5000 years ago? ______________________

ISBN: 978-1-98-856632-0

177 Mathematical Routines

Key Question: What mathematical process can be used to help data analysis?

Mathematics is used to analyze, interpret, and compare data. It is important that you are familiar with mathematical notation (the language of mathematics) and can confidently apply some basic mathematical principles and calculations to your data. Data collected in the field or laboratory is called raw data. It often needs to be transformed in order for trends or patterns to be revealed. Ratios and percentages are widely used. Large numbers may be transformed using logarithms. Log transformations reduce skew, make large numbers easier to work with, and can make data easier to interpret.

Using mathematical routines may include:

- Determining the best method to solve a mathematical problem, e.g. explaining the best way to compare coal use between countries.
- Applying appropriate mathematical routines or relationships to solve a problem, with working shown e.g. calculating population growth over time.
- Calculating a numeric answer to a problem, using the appropriate units, e.g. calculating the energy required to power a town for 10 years.

Conversion factors: metric to common units

LENGTH	Multiply by
Centimeters to inches:	0.393
Meters to feet:	3.280
Kilometers to miles:	0.621
VOLUME	
Milliliters to fluid ounces:	0.034
Liters to gallons:	0.264
AREA	
Square meters to square feet:	10.76
Hectares to acres:	2.471
Square kilometers to square miles	0.386

TEMPERATURE

°C to °F: Freezing point of water: 0°C = 32°F
Boiling point of water : 100°C = 212°F

Formula °C to °F: °F = °C x 1.8 + 32

Energy

BTU to joules 1055.0558

Percentages

Percentages are expressed as a fraction of 100 (e.g. 20/100 = 20%).

Percentages provide a clear expression of what proportion of data fall into any particular category, e.g. for pie graphs.

Allows meaningful comparison between different samples.

Useful to monitor change (e.g. % increase from one year to the next (example below)).

Example: A study of a bear population counts 75 bears living within a 300 km^2 forest. 25 of them were male:

1. Calculate the % of male bears in the population.
   25/75 x 100 = 33%
2. It is estimated that the bear population may be 20% larger than the raw count suggests. Calculate the new population:
   75 + (75 x 0.20) = 90 bears.
3. It is estimated the population has an annual growth rate of 3%. Calculate the bear population in five years time:
   $Pop_{future\ bears} = Pop_{present\ bears} \times (1 + 0.03)^5 = 75 \times (1.03)^5$
   = 87 bears in 5 years

Decimal and standard form

Decimal form (also called ordinary form) is the longhand way of writing a number (e.g. 15,000,000). Very large or very small numbers can take up too much space if written in decimal form and are often expressed in a condensed **standard form**. For example, 15,000,000 is written as 1.5×10^7 in standard form.

In standard form a number is always written as $A \times 10^n$, where A is a number between 1 and 10, and n (the exponent) indicates how many places to move the decimal point. n can be positive or negative.

For the example above, A = 1.5 and n = 7 because the decimal point moved seven places (see below).

$$1.5\,000\,000 = 1.5 \times 10^7$$

Small numbers can also be written in standard form. The exponent (n) will be negative. For example, 0.00101 is written as 1.01×10^{-3}.

$$0.00101 = 1.01 \times 10^{-3}$$

Adding numbers in standard form

Numbers in standard form can be added together so long as they are both raised to the same power of ten.
E.g: $1 \times 10^4 + 2 \times 10^3 = 1 \times 10^4 + 0.2 \times 10^4 = 1.2 \times 10^4$

Rates

Rates are expressed as a measure per unit of time and show how a variable changes over time. Rates are used to provide meaningful comparisons of data that may have been recorded over different time periods.

Often rates are expressed as a mean rate over the duration of the measurement period, but it is also useful to calculate the rate at various times to understand how rate changes over time. The table below shows the distance a fault line moves over a decade. A worked example for the rate at 4 years is shown.

Time (year)	Distance traveled (mm)	Rate of movement (speed) (mm/year)	Mean rate of movement (mm/year)
0	0	0	0
2	40	20	20
4	100	30*	25
6	120	10	20
8	170	25	21
10	200	15	20

*mm moved between 2 - 4 years: 100 mm – 40 mm = 60 mm

Rate of movement (speed) between 2 - 4 years
60 mm ÷ 2 years = 30mm/year

ISBN: 978-1-98-856632-0

Dealing with large numbers

- Environmental science often deals with very large numbers or scales. Numerical data indicating scale can often increase or decrease exponentially. Large scale changes in numerical data can be made more manageable by using log transformations.

Exponential function

- Exponential growth or decay occurs at an increasingly rapid rate in proportion to the increasing or decreasing total number or size.
- In an exponential function, the base number is fixed (constant) and the exponent is variable.
- The equation for an exponential function is $y = c^x$.
- An example of exponential decay is radioactive decay. Any radioactive element has a half-life, the amount of time required for its radioactivity to fall to half its original value.

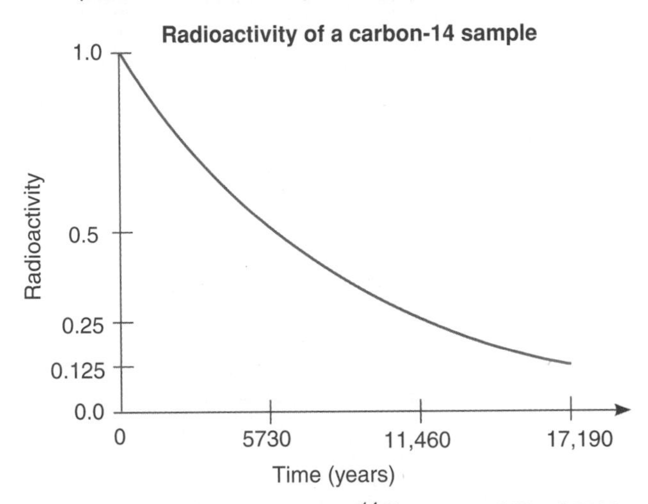

Example above: Carbon-14 (^{14}C) has a half life of 5730 years. If a sample with a mass of 10 g was left for 5730 years half the sample will have decayed, leaving 5 g of radioactive material. After another 5730 years, 2.5 g of radioactive carbon will be left.

Log transformations

- A log transformation can make very large numbers easier to work with.
- The log of a number is the exponent to which a fixed value (the base) is raised to get that number. So $\log_{10}(1000) = 3$ because $10^3 = 1000$.
- Both $\log_{10}$ and $\log_e$ (natural logs or *ln*) are commonly used.
- Log transformations are useful for data where there is an exponential increase or decrease in numbers. In this case, the transformation will produce a straight line plot.
- To find the $\log_{10}$ of a number, e.g. 32, using a calculator, key in log 32 = . The answer should be 1.51.
- Instead of transforming the data it can be plotted on a log grid, where grid lines are spaced out logarithmically either on both axes (log-log grid) or on one axis (semi-log grid).
- An example of the difference between raw numbers and log transformations is described below. The data shows the growth of a newly established squirrel population in a park.

Squirrel population		
Year (since establishment)	Population	$\log_{10}$ of population
0	10	
1	12	
3	17	
5	25	
7	37	
9	53	
12	93	

1. (a) Complete the table above right by calculating the $\log_{10}$ of the population:

   (b) Draw a line graph of the squirrel population using the raw data:

   (c) Draw a line graph of the squirrel population using the log transformed data:

   (d) Draw a line graph of the squirrel population on the semilog graph using the raw data:

   (e) Describe the difference in these graphs: ______________________________

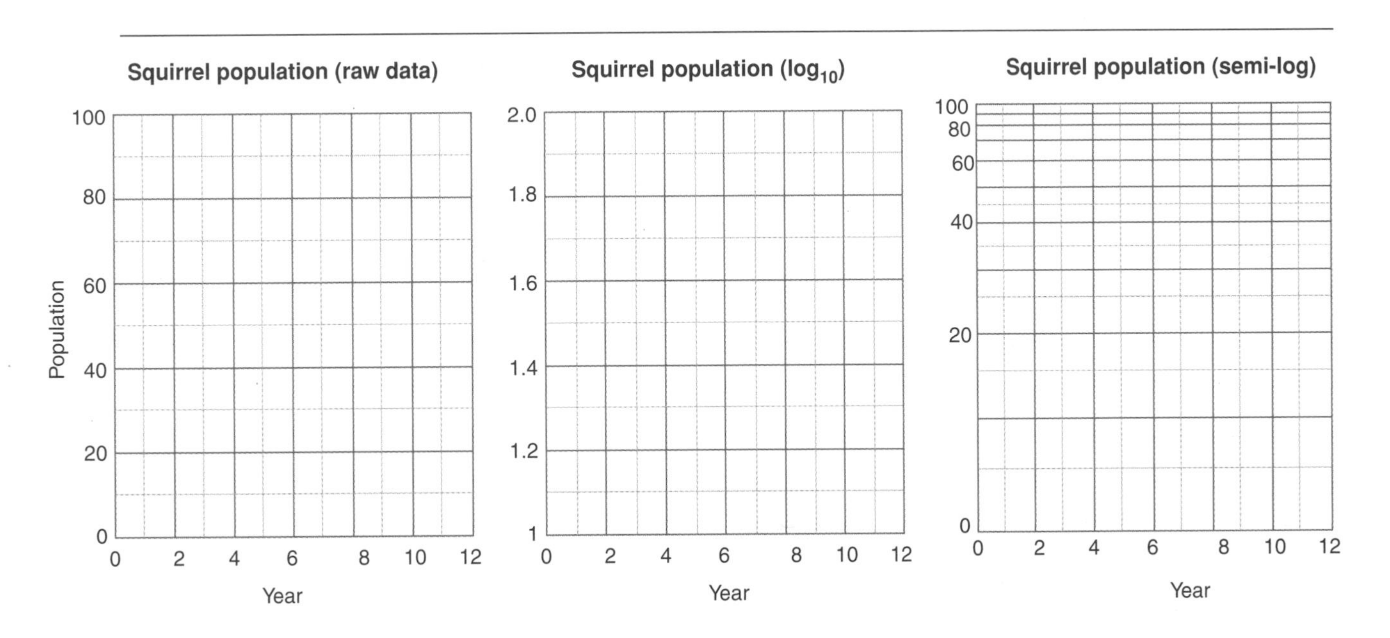

ISBN: 978-1-98-856632-0

178 Environmental Solutions

Key Question: What steps might be taken to solve an environmental problem?

An important part of environmental science is analyzing problems and proposing potential solutions. To do this you will need all the skills and knowledge gained in this program of study. Solving problems involves gathering and analyzing data, identifying a solution and its advantages and disadvantages, and justifying the potential outcome.

Solving environmental problems may include:

- Describing the problem:
  - Describing environmental problem, e.g. unsustainable population growth.
  - Describing potential responses to environmental problems, e.g. reducing human impacts on the environment.
  - Describing the advantages and disadvantages of a potential solution to an environmental problem, e.g. determining how realistic a proposed solution is.
- Using data:
  - Using data to identify and justify which solutions are viable.
  - Proposing solutions to environmental problems based on gathered data.
- Justifying a claim:
  - Proposing a solution to an environmental problem in an applied context (e.g. agriculture) and justifying the claim (e.g. explaining the advantages of a proposed irrigation practice).

Flood irrigation

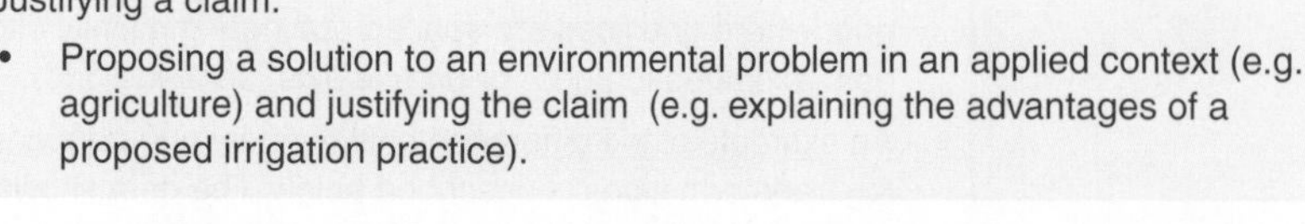

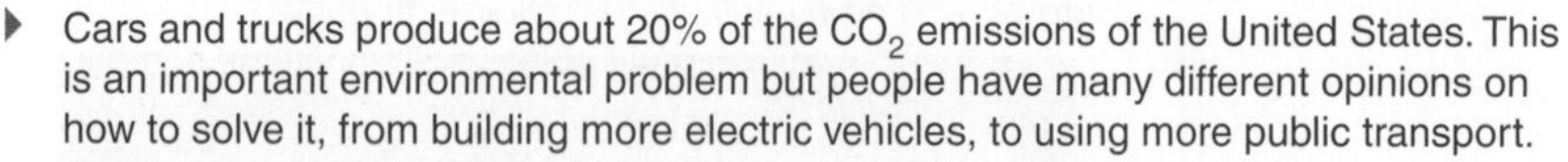

- Cars and trucks produce about 20% of the CO_2 emissions of the United States. This is an important environmental problem but people have many different opinions on how to solve it, from building more electric vehicles, to using more public transport.
- Some students were discussing how to reduce the air pollution caused by cars. Each made a claim (below):

Student 1: "Cars using gasoline have higher fuel consumption than cars using diesel. One liter of diesel takes you further than one liter of gasoline. Therefore all cars should run on diesel so that we use less fossil fuel, which produces less carbon dioxide and is better for the environment."

Student 2: "Diesels produce more particulate matter from the exhaust and more NOx gases than other fuels. This creates smog and more air pollution. Therefore diesels should be banned."

Student 3 : "We should use electric cars because they don't use fossil fuels or produce carbon dioxide."

Student 4: "If everyone used electric cars there would no off-peak time for electricity generation. Power stations would have to use more fuel, which can produce CO_2. And we don't know the environmental effect of used batteries."

Student 5: "People should be encouraged to use public transport. That would reduce the number of cars on the road."

Student 6: "People aren't going to want to give up their cars for something that's less convenient or more expensive."

Some of the opinions above present a solution, others present an argument for or against the solution. A solution to an environmental problem needs to be able to justify its use.

1. Choose two of the claims and explain what needs to be done to justify the claim:

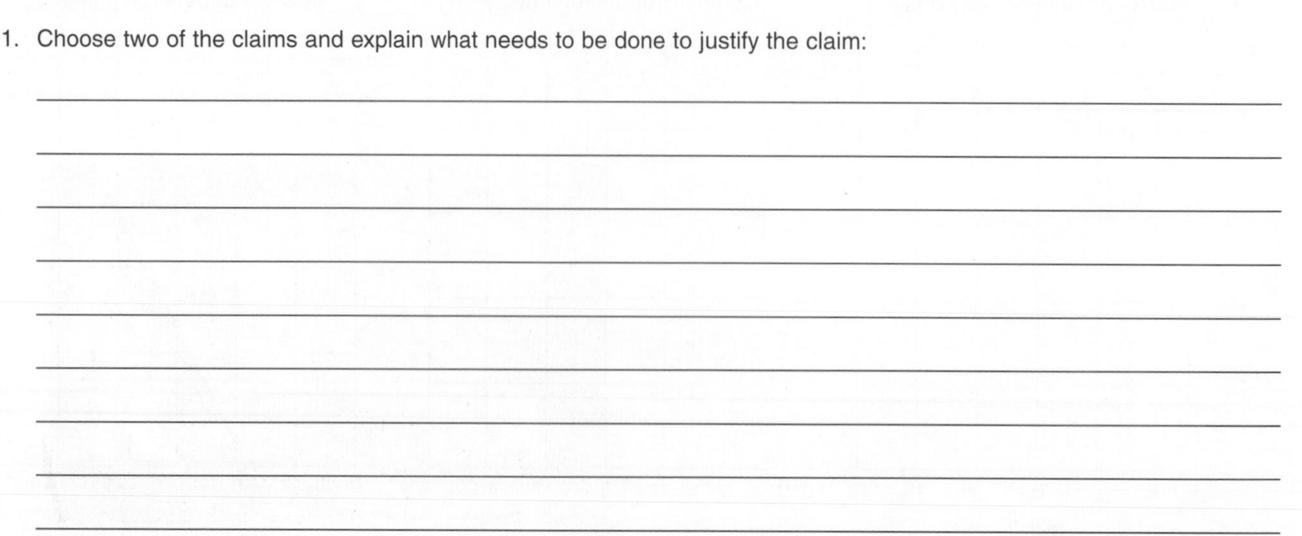

ISBN: 978-1-98-856632-0

Appendix 1: Assessing Invertebrate Diversity

Part of your experimental design task in chapter 2 (Personal Progress Check) requires you to sample invertebrates. Some methods are shown here along with a method of analyzing invertebrate diversity. Animals are highly mobile and present special challenges in terms of sampling them quantitatively to estimate their distribution, abundance and diversity. Invertebrates can be sampled using relatively simple equipment ranging from nets to traps as shown below. Invertebrate diversity can be measured using **Simpson's Diversity Index** (below).

Methods for sampling invertebrates

Sweep net

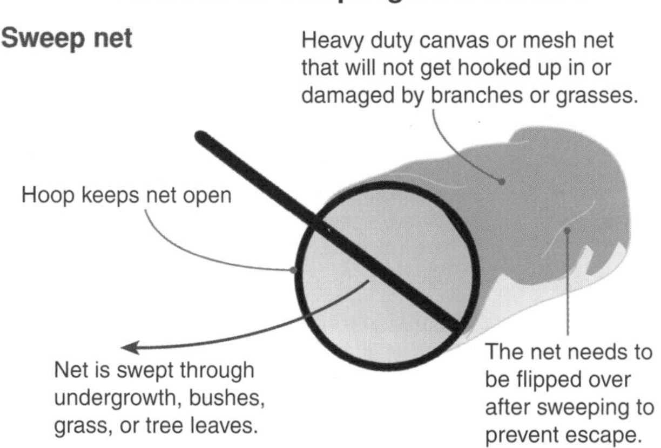

Pitfall trap

Pitfall traps are simple to make and use but need to be checked frequently so invertebrates don't escape or predatory invertebrates (e.g. centipedes) don't eat others in the sample.

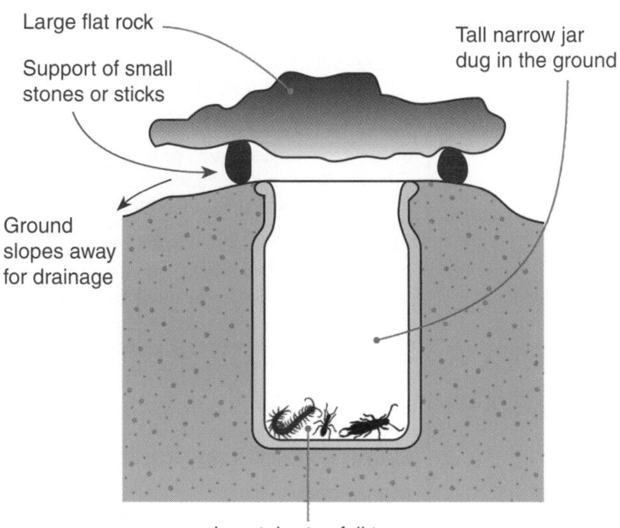

Pooter (aspirator)

Pooters can be used to suck up small fragile invertebrates for later identification

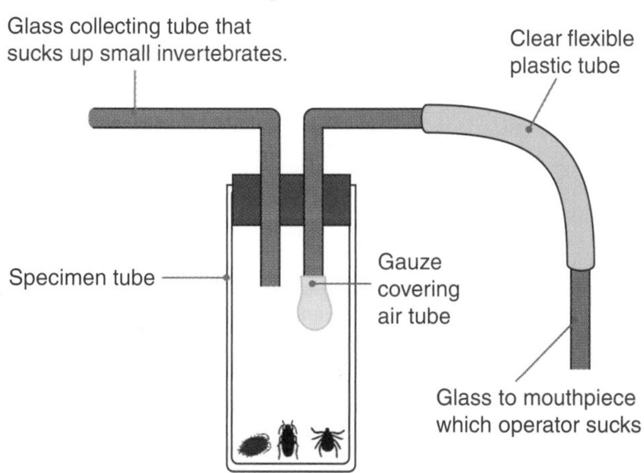

Simpson's Diversity Index

Simpson's Diversity Index (below) produces values ranging between 0 and almost 1. Communities with a wide range of species produce a higher score than communities dominated by larger numbers of only a few species.

Simpson's Diversity Index (D) is easily calculated using the simple formula below.

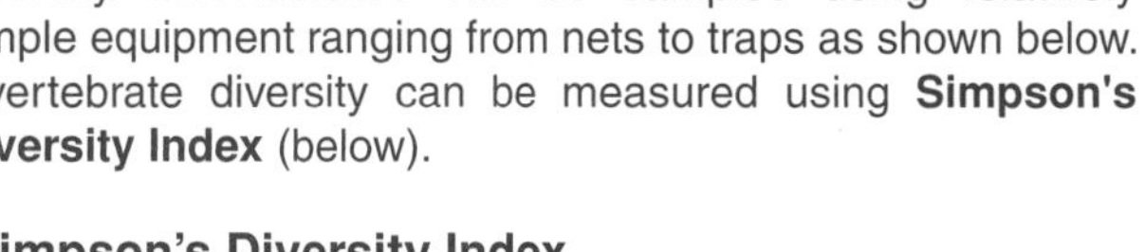

$$D = 1 - \frac{\Sigma n(n-1)}{N(N-1)}$$

D = Simpson's Diversity Index
N = Total number of individuals (of all species) in the sample
n = Number of individuals of each species in the sample

There are other variants of this index, but the more limited range of values provided by this calculation makes it more easily interpreted. No single index offers the "best" measure of diversity. Each is chosen on the basis of suitability to different situations.

Example of species diversity in a stream

The example below describes the results from a survey of stream invertebrates. It is not necessary to know the species to calculate a diversity index as long as the different species can be distinguished. For the example below, Simpson's Diversity Index using $D = 1 - (\Sigma n(n-1) \div N(N-1))$ is:

	Species	n	n(n–1)
A	Backswimmer	12	132
B	Stonefly larva	7	42
C	Silver water beetle	2	2
D	Caddisfly larva	6	30
E	Water spider	5	20
F	Mayfly larva	8	56
	N(N–1) = 1560	Σn = 40	Σn(n–1) = 282
	Σn(n–1)÷ N(N–1) =	282 ÷ 1560 =	0.18
	D =	1 – 0.18 =	**0.82**

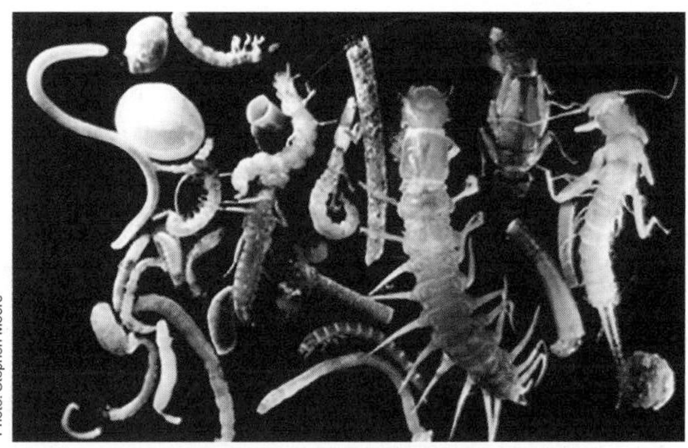

This community assemblage has a high index of diversity

Appendix 2: Glossary

A

abiotic factor
Non-living component of the environment.

acid rain
Rain containing acids that form in the atmosphere when industrial gas emissions combine with water.

adaptation
A genetically determined characteristic that improves an organism's ability to survive and reproduce under prevailing environmental conditions.

albedo
A measure of how much light that hits a surface is reflected without being absorbed.

anoxic
Having no oxygen

antigenic drift
A mechanism for variation by viruses, where incremental mutations cause small changes in the virus over time.

antigenic shift
Major, rapid change caused when two viral strains (or different viruses) combine to form a new subtype.

anthropogenic
Of, relating to, or resulting from the influence of human beings on nature.

aquaculture
The rearing of aquatic animals or the cultivation of aquatic plants for food.

asthenosphere
The upper layer of the Earth's mantle, which lies below the lithosphere and is fluid-like with viscous and elastic behavior.

atmosphere, Earth's
The envelope of gases surrounding Earth.

B

bioaccumulation
The accumulation over time of a substance (especially a contaminant, such as a heavy metal) in a living organism.

biofuel
A fuel derived from biomass, such as plant or algae material or animal waste.

biomagnification
The process by which pesticides and other substances become more concentrated in each link of the food chain.

biome
Major regional ecological community of plants and animals.

biotic factor
Living component of the environment.

biotic potential
The capacity of a population of organisms to increase in numbers under optimum environmental conditions.

biochemical oxygen demand (BOD)
The amount of dissolved oxygen needed by aerobic biological organisms to break down organic material in a given water sample at certain temperature over a specific time.

C

carrying capacity
Number of individual organisms the resources of a given area can support, usually through the most unfavorable period of the year.

chlorofluorocarbon (CFC)
Any of several simple gaseous compounds that contain carbon, chlorine, fluorine, and sometimes hydrogen; a major cause of stratospheric ozone depletion.

commensalism
Relationship between species that is beneficial to one, but neutral or of no benefit to the other.

community
The living component of an ecosystem.

competition
Any interaction that is mutually detrimental to both participants, occuring between species that share limited resources.

condensation
The transformation of water vapor to a liquid state.

consumer
Any organism that lives on other organisms, dead or alive.

control (experimental)
A 'treatment' in an experiment designed to evaluate the effect of independent variable on the response variable. It usually lacks the variable being tested but is otherwise the same as all other treatments.

convergent plate boundary
A tectonic boundary where two plates are moving toward each other and colliding.

Coriolis effect
Physical consequence of the law of conservation of angular momentum; as a result of the Earth's rotation, a moving object veers to the right in the Northern Hemisphere and to the left in the Southern Hemisphere relative to the Earth's surface.

crust, Earth's
The outermost layer of the Earth, composed of a great variety of igneous, metamorphic, and sedimentary rocks.

D

decomposer
Organism that obtains energy from the breakdown of dead organic matter to simpler substances; most precisely refers to bacteria and fungi.

denitrification
Reduction of nitrates and nitrites to nitrogen by microorganisms.

dependent variable
The variable being tested and measured in an experiment, whose value depends on that of the independent variable.

detritivore
Organism that feeds on dead organic matter; usually applies to detritus-feeding organisms other than bacteria and fungi.

divergent plate boundary
A tectonic boundary where two plates are moving away from each other and new crust is forming from magma that rises to the Earth's surface between the two plates.

E

ecological succession
The process by which the structure of a biological community evolves over time. May be primary or secondary.

endangered species
A species of animal or plant that is facing a very high risk of extinction in the wild.

endemic disease
A disease that is restricted to a given region.

El Niño–Southern Oscillation
A recurring climate pattern involving changes in the temperature of waters in the central and eastern tropical Pacific Ocean.

epidemic
Rapid spread of a bacterial or viral disease in a human population.

erosion
The action of surface processes (water, wind or ice) that removes soil, rock, or dissolved material from one location and then transports it to another location.

estuary
A partially enclosed embayment where freshwater and seawater meet and mix.

eutrophic
Term applied to a body of water with high nutrient content and high productivity.

eutrophication
Nutrient enrichment of a body of water.

evaporation
Loss of water vapor from soil or open water or another exposed surface.

exponential growth
Instantaneous rate of population growth, expressed as a proportional increase per unit of time.

extinction
The dying out or extermination of a species.

extirpation
Local extinction; when a species ceases to exist in a chosen area of study, but still exists elsewhere.

F

fertility
An organism's natural capacity to produce offspring.

fossil fuel
A natural fuel such as coal or gas, formed in the geological past from the remains of living organisms.

fracking
See hydraulic fracturing.

G

geosphere
The portion of the Earth system that includes the Earth's interior, rocks and minerals, landforms and the processes that shape the Earth's surface.

glacial
A glacial period is an interval of time within an ice age that is marked by colder temperatures and glacier advances.

gravitational potential energy
The energy stored in an object as the result of its vertical position or height.

gross primary productivity
The rate at which solar energy is captured in sugar molecules during photosynthesis (energy captured per unit area per unit time).

H

habitat fragmentation
The fragmentation of larger continuous tracts of habitat into a mosaic of smaller, often isolated areas. Compare habitat loss.

habitat loss
When a natural habitat is altered so dramatically that it no longer supports the species it originally sustained. Compare habitat fragmentation.

Hadley cell
A large-scale atmospheric convection cell in which air rises at the equator and sinks at medium latitudes.

half-life
The interval of time required for one-half of the atomic nuclei of a radioactive sample to decay.

halocline
Abrupt salinity gradient in a body of water.

hydraulic fracturing
The process of injecting liquid at high pressure into subterranean rocks, boreholes, etc. so as to extract oil or gas.

hydrosphere
All the waters on the Earth's surface, such as lakes and seas.

hypoxic
Having low oxygen (compare anoxic)

I

ice age
A geological period when there are substantial ice sheets and alpine glaciers on the planet.

independent variable
The variable set by an experimenter in an experiment, which is assumed to have a direct effect on the dependent variable.

indicator species
An organism that serves as a measure of the conditions in a given environment.

integrated pest management (IPC)
A pest management strategy that uses land management, physical and biological controls, and limited chemical controls to limit the economic damage of pests.

intensive agriculture
A system of cultivation using large amounts of energy, labour and capital relative to land area.

interglacials
A warmer period between glaciations in an ice age.

invasive species
A species that is not native to that ecosystem.

Intertropical Convergence Zone (ITCZ)
A planetary band of heavy precipitation close to the equator.

J

jetstream
Fast flowing, narrow atmospheric currents. On Earth, jetstreams are generally westerly.

K

keystone species
A species whose activities have a significant role in determining community structure.

kinetic energy
Energy associated with motion; performs work at the expense of potential energy.

Kyoto Protocol
An international climate change treaty that commits state parties to reduce greenhouse gas emissions.

L

lethal dose 50% (LD_{50})
The dose of a chemical that is lethal to 50% of the population of a particular species.

limiting factor
Factor or environmental condition that limits the abundance and distribution of an organism.

lithosphere
The rigid outer part of the Earth, consisting of the crust and upper mantle.

logistic growth
Population growth that follows a sigmoidal curve, plateauing at carrying capacity.

M

mantle, Earth's
The mostly-solid bulk of Earth's interior, which lies between the dense, super-heated core and the crust.

migration
Seasonal movement of animals from one region or habitat to another.

mortality
The death rate; the ratio of total number of death to the total population. The ratio of deaths in an area to the population of that area, expressed per 1000 per year.

municipal solid waste
A waste type consisting of everyday items that are discarded by the public.

mutualism
Relationship between two species in which both benefit.

N

natality
Production of new individuals in a population.

net primary productivity (NPP)
The rate of energy storage as organic matter after respiration.

nitrification
Biological oxidation of ammonia to nitrates and then nitrites.

nitrogen fixation
The process by which molecular nitrogen in the air is converted into ammonia (NH_3) or related nitrogenous compounds in soil.

O

ocean acidification
A reduction in the pH of the ocean over time, caused primarily by uptake of carbon dioxide from the atmosphere.

oil shale
An organic-rich fine-grained sedimentary rock from which liquid hydrocarbons can be produced, called shale oil.

oligotrophic
Term applied to a body of water with low nutrient content and high oxygen content.

oxygen sag curve
A plot of dissolved oxygen against distance from point source pollution.

ozone
The molecule O_3 formed in the stratosphere by the action of sunlight. Ground level ozone is a result of photochemical smog, and is a pollutant.

P

pandemic
Worldwide spread of a bacterial or viral disease, affecting an exceptionally high proportion of the population.

parasitism
Relationship between two species in which one benetfits while the other is harmed (although not usually killed directly).

permafrost
Permanently frozen soil.

persistent organic pollutants (POPs)
Organic compounds that are resistant to environmental degradation through chemical, biological, and photolytic processes.

pollution
The introduction of a contaminant into the natural environment that has harmful or poisonous effects.

population
A group of individuals of the same species living in a given area at a given time.

photovoltaics
The conversion of light into electricity using semiconducting materials that exhibit the photovoltaic effect.

precipitation
All the forms of water that fall to Earth, and the measured amounts of each.

predation
Relationship in which one living organism serves as a food source for another.

primary producer
Green plant or chemosynthetic bacterium that converts light or chemical energy into organic matter.

primary succession
Vegetational development starting on a new site never before colonized by life.

pycnocline
Abrupt density gradient in a body of water.

R

rainshadow
A dry region on the leeward side of a mountain range resulting from a reduction in rainfall.

remediation
The use of biological agents, such as bacteria or plants, to remove or neutralize contaminants, as in polluted soil or water.

resilience, ecosystems
Ability of a system to absorb changes and return to its original condition.

resistance, ecosystems
Ability of a system to resist changes from a disturbance.

riparian zone
Area of vegetation bordering a waterway or water body (typically a river or stream).

S

salinization
The process of accumulation of soluble salts in soil, usually by upward capillary movement from a salty groundwater source.

sanitation
the development and application of sanitary measures, related to clean drinking water and adequate disposal of sewage.

secondary succession
Development of vegetation after a disturbance.

sere
The series of successional stages on a given site that lead to a terminal community.

soil erosion
The removal of the most fertile top layer of soil through water, wind or tillage.

solar cell
An electrical device that converts the energy of light directly into electricity through the photovoltaic effect.

stratosphere
The layer of the Earth's atmosphere above the troposphere, extending to about 50 km above the Earth's surface.

subsistence agriculture
Growing food crops to meet the needs of the farmers and their families.Farm output is targeted to survival and is mostly for local requirements with little or no surplus.

T

thermocline
Abrupt temperature gradient in a body of water.

threatened species
See vulnerable species.

tillage
The agricultural preparation of soil by mechanical agitation, for the purpose of crop production.

toxicity
A measurement of the dosage of a particular substance needed to damage a living organism.

tragedy of the commons
The overexploitation of a shared resource by self-interested individuals, leading to the depletion of that resource.

transform plate boundary
A tectonic boundary where two plates are sliding past one another and crust is neither formed nor destroyed.

trophic efficiency
Ratio of productivity in a given trophic level with the trophic level on which it feeds.

troposphere
The lowest region of the atmosphere, extending from the Earth's surface to the lower boundary of the stratosphere.

U

urbanization
The movement of people out of small areas into cities.

V

vector (disease)
Any agent which carries and transmits an infectious pathogen into another living organism

vulnerable species
A species of plant or animal that is facing a high risk of extinction in the wild.

W

wastewater
Any water that has been contaminated by human use; a byproduct of domestic, industrial, commercial or agricultural activities.

watershed
Entire region drained by a waterway into a lake or reservoir; total area above a given point on a stream that contributes water to the flow at that point; the topographic dividing line from which surface streams flow in two different directions.

wetland
A general term applied to open-water habitats and seasonally or permanently waterlogged land areas.

Appendix 3: Equipment list

The equipment list provides the material and equipment needed per student, pair, or group.

1: The Living World: Ecosystems

INVESTIGATION 1.1
Carbon cycling simulation

Per student/pair
Computer
Spreadsheet application e.g. Excel

INVESTIGATION 1.2
Determining primary productivity in grass

Per student/pair
Pre-prepared plots of watered grass (20 x 40 cm)
Fertilizer (e.g. urea)
Light source (e.g. desk lamp)
Scissors
Ruler
Drying oven
Aluminum foil
Electronic balance

3: Populations

INVESTIGATION 3.1
Creating a model of logistic growth

Per student/pair
Computer
Spreadsheet application e.g. ®Excel

4: Earth Systems and Resources

INVESTIGATION 4.1
Identifying soil type part 1

Per student/pair
Samples of sand, silt, and clay.
Measuring cylinders
Stirring rods

INVESTIGATION 4.2
Identifying soil type part 2

Per student/pair
Three different soil samples.
Measuring cylinders
Stirring rods

INVESTIGATION 4.3
Measuring energy

Per student/pair
Torch
Protractor device to measure angles
Clamp stand or similar
Grid paper

5: Land and Water Use

INVESTIGATION 5.1
The Tragedy of the Commons

Per 4 students
Scissors. Packets of wrapped candy.

INVESTIGATION 5.2
Testing water runoff

Per student/pair
Container (500 mL yoghurt container. metal can or similar) with holes in the bottom for water to run through.
500 mL measuring cylinder.
Metal tray or ramp (or similar).
Container that will fit at bottom of ramp to collect water to drain to measuring cylinder.
Sponge or towel that will cover the metal tray of ramp.
Large floor tile that will cover the ramp.
Small tiles with enough total area to cover the ramp.
Enough gravel to cover the ramp.
Thin sponge or sponges that will cover the ramp.

6: Energy Resources and Consumption

INVESTIGATION 6.1
Home electricity survey

No equipment requirements

INVESTIGATION 6.2
Using M&M's® to model half lives

Per group
100 M&Ms®
1 x lidded container
1 x plate

INVESTIGATION 6.3
Solar heating house

Per student/pair
Computer
Energy 2D software
https://energy.concord.org/energy2d/

INVESTIGATION 6.4
Solar power

Per student/pair
Computer
Energy 2D software
https://energy.concord.org/energy2d/

7: Atmospheric Pollution

INVESTIGATION 7.1
Measuring particles in the air

Per student/pair
Thick cardboard sheets
Scissors
Grid paper
Petroleum jelly or similar
Stereomicroscope or magnifying glass
Tape or Blu-tak

8: Aquatic and Terrestrial Pollution

INVESTIGATION 8.1
Cleaning up oil spills

Per group of students
4 liter bucket or container
60 mL vegetable oil
Food coloring
Mixing container (e.g. 100 mL beaker)
Craft or ice block stick
Oil clean up material e.g. cotton or paper towels, straw,
Flexible straws
Detergent

INVESTIGATION 8.2
Recording your trash

Per student
Spill proof bags
Latex or chemical proof gloves

INVESTIGATION 8.3
The role of microbes in sewage treatment

Per student/pair/group
1 x stirring rod
8 x 1 L beakers
Aeration unit with four tubes
Plastic wrap
Water bath
Glucose test paper strips
14 g dried *Saccharomyces* yeast
40 mL warm water
500 mL glucose solution (100 g/L)

9: Global Change

INVESTIGATION 9.1
Albedo and ice cube melting

Per pair/group
2 x Florence or Erlenmeyer flasks
Black paint
Aluminum foil
Ice cubes
2 x thermometers
60W tungsten lamp (optional)
Timer

Image Credits

The writing team would like to thank the following people and organizations for their contributions to this edition:

• K Pryor • Stephen Moore for the aquatic invertebrate images • Gregg Segal (https://www.greggsegal.com/).

We also acknowledge the photographers who have made images available through Wikimedia Commons under Creative Commons Licences 0, 1.0, 2.0, 2.5, 3.0, or 4.0:

• Marco Vinci • Luc Viatour, www.Lucnix.be • Keith Williams (kdee64) • Althepal • viamoi • Gilles San Martin • Thomas Hahmann • Charles J Sharp • Saffron Blaze • Charles Robert Knight • CSIRO Marine Research • Dustin M. Ramsey • Jan Kronsell • NEON ja, colored by Richard Bartz • Bob Blaylock • Picturepest • Soricida • Lubasi • Jerald E. Dewey, USDA Forest Service, Bugwood.org • Mdf • Diogo Luiz • Nando cunha • putneymark • Matthew Field, www.photography.mattfield.com • Luca Galuzzi • Tomruen • P. Huybrechts (2002) Geology • Paul Gierszewski • John M • Janke • Daderot • Mikrolit • Rasbak • Matt Knoth • Stephen Moore • Alan Rockefeller • Walter Siegmund • Bertil Videt • National Archives and Record Administration • Larry Lamsa • Komencanto • Valerio Pillar • Heikki Valve • Billy Hathorn • Frank Vassen • Mnolf • Nicholls H • Derek Quinn • Matt Wasson • Sharon Loxton • Lorrie Graham / AusAID • Richard Ling • Wknight94 • Joseph Berger, Bugwood.org • Dhalusa • Tucker Lieberman • ©Entomart • Sharon Loxton • David Iliff • Wawny • Cunningham-Saigo • Siga • Institute for Transuranium Elements • Digital Gloce • Tetris L • IGV Biotech • MisterRichValentine • BS Thurner Hof • Fundy • Erik Friis-Madsen • QFSE Media • Mario Roberto Duran Ortiz • ynto • Tomskyhaha • Fidel Gonzalez • Johantheghost • SallyV • Peter Kelly, USGS • Marc St. Gil EPA • Andrew Dunn • Toby Hudson • Acropora • Blair Witherington, Florida Fish and Wildlife Conservation Commission/NOAA • Louisiana GOHSEP • US Coast Guard • Modified Copernicus Sentinel data (2020); processed by ESA • infrogmation • Chris Jordan • NordNordWest • David Ward, USGS • Emmanuelm • Boréal • Moni3 • Portal da Copa/ME • Alexandr Trubetskoy • Runner1928 • Guinther • Z22 • Nick Carson • Janice Haney Carr, CDC • SuSanA Secretariat • Alissa Eckert & Dan Higgins, CDC • Daniel Case • Humane Society of the United States • Ed Hawkins • Govt. Kiribati • Davidarfonjones • Brocken Inaglory • Boris Radosavljevic • Steve Jurvetson • Andreas Weith • Scott Ehardt • Scott Bauer, USDA • Dan Gustafson USFWS • James Morgan, WWF-US • Jacek Lesniowski • Xavierschmit at lb.wikipedia • Dan Bennett • Mike Dickison • Geoff Gallice • AnnieDick • Dartmouth Electron Microscope Facility

Contributors identified by coded credits are:

BLM: Bureau of Land Management • CBD: Convention on Biological Diversity • CDC: Centers for Disease Control and Prevention, Atlanta, USA • CSIRO: Commonwealth Scientific and Industrial Research Organization • ESA: European Space Agency • IAEA: International Atomic Energy Agency • IRRI: International Rice Research Institute • MIET: Member of the Institution of Engineering and Technology • NASA: National Aeronautics and Space Administration • NCI: National Cancer Institute • NIAID: National Institute of Allergy and Infectious Diseases • NIAID-RML: National Institute of Allergy and Infectious Diseases - Rocky Mountain Laboratories • NIH: National Institute of Health • NOAA: National Oceanic and Atmospheric Administration • NPS: National Park Service • USDA: United States Department of Agriculture • USDE: United States Department of Energy • USFWS: United States Fish and Wildlife Service • USGS: United States Geological Survey • WWF-US: World Wildlife Fund - United States

Royalty free images, purchased by BIOZONE International Ltd, are used throughout this workbook and have been obtained from the following sources: • Adobe Stock • iStock images • Corel Corporation from their Professional Photos CD-ROM collection; ©Digital Vision; PhotoDisc®, Inc. USA, www.photodisc.com • 3D images created using Bryce, Poser, and Pymol

Index